Numbers in **bold** type refer to colour plates

Penguins **1-2**

Storm-petrels **13-14**

Diving petrels **14**

Petrels,
Shearwaters,
Fulmars **7-12**

Tropic-birds **15**

Albatrosses
3-6

Pelicans **16-17**

Cormorants,
Shags
20-23

Gannets,
Boobies
18-19

Frigate-birds
24

Sheathbills **25**

Phalaropes **25**

Gulls **27-40**

Skuas **26**

Terns,
Noddies **41-45**

Skimmers **45**

Auks, Guillemots,
Puffins **46-48**

A FIELD GUIDE TO THE
SEABIRDS
OF BRITAIN AND THE WORLD

A FIELD GUIDE TO THE
SEABIRDS
OF BRITAIN AND THE WORLD

Captain G. S. Tuck
D.S.O., Royal Navy

Illustrated by
Hermann Heinzel

COLLINS
Grafton Street, London

William Collins Sons & Co Ltd
London · Glasgow · Sydney · Auckland
Toronto · Johannesburg

To

Past, present and future members

of

The Royal Naval Birdwatching Society

'I must go down to the seas again, for the call of the running tide
Is a wild call and a clear call that may not be denied;
And all I ask is a windy day and the white clouds flying,
And the flung spray and the blown spume, and the seagulls crying.'

John Masefield

First published 1978

Reprinted 1980
First published in limpback 1985

© in the text G. S. Tuck, 1978
© in the illustrations Hermann Heinzel, 1978

ISBN 0 00 219286 1

Filmset by Jolly & Barber Ltd, Rugby, Warwickshire

Made and Printed in Great Britain by
William Collins & Sons & Co Ltd Glasgow

CONTENTS

PREFACE

No field guide covering the world's seabirds as a whole has been published since W. B. Alexander's *Birds of the Ocean* in 1954. Since then many species have been studied intensively, primarily at breeding colonies, more recently in surveys in various ocean areas, and the general picture of seabird distribution is a good deal clearer. But the oceans over which seabirds are free to wander at will cover some seven-tenths of the whole surface of the globe; it will be many years, if ever, before these vast areas can be fully covered by seasonal observation, and then only from the decks of ships at sea.

There seemed to us a need for a guide book to help birdwatchers to identify the seabirds they see; to show a general pattern of their distribution around the world; and to provide an account for voyagers at sea along the principal ocean routes. For those who travel constantly at sea, birds provide more than purely scientific interest; they are indeed a ship's true companions in an otherwise empty vista of sea and sky. Those that arrive on board are treated as welcome visitors. Thus a few examples of notes taken, together with suggestions for the care and feeding of birds on board and simple forms for recording birds at sea, seemed worth including.

This is a practical handbook, not a work of systematics. Awesome numbers of subspecific titles have been assigned in works covering the seabirds of different countries. Many of these may well be justified. But in a book such as this the main object is to provide a guide to those seabirds which can be identified by field observation. Subspecific titles based on small taxonomic and plumage distinctions have been reduced in general to a minimum to embrace only those races whose variations are observable in the field.

Any writer on seabirds owes much to the many studies already published, and we owe a special debt, not only to W. B. Alexander's splendid book, but also to the *Preliminary Identification Manuals* published by the Smithsonian Institution; and to Captain P. P. O. Harrison's *Seabirds of the South Pacific*. The description of the sea route from New Zealand to Panama is derived largely from Captain Harrison's records. We are also grateful to many friends and correspondents for help generously given, particularly Mr. George Edwards, Mrs. M. K. Rowan, Mr. John Parslow, Dr. W. R. P. Bourne, Dr. D. L. Serventy, and Captain W. F. Mörzer-Bruyns and most of all to the members of the Royal Naval Birdwatching Society. Over a period of 18 years, ocean-going members of the R.N.B.W.S. have been sending back detailed seabird passage records of their voyages. Without this continual flow of information, much of this book could not have been compiled.

We are most grateful to Dr. C. J. O. Harrison for contributing notes on the nesting habits of seabirds. These have been incorporated in the introductions to families and in the descriptions of certain species.

In describing and compiling maps, we wish to acknowledge the help received from a study of many published works and papers on seabirds by a number of eminent ornithologists and authors. In particular we must thank Crispin Fisher for his meticulous and enthusiastic cartography. Any errors in the maps – as in the text – are the author's.

HOW TO USE THIS BOOK

The **endpapers**, inside the front and back covers, illustrate typical members of the principal seabird groups: at the front in flight, at the back standing or swimming. The numbers beside each caption refer to the colour plates on which that group is illustrated.

The **introduction**, pages xiii to xxviii, is a brief survey of the world's seabirds, their categories, physical characteristics and way of life.

The **description section**, pages 2–131, provides a systematic guide to the world's seabird species and distinct subspecies, with notes on size and measurements (see below); plumage and markings; flight and points of behaviour useful for identification; range and breeding areas. It is important to read the introductory notes given for each Family, since these are not repeated in the species descriptions. References to colour plates are given with the heading, to the world distribution maps after the notes on RANGE.

The following table has been used in quoting length. Length is measured between the tip of the bill and the tip of the longest tail feather. In tropic-birds the second measurement includes the elongated tail. Where the letter 'W' is included in captions, it indicates total wingspan.

Description	Length	
	ins	mm
Tiny	4-6	102-152
Very small	6-8	152-203
Small	8-12	203-305
Small-medium	12-16	305-406
Medium	16-20	406-508
Medium-large	20-24	508-609
Large	24-28	609-711
Very large	28-32	711-813
Outsize	above 32	813

In the case of Penguins their height has been indicated as follows:
Large: over 36 ins, over 915 mm.
Medium: 24-36 ins, 610-915 mm.
Small: 20 ins, 508 mm and below.

On the **colour plates**, between pages 133 and 229, the principal birds are painted to scale with each other; but subsidiary illustrations, e.g. to plumage and other variants, flight sketches, and other species added for the sake of comparison, are shown on a smaller scale.

The **caption pages**, facing each plate, gives the bird's names, diagnostic features, and references both to its distribution map and to the page on which it is described. Where a bird is also illustrated on another page, e.g. to show its winter or immature plumage, cross-references are given on the caption pages.

xi

The **distribution maps,** pages 229–260, indicate the breeding, non-breeding and migratory distributions. The maps are explained on page 229, and a map to principal islands is on pages 230–231.

British seabirds. On pages 261–285 is an account by John Parslow of the seabirds of the British Isles, with maps showing the main breeding sites around our coastline and the distribution of individual species.

The **index,** pages 286–292, has references to text descriptions in normal type, to the colour plates in bold, and to the distribution maps in italic.

INTRODUCTION

This book is concerned with true or *primary* seabirds: those for which the sea is the normal habitat and principal source of food: phalaropes are included for they spend the winter months outside the breeding season entirely in the open sea. *Secondary* seabirds are those whose habitats are confined chiefly to inland lakes, rivers and lagoons, such as divers, grebes, darters and sea ducks. Although these species resort at times to sea coasts, they are not true seabirds and are outside the scope of this book. Locally, the true seabirds may be divided broadly into three zones, depending on where their principal food is obtained:

INSHORE species are those which obtain their food near the coastline or by foraging inland: pelicans, cormorants, most gulls, coastal terns, skimmers.

OFFSHORE species are those which feed on fish offshore at no great distance from the coasts: penguins (also oceanic), diving-petrels (also oceanic), gannets, boobies, frigate-birds (also oceanic) terns (except on migration), noddies, auks and allies (also oceanic). But note that the Sooty Tern and Brown-winged or Bridled Tern are frequently seen far out to sea.

PELAGIC or OCEANIC species are those which obtain their food in the open oceans: albatrosses, petrels, shearwaters, prions, storm-petrels, tropic-birds, skuas (on migration), phalaropes (outside breeding areas), kittiwakes.

Within these broad groupings the different species have their particular distribution. Each seabird species and its allied races tend to spread and breed laterally around the world within the latitude belts they favour. At the end of breeding seasons, many species disperse from their congested breeding localities to find favourable climates and feeding areas for the winter. Some, particularly those which breed in the higher latitudes, undertake enormous trans-global seasonal migrations from their breeding grounds, many crossing the equator to similar latitudes at the other end of the world where suitable feeding areas occur.

Of course, all birds have to nest and rear their young on land; so during the breeding season all seabird species may be seen at, or close off coastal breeding areas.

SEABIRD CHARACTERISTICS

In the course of evolution seabirds have developed many different characteristics both in structure and habits. These are determined primarily by the types of sea food they have become adapted to consume, and the areas where this is most abundant. This in turn is associated with their adaptability to breed in large colonies whether on cliffs where in certain cases brood patch will only allow coverage of a single egg, in colonies on sand dunes or more independently where nesting material may be collected and two or three eggs laid, or the need to escape predation by nesting in burrows or crevices where only a single egg is laid. Some indeed nest in trees. Where different species nest together in large colonies, an ecological pattern can normally be found in which each requires a different type of sea food for its offspring. In this way, the adjacent sea provides enough food for all.

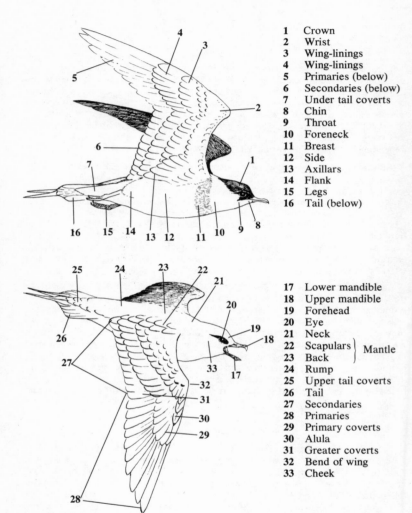

1 Crown
2 Wrist
3 Wing-linings
4 Wing-linings
5 Primaries (below)
6 Secondaries (below)
7 Under tail coverts
8 Chin
9 Throat
10 Foreneck
11 Breast
12 Side
13 Axillars
14 Flank
15 Legs
16 Tail (below)

17 Lower mandible
18 Upper mandible
19 Forehead
20 Eye
21 Neck
22 Scapulars ⎫ Mantle
23 Back ⎭
24 Rump
25 Upper tail coverts
26 Tail
27 Secondaries
28 Primaries
29 Primary coverts
30 Alula
31 Greater coverts
32 Bend of wing
33 Cheek

While all seabirds should be capable of resting on the sea, and make use of their preening gland – or in the case of petrels oil from their nostrils – to keep their plumage oiled, a few have become less adapted to do so. Frigate-birds do not have the oiled feathers to provide buoyancy. Cormorants would become waterlogged if they did not regain land frequently to preen and dry their feathers. Sooty Terns will rarely attempt to settle for long periods on the sea. It is said that the Ivory Gull in the high Arctic avoids wetting its feathers to prevent them becoming encrusted with ice.

Heat conservation

Heat conservation is an important requirement in all birds, but particularly so in seabirds. Their closely-knit oiled outer plumage, the filoplumes of their under-bodies and underlayers of fat and blubber help to insulate them, and species which inhabit higher colder latitudes are generally found to be larger than their counter-parts in lower latitudes. More rounded contours and "built-in" necks which help to conserve heat are noticeable in such species as the penguins and auks of high latitudes.

Legs and feet

A noticeable feature in different species is the position of the legs in relation to the underbody. Those which spend much time out of the water, particularly gulls, have sturdy legs placed centrally below their underbodies providing a horizontal carriage and balance suitable for foraging for food on tidelines or inland. Species which pursue fish underwater have shorter legs placed much further aft and wider webbed feet to act as paddles or rudders. This results in a more upright stance, evident particularly in the alcids (auks and allies) and penguins. Many truly oceanic species have not retained sufficient strength in their legs to bear the weight effectively on land, and are forced to shuffle forward helped by their wings. This makes them so vulnerable to predators that many petrels, shearwaters and storm-petrels have become adapted to approaching and leaving their enclosed nesting sites under cover of darkness.

Bills

The bills of seabirds vary to meet their particular mode of life. Penguins have caruncles on tongue and palate to grasp fish firmly. The bills of albatrosses and petrels are stout and hooked at the tip, those of shearwaters generally similar but more slender. A distinguishing feature in all species of the Order Procellariiformes is the presence of the two nostrils opening together at the end of a double tube on the upper mandible. Diving-petrels also possess a distensible pouch at the base of the lower mandible. The bills of tropic-birds, gannets and boobies are stout and dagger shaped, in keeping with the streamlined outline of these species which dive from considerable heights into the sea, and well suited for grasping quite sizeable fish. Cormorants and frigate-birds both have long slender bills sharply hooked at the tip. This helps cormorants to seize and pierce the gills of the fish they pursue, and serves frigate-birds as a weapon both for harrying other seabirds, and for snatching food from the surface, and indeed fledgling birds from nesting colonies of terns, without pausing in flight. The long powerful bill of the Pelican and its huge pouch serves to seize large fish on conclusion of its headlong dives and to scoop up smaller fry after driving them into the shallows. The fine needle-shaped bills of phalaropes have been adapted to probe for small marine animals at their breeding grounds and to peck for planktonic crustaceans on the surface of the sea. Skuas with their stout hooked bills pirate other seabirds and are great scavengers of both eggs and young.

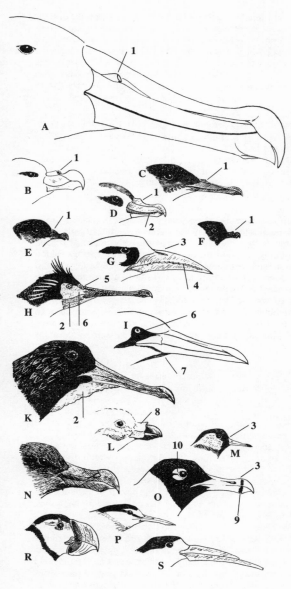

SEABIRDS' BILLS

A Albatrosses
   1 nostril

B Petrels

C Shearwaters

D Prions
   2 pouch

E Diving-petrels

F Storm-petrels

G Tropic-birds
   3 nostril
   4 saw bill

H Cormorants
   5 caruncles
   6 naked skin on face

I Gannets
   7 gular stripe naked

K Frigate-birds

L Sheathbills
   8 'sheath'

M Phalaropes

N Skuas

O Gulls
   9 under mandible
      often with red spot
   10 eye-ring

P Terns

R Puffins

S Skimmers

The strong bills of the larger gulls are equally suitable for scavenging on the tidelines, tearing at refuse and killing fledgling seabirds. The finer bills of terns are sufficient for the capture of fry and eels. Puffins have backwardly directed spines on their tongues enabling them to hold each small fish caught separately until six or more may be seen dangling crosswise in their bills. The bills of skimmers are useful for scooping up fish in flight, with the lower and longer mandible skimming below the surface while the bird maintains its flight.

FEEDING

The Oceans

The existence of life in the surface layers of the oceans depends upon the presence of dissolved nutrient salts, largely nitrates and phosphates from the deep layers of the ocean being brought to the surface. Here by a process of photosynthesis, through the energy of sunlight together with dissolved carbon dioxide and oxygen, phytoplankton multiplies. From this basis arises the food-chain of life in the upper layer of the sea. Microscopic zooplankton, crustacea, copepods and the like, and finally fish consume each other, providing food for seabirds, until the last in the food chain dies, sinks below the surface to recreate the cycle. The immense quantities of guano from the excreta of seabirds on islands also get washed into the sea to augment the nutrient salts.

To provide for these conditions, nutrient-rich deep water must be brought to the surface in circumstances known as "up-welling". Such areas occur in high polar latitudes near moving ice masses; where strong constant winds and rough weather persist; where winds or surface currents deflect surface water away from coasts; where cool currents flow past coastal land masses; in the warm tropical oceans where deep water strikes an incline around islands; and in the open oceans where converging or crossing currents occur.

While winds and currents affect particular areas in this way a broad pattern of rich surface feed zones or 'convergencies' emerges between the Poles and the Equator. These may be summarised as follows: Polar zones around the ice edge; Arctic and Antarctic convergencies at about 55 degrees latitude; Sub-arctic and Sub-antarctic zones between 55 and 35 degrees latitude; and Sub-tropical zones between 35 degrees and 10 degrees latitude. Within the doldrums near the Equator in the open oceans, the warm surface water however provides little surface feed.

As a general guide, the principal areas over which oceanic seabirds tend to feed are:

PACIFIC OCEAN. The Arctic convergence about 55° N. and into the Bering Sea. The converging currents east of Japan. Off west coast of British Columbia. Along the equatorial counter current between 6° and 8° N. Along the west coast of South America in the Humboldt Current. New Zealand seas. Around tropical pacific Islands.

INDIAN OCEAN. The south-east coast of Arabia during the south-west monsoon. The north-east coast of Arabia and Mekran coast during the north-east monsoon. Along the equatorial counter current, especially around islands. Off the west coast of Australia. Off the southern tip of South Africa.

ATLANTIC OCEAN. The confluence of the Labrador Current and the Gulf Stream. Upswellings off islands and off the north-west coast of Africa. In the Buenguela Current off the west coast of South Africa. In the Falkland Current.

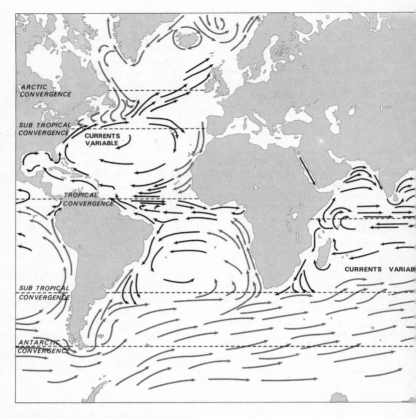

OCEAN CURRENTS AND SURFACE FEED

The map above shows the course of the principal surface currents in the world's oceans. The warm currents are indicated by solid black arrows, the cool or cold by lighter arrows.

The direction and strength of surface current result from the effects of constant winds and of the rotation of the earth. These cause the currents to circulate generally clockwise in the northern hemisphere and anti-clockwise in the southern.

Areas of turbulence and upwelling yield the richest supplies of surface feed for seabirds. Their main causes and areas are:

1. In the high latitudes near the Poles, with easterly winds and floating ice.

2. The Arctic and Antarctic convergences, with high winds and strong surface currents.

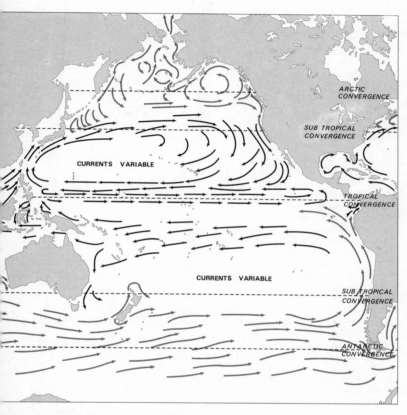

3. The subtropical convergences at about 35° Lat.

4. The cold currents flowing northwards off the southern hemisphere continents – the Humboldt Current of the west coast of South America and the weaker Falkland Current off the south-eastern coast, and the Benguela Current passing up the west coast of Africa.

5. Where opposite currents converge or overlap, e.g. off Labrador the cold, southward-flowing Labrador Current impinges on the Gulf Stream, causing considerable turbulence.

6. Currents flowing sharply away from coastlines, e.g. the strong South West Monsoon off the coast of South-east Arabia during the northern summer months causes upwelling close offshore.

7. Where currents are deflected off islands, e.g. tropical oceanic islands.

Where variable weak winds and currents occur in warm tropical and sub-tropical zones, little surface feed is present in the open ocean.

SOUTHERN OCEAN. Along the belt of the Antarctic convergence at about 55° S. Along the seaward edge of the pack-ice.

In the Sub-arctic zones certain southern hemisphere migratory petrels and shearwaters spend the northern summer months.

The Food

The following list provides a general outline of the kind of food taken by different groups:

Penguins: Fish, squid and krill, propelling themselves underwater with their flippers and using their feet as rudders.

Albatrosses: Fish, squid, garbage, settling on the water with raised wings and submerging a little way below the surface.

Petrels and **Shearwaters:** Mainly fish, squid and crustaceans, but some will also eat garbage. Food is obtained mainly from close to the surface, but they often settle and submerge freely.

Prions: Mainly small crustaceans, often obtained by running along the surface and scooping up food with their heads submerged.

Storm-petrels: Planktonic crustaceans, fish eggs, oily scum obtained from the surface.

Tropic-birds: Squid and fish near the surface obtained by diving from a height.

Gannets and **Boobies:** Fish, by diving from a height. Boobies frequently capture flying fish in the air.

Pelicans: Fish, either by diving from a height, or scooping fish into their pouches when several work in unison driving shoaling fish into shallow water.

Cormorants: Fish, by diving from the surface and propelling themselves chiefly with their legs.

Frigate-birds: Pirate other seabirds and snatch up food vomited. Snatch offal from the surface and eat fledgling seabirds.

Phalaropes: Planktonic crustaceans obtained from the surface.

Skuas: Pirate other seabirds, offal, garbage, fledgling seabirds.

Gulls: Scavenge for molluscs and worms on tide lines; feed inland on refuse. Large gulls will kill and eat fledgling seabirds.

Terns: Small fish near surface. Terns often hover with head slanting downwards searching for fish before diving just below the surface.

Noddies: Fish, probably squid also. Noddies usually fly close above the surface unlike terns.

Alcids: Fish, small squid, crustaceans, diving from the surface.

Drinking

Seabirds will drink fresh water where this is available in preference to salt water. Pelagic seabirds have become adapted to drinking sea water and have developed a salt water excreting gland in the nose which extracts the surplus salt from the water taken in and empties it back into the sea.

With a very few exceptions there is not noticeable plumage difference between the sexes of adult seabirds. Frigate-birds are a notable exception. The plumage of immature birds however is often entirely different from that of mature adults. Many immatures take several years to assume full adult plumage, and these differences are a frequent cause of perplexity to observers.

During the course of a year all birds moult their feathers, but there is a considerable variation in the extent and period in which different species elect to moult. Some species moult more than once in a year. The moult of wing and tail feathers is arranged so that not more than one or two feathers are missing from each side at one time. A common time for moulting to commence is shortly after the mating season, and this appears more applicable to the inshore and residential species. Species which undertake distant migrations immediately after the breeding season, such as the migratory shearwaters, retain their original wing and tail feathers until reaching or approaching their contra-nuptial feeding grounds. The periods and extent of moulting however varies in many cases. Penguins for example slough all their feathers at once, lose much weight and are unable to go to sea to feed for several weeks.

Most adult seabirds retain the same plumage throughout the seasons, but there are notable exceptions. In particular cormorants, phalaropes, the dark hooded gulls and terns and the auks. In the contra-nuptial season certain cormorants lose their distinctive white plumage patches, dark hooded gulls and terns lose their dark hoods and retain only dusky patches about their heads. Phalaropes assume an entirely different plumage, and many auks and murrelets shed their crests or facial adornments. At this season there is a general tendency in birds with bright coloured bills and legs to revert to duller colours.

IDENTIFYING SEABIRDS

Naturally the first object when sighting a seabird is to be able to put a name to it. As a first step it is helpful to know the general characteristics of the different Families in which seabird species are grouped:

PENGUINS. Family Spheniscidae. Medium to outsize. Stout bodied and short necked, standing upright on land on short webbed feet set very far back. Penguins differ from all other seabirds in having 'flippers' instead of quilled wings. When at the surface they swim very low in the water with only the head or part of the back showing, and are sometimes seen 'porpoising' in and out of the water. Confined to the Southern Hemisphere, except for the Galapagos Penguin.

ALBATROSSES and MOLLYMAWKS. Family Diomedeidae. Very large to outsize. Distinguished at sea by their large size, long slender wings, stout bills with upper mandible slightly hooked, short tails and characteristic gliding flight. The different colouring of the bills and pattern of the underwing margins helps to distinguish species. The smaller species are often referred to as 'Mollymawks'.

TRUE PETRELS and SHEARWATERS. Family Procellariidae. Medium size with long narrow wings held out straight or angled in flight. Fly low over the sea in tilted glides on extended wings alternating with a few wing beats. (Some 'gadfly' petrels of the genus *Pterodroma* tend to swoop and soar.) Distinguished at close quarters by their tubular nostrils.

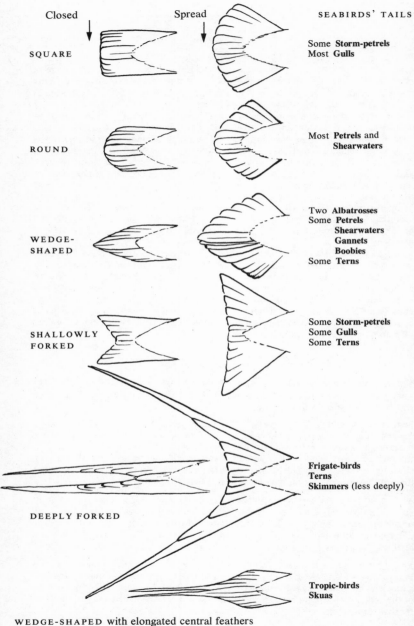

Closed   Spread   SEABIRDS' TAILS

↓   ↓

SQUARE   Some **Storm-petrels**
Most **Gulls**

ROUND   Most **Petrels** and
Shearwaters

WEDGE-
SHAPED   Two **Albatrosses**
Some **Petrels**
     Shearwaters
     Gannets
     Boobies
Some **Terns**

SHALLOWLY
FORKED   Some **Storm-petrels**
Some **Gulls**
Some **Terns**

DEEPLY FORKED   **Frigate-birds**
Terns
Skimmers (less deeply)

    Tropic-birds
Skuas

WEDGE-SHAPED with elongated central feathers

xxii

STORM-PETRELS. Family Hydrobatidae. Very small dark birds usually to be seen flitting back and forth close to the sea, sometimes close in the wake of a ship, or pattering the surface with their webbed feet. Tubular nostrils.

DIVING-PETRELS. Family Pelecanoididae. Small stumpy little birds, blackish above and white below with short bills and wings, legs placed far back. Usually seen in flocks resting on the surface of the water. Fly short distances with rapidly beating wings and usually dive on alighting. Confined to Southern Oceans. Tubular nostrils.

TROPIC-BIRDS. Family Phaethontidae. Medium size, graceful white birds with greatly elongated central tail feathers. High flying with quick powerful wing beats.

PELICANS. Family Pelecanidae. Outsize birds with broad rounded wings, heavy bodies and huge pouched bills. In flight heads are thrust back on shoulders. Plunge clumsily into sea for food.

GANNETS and BOOBIES. Family Sulidae. Very large. Cigar-shaped with long narrow wings, short necks and stout conical pointed bills. Flight is stately with regular wing beats. Plunge headlong into sea for food.

CORMORANTS and SHAGS. Family Phalacrocoracidae. Medium large to large. Dark birds with long necks and wings and slender hooked bills. Fly low over surface with regular wing beats. Dive from surface of water for food.

FRIGATE-BIRDS. Family Fregatidae. Very large almost black plumaged birds with very long narrow wings, long forked tails and long slender hooked bills. Circle for hours overhead, tails opening and closing scissor-fashion. Chase and pirate other seabirds.

PHALAROPES. Family Phalaropodidae. Very small delicate rather long-necked waders. Winter at sea in favoured localities. Usually seen in flocks either swimming buoyantly on the sea or flying with rapid flight for short distances.

SKUAS and JAEGERS. Family Stercorariidae. Medium size. Dark uniform brown or in the light phase with yellowish sides and neck and pale underparts. Long wings, slightly hooked bills. The Great Skua is much larger than the three Jaegers, and is uniform brown with broad rounded wings and pale wing patches. Chase and pirate other seabirds.

GULLS. Family Laridae. Medium to large. In most cases in adult plumage have head, body and tail white, and the upper wings grey or black. The tail is nearly always square. Some of the smaller gulls acquire a dark hood in the breeding season. The majority of the immature birds are mottled brown overall.

TERNS. Family Sternidae. Small to medium. Graceful seabirds distinguished by their long narrow wings, short legs and long deeply forked tails. The majority have the crown black in the breeding season and the remainder of the plumage a mixture of pale grey and white. A few species, e.g. Noddies, are mainly sooty-brown. Fly with rapid wing beats. Hover and plunge into sea for food.

SKIMMERS. Family Rhynchopidae. Medium size. Somewhat like large terns with very long narrow wings; short legs and slightly forked tails. Blackish above with white foreheads and underparts and long bills usually orange or yellow with dark tips, the lower mandible extending well beyond the upper.

AUKS. Family Alcidae. Small to medium size. Short-winged, usually dark above and white below. Often to be seen in flocks swimming buoyantly. When disturbed they dive or fly with a rapid whirring flight straight and low over the sea. Obtain food by diving from surface.

Once one has grasped the general characteristics of the Families, it is usually not difficult to decide within which a bird belongs. But to identify the individual species a selective eye to concentrate upon the particular characteristics and field markings which will serve to identify it.

At sea, when the birds are nearly always seen on the wing and glimpses of upperparts and underparts may be fleeting, a good pair of binoculars of, say, 7 × 50 magnification and diameter is essential.

Taking notes of seabirds seen is always a good plan. It provides a record, avoids the pitfalls of wishful thinking, and is invaluable for later verification. The following points should be noted, and if possible accompanied by a sketch, with arrows pointing to any principal features of plumage colours, and wing and tail shape:

1. **Size** and **build**.	Size: very large, large, medium, or small. Build: heavy, compact, light or slender.
2. **Manner of flight**.	Wings: straight or angled. Wing beats: slow, rapid, fluttering or gliding on fixed pinions. Height: above ship or close to surface.
3. **Wings**.	Short and broad, or long and narrow.
4. **Tail**.	Very long, short and round, square or wedge-shaped.
5. **Plumage colours**.	Head; back and upperwing; underparts and underwing; rump; tail; bill and legs.
6. **Behaviour** and **voice**.	Behaviour; solitary or in flocks, active or sluggish. Voice: noisy or silent, harsh or pleasing.

SEABIRD SURVIVAL

The number of different seabird species is very small in comparison with landbirds, and yet the total number of seabirds in the world far exceeds that of landbirds. The wide global distribution and close association with the sea favours suitable breeding localities remote in many cases from civilisation or inaccessible from interference. Moreover, the sea provides an inexhaustible food supply under all conditions irrespective of extremes of weather.

Selective diets: Viewing the immense colonies of breeding seabirds, not only of identical species, which pack every ledge on the high cliffs of mainlands or remote islands, one might question the inexhaustibility of the adjacent food supply. Yet an ecological balance is achieved, for each species demands its own particularly selective diet. One species will be seen to be bringing back small sprats to its young caught from near the surface, another species will be pursuing larger fish or marine life among the shallow bottom weed, whilst a third will be working further to seaward watching for shoals of larger fish, either diving from a height or pursuing them at deeper depths. It has been noticed that, where mass breeding colonies of different species of terns nest in close proximity, some species will fly further afield than others to collect food suitable for their young.

Natural hazards: As in all other wildlife a chain of predation is equally applicable to seabirds. Giant petrels, Skuas, Frigate-birds and the larger gulls pirate both eggs and young of more defenceless species. Attack may occasionally come from beneath the sea for both seals and large predatory fish may drag some unsuspecting seabird beneath the surface. The penguins are particularly vulnerable to the Leopard Seal. Such hazards have little effect on ultimate numbers.

Disasters: Local disasters from uncontrollable elements have occurred occasionally. At rare intervals obscure changes in the direction and surface temperature of ocean currects, the warm surface water causing the destruction of both plankton and small fish has caused mass starvation to millions of seabirds. Such a case has occurred off the west coast of South America in the region of Peru on more than one occasion, where a warm tropical current has unexpectedly intruded into the cold Humboldt current. Huge numbers of Peruvian Boobies starved or were unable to feed their offspring. In another form a phenomenon known as 'The Red Tide' occurred off the coast line of South Africa, caused, it was believed, through an unusual outfall of silt from flooded rivers. This created a multiplication of one-celled organisms containing a substance highly poisonous to seabirds. A more recent cause of local disasters has arisen from the great increase in the number of oil tankers now delivering oil to almost every commercial port in the world. Although waste oil on flushing out tanks on departure should not be carried out until ships are far out to sea, this has frequently been disregarded. Floating oil slicks close to coasts have resulted in very large numbers of seabirds, alcids in particular, being contaminated with fatal results. The dangers from floating oily and chemical pollution of the sea through dumping highly toxic waste locally offshore, although very real, fortunately affects only local colonies of seabirds; in view of their vast distribution elsewhere the danger of extinction is small.

SEABIRDS ON THE DANGER LIST. The following list at present quoted in the Red Data Book by the International Union for the Conservation of Nature and the International Council for Bird Preservation shows these species whose future existence may be in danger. Not all are given the same status, some being severely threatened while others have small and vulnerable populations which require to be watched:

Short-tailed Albatross (*Diomedea albatrus*), Audouin's Gull (*Larus audouinii*), Abbott's Booby (*Sula abbotti*), King Shag (*Phalacrocorax c. carunculatus*), Black-capped Petrel (*Pterodroma hasitata*), Ascension Frigate-bird (*Fregata aquila*), Reunion Petrel (*Pterodroma aterrima*), Galapagos Penguin (*Spheniscus mendiculus*), Waved Albatross (*Diomedea irrorata*), Hawaiian Petrel (*Pterodroma phaeopygia*), Flightless Cormorant (*Nannopterum harrisi*), Cahow (*Pterodroma cahow*), Macgillivray's Petrel (*Pterodroma macgillivrayi*).

SEABIRDS ON BOARD

Seabirds, unlike land birds at sea, have no need to use ships as resting places. Usually when they are found on deck they have arrived during the night, either attracted by the ship's lights or, perhaps, blown across the ship in heavy weather and striking some portion of the ship's structure have come to grief.

Shearwaters and petrels and even tropic-birds are quite unable to take wing of their own accord from the deck, shuffling forward awkwardly on their webbed feet which are set far back in the body, and trailing their long wings. Storm-petrels and tropic-birds are the species most often found on ships, followed by Sooty Terns. Tropic-birds often follow ships at night and Sooty Terns have a similar habit though to a lesser extent. They are both known to feed off squid, which tend to rise to the surface at night, and the birds may pick up the ships during dusk and search for squid churned up by the propellers.

Southern Great Skuas have also been known to alight on board when they occur at sea off southern Australia.

There is one family however that quite frequently and deliberately makes use of a ship at sea – the boobies – and particularly the Red-footed Booby. In the tropics boobies will perch usually on the forecastle head from which vantage point they will plummet again and again as flying fish break water from the bow, catching them in the air, landing in the sea to devour them, and returning once again to their perch. They have been known to remain on board for hours.

When ships are in harbour gulls which are constantly foraging for scraps of food become unusually tame and use a ship's structure or any other handy perching place. This is not so at sea; gulls will follow astern or sail above a ship but usually will not perch on board although they may be tempted to alight momentarily on the bulwarks where food has been specially placed.

LAND BIRDS AT SEA

A passenger in a ship at sea may be quite unaware of land birds in flight in the sky above and may not even notice a little bird flying at low level close alongside the ship making desperate efforts to alight on board. But vary large numbers of land birds alight on ships, not only when the ship's route coincides with a particular migration fly path, but also far out in the oceans where their presence may be least expected.

For land birds, particularly on migration, the presence of a ship at sea must be hailed as a haven of rest, for a great many birds that take shelter are lost or storm-driven and exhausted, and so often appear remarkably tame. Frequently they feel no compulsion to leave, and find themselves being given assisted passages far from their intended destinations. A racing pigeon found on board a ship 400 miles west of Spain and, from its ring number, due to go home to Manchester should have known better – for it was perfectly free to fly away. It stayed on board through the Panama Canal and finally took off towards the Galapagos Islands. Months later its owner was informed!

Three Indian Crows remained with a ship from the moment it left Colombo until its destination in Geelong Harbour, in Victoria, Australia.

One could quote many other such cases and others where land birds varying from White Storks, Egrets, Bitterns, Ospreys and exotic birds have come on board far out to sea, but perhaps the relatively common occurrence of the Peregrine Falcon deserves mention. Peregrines have alighted on ships well out in the ocean – certainly in the Atlantic, Pacific and Indian Oceans, Mediterranean and Red Seas – and made themselves entirely at home perching nearly always high up on the fore truck or platform below the emergency steaming light.

The routes on which the greatest number and variety are likely to occur are primarily those passing through the Mediterranean; the Red Sea; the sea route from the British Isles to Cape Town while passing the bulge of northwest Africa; and off the east coast of North America and Canada.

CARE AND FEEDING

Birds which arrive on board ships at sea and allow themselves to be collected in the hand are usually in an exhausted state, often wet and bedraggled, and all primarily in need of rest, warmth and shelter.

In Ocean Weather Ships on station at sea, where a considerable number and variety of small landbirds seek shelter at intervals, the most convenient arrangement is to construct a commodious cage some 36 inches long, 20 inches high and 14 inches in depth, the floor, ends and back of plywood, the roof of hardboard, the front of vertical wire rods, i.e. barred ½" apart. A vertical barred front is preferable to wire netting as birds fluttering against bars do not injure their faces so easily. If an entrance flap is fitted in the roof it can be large enough to collect birds from all quarters of the cage. A muslin front cover should be arranged which will let in light and yet give air and a feeling of seclusion and keep the birds quiet. The cage should be placed in a secure warm place, and judgment must be used as to the types of birds which can be placed together. At this stage a little water should be provided in a receptacle which will not easily tip up.

As an ad hoc arrangement any open topped large cardboard box perforated plentifully with air holes and covered with muslin will do.

When birds are seen to have 'perked up' the moment has come to provide food. At NO times should oceanic seabirds be placed in a bath of water.

It is rarely possible to provide the natural diet which most species would feed upon in normal freedom. The following suggestions aim to cover a possible 'best' where feed can be stocked in advance, as in Ocean Weather Ships. A good general point in the case of the smaller insectivorous and seed eating landbirds is to remember that they may not recognise inert food, but that their attention may be stimulated by mixing among the feed a number of nice wriggling mealworms or maggots.

Seed-eating small landbirds. Millet on the stalk is always an attraction. In addition canary seed, white millet, and hemp seed can be obtained as mixtures sold by dealers as 'Aviary Mixture', 'Finch Mixture', 'Swoop' etc. Large seed eating birds such as Jays, less likely to come on board, can be tempted with grain. Pigeons will also take readily to uncooked rice.

Insectivorous birds. Mealworms are valuable. Suitable proprietary foods are 'Activite', 'Stimulite', 'Prosecto' or 'Sluis'. Soaked chopped currants and dried or fresh fruit chopped small. 'Starter Crumbs' used for rearing poultry chicks, finely chopped hard-boiled egg or finely grated cheese are valuable alternatives.

Ducks, geese, herons, egrets. Soaked bread, cereals, chopped green vegetable for ducks and geese; finely minced raw meat without fat or tissue and hard-boiled egg for herons, egrets.

Waders, hawks, owls, large thrushes. Finely minced raw meat without fat or tissue, for hawks and owls small squares of raw meat.

Seabirds. Chopped fresh raw fish, finely chopped minced raw meat. Seabirds frequently need feeding forcibly at the outset.

In the absence of special foods. For small landbirds soft breadcrumbs and finely chopped hard-boiled egg or finely grated cheese. For larger seed-eating landbirds – softly-boiled rice or porridge oats can be tried.

Feed should be put in the cages or boxes making sure there is sufficient light and not too much at once. Where birds are too big to cage their radius of action should be restricted so that food is always in view.

Water must always be available.

Mealworms require warmth to keep them alive and should be kept in a tin with holes pierced in the lid at a temperature of say 60°F. They should also be provided with some food, i.e. porridge oats, and occasionally fresh pieces of apple skin, skin will make them fatter. The skin should be removed before it goes mouldy. Maggots can be kept alive for some time but they must be kept in a cool temperature to prevent them pupating.

Mealworms can be bred under the following conditions: Put about 3 inches of barley meal mixed with maize meal in a shallow wooden box covered securely with gauze or muslin for ventilation. Put sheets of crumpled newspaper amongst the meal in layers. Put ½ inch slices of carrot on top of bran and add fresh slices occasionally.

¼lb of mealworms is sufficient to start a colony which takes a little time to get started. Keep in a warm place, 85°F is optimum temperature. Extreme cold will kill colony. Mealworms should not be used as feed until adult beetles have developed and are breeding.

TREATMENT OF OILED SEABIRDS ON BOARD SHIP

An increasing number of seabirds contaminated with oil are arriving on board ships at sea. Ships are not in a position to undertake lengthy rehabilitation but the following action and treatment has proved successful in several cases.

Attempts to clean should not start immediately. At first the bird should be kept *warm* and *quiet* securely wrapped in a cloth with its head and legs only protruding to prevent it preening and thus swallowing more oil, and placed in a suitable cardboard box with ventilation. The feet should be treated with a little ointment or hand cream to prevent cracking.

After the bird has rested an attempt should be made first at suitable feeding or force feeding. Thereafter wash the affected parts in a warm solution of commercial washing-up liquid, ⅛th pint of detergent to 1 gallon of hand hot water at about 105°F holding the affected parts submerged, separating the feathers. A second similar wash is needed usually. Finally rinse in clean hand hot water. Dry by mopping with a clean cloth or in front of a warm 'air duct' and place at once in a *really warm place* in its covered box, e.g. under a hot towel rail, to rest.

Allow the bird to preen and to continue feeding as it gains strength and mobility. Do not launch it into the air until it shows clearly through wing flapping that it is ready and eager to fly away.

THE BIRDS

An Emperor Penguin rookery, with a McCormick's Skua looking for unprotected eggs or dead chicks.

PENGUINS   Spheniscidae

Penguins occur solely in the southern hemisphere, breeding and ranging from the Antarctic continent throughout the sub-antarctic islands from Cape Horn to New Zealand, extending to the southern coasts of S. America, S. Africa, Australia and New Zealand. Only the Emperor Penguin and Adelie Penguin breed on the south polar continent itself. The Galapagos Penguin takes advantage of the northern limit of the cold Humboldt Current to breed on the Galapagos Is., ranging only a few degrees south of the Equator.

Apart from the breeding and moulting period at their rookeries penguins spend their entire time at sea, dispersing in some cases northwards during the southern winter.

They are seldom seen on the sea routes. When they are observed, usually at no great distance from coasts, they are not easy to identify except by close observation of the pattern of their head, neck and bill, for they swim low in the water.

Penguins travel at great speed underwater using their flippers to propel them and their feet stretched out behind as rudders. They are sometimes seen progressing in a series of leaps clear of the water in the manner of porpoises. They feed principally on fish.

ADULT PENGUINS
Swimming

Emperor, p.7

King, p.7

Gentoo, p.7

Chin-strap, p.8

Adelie, p.7

Jackass, p.11
other *Spheniscus*
similar

Rock-hopper, p.9

Macaroni, p

JUVENILE PENGUINS
Swimming

Emperor, p.7

King, p.7

Gentoo, p.7

Adelie, p.7

Royal, p.9

Jackass, p.11 other *Spheniscus* are similar

Nesting and young

These species nest in colonies on or near the shore, on islands or coasts. They may take *c*. 4–7 years to reach maturity before breeding. The largest species have no nest; some species have open nests on bare ground lined with nearby material such as plant fragments or stones; while others nest among rocks, in crevices and hollows, or in burrows, and nests are composed of a variety of debris carried into these. The species using more open sites often nest very close together. The eggs of the largest species are pear-shaped but those of smaller species are more rounded. The eggs have an irregular white, chalk-like outer layer on a greenish-white shell, and often become very dirty during incubation. The clutch varies from 1 in the larger species to 2–3 in the smaller penguins, but *Eudyptes* species usually lay two, generally discarding the first egg and only incubating one. The Emperor and King Penguins incubate with the egg resting on top of the feet and covered by a fold of feathered skin from the belly. The other species incubate in a more normal manner. The Little or Blue Penguin is double-brooded.

Incubation in smaller species is from 33–40 days. Both adults incubate, the periods of alternate sitting varying with the species from 1 to 2½ weeks. The chicks have two successive coats of thick grey or brown down. They are brooded by the adults for 2–3 weeks. After this those nesting in more open colonies gather together in large numbers where they are visited by the parents for feeding. Those nesting in burrows tend to remain there until fledged. The young are fed by regurgitation, taking the food from inside the mouth of the adult. They become very large and fat before the final growth of feathers, appearing larger than the parents. The fledging periods usually varies from 7–10 weeks.

The King and Emperor Penguins have highly specialised breeding cycles. The growth period of the young necessitates a cycle including the winter months. In the King Penguin eggs may be laid from late November to April (late spring to early autumn in the southern hemisphere), and two cycles may be fitted into a three-year period. Incubation is shared by both birds sitting for periods of *c*. 2 weeks, and lasts for 53–55 days. The young are fed sparingly during the winter months and lose considerable weight, regaining this in the spring, but having remained with the adults for 10–13 months before leaving. The Emperor Penguin eggs are laid in the autumn (April onwards in the southern hemisphere). The female leaves and the male incubates alone for *c*. 64 days (during winter darkness), and then begins feeding the newly-hatched young with a crop secretion. The female then returns and feeds the chick for 2–3 weeks. Then both adults feed it and the chick grows rapidly. After *c*. 4 months the chick feathers and leaves, although only partly grown, continuing to grow in its first year.

General Distribution of Penguins on Continental Coasts

B = breeds. *S* = straggler. *W* = in southern winter months.

ANTARCTIC MAINLAND Emperor Penguin. Adelie Penguin.

AUSTRALIA Little or Blue Penguin, southern coasts, *B*. Fiordland Crested Penguin *S*, *W*.

NEW ZEALAND Little or Blue Penguin *B*. Erect-crested or Big-crested Penguin *W*. Fiordland Crested Penguin *B*. White-flippered Penguin *B*. Yellow-eyed Penguin *B*. Snares Crested Penguin *S* (breeds on Snares Is.). Royal Penguin *S*.

SOUTH AMERICA Humboldt Penguin, west coast, *B*. Magellan Penguin, southern east and west coasts *B*. Rock-hopper Penguin, southern east coast *W*.

SOUTH AFRICA Jackass Penguin, southern east and west coasts, *B*. Rock-hopper Penguin *S*, *W*.

For the purpose of defining height, penguins have been indicated as follows: Large: over 36 ins, 91 cm. Medium: 24–36 ins, 61–91 cm. Small: 20 ins, 51 cm and below.

KING PENGUIN *Aptenodytes patagonica* **Pages 4, 5 and Pl. 1**
Large, 36–38 ins, 91–96 cm. A handsome penguin rather smaller than Emperor Penguin. Top of head, cheeks and throat black; remainder of upperparts bluish-grey. Foreneck edged on each side by an orange band extending into a lozenge-shaped orange patch around the sides of the back of the head. An orange patch on foreneck, below which underparts white with narrow black line down each side of breast. Bill long, black with an orange-reddish slash at base of lower mandible. Legs black. Immatures similar but patches on foreneck yellow, and bill entirely black.

Stance very erect. Incubates egg in similar manner to Emperor Penguin.
RANGE: Southern oceans breeding on Staten I. South Georgia, Falkland Is, Marion, Crozet, Kerguelen, Heard, and Macquarie Is. Map 1.

EMPEROR PENGUIN *Aptenodytes forsteri* **Pages 4, 5 and Pl. 1**
Large, 48 ins, 122 cm. The largest penguin, and with the much smaller Adelie Penguin the only penguin species which breed on the antarctic continent. Top of head, cheeks, chin and throat black; remainder of upperparts bluish-grey. A wide orange-yellow semi-circular band sweeps around the sides of the upper neck merging into the white foreneck, and a black band borders the front of the shoulder ending in a point at the lower neck. Underparts and under-surface of flipper white. Bill long, bluish-black, curving downwards towards tip, showing a red slash along base of lower mandible. Legs black. Immature similar but band on sides of neck white.

Unique among penguins in incubating its one egg during period of total antarctic winter darkness. Stands upright with egg balanced on feet and covered by pouch of skin.
RANGE: Antarctic continent and seas to edge of pack ice. Map 2.

GENTOO PENGUIN *Pygoscelis papua* **Pages 4, 5 and Pl. 1**
Medium, 30 ins, 76 cm. Head, neck and throat brownish-black. A conspicuous white band extends over the back of the head from eye to eye. Remainder of upperparts slate-grey; underparts white. Flipper edged with white, underside white, black at tip. Bill orange or red, upper edge of upper mandible black. Legs orange. Immature similar but some grey mottling on throat. Easily distinguished at a distance by white band on head. Swims with head and back above water.
RANGE: Islands adjacent to Antarctica, breeding also at S. Shetlands, S. Orkneys, S. Georgia, Falkland, Staten, Bouvet, Marion, Crozet, Kerguelen, Heard and Macquarie Is. Map 3.

ADELIE PENGUIN *Pygoscelis adeliae* **Pages 4, 5 and Pl. 1**
Medium, 30 ins, 76 cm. Top of head, cheeks and throat black, the black extending to a point on foreneck, eyelids white. Upperparts bluish-black. Underparts conspicuously white. The stubby bill brick red; legs pinkish-white; tail noticeably long.

Immature similar but throat white; eyelids black; bill black.

A most engaging and inquisitive penguin. Stance upright; walks with waddling gait, frequently tobogganning over snow on its breast; swims very low in water with back submerged; 'porpoises' out of water at times.

RANGE Antarctic seas to outer edge of pack ice. Breeds on coast of Antarctica, and adjacent sub-antarctica islands, S. Shetlands, S. Orkneys, S. Sandwich Is. and Bouvet I.　Map 4.

CHIN-STRAP or BEARDED PENGUIN *Pygoscelis antarctica*

Page 4 and Pl 1

Medium, 30 ins, 76 cm. Crown and forehead black, remainder of upperparts bluish-grey. Sides of head, throat, neck and underparts white. A black line like a chin-strap extends round the throat from ear to ear. Under-surface of flipper white, outer margin black. Bill black, legs pinkish-white. Immatures similar.

Facial marking and chin strap unlike any other penguin.

RANGE: Antarctic seas and adjacent islands, breeding also at S. Shetlands, S. Orkneys, S. Sandwich Is., S. Georgia, Bouvet and Heard Is.　Map 5.

FIORDLAND CRESTED PENGUIN *Eudyptes pachyrhynchus*　Pl. 2

Medium, 28 ins, 71 cm. Forehead and crown bluish-black, cheeks, chin and throat dark slate-grey, white streaks showing on cheeks. Pale line of yellow feathers extends from nostril, above the eye, along sides of crown, the posterior feathers neither elongated nor drooping. Underparts white; iris bright reddish-brown; bill reddish-brown; legs pale flesh-colour, soles black. Immatures similar but chin and throat whitish, and features of crest only partially developed.

RANGE: Breeds on southern and south-western coasts of South Island, New Zealand. Occurs occasionally on coasts of Tasmania and Southern Australia.　Map 6.

SNARES CRESTED PENGUIN *Eudyptes robustus*　Pl. 2

Medium, 29 ins, 73 cm. Similar to the Fiordland Crested Penguin but more robust, darker in colour, especially about the chin, throat and cheeks which are almost black, feathers being dark based. The yellow superciliary crest is brighter and narrower with a more bushy end. Bill large with pink not grey skin at the corner; light reddish-brown. Legs flesh-colour. Immatures similar but chin and throat whitish, and feathers of crest only partially developed.

RANGE: Breeds only at Snares Is., New Zealand, and wanders to nearby parts of South Island.　Map 7.

ERECT-CRESTED or BIG-CRESTED PENGUIN *Eudyptes sclateri* Pl. 2

Medium, 28 ins, 71 cm. Whole head, chin, throat and upperparts bluish-black; underparts white. A bright yellow crest extends on each side from the base of the bill, above the eye to the back of the crown. When erected, this curves up sharply from the gape culminating as a bristle at the back of the crown. Iris red; bill light brown; legs pale flesh-coloured with black soles.

Immatures are similar but the chin and throat are mottled and the yellow crest is barely visible.

RANGE: Breeds on Bounty Is., Antipodes, Campbell and Auckland Is. Visits Cook Strait in southern winter. Stragglers reach Tasmania and Southern Australia.　Map 8.

ROCK-HOPPER PENGUIN *Eudyptes crestatus*   **Page 4 and Pl. 2**
Medium, 25 ins, 63 cm. Head, sides of face, chin and throat blackish-slate, blacker
on crown with slightly elongated feathers. Remainder of upperparts bluish-grey;
underparts pure white. A narrow line of golden-yellow feathers extends from
behind the nostril feathers, above the eye and along the sides of the crown terminating in greatly elongated plumes. Iris red; bill dull orange-red; legs flesh-colour,
soles black.

Immatures are similar but show an ashy-white chin, and a faint whitish-yellow
eyebrow with no elongated plumes.

RANGE: Breeds at Tierra del Fuego, Falkland Is., Tristan da Cunha, Gough, Prince
Edward, Marion, Crozet, St Paul, Amsterdam Is., Kerguelen, Heard Is. and
Bounty, Antipodes, Aukland, Campbell, Snares and Macquarie Is. off New Zealand. Stragglers sometimes occur off the southern tip of Africa and western and
southern coasts of Australia.   Map 9.

ROYAL PENGUIN *Eudyptes schlegeli*   **Page 5 and Pl. 2**
Medium, 26–30 ins, 66–76 cm. Upperparts light bluish-grey; sides of head and neck,
chin, throat and underparts white. Some species have the sides of the face grey but
there may be considerable variation. An orange crest of elongated plumes extends
from the centre and sides of the forehead backwards and downwards on either side
behind the eye. Eyes bright geranium-red; bill pale reddish-brown; legs
flesh-coloured, soles black. Immatures similar to adult but lack the golden plumes.

Adults differ from other crested penguins in their white or partially grey cheeks
and throats.

RANGE: Breeds on Macquarie I. A straggler to New Zealand coasts.   Not mapped.

light phase   dark phase

ROYAL PENGUIN. There is considerable variation in the pattern of facial and head plumage.
Most have chin, throat and side of head white; others are more or less greyish and some even
dark slate grey, almost like a Macaroni Penguin.

MACARONI PENGUIN *Eudyptes chrysolophus*   **Page 4 and Pl. 2**
Medium, 26–30 ins, 66–76 cm. Head, chin and throat black, remainder of upperparts dark bluish-grey. Underparts white. Across the forehead and along the sides
of the crown a series of long golden feathers occur having black pointed tips. The
longest golden plumes extend above and behind the eye. Flipper bluish-grey above,
inner margin with white edge, underneath white with black outer margin. Bill black
with reddish tip, pink at base. Legs pinkish. Immatures similar but plumes only
partially developed and yellow.

Plumes in the Rock-hopper Penguin are pale yellow and do not meet across the forehead.

RANGE: Islands adjacent to Antarctica, and breeds also at S. Shetlands, S. Orkneys, S. Sandwich Is., S. Georgia, Falkland Is., Bouvet, Prince Edward, Marion, Kerguelen and Heard Is.   Map 10.

YELLOW-EYED PENGUIN   *Megadyptes antipodes*   Pl. 2

Medium, 30 ins, 76 cm. Upperparts slate-grey. Forehead and crown pale golden showing black shaft stripes; cheeks and chin pale golden; throat and sides of neck brown; remainder of underparts white. A pale yellow band of short feathers extends from behind the eye backwards encircling the crown. Iris yellow; bill flesh-coloured, dull brown on culmen and at tip of mandibles; legs pale flesh-coloured.

Immatures are similar but yellow band is confined to the sides of the head only.

RANGE: Breeds on east coast of South Island, New Zealand, and at Stewart I., Auckland and Campbell Is., and occurs occasionally in the Cook Strait.   Map 11.

LITTLE or BLUE PENGUIN   *Eudyptula minor*   Pl. 2

Small, 16 ins, 40 cm. Crown, hindneck and upperparts deep slate-blue; sides of face below eyes grey; remainder of face, chin, throat and underparts white. Iris silver-grey; bill short and stout, black; legs pale flesh-coloured, soles black. Immatures similar but upperparts brighter blue.

RANGE: Breeds all round coast of South Island, New Zealand, Tasmania and southern and south-western coasts of Australia.   Map 12.

WHITE-FLIPPERED PENGUIN   *Eudyptula albosignata*   Pl. 2

Small, 16 ins, 42 cm. Crown, hindneck and upperparts pale slate-grey; sides of face below eyes, chin, throat and underparts white. Iris silver-grey; bill black; legs pale flesh-coloured, black on soles. Immatures similar.

Very similar and cannot be distinguished from Little Penguin in the water. On land a broad white margin on the upper side of both edges of the flippers, and in males a central white patch also serves to distinguish it.

RANGE: Breeds on Banks Peninsula on east coast of New Zealand and occurs in the Cook Strait.   Map 13.

normal   flavistic   albino

All penguins could show flavistic or albino phases like these Jackass Penguins. Where more than one species occurs, identification of these rare colour mutations is very difficult, except by size and bill shapes.

JACKASS PENGUIN *Spheniscus demersus*   **Pages 4, 5, 10 and Pl. 1**
Medium, 25–27 ins, 63–68 cm. Forehead, crown, sides of face, chin, throat and
remainder of upperparts black; underparts white. A white band extends from the
base of the upper mandible, above the eye, curving downwards dividing the black
crown from the black sides of face and joining the white underparts. A very narrow
black horseshoe band crosses the breast and extends along the sides to the flanks.
Bill stout and rather long, black with a grey transverse bar. Legs black, mottled with
grey, soles black. Immatures have black upperparts and plain white underparts.
    The only penguin common to the southern coasts of South Africa.
RANGE: From Angola on west coast to Natal on east coast. Breeds on islands off
the S. African coast.   Map 14.

HUMBOLDT PENGUIN *Spheniscus humboldti*   **Pl. 1**
Medium, 27 ins, 68 cm. Forehead, crown, sides of head and throat black, upperparts slate-grey. Chin and underparts white. A narrow white band extends from the
base of the bill around the sides of the crown on each side continuing round the
black throat.
    A single black horseshoe band surrounds the breast extending down the sides to
the tail. Bill stout, blackish, flesh-coloured at base; legs blackish, soles black.
    Immatures show no horseshoe band. The chin, throat and sides of head are grey;
sides and front of neck dark brown.
    Considerably larger than Galapagos Penguin, has one horseshoe band only and
ranges much further to the south.
RANGE: West coast of S. America from Peru to about 35°S. where it overlaps with
Magellan Penguin.   Map 15.

MAGELLAN PENGUIN *Spheniscus magellanicus*   **Pl. 1**
Medium, 28 ins, 71 cm. Crown, sides of face and throat black; chin white. Remainder of upperparts slate-grey. A white band extends from the base of the bill above
the eye, curving downwards dividing the black crown from sides of face and
running under the black throat. A black band extends around the white foreneck,
and an additional black horseshoe band crosses the breast and extends down the
sides to the flanks. Bill blackish; legs mottled blackish, soles black.
    Immatures are similar but the throat and the upper band on foreneck dark grey.
    Overlaps at its extreme northern range on west coast of S. America with Hum-
boldt Penguin which shows only a single horseshoe band.
RANGE: Breeds on coasts and islands on west coast of Chile and Juan Fernandez,
on Staten I., Tierra del Fuego, Falkland Is., and on east coast north to Point
Tombo, 44°S., 65°20'W.   Map 16.

GALAPAGOS PENGUIN *Spheniscus mendiculus*   **Pl. 1**
Small, 20 ins, 50 cm. Forehead, crown, sides of head and throat black, upperparts
slate-grey. Chin and underparts white. A narrow white band extends from the base
of the bill around the sides of the crown on each side, continuing round the black
throat. A black band surrounds the white underparts beneath the foreneck, and an
additional black horseshoe band surrounds the breast extending down the sides.
Bill has a black upper mandible and yellow lower mandible with black tip. Legs
black with white mottling, soles black.
    Breeds only on the Galapagos Is. and rarely seen at any distance from the islands.
Cannot be confused with any other penguin.   Not mapped.

Black-browed Albatrosses

ALBATROSSES   Diomedeidae

Albatrosses are easily recognised in flight by their large size, very long narrow wings and distinctive flight. The smaller albatrosses, those having dark backs and upperwings, are often referred to by seafarers as "Mollymawks". Of the thirteen species, nine are confined to the southern oceans, three to the N. Pacific and one to the tropics.

In the most usual flight pattern they plane on flexed pinions with barely a wing beat, gaining height into the wind while losing some air speed, then turning across wind, swooping downwards towards the sea to leeward, thus gaining speed, before banking sharply again into the wind. This they repeat for hours on end. In high winds their wings may be raked back steeply from the carpal joint. They will alight readily on the sea, and find it necessary to run along the surface into the wind before becoming airborne. Their webbed feet are carried open in flight on each side of the tail.

A distinctive feature is the nature of the stout hooked bill, consisting of a number of horny plates, the nostril openings being placed on each side of the middle plate of the upper mandible in short tubes.

In adults the colour pattern of upper- and underwing and the particular colour of their bills provides the best clue to their identity, but the variable colour of immature plumage can be confusing.

In the open sea albatrosses feed from the surface largely on squid and krill, also eating fish, usually only dipping the head and bill beneath the surface. They are equally ready to eat blubber and floating refuse. Probably for this reason they will follow ships for long distances by day, alighting at the stern with wings raised and joining with Giant Petrels, Cape Pigeons and other species in a scramble for scraps thrown overboard from the galley.

Nesting and young

These nest on islands where sites provide good facilities for take-off. In general the incubation, fledging and maturation periods are longer in the larger species. Maturation is slow and birds may not breed until 6–10 years old. Nest sites may be bare hollows in tropical species but are usually largish cones of mud and vegetable matter with a hollow in the top. A single large egg is laid, white or finely marked with red at the larger end. Incubation varies from 60–70 days in smaller species to c. 80 days in larger ones. The male takes the first period after the female has laid the egg. Periods of alternate sitting may be 1½–3 weeks long. The chick has two successive coats of pale grey or whitish down, and is brooded by a parent for the first 3–5 weeks after which it is visited and fed at intervals, with apparently no desertion period, chicks having been seen to be fed at intervals until the time of departure. The chicks are fed on regurgitated food, placing the bill inside the adult's and at right angles to it. Fledging varies from 4–4½ months in smaller species to 9 months in the Wandering Albatross. In the latter the total cycle is 11 months, and successful breeders breed only once in two years.

14

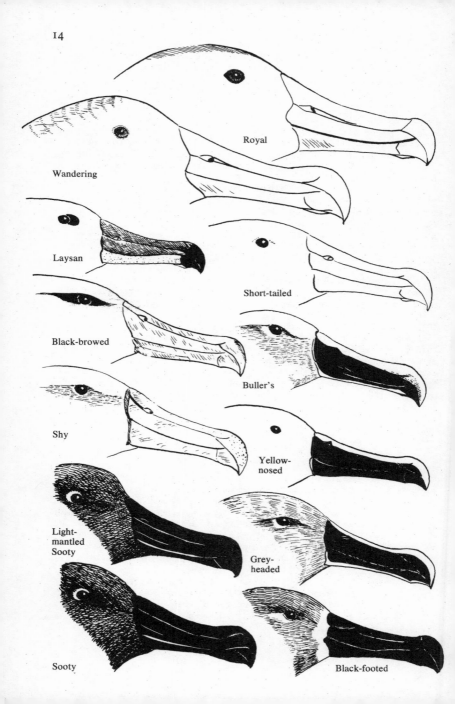

After the wing pattern, the colour of albatross bills are a very important character for the identification of species.

Royal Albatross, *Diomedea epomophora*, p.17
Bill faintly pink, cutting edges of both mandibles black.

Wandering Albatross, *Diomedea exulans*, p.16
Bill flesh-coloured.

Laysan Albatross, *Diomedea immutabilis*, p.18
Bill greyish; base of the mandible yellow.

Short-tailed Albatross, *Diomedea albatrus*, p.17
Bill flesh-coloured.

Black-browed Albatross, *Diomedea melanophris*, p.18
Bill yellow with a pink tip.

Shy Albatross, *Diomedea cauta*, p.19
Bill grey, with distinct orange tip; bluish lateral plates run up in front of eye; dark horseshoe stripe behind nostril.

Buller's Albatross, *Diomedea bulleri*, p.19
Bill greyish black, with a yellow stripe along the upper and mandibles. Upper plate widens noticeably at base.

Yellow-nosed Albatross, *Diomedea chlororhynchos*, p.19
Bill black, with a bright yellow line along the ridge of the upper mandible; bright orange tip.

Grey-headed Albatross, *Diomedea chrysostoma*, p.20
Bill blackish; yellow stripe along upper and lower mandibles, ending with bright pink tip.

Light-mantled Sooty Albatross, *Phoebetria palpebrata*, p.21
Bill black with pale blue line along the side.

Sooty Albatross, *Phoebetria fusca*, p. 20
Bill black, with a yellow line along lower mandible.

Black-footed Albatross, *Diomedea nigriceps*, p.17
Bill dark brown.

WANDERING ALBATROSS *Diomedea exulans* **Page 14 and Pl. 3**
Outsize, 44–48 ins, 117 cm. Wing-span 114–130 ins, 324 cm. The Wandering Albatross takes many years to adopt full adult plumage and is more often seen in one of its intermediate phases. The full adult is pure white below, except for a narrow black border along the trailing edge of the wing and the black primary wing tips. Back is pure white in extreme southern breeding birds, in others shows a few dark vermiculations. Upper wing surfaces white with a little dark speckling. Females sometimes carry a dark crown patch on their white heads. Eyes are dark brown; bill massive, pale flesh-coloured; legs pale flesh-coloured.

In the youngest immatures only the side of the face, throat and part of the underwing are white, the remainder of the body, wings and tail brown. At a later stage the underparts become progressively whiter, the last brown appearing as a mottled brown band across the chest. On the upperparts the mantle is the first to become mottled white, the brown receding from neck to tail. The upper wings do not begin to turn white until the body is more or less clear of mottling. At this stage a white patch appears on each upper wing as the white plumage spreads across the wings. Finally the brown tail is replaced by white. The bill, whitish in young birds becomes flesh-coloured as do the legs. The whole development to full adult plumage will cover probably not less than five years.

Note: In flight the bill is usually angled slightly downwards, and at a distance the heavy bill, peaked crown and humped back are characteristic.

RANGE: Throughout the southern oceans between approximately 60°S. and 25°S.; but tends to disperse further north in the southern winter and has been met with at 15°S. Breeds at S. Georgia, Tristan da Cunha, Gough, Marion and Crozet Is., Amsterdam and St. Paul Is., Kerguelen I., Campbell, Antipodes and Auckland Is. and Macquarie I. Map 17.

WANDERING ALBATROSS. Typical courting display at breeding colonies accompanied by hoarse cries and groaning prior to mating.

ROYAL ALBATROSS *Diomedea epomophora*   **Page 14 and Pl. 3**
(A) outsize, 48 ins, 122 cm. Wing-span 120 ins, 305 cm. Adult; (B) mostly white, primaries and secondaries black, thin dark margin to trailing edge of underwing; (C) bill faintly pink, cutting edges of both mandibles black, observable at sea at close range; (D) legs bluish-white; (E) immatures similar to adults.
RANGE: Largely localised to seas around New Zealand, although a few reach the coastal waters off the south of S. America, and stragglers off southern Australia.
RACES:
> ROYAL ALBATROSS   *Diomedea e. epomophora*   **Page 14 and Pl. 3**
> Breeds on Campbell and Auckland Is.; (B) Traces of grey on some scapulars and wing-coverts, pure white in most southerly ranging birds.   Map 18.
> ROYAL ALBATROSS (Northern Race)   *Diomedea e. sanfordi*   **Pl. 3**
> Breeds on Chatham I. and Otago Peninsula; (B) upperwings show variable dark flecking, sometimes entirely dark blackish-brown.   Map 18.

WAVED ALBATROSS *Diomedea irrorata*   **Pl. 4**
Very large, 35 ins, 89 cm. Wing-span 82 ins, 208 cm. In adults the head and neck are white, nape noticeably tinged with buff, upper back and rump dusky. The back, wings and tail are greyish-brown, and the underparts and underwings dusky-white. The bill is yellow and legs bluish-white. Young birds have an overall brownish plumage.
  Note: The Waved Albatross is the only albatross existing entirely within the tropics.
RANGE: Breeds on the Galapagos Is. and winters over the Humboldt Current off Ecuador and Peru.   Map 19.

SHORT-TAILED ALBATROSS *Diomedea albatrus*   **Page 14 and Pl. 3**
Outsize, 37 ins, 94 cm. Wing-span 84 ins, 213 cm. Adult in fully developed plumage is white except for totally black upperwings and a black band on tail. The back between the wings is white. The white head and nape are diffused with yellow. The bill is pink and proportionally large; around its base a thin conspicuous black line extending back along edge of mouth to gape. Legs flesh-colour. Fully fledged juveniles are completely black, replaced progressively as they grow older by white, beginning with bill, face and legs. Birds become breeding adults before the fully developed black-and-white pattern is reached.
  In their earlier dark stage they may resemble the Black-footed Albatross, but their pale bills and legs distinguish them.
RANGE: Confined to the North Pacific, possibly spreading throughout the Western quarter. A very rare species breeding only on Torishima I. in the Isa Is. Recent reports indicated a total breeding population of about 57 pairs.   Map 20.

BLACK-FOOTED ALBATROSS *Diomedea nigripes*   **Page 14 and Pl. 6**
Large, 28 ins, 71 cm. Wing-span 80 ins, 203 cm. Overall sooty-brown plumage, slightly paler on forehead and cheeks, and with a white area around the base of the dark brown bill. Legs black. Adults are easily identifiable.
  Young birds usually have a more extensive white area around the forepart of the head and whitish upper tail-coverts. Young birds of the race Short-tailed Albatross *Diomedea albatrus* are similar but rather darker and can be distinguished by their pink bills and flesh-coloured legs, and lack of white on face or rump.
  The Black-footed Albatross is an inveterate ship follower and is usually to be seen gliding back and forth across the wake looking for garbage. When alighting on

the sea it usually keeps its wings spread unless remaining on the water for some time. It is bolder than the Laysan Albatross which may be seen in company but which tends to hold off further from a ship.
RANGE: Across the entire breadth of the N. Pacific from approximately 20°N. to 55°N. and commonly seen between 30°N. and 45°N. in summer on completion of its breeding season. Breeds on the leeward Hawaiian Is.   Map 21.

LAYSAN ALBATROSS *Diomedea immutabilis*   **Page 14 and Pl. 4**
Large, 32 ins, 81 cm. Wing-span 80 ins, 203 cm. In adults the head, neck, rump, upper tail-coverts and underparts are white. A dark spot shows in front of the eye. The back and upperwings are dark sooty-brown, and the white tail carries a dark terminal band. Underwings have broad dark margins with dark areas encroaching into the white central lining from the leading edge. The bill is greyish with the base of the mandible yellow. Legs flesh-coloured.
    Young birds are similar.
    The Laysan Albatross may often be seen following ships in the N. Pacific and is the only white albatross with sooty-brown upperwings and back in the N. Pacific.
RANGE: Across the entire breadth of the N. Pacific from approximately 30°N. to 45°N., extending to 55°N. in the northern summer after the breeding season. Breeds on the leeward Hawaiian Is.   Map 22.

BLACK-BROWED ALBATROSS *Diomedea melanophris* **Page 14 and Pl. 5**
Very large, 32–34 ins, 81–86 cm. Wing-span 90 ins, 229 cm. Head, neck, rump, upper tail-coverts and underbody white. Upperparts and upper wing surfaces brownish-black, back and tail slightly greyer-black. Central white underwing linings are edged by broad smudgy blackish margins, wider in front. The yellow bill is stout and has a pink tip. Legs pinkish, webs pale blue. At close quarters a dark streak shows above and behind the eye tending to give a 'frowning' appearance. Young birds have dusky-grey heads and necks, and grey merging gradually into the white of the underbody, greyish-black bills, and the undersurface of the wings mainly dark. In many sub-adults the bill appears yellow with a dark tip.
    Its thick 'neckless' and 'hump-backed' appearance, yellow bill and much broader dark underwing margins distinguishes it from the more slender and black-billed

BLACK-BROWED ALBATROSS. In calm weather heavy flapping and violent leg action is used to become airborne. The beating of their feet can be heard at a considerable distance.

Yellow-nosed Albatross. Immature Black-browed Albatrosses are difficult to distinguish from immature Grey-headed Albatrosses (see Grey-headed Albatrosses, pp. 14 and 20).
RANGE: S. Pacific, S. Atlantic and S. Indian Oceans and Australian and New Zealand seas from approx. 55°S. to 30°S. but dispersing even further than northern limit during the southern winter in areas of cold currents. Breeds on Staten I. and islands off Cape Horn, the Falkland Is., S. Georgia, Kerguelen and Heard Is., Campbell, Antipodes and Macquarie Is. Map 23.

BULLER'S ALBATROSS *Diomedea bulleri*   **Page 14 and Pl. 4**
Very large, 34 ins, 86 cm. Wing-span 84 ins, 213 cm. Buller's Albatross is the rarest of the southern ocean albatrosses. In adult plumage the cheeks and hindneck are grey (reported from sea as appearing a delicate pale blue-grey), the forehead white. A dark patch shows in front of the eye. Back and upperwings are sooty-brown, rump, upper tail-coverts and underparts white. The central portion of the underwing is white, the leading edge carrying a dark margin, the trailing edge a fine dark margin. Bill greyish-black with a yellow band along both the upper and lower mandibles. The upper plate of the bill widens noticeably at its base. Legs bluish-white. Tail sooty-brown.
    Adult Buller's and Grey-headed Albatrosses may easily be confused unless the particular differences in plumage are studied.
RANGE: Like the Royal Albatross it is to be seen chiefly in the seas closely surrounding New Zealand, but has also been reported eastwards off the southern coast of Chile. Rarely strays north of 40°N. Breeds on Chatham Is., Solander and Snares Is. Map 24.

SHY or WHITE-CAPPED ALBATROSS *Diomedea cauta* **Page 14 and Pl. 4**
Outsize, 35–39 ins, 89–99 cm. Wing-span 96 ins, 243 cm. Considerably larger than other southern ocean 'Mollymawks'. In adults the forehead white, and, in birds seen in southern seas around Australia and New Zealand, the crown and neck are white. Head, nape and cheeks grey. Upperwings and tail greyish-brown, back pale greyish. Remainder of body white. The whole underwing is white except for very narrow dark margins and a dark tip. The eye shows a greyish-black eye socket. Bill grey with distinct orange tip, deep at base, with bluish lateral plates running up in front of the eye and a dark horseshoe stripe behind the nostrils. An orange stripe shows behind the base of lower mandible. Legs bluish-flesh-coloured. Immatures similar but have dark grey bills. Breeds on Albatross Rock in Bass Strait, off Tasmania and Auckland I. off New Zealand. Map 25.
    The flight is similar to the Wandering Albatross with a tendency to turn and bank more sharply. The Shy Albatross usually keep well clear of ships.
RANGE: Southern oceans ranging as far north as 25°S. Breeds on islands in the Bass Strait, off the southern coast of Tasmania and on the Auckland Is. Occurs at sea off both sides of S. Africa. Map 25.

YELLOW-NOSED ALBATROSS *Diomedea chlororhynchos* **Page 14 and Pl. 5**
Very large, 29–34 ins, 74–86 cm. Wing-span 80 ins, 20 cm. A noticeably neater and more slender bird than the Black-browed Albatross, lacking the thick 'neckless' and 'hump-backed' appearance of the latter.
    Head and neck white, sides and back of head slightly pale grey. Dark feathers around the eye appear as a triangular patch. The back is sooty-black, the upper wings and tail dark brownish-black, as in Black-browed Albatross. The underwing

has much more white than either the Black-browed or Grey-headed, edged with a clearly defined thin black margin in which the leading edge is broader than the trailing edge. The black underwing tip is formed by a sudden widening of the black margin along the trailing edge. The bill is more slender than that of the previous species, is black with a bright yellow line along the ridge of the upper mandible, and terminates in a bright orange tip. Legs flesh-colour.

Immatures are similar with pure white heads and entirely black bills.

RANGE: S. Atlantic and Indian Oceans eastwards to Australia and New Zealand seas between approximately 50°S. and 25°S., extending further north in the southern winter. Breeds on Tristan da Cunha and Gough Is. and Amsterdam and St. Paul Is.

Is often the first species of Albatross to be observed by ships on southerly sea routes to S. Africa, Australia and S. America appearing sometimes within the Tropic of Capricorn (23½°S.). Map 26.

GREY-HEADED ALBATROSS *Diomedea chrysostoma* Page 14 and Pl. 5

Large, 28–32 ins, 71–81 cm. Wing-span 80 ins, 203 cm. In adult plumage the whole head and neck are dusky-grey, or slate-grey. A distinct half circle of white feathers surrounds the back of the eye. Upperwings sooty-brown; back and tail dark grey, rump, upper tail-coverts and underparts white. The central portion of the underwing is white with dark tips and margins on both leading and trailing edges, wider from the carpal joint inwards on the leading edge. The bill is blackish with a yellow stripe along the upper and lower mandibles ending with a bright pink tip, a feature visible at some distance in good light. Immature birds resemble adults but are somewhat browner above, with slaty-grey heads, the underwings with considerably broader dark margins and bills greyish-black.

The early immature plumages of the Grey-headed and Black-browed Albatrosses are very similar. In the Grey-headed Albatross the whole head and neck looks brownish-grey and is sharply divided from the white on throat and breast, quite distinct from the manner in which the grey blends gradually into the white in the young Black-browed Albatross. At a later stage the head of the Black-browed Albatross becomes white and bill more yellow, while the head of the Grey-headed Albatross always remains grey and the bill dark.

RANGE: Remains in high southern latitudes throughout the year, dispersing throughout the southern oceans between 60°S. and 40°S. Reaches the seas off southern Australia in winter. Breeds at Cape Horn, Falkland Is., S. Georgia, Prince Edward and Crozet Is., Kerguelen, Campbell, Antipodes and Macquarie Is. Map 27.

SOOTY ALBATROSS *Phoebetria fusca* Page 14 and Pl. 6

Large, 32 ins, 81 cm. Wing-span 78 ins, 198 cm. Sooty-brown overall, the wings and head being darker, the back and underparts slightly paler. As in the Light-mantled Sooty Albatross a white ring of short feathers almost encircles the eye and the long tail is wedge-shaped. The bill is black with a yellow line along the lower mandible. The legs are pale flesh-coloured. Young birds are brown overall and indistinguishable from young Light-mantled Sooty Albatrosses.

The flight is similar to that of the Light-mantled Sooty Albatross and excels that of the larger albatrosses in grace and variation. This is the bird into which the ancient seafarers believed that the souls of men drowned overboard passed and that intended in 'The Rime of the Ancient Mariner'.

RANGE: Eastern S. Atlantic eastwards through S. Indian Ocean between 50°S. and 30°S. Ranges further north than the Light-mantled Sooty Albatross. Breeds at Tristan da Cunha and Gough Is., St. Paul and Amsterdam Is. Map 28.

LIGHT-MANTLED SOOTY ALBATROSS *Phoebetria palpebrata*
Page 14 and Pl. 6

Large, 28 ins, 71 cm. Wing-span 82 ins, 208 cm. The two dark mollymawks, the Light-mantled Sooty Albatross and the Sooty Albatross of the southern oceans are somewhat similar.

In the Light-mantled Sooty Albatross the head is dark greyish-brown, the back and underparts ash-grey, and the wings greyish-brown with blacker primaries. A conspicuous white ring encircles the eye, broken in front. The noticeably long wedge-shaped tail appears black, the bill also is black and shows a pale blue line along its side. The legs are pale flesh-coloured. Young birds of both species are browner overall and indistinguishable at sea.

The two species are the most graceful of all the albatrosses in flight having a quality of manoeuvre unequalled by the larger albatrosses.

RANGE: Disperses throughout the southern oceans between 55°S. and 35°S., breeding on islands in the higher latitudes and dispersing towards its northern limits in the southern winter. Ranges further south than the Sooty Albatross. Breeds at S. Georgia, Bouvet, Kerguelen and Heard Is., Campbell, Auckland, Antipodes and Macquarie Is. Map 29.

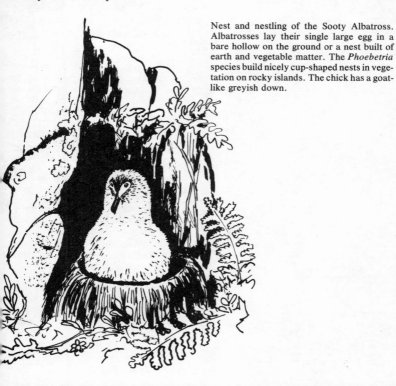

Nest and nestling of the Sooty Albatross. Albatrosses lay their single large egg in a bare hollow on the ground or a nest built of earth and vegetable matter. The *Phoebetria* species build nicely cup-shaped nests in vegetation on rocky islands. The chick has a goat-like greyish down.

Manx Shearwaters returning to their nesting burrows at night.

PETRELS and SHEARWATERS   Procellariidae

The principal distinguishing feature of this family of oceanic seabirds is in the character of the bill which is slightly hooked at the tip and with two nostrils opening together at the end of a double tube on the upper mandible. For this reason they are sometimes referred to as 'tube-noses'.

Except when breeding they spend their whole life at sea adapting themselves to the severest storms, constantly on the wing gliding, banking, shearwatering, or swooping in high arcs making use of the up currents of wind along the weather side of the troughs of the swell, and rising above the breaking crests of the comers. Indeed it appears that they must be able to exist without true sleep for long periods. Their food consists chiefly of crustacea, organic plankton, squids, and fish, diving below the surface as necessary, and in some cases floating scraps which come their way.

Viewed as they so often are at some distance from a ship the particular characteristics of their flight assists in differentiating between them.

Nesting and young

A few species nest on open ground or on ledges, but most nest in burrows or natural crevices and cavities in rocks. The breeding sites are usually in colonies, often large, on islands, rocky shores, cliff-tops and screes, usually on the coast but in some instances well inland on mountain slopes, sometimes necessitating a flight over forest. The burrow may be dug by the birds themselves. Plant material from around a burrow mouth may be gradually dragged down to form a nest pad. The single white egg is large for the size of the bird. Incubation varies from $c.$ 40–60 days, according to species, and both birds sit for alternate periods of 2–12 days. The eggs and young can survive periods of neglect and chilling, presumably an adaptation to the long gaps between change-over of incubation and the infrequent visits of the parents. Young in burrows are only brooded for the first 2–3 days, and then only visited at intervals for feeding, but species nesting in open sites may guard the young for the first fortnight. The young have two successive thick coats of greyish or brownish down. They are fed by regurgitation, placing their bills crosswise in those of the adults. In many species they can defend themselves by spitting quantities of oil. They become very large and fat but lose this while the feathers are growing. The adults may continue to visit the young until they leave the nest. Fledging takes 45–55 days in the smaller species, and up to 100–135 days in the largest.

SOUTHERN GIANT PETREL *Macronectes giganteus*   **Pl. 7**
Outsize, 33–36 ins, 84–92 cm. Wing span 84 ins, 213 cm. The Giant Petrel is as large
as a small albatross, males being larger and with heavier bills than females. The
more normal plumage is a dusky grey-brown, much paler on the head, neck and
throat. As feather plumage wears, a more mottled appearance is frequently apparent. A noticeable feature is its enormous plated bill, usually greenish-yellow, and its
elongated nasal tube. Its small pale eyes are shrouded by a ridge of feathers, giving
the bird an unpleasant frown. Legs vary from brown to sooty-black. Young birds
are uniformly rich chocolate-brown with darker eyes, but otherwise similar to
adults. Its wings are narrower than those of albatrosses, and its flight appears
ungainly in comparison, flapping awkwardly or gliding in a stiff-winged attitude
with humped back and head held low. It frequently follows ships in search of refuse.
Amongst the more southerly breeding colonies birds with predominantly white or
almost pure white plumage occur, and may be seen occasionally in the higher
latitudes.
RANGE: Throughout the southern oceans from the Antarctic to the Tropic of
Capricorn and even further north. Breeds on the antarctic continent, on many
sub-antarctic islands, S. Shetlands, S. Orkneys, S. Sandwich Is., S. Georgia.
Falkland Is., Bouvet and Heard Is. and Macquarie Is. Nests socially, eggs in late
October.   Map 30.

Giant Petrels scavenging on a dead seal washed onto the beach.

NORTHERN GIANT PETREL *Macronectes halli*   **Pl. 6, 7**
Outsize, 33–36 ins, 84–92 cm. Wing-span 84 ins, 213 cm. The northern species has a
darker brown body and head, pale face and freckled cheeks and a darker
yellowish-brown bill with dark marks at tip. Young birds however show a less dark
plumage than those of the southern species. In flight its characteristics are similar to
the southern species. There is no white phase.
RANGE: Breeds on islands chiefly north of the Antarctic Convergence on Gough,
Marion and Crozet Is., Kerguelen Is., Chatham, Stewart, Snares, Auckland,
Campbell and Macquarie Is. Some overlapping occurs. Nests singly unlike the
social habits of the southern species and earlier in the year. Eggs from late August.
    Both species overlap at sea, more particularly immatures of the southern species
which disperse northwards, but to an observer at sea the differences will not be
apparent except in the case of a white bird of the southern species.   Map 31.

NORTHERN FULMAR *Fulmarus glacialis* **Pl. 11**
Medium size, 19–20 ins, 48–51 cm. Wing span 42 ins, 107 cm. At a distance its pearl-grey upperparts, white head, neck and underparts in its light phase give it a resemblance to a gull. At closer quarters its thick neck, stout yellowish slightly hooked tubenose bill, dusky spot in front of its dark eye, slate-grey primaries and pale patch near the tip of each wing are distinctive. Its legs are pale flesh-coloured or bluish. In its northern range some 'dark' or 'blue' forms occur with the head and underparts bluish-grey. In flight it planes continuously on stiffly held wings, making use of every variation in wind currents to bank and soar with a characteristic mastery of flight.
RANGE: N. Atlantic and N. Pacific Oceans and adjacent arctic seas. Map 32.

SOUTHERN FULMAR or SILVER-GREY PETREL **Pl. 11**
Fulmarus glacialoides
Medium, 18 ins, 46 cm. Wing-span 42 ins, 107 cm. The forehead, cheeks and underparts are white. The upperparts and tail are pearly-grey slightly paler on the crown and neck. A dark spot shows before the eye. The primary flight feathers are dark, a white patch showing on the upperwings in flight. The tubenose bill is horn-coloured, bluish on the nostril, tip dark; legs pale flesh-coloured. In flight it planes continuously on stiffly held wings making use of every variation in wind currents to bank and soar with a characteristic mastery of flight.

Closely related to the Fulmar Petrel of the northern hemisphere with a paler pearly-grey appearance. It has no dark phase.
RANGE: Antarctic seas and southern oceans rarely north of 40°S. Breeds as far south as the antarctic continent and on S. Orkney and S. Shetland Is., Bouvet and Kerguelen Is. Map 33.

CAPE PIGEON or PINTADO PETREL *Daption capensis* **Pl. 11**
Small–medium, 14 ins, 36 cm. Wing-span 35 ins, 89 cm. A medium built petrel with broad wings and short round tail. Quite unmistakable with the dark brown and white chequered pattern of its upperwing surfaces showing two large white patches on each wing, and the sooty-brown head, chin, sides of neck and back. The upper tail-coverts are white. Beneath the chin the underparts are pure white save for dark brown margins to its underwings. Bill short and brown; legs dark brown. In flight it proceeds with periods of stiff-winged flapping and shorter glides usually at 'deck level'.

Known to seafarers as the 'Cape Pigeon' it habitually follows ships in flocks and is seen more regularly in the southern oceans than any other species of petrel.
RANGE: Throughout the southern oceans from the antarctic ranging north to the Tropic of Capricorn. Breeds on the antarctic continent and adjacent sub-antarctic islands, S. Shetlands, S. Orkneys, S. Sandwich Is., S. Georgia, Bouvet, Crozet, Kerguelen, Heard, New Zealand adjacent islands and Macquarie I. Map 34.

SNOW PETREL *Pagadroma nivea* **Pl. 11**
Small–medium, 14–16 ins, 36–41 cm. This beautiful pure white petrel with its black bill and dark grey legs is unmistakable.

Snow Petrels rarely range beyond the pack ice.
RANGE: Antarctic seas. Breeds in antarctic continent and also on S. Shetlands, S. Orkneys, S. Sandwich Is., and Bouvet I. Map 35.

ANTARCTIC PETREL *Thalassoica antarctica*　　　　　　**Pl. 11**
Medium, 17 ins, 43 cm. Wing-span 36 ins, 92 cm. Head, upper neck and back brown, sides of neck and throat slightly paler. Upperwings brown showing a broad white outer area caused by shafts and inner webs of primaries, all secondaries and greater wing-coverts being white. Leading primaries show brown tips. Upper tail-coverts and tail white, tail feathers tipped brown. Underparts and underwing-coverts white. Bill black; legs yellowish.
　The brown upperparts and white area on wings and tail are unmistakable.
RANGE: Breeds on antarctic continent and rarely ranges more than 100 miles to seaward of the pack ice. Map 36.

BLUE PETREL *Halobaena caerulea*　　　　　　**Page 42 and Pl. 11**
Small, 11 ins, 28 cm. Wing-span 19 ins, 48 cm. A small stocky petrel with moderately long wings and a short square tail. The crown, nape and shoulders appear dark against the blue-grey of the upperparts and tail. The forehead is generally white with some freckling. The leading primaries are brownish-black and a distinct dark 'W' pattern is formed by a darker band from the carpal joint across the wing-coverts. The secondaries and scapulars show white tips. The throat and whole of the underparts and underwings are white. Bill short black with a bluish-grey line along the lower mandible. Legs blue with flesh-coloured webs. The central tail feathers are white tipped and two outer tail feathers white forming a white terminal band.
　Very similar to the prions in plumage but distinguished by the squareness of its tail and its white terminal band.
RANGE: Antarctic seas rarely north of 40°S. Breeds in the Falkland Is., Marion and Crozet Is., Kerguelen and Macquarie Is. Map 37.

PRIONS

Prions were known to seagoing whalers and sealers as 'Whale-birds', 'Ice-birds' or 'Fire-birds', the latter title derived from their habit of being attracted to and flying into fires at night at the whaling stations while they came and went to and from their breeding burrows in the dark. All are very small petrels varying between 10–11 ins, 254–280 mm in length, wing span 16–18 ins, 407–457 mm, and are of such similar plumage that it is virtually impossible to distinguish between them at sea. The particular feature which determines each species is in the considerable variation in the breadth and proportion of their bills. One overall description follows:
　Small, 10 ins, 25 cm. Upperparts delicate blue-grey slightly darker on the crown. Sides of face grey with a black patch behind and below the eye. Edge of shoulders, scapulars and outer primaries black, forming a distinct 'W' pattern across the upperwings. Underparts and underwings white, bluish on flanks. Upper tail-coverts and tail grey, the tail feathers with broad black tips showing as a black terminal band. Tail wedge-shaped. Bill bluish-grey; legs blue. Flight very fast and erratic, birds frequently in flocks, banking and zig-zagging low over the sea, appearing and disappearing as they show their white underparts then grey-blue backs which tone in with the colour of the sea.

BROAD-BILLED PRION *Pachyptila vittata*　　　　　　**Page 27**
Bill length 1.5 ins, 38 mm, breadth at base 0.7–0.8 ins, 18–21 mm. Bill steel-grey above, bluish yellow below.

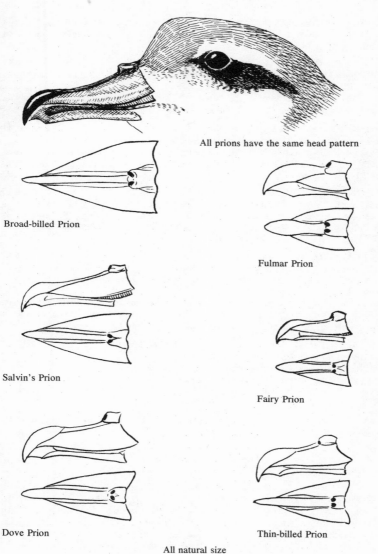

All prions have the same head pattern

Broad-billed Prion

Fulmar Prion

Salvin's Prion

Fairy Prion

Dove Prion

Thin-billed Prion

All natural size

Prion bills, *Pachyptila* species (p.28). The upper figures show the bill from the side; the lower figures the bill from above.

RANGE: Southern oceans north to 30°S. Breeds on Tristan da Cunha and Gough Is., Amsterdam and St. Paul Is. and on South I., New Zealand and adjacent islands. Map 38.

SALVIN'S PRION *Pachyptila salvini*　　　　　**Page 27**
Bill length and breadth at base slightly less than *P. vittata*. Bill bluish-grey above and below.
RANGE: Southern Indian Ocean. Breeds on Marion and Crozet Is. and extends its range to New Zealand seas. Map 39.

DOVE PRION *Pachyptila desolata*　　　　　**Page 27 and Pl. 11**
Bill length 1.5 ins, 38 mm, breadth at base 0.5–0.6 ins, 13–15 mm.
RANGE: Sub-antarctic and southern oceans north to 35°S. Breeds in sub-antarctic zone, in Antarctic Peninsula, S. Georgia, Kerguelen, Heard, Macquarie and Auckland Is. Map 40.

THIN-BILLED PRION *Pachyptila belcheri*　　　　　**Page 27**
Bill length 1.5 ins, 38 mm, breadth at base 0.3 ins, 8 mm. Very narrow bill.
RANGE: Southern coasts of S. America, Australia and New Zealand seas. Breeds on Falkland Is. and Kerguelen I. and extends its range to New Zealand seas. Map 41.

FAIRY PRION *Pachyptila turtur*　　　　　**Page 27**
Bill length 0.9 ins, 23 mm, breadth at base 0.4 ins, 10 mm. Bill blue.
　　A smaller stockier prion than the former species with a paler crown, and a very wide black band on end of tail.
RANGE: Sub-antarctic to 35°S., common in S. Australian and New Zealand seas. Breeds on islands in the Bass Strait and on islands off New Zealand from Poor Knights Is. to Snares and on Chatham and Antipodes Is. Map 42.

FULMAR PRION or THICK-BILLED PRION　　　　　**Page 27**
Pachyptila crassirostris
Bill length 0.9 ins, 23 mm, breadth at base 0.6 ins, 15 mm.
　　Distinguished from other prions by enlarged swelling of bill plates.
RANGE: Sub-antarctic rarely range north of 40°S. Breeds on Kerguelen and Heard Is. and on Chatham, Bounty and Auckland Is. Map 43.

Note: The Blue Petrel closely resembles the prions but can be distinguished by observing its square white-tipped tail.

BROWN PETREL *Procellaria cinereus*　　　　　**Pl. 10**
Medium, 19 ins, 48 cm. Wing-span 48 ins, 122 cm. A large heavily built petrel with long broad wings. The sides of the face and neck are grey; the upperparts greyish-brown, darker on the head, wings and tail. The underparts are white. The underwing-coverts and under tail-coverts are grey. The massive bill is horn-coloured on the nail, tip, side plates and bottom of the lower mandible, with blackish nostril and upper ridge. Legs are bluish and tail medium-round. In flight it alternates between rapid flaps, long glides and some shearwatering.
　　With newly moulted feathers in May when breeding season starts it appears

considerably greyer, and browner when plumage has become worn. Known by
seafarers as the 'Pediunker' or 'Cape Dove' it frequently follows ships.
RANGE: Southern oceans rarely north of 30°S. Breeds at Tristan da Cunha, Gough,
Marion, Kerguelen, Campbell, Antipodes and Macquarie Is.   Map 44.

WHITE-CHINNED PETREL *Procellaria aequinoctialis*   **Pl. 7**
Medium large, 21 ins, 53 cm. Wing-span 53 ins, 135 cm. A large heavily built petrel
with long broad wings and a medium round tail. It is seen most usually in an overall
black to sooty-brown plumage offset by a distinctive white chin. The white at the
chin is however variable; in the S. Atlantic birds may sometimes be seen with the
white extending over the face giving a spectacled appearance; in the seas around
New Zealand the white on the chin is frequently almost lacking and may not be
visible at sea. Its bill is long and massive, yellowish or horn-coloured with dark
nostrils and black ridge on the culmen, a noticeable feature at some distance. In
flight it proceeds with loose flaps and glides, is a persistent follower of ships, and
one of the commonest petrels throughout the southern oceans.
    Known by seafarers as the 'Cape Hen' or 'Shoemaker'.
RANGE: Southern oceans ranging from the edge of the pack ice to 30°S. Breeds on
Falkland Is., S. Georgia, Tristan da Cunha, Marion and Crozet Is., Kerguelen,
Macquarie, Campbell, Auckland and Antipodes Is.   Map 45.

PARKINSON'S PETREL *Procellaria parkinsoni*   **Pl. 7**
Medium, 18 ins, 46 cm. Stoutly built with long narrow wings. Overall plumage dark
blackish-brown. Bill yellowish horn-coloured with a dark nostril and line along
ridge of culmen, and a dark tip. Tail medium round. In flight in moderate winds it
tends to swoop and soar. It has been identified rarely at sea and is easily confused
with the larger White-chinned Petrel and cannot be distinguished from the Westland
Petrel.
RANGE: Disperses eastwards and northwards from its breeding grounds during the
contra nuptial periods. Breeds in mountain tops in both North and South Is. of New
Zealand. Eggs in December.   Map 46.

WESTLAND PETREL *Procellaria westlandica*   **Pl. 7**
Medium, 20 ins, 51 cm. Slightly larger but otherwise identical with Parkinson's
Petrel. Eggs however in May.
RANGE: Disperses into the Tasman Sea from breeding grounds inland on the W.
coast of South Island, New Zealand.   Map 47.

WHITE-FACED or STREAKED SHEARWATER   **Pl. 8**
Calonectris leucomelas
Medium, 19 ins, 48 cm. Wing-span 48 ins, 122 cm. Upperparts generally brown with
pale speckling on back and upper wings. Front and sides of head and neck whitish,
showing dark streaks. Primaries blackish. Underparts and under surface of wings
white with darker streaked underwing margins. Bill horn-coloured. Legs
flesh-coloured. Tail brown. Flies lightly with long easy wing-beats and glides,
wrists bent.
    A rather large shearwater easily distinguished by its white streaked face and
white underparts. Very large flocks occur off Japan and in the China Sea in summer
months.
RANGE: N.W. Pacific Ocean, dispersing southwards in winter to areas off the
Philippines and N. Borneo. Breeds on the Pescador Is., and islands off north of
Japan.   Map 48.

CORY'S SHEARWATER *Calonectris diomedea* **Pl. 9**

Medium, 18–22 ins, 46–56 cm. Wing-span 44 ins, 112 cm. A rather large shearwater with broad wings and heavy body. Its upperparts are medium-brown with pale flecking on the back and wing-coverts and rather darker head, wings and tail. In some lights the upperparts appear lightish-brown. The underparts are pure white; most of the underwing whitish, slightly darker on the edges. A narrow-curved white band of feathers is sometimes noticeable above the base of the tail. The bill is stout and yellow and can be observed at some distance. Legs yellowish. Its flight is unhurried and effortless, gliding for long periods low over the sea, occasionally making easy shallow wingbeats. While planing and shearwatering in this way its wings often seem to project slightly forward and droop, the tips lower than the belly.

Rather similar in appearance to the Great Shearwater but the throat and sides of the neck are greyish, and it lacks the distinctive dark capped appearance of the Great Shearwater.

RANGE: N. to S. Atlantic Oceans and Mediterranean Sea, dispersing southwards during northern autumn and winter to W. coast of southern Africa. Breeds on Azores, Madeira, Salvage, Canary and Cape Verde Is., coast of Portugal and in the Mediterranean, recently on Filfla Rock, Malta. Map 49.

PINK-FOOTED SHEARWATER *Puffinus creatopus* **Pl. 8**

Medium, 20 ins, 51 cm. Wing-span 43 ins, 109 cm. A heavily built shearwater with long narrow wings, similar in build and flight pattern to the Pale-footed Shearwater from which it can be distinguished by its whitish underparts and mottled-white underwings (both underparts and underwings are brown in the Pale-footed Shearwater).

The crown and sides of neck are dark grey, upperparts dark greyish-brown, rump black. The throat, breast and flanks are mottled-grey, remainder of underparts white. The bill is long, massive and pale pink with a black tip. Legs pink and tail short and round.

Distinguished from the pale phase of the Wedge-tailed Shearwater by its larger size, round as opposed to long wedge-shaped tail and slower deliberate and less graceful flight.

RANGE: Eastern S. Pacific, migrating north of the Equator during the southern winter. Breeds on the Juan Fernandez Is. and Mocha I. Map 50.

PALE-FOOTED SHEARWATER *Puffinus carneipes* **Pl. 8**

Medium, 20 ins, 51 cm. Wing-span 43 ins, 109 cm. A large heavily built uniform chocolate-brown shearwater with long narrow wings and a short round tail. Its most conspicuous feature is its long straw-coloured bill ending in a brown tip. Legs yellowish-flesh coloured. Its flight is deliberate consisting normally of a few powerful wingbeats interspersed with short glides low over the sea.

It is liable to be confused with the dark phase of the Wedge-tailed Shearwater which however has a long wedge-shaped tail, long slender grey bill and a lighter more graceful flight.

RANGE: S. Indian and S. Pacific Oceans. Migrates north of the Equator to Arabian Sea and central Pacific during southern winter. Breeds on the S. coast of Western Australia, North Island of New Zealand and Lord Howe I. Map 51.

GREAT SHEARWATER *Puffinus gravis* **Pl. 9**
Medium, 18–21 ins, 46–53 cm. Wing-span 45 ins, 111 cm. The Great Shearwater is in many respects very similar to Cory's Shearwater with brown upperparts, darker on wings and tail and with a noticeably darker crown and white cheeks. The neck is white nearly all round. The underparts are white flecked with darker feathers in the centre of the abdomen. The longer upper tail-coverts are tipped white forming a white band across the rump. The underwing is not as white as in the case of Cory's Shearwater, and shows brown streaking. The bill is long, slender and dark and legs flesh-coloured. In flight it glides on stiff pinions beating its wings rather more rapidly than Cory's.
A distinguishing feature is its 'dark capped' appearance, the white of the neck contrasting with its dark crown.
RANGE: S. and N. Atlantic Oceans, undertaking transequatorial migration during southern winter. Breeds on the Falkland Is., Tristan da Cunha and Gough Is. Map 52.

WEDGE-TAILED SHEARWATER *Puffinus pacificus* **Pl. 7**
Medium, 15.5 ins, 39 cm. Wing-span 38 ins, 97 cm. This is a variable species occurring in both pale and dark phases. Lightly built it has long broadish wings, a long slender bill and noticeably long wedge-shaped tail. In the dark phase it is a uniform dark chocolate-brown overall plumage, long slender grey bill, and flesh-coloured legs. In the pale phase it is slightly paler above, has white underparts and white underwings showing dark margins, dark under tail-coverts and some-times a pale flesh-coloured bill. It usually flies low over the sea with little upward movement frequently banking from side to side holding its long bill horizontal and tending to throw its head upwards during shallow wingbeats. When shearwatering and banking in calm weather it has been seen to touch the water with its lower wing leaving a trace behind it. In stronger winds it tends to bank more steeply in easy graceful flight.
In the dark phase it is liable to be confused with the Pale-footed Shearwater where both occur together, but its long wedge-shaped tail, slender grey bill and swifter and more graceful flight should serve to distinguish it.
RANGE: Ranges widely over the Indian and Pacific Oceans. Breeds throughout range. Map 53.

GREY-BACKED SHEARWATER *Puffinus bulleri* **Pl. 8**
Medium, 16.5 ins, 42 cm. Wing-span 42 ins, 107 cm. The outstanding feature of this lightly built long-winged shearwater is the contrast between the completely white underparts and underwings and the sooty-black and grey pattern of its upperparts. The back of the head and neck, lesser wing-coverts, primaries and tail are dark, the back, greater wing-coverts and upper tail-coverts grey, showing a dark '**W**' upper wing pattern in flight. The bill is long, bluish in colour, legs flesh-coloured and tail long and wedge-shaped. In fresh winds it swoops and soars on stiffly held wings, but in light wings it glides between wingbeats, its body appearing to dip and rise with each wingbeat cycle.
RANGE: S. Pacific Ocean, migrating northwards towards the Equator from its breeding quarters on Poor Knights Is. off the North Island of New Zealand during non-breeding season. Map 54.

SOOTY SHEARWATER   *Puffinus griseus*   **Pl. 8**
Medium, 16–20 ins, 41–51 cm. Wing-span 43 ins, 109 cm. A rather heavily built
shearwater with long narrow wings, uniformly sooty-brown upperparts and
greyish-brown underparts, paler under the chin. The central portion of the underwing lining is very distinctly pale, almost silvery, and considerably paler than in the
smaller Short-tailed Shearwater. The bill is blackish, long and slender, legs bluish
and tail short and round. In calm weather in flight it proceeds with a few quick
wingbeats followed by short glides with wings bent at the wrists. In moderate to
high winds it is capable of much soaring and shearwatering on stiff wings.
   This is the 'Mutton Bird' of New Zealand. It may easily be confused with the
Short-tailed Shearwater where both occur in the Pacific Ocean for its characteristics are similar. Its much larger size, the silvery lining of its underwing, and, where
this is observable, its pale chin, help to distinguish it.
RANGE: S. Atlantic and S. Pacific Oceans migrating north of the Equator in the
southern winter. Breeds in New Zealand and adjacent sub-antarctic islands, on
islands off Tasmania and south-eastern Australia, Falkland Is., and islands off the
W. coasts of Chile.   Map 55.

SHORT-TAILED SHEARWATER   *Puffinus tenuirostris*   **Pl. 8**
Small–medium, 13 ins, 33 cm. Wing-span 38 ins, 97 cm. A medium built shearwater
with long narrow wings, sooty-brown upperparts, greyish underparts and a greyish
central lining to the underwings. Due to its short round tail its body looks extremely
short behind the wings. The bill is medium long and dark and legs bluish-grey. In
calm weather in flight it proceeds with flaps and glides. In moderate to high winds its
flight is fast and effortless with much soaring and shearwatering interspersed with
rapid stiff wingbeats.
   The Short-tailed Shearwater is known as the 'Mutton Bird' in Tasmania and the
islands in the Bass Strait. During the breeding season the sea is sometimes churned
white with plunging birds. See also Sooty Shearwater.
RANGE: S. Pacific Ocean, migrating north of the Equator in the southern winter.
Breeds on islands in the Bass Strait and on the coasts of New South Wales, Victoria
and S. Australia.   Map 56.

CHRISTMAS SHEARWATER   *Puffinus nativitatis*   **Pl. 7**
Small–medium, 14 ins, 36 cm. Wing-span 32 ins, 82 cm. A medium sized lightly built
shearwater of overall chocolate-brown colour with long broadish wings, a long dark
slender bill, brown legs and short rounded tail. A white edge to the wing-coverts and
secondaries has been reported in flight but is unconfirmed. In flight it glides easily
with rather stiff wingbeats close over the surface.
   It resembles the dark phase of the Wedge-tailed Shearwater but is smaller, more
chestnut in colour, with only half the length of tail, and has dark legs as opposed to
flesh-coloured legs, and a faster wing-beat.
RANGE: Tropical Pacific Ocean with a limited range away from land. Breeds
throughout range. Recently found breeding on Easter I.   Map 57.

MANX SHEARWATER   *Puffinus puffinus*
Small–medium, 12–15 ins, 31–38 cm. Dark upperparts, white underparts (except
P.p. opisthomelas and *P.p. mauretanicus*). Dark crown extends below level of eye.
Bill long, slender, leaden-black. Legs pinkish flesh-coloured. Wings long and
narrow. In flight it planes (except *P.p. gavia*) on rigid wings close above the sea,

tilting from side to side, showing first white, then black, with three or four rapid wing-beats at intervals.

RANGE: Atlantic, Pacific, Mediterranean.

RACES:

MANX SHEARWATER *Puffinus p. puffinus* **Pl. 9**
Atlantic, Mediterranean. Black upperparts. Legs pinkish, webs blue. Breeds in British Is., Azores, Madeira and Salvage Is. Map 58.

LEVANTINE SHEARWATER *Puffinus p. yelkouan* **Pl. 9**
E. Mediterranean, extending into Sea of Marmora. Recently on Filfla Rock, Malta. Dark upperparts rather browner. Breeds in Aegean Is. Map 59.

BALEARIC SHEARWATER *Puffinus p. mauretanicus* **Pl. 9**
Balearic Is., extending into N. Atlantic in autumn. Brownish-black upperparts and pale brown underparts. Breeds in Balearic Is. Map 60.

RACES IN N. PACIFIC:

TOWNSEND'S SHEARWATER *Puffinus p. auricularis* **Not illustrated**
E. Pacific. Breed on Rivella, Gizedo and Clipperton Is. Like *P.p. puffinus* but with black legs and under tail-coverts. Map 61.

NEWELL'S SHEARWATER *Puffinus p. newelli* **Not illustrated**
Breeds on Kanai Is. and possibly other Hawaiian islands. Common within 200 miles of them May–October. Two small white patches on the dark back, though too hard to distinguish at sea. Map 62.

BLACK-VENTED SHEARWATER *Puffinus p. opisthomelas* **Pl. 9**
E. Pacific. Breeds on coast of Lower California. Upperparts brownish-black. Under tail-coverts and flanks dark. Tail long. Map 63.

RACES IN S. PACIFIC:

FLUTTERING SHEARWATER *Puffinus p. gavia* **Pl. 10**
New Zealand coastal waters, extending N.W. to Australia. Breeds on islands off North Island of New Zealand. Smaller than other races (12–14 ins, 31–36 cm) with shorter (30 ins, 76 cm) and broader wings, upperparts brown. Underwings have narrow dark margins. Sides of head and neck mottled. Legs flesh-coloured. Flight fluttering except in strong winds, with short glides close to the surface. Frequently gathers in flocks on the water, diving and feeding. Map 64.

HUTTON'S SHEARWATER *Puffinus p. huttoni* **Pl. 10**
Cook Strait and E. Coast of New Zealand, extending to S. Australia. Like *P.p. gavia* but uniformly darker brown and breeding season two months later. Map 65.

LITTLE SHEARWATER *Puffinus assimilis* **Pl. 9**
(A) Small, 10.5–12 ins, 26–30 cm, wing-span 21 ins, 53 cm; (B) Upperparts slaty-black; (C) Underparts, sides of cheeks, neck, under tail-coverts white; (D) Underwings white; (E) Bill, legs bluish-black, the latter observable against white under tail-coverts; (F) Tail short; (G) Flight: very rapid wing-beats, short glides on stiff wings.

BREEDS (Map 66):

S. Atlantic – Tristan da Cunha and Gough Is.

S.W. Pacific – Lord Howe, Norfolk, Kermadec and Austral Is.

Australia – islands off S.W. Australia.

New Zealand – off N.E. coast of Auckland Province and Bay of Plenty. Individual races off Australia and New Zealand cannot be identified as such at sea.

N. Atlantic – P.a. baroli: Madeira, Azores, Salvage and Canary Is. (C).
　Shows more white in front of eye.
P.a. boydi: Cape Verdi Is. (C). Under tail-coverts.

AUDUBON'S SHEARWATER　*Puffinus l'herminieri*

(A) Small, 12 ins, 31 cm. Wing-span 27 ins, 69 cm; (B) Sturdily built, wings rather short, narrow; (C) Upperparts dark brown; (D) Underparts white, dark shoulder patch; (E) Underwings white, under tail-coverts black; (F) Bill long, slender, black, legs whitish flesh-colour; (G) Tail rather long, rounded; (H) Flight: six or seven rapid wing beats followed by short glides close over the sea. Swims and dives freely.

　Much smaller and browner than Manx Shearwater *Puffinus puffinus*, with shorter wings and longer tail. The smaller Little Shearwater *Puffinus assimilis* has black upperparts, white under tail-coverts and bluish legs; a point to look for.

RANGE:　Tropical W. Atlantic, Indian and Pacific Oceans.

RACE IN ATLANTIC, INDIAN AND PACIFIC OCEANS:

　AUDUBON'S SHEARWATER　*Puffinus l'h. l'herminieri*　　　　　**Pl. 9**
　Tropical W. Atlantic, Caribbean, breeds throughout W. Indies, Bahamas, and islands off Central America and Venezuela, and on islands in Indian and Pacific Oceans.　Map 67.

RACE IN ARABIAN SEA AND PERSIAN GULF:

　PERSIAN SHEARWATER　*Puffinus l'h persicus*　　　　　　**Pl. 10**
　Southern quarter of Red Sea, Gulf of Aden, N. Arabian Sea, Gulf of Oman, Persian Gulf. (A) 12–13 ins, 31–33 cm; (C) Sooty-brown; (D) Central portion of abdomen white, upper parts of sides and flanks brown; (E) Central portion of underwing white, merging into wide brown margins, axillaries brown, under tail-coverts brown; (F) Bill dusky, legs flesh-colour; (G) Tail short, rounded.　Map 68.

HEINROTH'S SHEARWATER　*Puffinus heinrothi*　　　　　**Pl. 9**

Very small, 7.5 ins, 19 cm. This species is known only from specimens from the coast of New Britain.

　Its general plumage is similar to the Short-tailed Shearwater, brownish-black above, underparts slightly paler, throat and chin grey, and showing pale underwing-coverts. Bill greyish-black, relatively long and slender. Legs flesh-coloured.

　Due to its very small size it might be confused with Bulwer's Petrel, but its long slender bill and shorter tail should be looked for.

RANGE:　Unknown.　Not mapped.

GREAT-WINGED or GREY-FACED PETREL　　　　　**Pl. 10**
Pterodroma macroptera

Medium, 15–16 ins, 38–41 cm. Wing-span 42 ins, 107 cm. A rather heavy long winged petrel of overall dark brown plumage with a grey patch around the base of the bill and throat, sometimes extending above the bill to the forehead. Its dark wings are exceptionally long and narrow. Its bill is short and black and legs black. In flight in calm weather it flaps and glides, but in moderate winds it swoops and soars in fast high towering arcs well above the horizon, the wings looking like great scythes.

It pays no attention to ships. New Zealand breeding birds show more grey on the forehead, face and throat than those seen in the S. Atlantic and S. Indian Oceans.
RANGE: Southern oceans between 50°S. and 30°S. Breeds on islands in the southern S. Atlantic and S. Indian Oceans, the S. coast of Western Australia and North Island of New Zealand. Map 69.

WHITE-HEADED PETREL *Pterodroma lessoni*   Pl. 11
Medium, 18 ins, 46 cm. Wing-span 36 ins, 92 cm. A medium built rather large petrel with long narrow wings and a medium round tail. The crown, hind neck and upper tail-coverts are pale grey, the back greyish and upperwings sooty-brown. The front of the head, face, throat, underparts and base of tail are white, a dark patch showing around the eye. The underwings are grey. Bill short and black; legs flesh-coloured. Its flight is fast with much banking and swooping.
Easily recognised by its rather large size, large amount of white on the head and pale hind neck and pale tail.
RANGE: Antarctic seas ranging to the edge of the pack ice. New Zealand waters and north to about 34°S. Breeds in Kerguelen I. and in Auckland, Antipodes and Macquarie Is. Map 70.

SCHLEGEL'S PETREL *Pterodroma incerta*   Pl. 10
Medium, 17.5–18 ins, 45–46 cm. A stoutly built petrel with long narrow wings and a medium round tail. The whole head, neck and upperparts are brown, rather paler on the hindneck. The throat and foreneck are brown sharply divided from the white of the lower neck, breast and abdomen, which in turn contrast with the dark brown underwings and under tail-coverts. Bill black; legs yellowish.
It has been seen following ships and is easily distinguished.
RANGE: S. Atlantic Ocean. Breeds in Tristan da Cunha. Map 71.

SOLANDER'S PETREL *Pterodroma solandri*   Pl. 12
Medium size, 16 ins, 41 cm. Wing-span 37 ins, 94 cm. A heavily built petrel with slaty-grey upperparts contrasting with a darker brown head, wings and tail. The forehead and throat are white, a dark patch noticeable in front of the eye. The underparts and underwings are greyish-brown, some white feathers showing as a white oval patch towards the centre of the underwing. Bill short and black; legs flesh-coloured. Flight normally consists of long glides and upswinging banking turns.
The grey appearance of the back and the white oval patches on the underwings help to distinguish it.
RANGE: Sub-tropical S. Pacific Ocean dispersing northwards across the Equator during the southern winter. Breeds on Lord Howe I. Map 72.

MURPHY'S PETREL *Pterodroma ultima*   Pl. 12
Medium, 15 ins, 38 cm. Wing-span 38 ins, 97 cm. A medium built petrel with narrow wings and medium round tail. At sea it appears as an overall greyish-brown petrel with a short black bill and flesh-coloured legs. At close quarters the crown and nape appear darker, and the back, scapulars and upperwing coverts greyish-brown.
The throat is mottled with white and a dark patch shows before and under the eye. The feathers of the forehead and lores appear greyish. Bill short and black; legs flesh-coloured. Flight in moderate winds fast, swooping, banking and soaring.

Somewhat similar to Solander's Petrel, but is smaller and shows no white underwing patch.

RANGE: Central sub-tropical Pacific Ocean. Breeds in Tuamotu, Austral Is., Ducie I. and Oeno I. Map 73.

PEALE'S PETREL or MOTTLED PETREL   Pl. 12
Pterodroma inexpectata

Small–medium, 14 ins, 36 cm. Wing-span 30 ins, 76 cm. A fairly small medium build petrel with long narrow wings and a medium round tail. The crown, nape, upper-parts and upper surface of tail are grey, the scapulars and wings darker, and a '**W**' pattern is observable across the upperwings. The forehead, throat, breast and under tail-coverts are white. A conspicuous dark patch surrounds the eye showing against the whitish sides of the face. The forward portions of the underparts are white, but a distinct grey patch shows on the after portion of the underbelly. The axillaries are black, the centre of the underwing is white with thick black edging on the forward edge, finer on the trailing edge, and a noticeable dark band cuts across the white central lining from the carpel joint to the abdomen. Bill short and black; legs flesh-coloured. Flight fast, swooping and soaring in high arcs, wrists bent, well above the horizon.

Known as the 'Rainbird' in New Zealand. At sea in flight its most distinctive feature is its underwing pattern.

RANGE: Breeds on Stewart and Snares Is., migrating northwards from New Zealand waters widely into the western North Pacific to 55°N, extending eastwards towards the west coast of North America. Map 74.

KERGUELEN PETREL *Pterodroma brevirostris*   Pl. 11

Small–medium, 13 ins, 33 cm. Wing-span 26 ins, 66 cm. An almost uniformly dark slate-grey petrel with slight mottling on forehead and face, and in some cases on flanks. Slightly darker grey on wings and tail. Bill black, narrow and compressed; legs purplish flesh-coloured.

Its overall grey appearance distinguishes it from other petrels.

RANGE: S. Atlantic and S. Indian Oceans from 60°S. to about 40°S. Occasionally reaches the pack ice. Ranges east to New Zealand occasionally. Breeds on Gough, Kerguelen and Marion Is. Map 75.

SOFT-PLUMAGED PETREL *Pterodroma mollis*   Pl. 10

Small–medium, 13.5–14 ins, 34–36 cm. Wing-span 26 ins, 66 cm. The back of the head and back are slate-grey, the tail dark grey and the upperwings brown. The face and throat are white, a dark patch showing below the eye. The underparts are greyish-white and a darker band occurs across the chest. The under surface of wings dark brown; bill short and black; legs flesh-coloured. Its flight is fast with rapid wingbeats and much zig-zagging while planing on angled wings close over the sea.

RANGE: Atlantic and S. Indian Oceans. Breeds in Madeira, Cape Verde and Tristan da Cunha in the Atlantic, and in Kerguelen and St. Paul Is. in the southern Indian Ocean. Map 76.

TAHITI PETREL *Pterodroma rostrata*

(A) Small–medium, 14 ins, 36 cm. Wing-span 33 ins, 84 cm. Stockily built with moderately long wings and tail; (C) Head, neck, upperparts dark brown; (D) Upper breast dark brown with a sharp dividing line between dark breast and remainder of white underbody and under tail-coverts; (E) Underwings dark brown; (F) Bill massive, short, black, legs flesh-colour, feet black; (G) Flight: banks, arcs and glides seldom above horizon, interspersed with deep wing-beats. Distinguished from Phoenix Petrel *Pterodroma alba* by its heavier build, darker brown plumage and lack of any white on chin and throat.

RANGE: Tropical and sub-tropical central and western Pacific south of the Equator. Breeds on Marquesas Is., Society Is., New Caledonia and possibly Solomon Is.

RACES:

TAHITI PETREL *Pterodroma r. rostrata* **Pl. 12**
Not reported breeding on Solomon Is. Map 77.

BECK'S PETREL *Pterodroma r. becki*
Little known, only two specimens recorded N. of Solomon Is. (A) Smaller with shorter wings and tail; (D) Flanks and white under tail-coverts show some brown streaking. Not mapped.

REUNION PETREL *Pterodroma aterrima* Pl. 12

Small–medium, 14 ins, 36 cm. The present existence of this Indian Ocean Gad-fly Petrel remains uncertain. In appearance it is a stockily built black petrel with a short massive black bill, moderately long wing and rather long slightly pointed tail. Legs dark reddish; inner third of inner part of toe pink, outer toe and webs black with sharp dividing line. Its flight may be expected to be fast with swooping and arcing above the horizon.

In the Indian Ocean it might be confused with the dark phase of the Trinidade Petrel *Pterodroma arminjoniana* which is also likely to be somewhat rare and has much the same area of distribution.

RANGE: In the Indian Ocean it may still breed in the Mascarene Is., probably Reunion where petrels are said to breed in inland cliffs. Not mapped.

PHOENIX PETREL *Pterodroma alba* Pl. 12

Medium, 15 ins, 38 cm. Wing-span 33 ins, 84 cm. A medium built petrel with long narrow wings and medium round tail. The whole head, neck and upperparts are dark sooty-black. The throat, lower breast, abdomen and under tail-coverts are white. A distinguishing feature is a broad dark band across the chest, always present. Axillaries are white and the under surface of wings all dark. Bill short, stout and black; legs flesh-coloured or yellowish. In flight tends to glide and bank in steep arcs, its long sickle-shaped wings bent at the wrists, between loose wing-beats.

The Herald, Kermadec, Tahiti and Collared Petrels in the Pacific Ocean, the Soft-plumaged Petrel in the S. Atlantic and S. Indian Oceans frequently have similar dark breast bands. Of these only the Tahiti and Soft-plumaged Petrel has a completely dark underwing however the latter does not range into the Pacific Ocean. The Phoenix Petrel is best recognised by its sickle-shaped wings, very dark head and black underwings.

RANGE: Ranges widely throughout sub-tropical and tropical belt of the Pacific Ocean. Map 78.

KERMADEC PETREL *Pterodroma neglecta* Pl. 12

Medium, 15.5 ins, 89 cm. Wing-span 36 ins, 92 cm. A lightly built petrel with long narrow wings and a medium round tail. Head usually freckled whitish-brown. Upperparts brown, upperwings and tail blackish-brown. The underbody varies considerably; sometimes white with brownish feathers on breast and flanks, at other times entirely brown. The underwing is always brown, showing a white area near the tip of the underwing due to the white shafts of the primaries. Bill black. Legs black or yellow. Flight unhurried with deep wingbeats alternating with steep banked arcs and glides, wings bent at the wrists.

Can be confused with the smaller Herald Petrel, but is a somewhat paler brown above, and can be distinguished by its entirely brown underwings which show a distinct white patch near the tip.

RANGE: Sub-tropical and tropical zone of the Pacific Ocean. Breeds on Lord Howe and Kermadec Is., Austral and Tuamotu Is., Ducie and Oeni Is., and in the Juan Fernandez Group off the west coast of S. America.   Map 79.

TRINIDADE PETREL *Pterodroma arminjoniana*
Small–medium, 16 ins, 41 cm. Wing-span 38 ins, 97 cm. Lightly built with long narrow wings. Occurs in variable plumage.
DARK PHASE: (A) Dark brownish overall; (B) Underwing mottled-brown showing a white area towards tip; (C) bill short, black; (D) tail medium length, rounded.
PALE AND INTERMEDIATE PHASE: (A) Brownish-grey or brown upperparts, face and chin paler; (B) Underbody either white or more often white with dark breast band and flanks, or whole breast and flanks brown, abdomen mottled-white, underwing as in dark phase; (C) bill short, black, legs black or pinkish; (D) Flight: graceful swoops and banks close over the sea with wings bent at the wrists.
RANGE: Indian, S. Atlantic and Pacific Oceans.
RACE IN INDIAN AND S. ATLANTIC OCEANS:
   TRINIDADE PETREL   *Pterodroma a. arminjoniana*   **Pl. 10**
   Reported breeding on Round I., Mauritius, and possibly Reunion I. in the Indian Ocean, and at Trinidad and Martin Vas Is. in the S. Atlantic. Little is known of its oceanic range.   Map 80.
RACE IN PACIFIC:
   HERALD PETREL   *Pterodroma a. heraldica*   **Pl. 10**
   Breeds on Easter I., Ducie, Oeno, Henderson, Tuamotu, Chesterfield, Tonga and Marquesas Is., and disperses northwards into N. Central Pacific. (B) Both phases, underwing mainly dark with a thin irregular white centre line.   Map 81.

WHITE-NECKED PETREL *Pterodroma externa*   **Pl. 11**
Medium, 17 ins, 43 cm. Wing-span 38 ins, 97 cm. A rather large but lightly built petrel with long narrow wings and short wedge-shaped tail. The crown and nape are brownish-black, and a greyish-white collar around the neck separates the nape from the grey back and rump. The upperwings are medium-grey with darker 'W' pattern across wings and back. Tail black. The forehead and face are white, the area around the eye dark grey. The underparts and under-surface of wings are white with dark margin between bend of wing and leading primary. Bill short, heavy and black; legs yellowish. Its flight is fast with much banking and swooping on wings bent at the wrist often rising high above the horizon.

Distinguished from the White-headed Petrel by its very dark crown, whitish collar and white underwings. Those breeding at Juan Fernandez Is. tend to have greyish neck collars but turn whitish with feather wear, sometimes known as Juan Fernandez Petrels.
RANGE: Pacific Ocean from western sector of S. Pacific and from west coast of Chile, ranging northwards into central Pacific during southern winter. Breeds in the Kermadec Is. and in Mas Alfuera I. in the Juan Fernandez group.   Map 84.

BLACK-CAPPED PETREL *Pterodroma hasitata*
(A) Medium, 16 ins, 41 cm; (B) Upperparts sooty-brown, crown darker blackish-brown; (C) Forehead white, a whitish collar surrounds the nape; (D) Upper tail-coverts and base of tail white; (E) Underbody, under tail-coverts white, sides of breast greyish-brown; (F) Central linings to underwings white, with broad dark leading margins, axillaries white; (G) Bill short, stout, black, legs flesh-colour, webs black; (H) Flight: series of rapid wingbeats and arcs on angled wings. Distinguished by its white collar and white rump patch (the rather similar Bermuda Petrel *Pterodroma cahow* has dark nape and rump, the Great Shearwater *Puffinus gravis* has a long slender bill).
RANGE: Within the Caribbean and wanders northward occasionally off Florida and S. Carolina.
RACES:

    BLACK-CAPPED PETREL   *Pterodroma h. hasitata*   **Pl. 10**
    Breeds in Hispaniola.   Map 82.
    JAMAICA PETREL   *Pterodroma h. caribbaea*   **Pl. 10**
    Possibly now extinct, once bred in Jamaica. (C), (D), (E), (F) all dark sooty-brown, but shows an indistinct pale rump.   Not mapped.

BERMUDA PETREL *Pterodroma cahow*   **Pl. 10**
Small–medium, 14–15 ins, 36–38 cm. Wing-span 36 ins, 92 cm. A dark capped petrel with sooty-grey crown, upperparts and tail. Upper tail-coverts sooty-grey. Forehead, lower sides of face, underbody and under tail-coverts white. Axillaries white. Central linings to underwings white with broad dark margins. Sides of breast dusky. Bill short, stout, black. Legs pink, webs dark. In flight it swoops and glides in arcs low over the water on long angled wings followed by a short series of rapid wing-beats.
    Very similar to the Black-capped Petrel which occurs in the Caribbean but is larger and heavier in build and lacks white above rump and white on nape.
RANGE: Breeds on Bermuda and appears to range at no great distance from the islands.   Not mapped.

HAWAIIAN PETREL *Pterodroma phaeopygia*   **Pl. 12**
Medium, 17 ins, 43 cm. Wing-span 36 ins, 92 cm. A medium built petrel with long narrow wings and short wedge-shaped tail. Its upperparts are dark greyish-brown with black upperwings and tail; its forehead white, the cheeks and area around the eye black. Its underparts and the central portion of its underwing white with broad dark edges. Bill short and black; legs pink. In flight it swoops and soars in steeply banked arcs, its wings bent at the wrists.
    It is liable to be confused with the larger White-necked Petrel and is best distinguished from it by its very dark brown coloration above, and thick dark underwing margins.
RANGE: Sub-tropical and tropical waters of the Pacific Ocean. Breeds on Hawaiian and Galapagos Is.   Map 83.

BARAU'S PETREL *Pterodroma baraui*   **Pl. 10**
Medium, 15 ins, 38 cm. A rather lightly built petrel with long narrow wings and a noticeably short round tail. The forehead and cheeks below the eye are white and the whole underbody and under tail-coverts white. The crown and nape are brownish-black, contrasting with the greyish back; upperwings sooty-brown, rump and upper tail coverts sooty-brown. The central underwing linings are white with

dark leading and trailing margins combining in a dark underwing tip. Bill short, black. Legs yellowish, webs yellow at base with broad black tips. Flight fast, banking and swooping.

A recently discovered species closely associated with a group of tropical petrels of the type of the Black-capped Petrel and Cahow but occurring in a different ocean. RANGE: Found breeding on Reunion I., Indian Ocean, and probably ranges eastwards along the sub-tropical convergence. Map 85.

BONIN PETREL *Pterodroma hypoleuca*   **Pl. 12**
Small–medium, 12–13 ins, 31–33 cm. Wing-span 27 ins, 69 cm. A lightly built petrel with long narrow wings and a short round tail. The forehead and cheeks are white, the remainder of the upperparts mid-grey, darker on crown and nape. The upper surface of the wings is sooty-grey with lighter coverts so that an inconspicuous 'W' pattern is discernable in flight. The underparts and under tail-coverts are white. The central portion of the underwing is white with a thick black band to the leading edge and dusky-grey band to the trailing edge. Underwing axillaries usually white. Bill stout and black; legs flesh-coloured with dark tip to toes; tail sooty-black. Flight in light airs consists of flaps and glides, dipping and rolling; in moderate winds fast, swooping, soaring and banking.

Bonin Petrel is difficult to distinguish from other petrels of the 'Cookilaria' group of genus *Pterodroma*, Cook's, Gould's, Collared, Black-winged and Stejneger's, but is larger with a stouter bill and more flesh-coloured legs than the latter species. RANGE: Western N. Pacific. Breeds on the leeward Hawaiian Is., Bonin and Volcano Is. Observed regularly between 25°N. and 35°N. between breeding area and Japan. Map 86.

BLACK-WINGED PETREL *Pterodroma nigripennis*   **Pl. 12**
Small–medium, 12 ins, 31 cm. Wing-span 26 ins, 66 cm. Small, lightly built with long narrow wings and short round tail. Crown, hind neck, back and upper tail-coverts grey. Upper wings slaty-black. Forehead mottled, dark patch around eye, cheeks and underparts, including underwing-coverts white; a dark patch shows on sides of cheeks. Underwings have thick prominent dark margins, white axillaries. A prominent dark 'W' band shows across upperwings. Bill short, stout and black; legs flesh-coloured. Flight fast and erratic in steep arcs, wings bent at the wrists, with some rapid deep wingbeats.

Very similar to Gould's, Cook's and Stejneger's Petrels and difficult to separate species at sea. Distinguished from Chatham Petrel which has *black* axillaries. RANGE: Breeds in Kermadec and Three Kings Is. off N. coasts of New Zealand and migrates to N. Central Pacific from May to September ranging there between 5°N. and 30°N. Map 87.

CHATHAM ISLAND PETREL *Pterodroma axillaris*
Small–medium, 12 ins, 31 cm. A small lightly built petrel. Crown, nape, back and upper tail coverts medium-grey, wings dark slaty-black. A dark 'W' band across upperwings. Forehead, underparts and underwing white. Axillaries black. Bill short, stout, black. Legs flesh-coloured, webs with dark outer ends. Flight fast, swooping and arcing.

The black axillaries which can be observed at sea with birds on the wing at close quarters distinguishes it from the Black-winged Petrel which has white axillaries. RANGE: Breeds on Chatham Is. Range at sea uncertain, probably over the cool waters of the S. Pacific. Not mapped.

'*Hypoleuca*' and '*Cookilaria*' petrels in flight showing underwings.
1 Bonin Petrel, *Pterodroma hypoleuca*, p.40. Broad dark band on leading edge, dusky grey trailing edge.
2 Gould's Petrel, *Pterodroma leucoptera*, p.43
3 Collared Petrel, *Pterodroma leucoptera brevipes*, p.43
4 Stejneger's Petrel, *Pterodroma longirostris*, p.42
5 Black-winged Petrel, *Pterodroma nigripennis*, p.40
6 Chatham Island Petrel, *Pterodroma axillaris*, p.40. Medium dark band, black axillaries.
7 Cook's Petrel, *Pterodroma cooki*, p.42

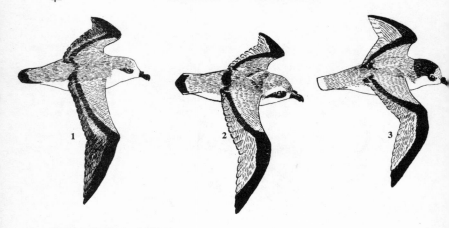

Petrels with **W** wing pattern
1 Cook's Petrel, *Pterodroma cooki*, and allies have this pattern fairly conspicuously; see Plate 12 and below.
2 Prions, *Pachyptila* species, always show the W wing pattern clearly; see Plate 11 and pages 26–8.
3 Blue Petrel, *Halobaena caerulea:* W pattern and dark cap, pale tail. See Plate 11 and page 26. Some *Pterodroma* species also have dark cap and back; see Plates 10–12 and pages 34–43.

COOK'S PETREL   *Pterodroma cooki*   Pl. 12

Small, 11 ins, 28 cm. Wing-span 26 ins, 66 cm. A small lightly built petrel with long narrow wings and short round tail. Crown, nape, sides of neck and breast light grey, tinged brown. Dark area before the eye. Forehead white or finely freckled grey and white. Back, rump and upper tail-coverts pale grey. Upper wing-coverts slightly darker grey, a very distinct '**W**' pattern showing across the wings. Primaries dark with white inner webs. The underparts, axillaries and underwings are white, the underwings showing thin dark edges. Bill short and black; legs pale blue; end of webs black. Tail very dark grey, outer feathers white. Flight in light airs languid and rolling; in moderate winds fast and erratic with steep banks and arcs showing alternatively the white underparts and upper wing pattern.

Distinguished from Gould's Petrel by its paler upperparts and clear '**W**' pattern on back.

RANGE: S. Pacific Ocean from New Zealand to west coast of S. America migrating northwards into N. Pacific during southern winter. Breeds on Little Barrier I. and Stewart I., New Zealand, and Juan Fernandez I. off S. America.   Map 88.

STEJNEGER'S PETREL   *Pterodroma longirostris*

(A) Small, 10 ins, 25 cm. Wing-span 28 ins, 71 cm; (B) Slightly built, long narrow wings; (C) Forehead white, head and nape dark grey; (D) Back, wing-coverts, upper tail-coverts light grey; (E) Wing quills slaty-black; (F) distinct '**W**' pattern across wings and back; (G) Underparts, under tail-coverts white, underwing white

with narrow dark margin to leading edge; (H) Bill short, black, legs blue; outer toes black, webs white; (K) Tail short, blackish-grey, outer tail feathers grey, rounded; (L) Flight fast, buoyant, rapid wing-beats and steep upward banks, wings bent.
RANGE: S. Pacific dispersing into N. Central Pacific during non breeding season.
RACES:

STEJNEGER'S PETREL   *Pterodroma l. longirostris*   **Pl. 12**
Breeds only in Mas Afuera I. in the Juan Fernandez group west of Chile, dispersing northwards and westwards and crossing the Equator during non breeding season.   Map 89.

PYCROFT'S PETREL   *Pterodroma l. pycrofti*   **Not illustrated**
Breeds in Poor Knights Is. and Hen and Chicken Is. off North Island of New Zealand. Full range uncertain, probably disperses northwards and eastwards during non breeding season. (A) 11 ins, 28 cm; (B) Wings slightly shorter; (H) Bill slightly shorter; (K) Tail longer.   Map 90.

GOULD'S PETREL   *Pterodroma leucoptera*

(A) Small, 12 ins, 31 cm. Wing-span 28 ins, 71 cm. Slightly built with long narrow wings and short rounded tail; (B) Forehead white with some speckling, face white, dark area before eye; (C) Crown, nape, sides of neck sooty-black; (D) Upperwing-coverts medium-grey, an indistinct '**W**' pattern showing across wing-coverts and back, primaries black, inner webs white at base; (E) Back, rump, dark grey, tail slaty-black; (F) Underparts vary, shoulders grey, underbody sometimes white, more often with dusky patch on breast and flanks; (G) Underwings white with thin dark margin on leading edge; (H) Bill short, black, legs bluish; (K) Flight: rapid wing-beats and steep banks and arcs, wings bent at wrists.
RANGE: Western Pacific in sub-tropical and tropical waters.
RACES:

GOULD'S PETREL *Pterodroma l. leucoptera*   **Pl. 12**
From eastern Australia, eastwards into sub-tropical Pacific. Breeds on Cabbage Tree I.   Map 91.

COLLARED PETREL   *Pterodroma l. brevipes*   **Pl. 12**
Sub-tropical and tropical western Pacific. Breeds on New Caledonia, New Hebrides and Fiji. (D) Slaty-grey; in good light the area forward of '**W**' appears paler accentuating the '**W**' pattern; (F) Dusky band across breast, occasionally entire underbody dusky; (G) Dark wedge along forewing from body to carpal joint, thin dark trailing edge.   Map 92.

JOUANIN'S PETREL   *Bulweria fallax*   **Pl. 9**

Small–medium, 14 ins, 36 cm. Jouanin's Petrel is a larger Indian Ocean representative of Bulwer's Petrel of the Atlantic and Pacific Oceans.

A lightly built small–medium petrel uniformly brownish-black overall, sometimes showing paler upper wing-coverts, with a noticeably short thick black bill and flesh-coloured legs with darker edges to the tarsus and toes. Its wings are long and slender, its tail long and wedge-shaped. Its flight is very fast and mobile, swooping and rising high over the horizon on the upswing, and it tends to point its short stout bill downwards during flight.

In the Arabian Sea it is most likely to be confused with a dark phase of the Wedge-tailed Shearwater, which however can always be distinguished by its long slender bill, and heavier slower flight.
RANGE: Arabian Sea and Gulf of Aden.   Map 93.

BULWER'S PETREL *Bulweria bulwerii*   **Pl. 9**
Small, 10.5–11 ins, 27–28 cm. Wing-span 24 ins, 61 cm. A small sooty-brown
petrel with slightly paler underparts. A pale band on the upperwings can usually be
discerned. The dark wings are long, narrow and slender, and a distinguishing
feature is its rather long wedge-shaped tail. Bill black. Legs flesh-coloured. In
moderate winds it flies in shallow swooping arcs and glides low over the water with
occasional rapid wing-beats. In light winds it employs easy deep irregular wing-
beats.
    It is only slightly larger than the dark storm-petrels but its flight is stronger and of
a different character. Its long tail helps in identification.
RANGE: N. Atlantic and N. Pacific Oceans. Breeds on the eastern N. Atlantic Is.,
leeward Hawaiian Is., Bonin and Volcano Is., Phoenix and Marquesas Is. and on
the coast of China. Frequently seen west of the Hawaiian Is. towards Japan and in
the China Sea.   Map 94.

Bulwer's Petrel   Macgillivray's Petrel   Storm Petrel

The Macgillivray's Petrel illustrated here is possibly not a full species: it is only known from a
single specimen. Identification at sea would be very difficult.

MACGILLIVRAY'S PETREL *Bulweria macgillivrayi*
Small, 11.5 ins, 29 cm. Plumage uniformly sooty-black overall with a relatively long
wedge-shaped tail and stout black bill. Lacks paler band on upperwings.
    At present only known from a single specimen from the Fiji Is. Very similar but
larger than Bulwer's Petrel with a larger bill.
RANGE: Tropical zone of Pacific Ocean but extent of range unknown.   Not mapped.

STORM-PETRELS Hydrobatidae

Storm-petrels or 'Mother Carey's Chickens' as they are known to seafarers are the smallest of oceanic seabirds, sometimes compared in size to large stocky swallows, and their flight to that of butterflies. The majority have overall sooty-black or sooty-brown plumage showing white patches above the rump; others are sooty-black altogether and yet others have white or partially white underparts. Their flight is generally weaker, more erratic and fluttering than true petrels, and they may be seen weaving across the wake of ships dropping their legs to touch the water and hopping or skipping as they search for minute crustaceans or other food particles. Their bills are short and black, the tube-nosed nostrils forming a single orifice. Legs which are black vary considerably in length.

WILSON'S PETREL. Storm petrels are very small seabirds. They all look similar: watch for the wing pattern, rump colour, and the shape of the tail.

Nesting and young

These nest on rocky shores and islands; nesting in crevices, cavities, burrows and sometimes in stone walls, either natural or excavated by the birds themselves. Sometimes small amounts of nest material may be pulled into burrows. Breeding usually occurs in colonies, and the birds may not breed until 2–3 years old. The eggs and young can withstand periods of neglect, eggs have been recorded as left for up to 11 days, and this usually only delays incubation and development. The single white egg is incubated for 38–40 days, or occasionally up to 50 days, by both birds, taking alternate periods of several days. Young are brooded for the first week and fed daily at first but later at several day intervals The young have thick grey or brownish down, in two successive coats. They become very large and fat, heavier and apparently larger than the adults; but lose this when they feather, although they may be fed to within a day of leaving. The fledging period is from 56–70 days.

WILSON'S STORM-PETREL   *Oceanites oceanicus*   **Pl. 13**
Very small, 7–7.5 ins, 18–19 cm. Wing-span 16 ins, 41 cm. Upperparts sooty-black, a palish brown band showing across the greater wing-coverts, and sometimes a pale line noticeable across the upperwings at the base of the secondary wing feathers. A clear patch of white feathers shows above the rump, formed by the upper tail-coverts, the upper and lower limits appearing slightly curved; some white feathers extend to the lower flanks on either side. Underparts sooty-brown. The tail is black and square, but appears rounded at the tips. A distinguishing feature in flight at close quarters is the sight of the feet just protruding beyond the tail, for it possesses. exceptionally long legs. When examined in the hand the webs of the feet will be seen to be yellow. Bill black. Flight normally consists of short glides interspersed with loose wingbeats with a tendency to tilt and roll from side to side. When searching for food it hops and flutters paddling along the surface with its long legs touching the water. Wilson's Storm-petrels regularly follow ships.
   Particularly in the N. Atlantic where the British Storm-petrel, Madeiran Storm-petrel, Leach's Storm-petrel and Wilson's Storm-petrels may occur in the same area, identification at sea is very difficult. Both the British and Wilson's are likely to follow ships, the British being the smaller, the Madeiran and Leach's have freer flight and Leach's appears browner and larger with the most dashing flight.
RANGE: Breeds on the antarctic continent in Adelie Land, Haswell I., islands off Graham Land, adjacent sub-antarctic islands, S. Shetlands, S. Orkneys, S. Sandwich Is., S. Georgia, Falkland Is., Kerguelen, Heard and Bouvet Is. Migrates far north of the Equator in Atlantic, Indian and Pacific Oceans.   Map 95.

ELLIOT'S STORM-PETREL   *Oceanites gracilis*   **Pl. 13**
Tiny, 5.8 ins, 148 mm. An extremely small dark storm-petrel, sooty black above with browner upperwing-coverts, and a white patch above the rump extending around the sides. The central portion of the underparts is white, remainder sooty-black; underwings black. Bill black; legs black, middle of webs yellow. Tail square, slightly indented and glossy black. Flight weak, fluttering, legs frequently pattering on the water.
   Its plumage is very similar to Wilson's Storm-petrel, but it is much smaller, its flight weaker. Its range is liable to clash with Wilson's Storm-petrel.
RANGE: Pacific coast of S. America from the Galapagos Is. southwards to Chile. Breeds in the Galapagos Is.   Map 96.

GREY-BACKED STORM-PETREL   *Garrodia nereis*   **Pl. 14**
Very small, 6.5–7 ins, 165–178 mm. A very small species. The head, neck and breast are sooty-grey. The back is ashy-grey, the rump, upper tail-coverts and tail a paler grey. The upperwings, with the exception of the secondary wing-coverts which are also pale grey, are brownish-black, and the grey portions having white edges give a scaly grey appearance to the bird. Below the breast the underparts including the inner underwing linings and under tail-coverts are white. A noticeable feature is the black terminal band on the tail. Bill and legs black.
   Its greyish appearance, lack of any white patch above the rump and black tail band help to distinguish it.
RANGE Southern oceans ranging north to 35°S. Breeds in Falkland Is., S. Georgia, Gough I., Kerguelen I. and Chatham, Antipodes and Auckland Is.   Map 97.

WHITE-FACED STORM-PETREL *Pelagodroma marina* **Pl. 13**
Small, 8 ins, 20 cm. Wing-span 17 ins, 43 cm. Easily recognised by its distinctive plumage pattern. The crown and nape are greyish-brown, darker on the crown, the back of the neck and upper part of the back grey. The upperwings are brown, primaries black. Further aft again the rump and upper tail-coverts are ashy-grey contrasting with the short black square tail. The most distinctive features are the white forehead and face showing a dusky patch beneath the eye and the completely white underparts and underwing-coverts. Bill and legs black; legs long, webs yellow. Its flight is fast and erratic, darting from side to side, sometimes hopping over the water with legs dangling. It does not follow ships.

Birds breeding in the Kermadec Is. have white rumps and upper tail-coverts.
RANGE: N. and S. Atlantic Ocean, western S. Pacific and tropical Pacific and Indian Oceans, ranging north of the Equator to the Arabian Sea in the southern winter. Breeds in the N. Atlantic Is., Tristan da Cunha and Gough Is., S.W. and southern coasts of Australia. New Zealand, Chatham, Auckland and Kermadec Is. Map 98.

WHITE-BELLIED STORM-PETREL *Fregetta grallaria* **Pl. 13**
Small, 7.5–8.5 ins, 19–22 cm. Wing-span 19 ins, 48 cm. The head, neck and upperparts are sooty-black, greyish-black on the back. Wings and tail black. The upper tail coverts are white, showing a rather indistinct white patch above the rump. Abdomen is white, the flanks sometimes dusky. The under tail-coverts and inner underwing-coverts are white. Bills and legs black. Tail square. Its flight is weak; it is usually seen fluttering and hopping, both feet touching the water together, and is inclined to follow in the wake of ships.

See Black-bellied Storm-petrel (p. 47).
RANGE: Southern oceans from about 35°S., ranging northwards to the tropics, apparently crossing the Equator in the Indian Ocean during the southern winter. Breeds in Tristan da Cunha and Gough Is., Lord Howe I. Austral Is. and Mas a Tierra I. in the Juan Fernandez group. On Lord Howe I. a dark phase occurs having a dark underbody. Map 99.

White-bellied   Black-bellied

These two species are best identified by the different shapes of their 'noses'.

BLACK-BELLIED STORM-PETREL *Fregetta tropica* **Pl. 13**
Small, 8 ins, 20 cm. Wing-span 19 ins, 48 cm. The head and upperparts are sooty-black, rather paler on the median wing-coverts. The upper tail-coverts are white forming a white patch above the rump. The distinctive features are the white flanks and sides of the abdomen and a longitudinal dark band in the centre. The axillaries are white and a whitish central area of the underwing shows indistinctly. Bill and legs are black. The flight appears distinctly erratic, the bird usually swinging from side to side and zig-zagging exposing its white underside.

The Black-bellied Storm-petrel and the White-bellied Storm-petrel are exceedingly difficult to differentiate between at sea, and indeed the Black-bellied species may show no dark central feathers under the belly on occasions. Both species are in the habit of following ships.

RANGE: Southern oceans from the sub-antarctic ranging northwards and apparently crossing the Equator during the southern winter in the Indian Ocean. Breeds in sub-antarctic islands, S. Shetlands, S. Orkneys, S. Sandwich Is., S. Georgia, Crozet Is., Kerguelen Is., and in Auckland, Bounty and Antipodes Is. Reported breeding on Amsterdam I. Map 100.

WHITE-THROATED STORM-PETREL *Nesofregetta fuliginosa* **Pl. 13**
Small, 8.5 ins, 216 mm. Wing-span 20 ins, 51 cm. Head, neck, upperparts and wings above sooty-black, greater wing-coverts paler. A narrow white patch on rump. Underparts are very variable. Pale birds have white throats and underparts and broad sooty breast bands. Intermediate birds have dark streaking on throat and underbody. In the central Pacific some birds may be melanistic and entirely dark. Underwings are greyish-white, under tail-coverts usually white with dark tips. Legs long, black and noticeably flattened. Tail black, deeply forked. In flight it bounds and skips with fluttering wings in an erratic manner.

The Samoan and Striped Storm-petrels are now considered to be simply melanistic White-throated Storm-petrels.

RANGE: Tropical central and western Pacific Oceans. Breeds on New Hebrides, Fiji, Marquesas, Phoenix and Line Is. Map 101.

BRITISH STORM-PETREL *Hydrobates pelagicus* **Pl. 13**
Very small, 5.5–7.5 ins, 14–19 cm. Wing-span 14 ins, 36 cm. A small dark storm-petrel, with sooty-black upperparts usually showing a narrow pale line across the upper wing-coverts. Underparts sooty-brown. It has a clear patch of white feathers above the rump, the forward and after limits appearing slightly curved towards the tail. A distinguishing feature when its wings are raised is a small patch of white feathers at the base of the underwing. Some white shows in the under tail-coverts. Tail black and square; legs black. Its flight is weak and fluttering with short glides, occasionally pattering over the water. It sometimes follows in the wake of ships.

Smaller than the dark Wilson's and Madeiran Storm-petrels but may easily be confused with them at sea. See note under Wilson's Storm-petrel (p. 46).

RANGE: Eastern N. and S. Atlantic Oceans and Mediterranean sea. Migrates southwards reaching the west coast of southern Africa in winter. Breeds in British Isles, Brittany, Canary Is. and Mediterranean. Recently on Filfla Rock, Malta. Map 102.

LEAST STORM-PETREL *Halocyptena microsoma* **Pl. 14**
Tiny, 5.5–6 ins, 140–152 mm. This tiny storm-petrel is the smallest of the storm-petrels with dark sooty-black upperparts, slightly brownish-grey greater wing-coverts and dark brownish underparts. Its tail is wedge-shaped scarcely visible at sea. Its flight is weak and fluttering.

Its overall dark plumage and tiny size readily distinguish it.

RANGE: Pacific coast of America from Lower California to Equator. Breeds on San Benito Is., Lower California. Map 103.

GALAPAGOS STORM-PETREL *Oceanodroma tethys* **Pl. 13**
Very small, 6.5–7 ins, 165–178 mm. This very small storm-petrel has a sooty-black plumage, slightly browner on the upperwing-coverts, a very slightly forked tail and a white somewhat triangular patch above the rump. Bill black; legs very short and black. Its flight, as in other very small storm-petrels, is weak and fluttering.

The greater fore and aft length to its triangular white patch is a guide in identification.

RANGE: Sea areas around the Galapagos Is. extending at times from Lower California to Peru. Breeds in the Galapagos Is. Map 104.

MADEIRAN STORM-PETREL *Oceanodroma castro* **Pl. 13**

Very small, 7–8 ins, 178–203 mm. Wing-span 18 ins, 46 cm. A dark storm-petrel with sooty-black upperparts, the wing-coverts somewhat browner and sooty-brown underparts. It has a clear cut square white patch above the rump, the upper and lower limits appearing straight and parallel. A few white feathers occur on the flanks and under tail-coverts. A slight cleft in the tail cannot be called forked and is not observable at sea. Its flight is more direct and fast than in many storm-petrels with more constant wingbeats, and it takes no notice of ships.

It looks larger than Wilson's and certainly larger than the British Storm-petrel but is most elusive and difficult to identify. Leach's Storm-petrel looks browner and has a distinctive buoyant free flight.

RANGE: Eastern N. Atlantic and eastern and western N. Pacific Oceans. Breeds in the N. Atlantic Is., Ascension and St. Helena. Galapagos and Hawaiian Is. and in Japan. Map 105.

LEACH'S STORM-PETREL *Oceanodroma leucorhoa* **Pl. 13**

Small, 8–9 ins, 20–23 cm. Wing-span 19 ins, 48 cm. A medium sized storm-petrel, blackish-brown above with a rather broad prominent paler band across the upperwing-coverts, which varies with feather wear. Underparts sooty-brown. A white patch above the rump is oval in shape, indistinctly divided down the centre by a few dark feathers, not always visible at sea. Some white feathers extend to flanks below rump. Wings long, pointed and rather broad at the base. Tail distinctly forked, broadening towards the tips and noticeable at close range.

Flight fast and buoyant, often swooping steeply between short glides and alternate fast-wing-beats. Sometimes follows ships, at other times pays little attention.

In the southern and western tropical Pacific Leach's Storm-petrels occur with dark rumps, and are smaller than Tristram's and Matsudaira's Storm-petrels or Bulwer's Petrel.

RANGE: Ranges widely over Atlantic and Pacific Oceans. Breeds on both sides of the N. Atlantic and on the coasts of both western N. America and Canada and eastern Asia. In the Pacific Ocean occurs regularly in the central tropical zone. Map 106.

GUADALUPE STORM-PETREL
Oceanodroma macrodactyla

Small, 8.5 ins, 22 cm. Very similar to Leach's Storm-petrel with somewhat blacker upperparts and greyer underparts and underwings. The white upper tail-coverts show broad dusky tips.

Possibly now extinct. Could not be distinguished from Leach's Storm-petrel at sea.

RANGE: May breed on Guadaloupe I. Range at sea unknown. Not mapped.

SWINHOE'S STORM-PETREL *Oceanodroma monorhis*   **Pl. 14**
Very small, 7–7.5 ins, 178–191 mm. Swinhoe's Storm-petrel is virtually identical in
plumage to the Tristram's Storm-petrel, but considerably smaller, with shorter
wings and a shorter medium-forked tail. Bill and legs black. It has a distinctive
flight, bounding and swooping over the water like a tern, and never pattering.
    See note under Tristram's Storm-petrel. An additional species of storm-petrel,
Oceanodroma matsudairae, is reported to occur in the same area as Swinhoe's
Storm-petrel, but is so similar that identification between them at sea is probably
impossible.
RANGE: South and west of Japan and S. China Sea, penetrating across the N.
Indian Ocean. Breeds on Pescador Is.   Map 107.

TRISTRAM'S STORM-PETREL *Oceanodroma tristrami*   **Pl. 14**
Small, 9–10 ins, 23–25 cm. Wing-span 22 ins, 56 cm. A large storm-petrel. Plumage
sooty-brown, a pale brown band showing across the upperwing-coverts. Underwings a shade paler. The black tail is deeply forked. Bill and legs black.
    Flight freer than the smaller storm-petrels, gliding and banking more often and
occasionally fluttering.
    Formerly quoted as Sooty Storm-petrel.
RANGE: Western N. Pacific Ocean from the leeward Hawaiian Is. westwards
towards Japan. Frequently seen north of the Hawaiian Is. outside its breeding
season. Breeds on the leeward Hawaiian Is. and on Volcano Is.   Map 108.

MARKHAM'S STORM-PETREL *Oceanodroma markhami*   **Pl. 14**
Small, 9–10 ins, 23–25 cm. Wing-span 22 ins, 56 cm. This species is similar to
Tristram's Storm-petrel but ranges in the cool waters off the coasts of Peru. It is
doubtful if it could be distinguished from Tristram's Storm-petrel but the two range
in widely separated zones.
    Formerly quoted as Sooty Storm-petrel. Breeding area unknown.   Map 109.

Matsudaira's Storm-petrel   Swinhoe's Storm-petrel

MATSUDAIRA'S STORM-PETREL *Oceanodroma matsudairae*   **Pl. 14**
Small, 10 ins, 25 cm. Wing-span 22 ins, 56 cm. A large sooty-brown storm-petrel
with forked tail. It may well be confused with Swinhoe's Storm-petrel
Oceanodroma monorhis which ranges into the same area. By close observation,

apart from its paler wing coverts which are also evident in Swinhoe's Storm-petrel, its white primary feather shafts show as a whitish area towards the ends of the wings.

RANGE: Breeds on Volcano Is. south of Japan, dispersing southwards to the area of the Philippines, and S. China Sea, a few probably spreading across the N. Indian Ocean. Map 110.

ASHY STORM-PETREL   *Oceanodroma homochroa*   Pl. 14

Very small, 7.5 ins, 190 mm. A very small sooty storm-petrel with short dark legs and a forked tail. The edges of the upperwing coverts and underwing coverts are slightly paler.

Its distribution may coincide with that of the Black Storm-petrel *Loomelania melania* which is noticeably larger with longer legs and more deeply forked tail. The even smaller Least Storm-petrel *Halocyptena microsoma* has a wedge-shaped tail and a more southerly general range.

RANGE: Off the coast of California. Breeds at Farallon and St. Barbara Is. Map 112.

HORNBY'S STORM-PETREL   *Oceanodroma hornbyi*   Pl. 14

Small, 8–9 ins, 203–229 mm. A distinctively plumaged species. The top of the head is chocolate-brown; forehead and sides of head white; chin, throat, breast and underbody white, with a clear cut brownish-grey band across the breast. The back is greyish-brown with upper tail-coverts darker. The upper wings are dark brown with greyer greater wing-coverts. The underwings are grey. A noticeable feature is the white collar which extends across the back of the neck. Bill and legs black. Tail dark brown and deeply forked. In flight it flutters and hops.

The white collar and dark band across the breast are the best diagnostic features at sea.

RANGE: Throughout the west coast of S. America. Breeds in the Chilean Andes. Map 113.

FORK-TAILED STORM-PETREL   *Oceanodroma furcata*   Pl. 14

Small, 8 ins, 203 mm. Wing-span 18 ins, 457 mm. Unique amongst storm-petrels in the pale grey of its plumage. The head and upperparts are pearl-grey, upperwing-coverts with paler edges. A black area shows below the eye. The underparts are even paler grey, appearing white on the throat and under tail-coverts. Axillaries and underwings are greyish-black, edged white. Bill black; legs black; tail noticeably forked. In flight it glides and weaves erratically, often fluttering with rapid wing-beats.

RANGE: N. Pacific and Bering Sea from 55°N. to 35°N. Breeds in the Kuril Is., Aleutian Is., southern Alaska southwards to Oregon. Map 114.

BLACK STORM-PETREL   *Loomelania melania*   Pl. 14

Small, 9 ins, 23 cm. This is one of the largest of all dark storm-petrels. The upperparts are sooty-black with uniform sooty-brown upperwing-coverts. Underparts brownish-black. Tail black and deeply forked; bill black; legs black and long.

It is liable to be confused with the rather smaller Markham's Storm-petrel which however has shorter legs and whose range does not overlap.

RANGE: Eastern N. Pacific Ocean between California and Peru and does not range any distance to the westward. Breeds in islands off Lower California. Map 111.

Diving Petrel coming to its nest site at night, the pouch is filled with food for the chick.

DIVING-PETRELS Pelecanoididae

Diving-petrels are small stubby birds and, with the exception of the Magellan Diving-petrel, are almost identical in plumage pattern and shape. They have short wings, black upperparts and white underparts. Their bills are short, black and hooked, broadening at the base; their legs short, blue, set far back in the body and their tails short and stumpy. Although resembling the Little Auks of the northern hemisphere, diving-petrels are confined to the southern hemisphere and are true tube-nosed petrels. Their nostrils however open upwards side by side from the base of the upper mandible, and between the sides of the lower mandible there is a distensible pouch. Although the Peruvian Diving-petrel is larger than the remainder, and the Magellan Diving-petrel may be distinguished by the white half collar on the sides of its neck, it is probably impossible to distinguish between them at sea. When examined in the hand the shape and size of the bill are diagnostic.

As their name implies, their principal preoccupation is in diving underwater using their wings to propel them, at other times resting on the surface. When disturbed they either dive or flutter along the surface, but once airborne they fly short distances close over the sea with rapidly whirring flight, usually diving on landing.

Diving-petrels usually keep close to the coasts and are very rarely seen on shipping routes except in New Zealand coastal waters. They feed on small fishes, crustaceans and other marins organisms.

Nesting and young

These breed on islands in the cooler parts of the southern hemisphere. They mature faster than other petrels and may breed in their second year. The nest is in a burrow several feet long dug by the birds themselves in open ground or under trees. Some nest material may be pulled into the burrow. There is a single large white egg which is incubated by both birds, alternating nightly, for c. 8 weeks. The chick's first down is sparse compared with that of other petrels, but the second coat is thicker. It is brooded for the first week or two, as compared with 2–3 days in other petrels. The chick is visited and fed daily and leaves the nest at 47–60 days.

PERUVIAN DIVING-PETREL *Pelecanoides garnoti* **Pl. 14**
Small, 8.2–9 ins, 209–229 mm. Bill length, 0.7–0.9 ins, 18–23 mm. Breadth at base, 0.35–0.4 ins, 9–10 mm. Similar to Common Diving-petrel but considerably larger. No band on foreneck.
Strictly limited to inshore waters of Humboldt Current.
RANGE: Coasts of Peru and Chile south to 50°S. A more northerly range than any other diving-petrel. Breeds in islands off the coast. Map 115.

MAGELLAN DIVING-PETREL *Pelecanoides magellani* **Pl. 14**
Small, 7.5–8.8 ins, 191–224 mm. Bill length, 0.6–0.7 ins, 15–18 mm. Breadth at base, 0.35–0.4 ins, 9–10 mm. Similar to the Common Diving-petrel but a conspicuous white collar on each side of the neck forms a partial collar, and foreneck is always white.
RANGE: From Cape Horn to about 50°S. Breeds on coasts of Straits of Magellan. Map 116.

GEORGIAN DIVING-PETREL *Pelecanoides georgicus*
Very small, 7–8.5 ins, 178–216 mm. Bill length, 0.5–0.6 ins, 13–15 mm. Breadth at base 0.35–0.4 ins, 9–10 mm. Similar to Common Diving-petrel, but its bill is wider at the base and tapers more sharply. Legs pale blue, webs black.
Can only be distinguished by the shape of its bill. See drawing opposite.
RANGE: Breeds on S. Georgia, Kerguelen and Heard Is., and Auckland Is. Map 117.

COMMON DIVING-PETREL *Pelecanoides urinatrix* **Pl. 14**
Very small, 7–8 ins, 178–203 mm. Bill length, 0.5–0.7 ins, 13–18 mm. Breadth at base, 0.25–0.35 ins, 6–9 mm. Head and upperparts black. Sides of neck and breast grey, foreneck sometimes mottled grey, the remainder of the underparts white, the sides of the flanks greyish. The underwing-coverts are a greyish-white. Bill black, short and hooked, the lower mandible broad and narrowing sharply towards the tip. Legs blue. Tail short and black.
The Common Diving-petrel tends to range further north than the other species except the Peruvian Diving-petrel.
RANGE: Southern oceans from 55°S. to 35°S. Local to breeding islands which stretch from the Falkland Is. eastwards through the S. Atlantic and S. Indian Ocean to S.E. Australia, Tasmania, New Zealand and adjacent islands. Map 118.

Diving-petrel bills. On the left the upper bill is shown from above; the lower from the underside. Note also the different patterns above the eye and at the collar.

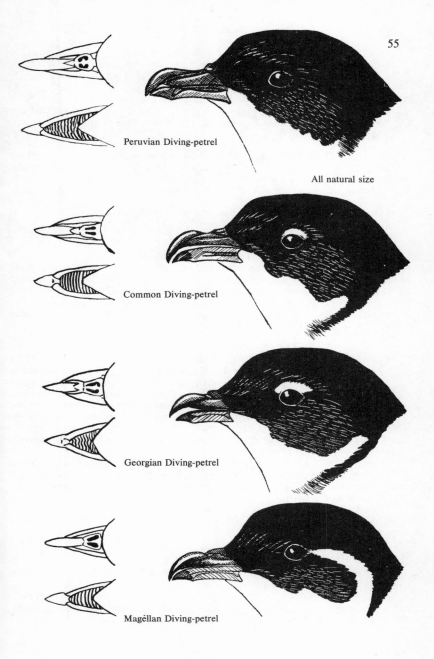

55

Peruvian Diving-petrel

All natural size

Common Diving-petrel

Georgian Diving-petrel

Magéllan Diving-petrel

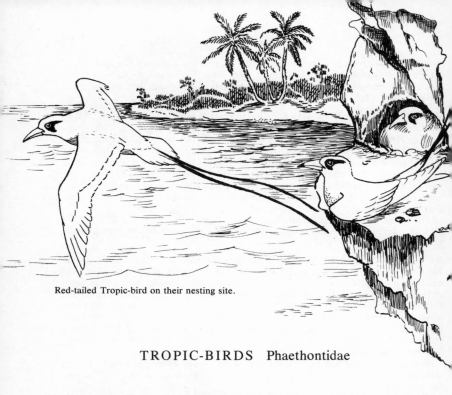

Red-tailed Tropic-bird on their nesting site.

TROPIC-BIRDS Phaethontidae

These beautiful white seabirds, distinguished in adult plumage by their immensely elongated two central tail feathers or 'streamers', are known as 'Bo'sun Birds' by seafarers, their central tails being likened to 'marlin-spikes'. They range far out into the ocean in the tropical belt and are usually seen flying high with powerful quick wingbeats. They are capable of twisting and turning sharply and plunge steeply to the water for food.

Tropic-birds feed chiefly on squid which rise to the surface at night. It is perhaps for this reason that tropic-birds frequently follow astern in the wake of ships at night, and becoming dazzled by the ship's lights, hit some part of the structure and are later found on board.

Viewed against a background of blue tropical sky it is no easy task to distinguish between the Red-billed and White-tailed species. All tropic-birds swim with their tails cocked.

Nesting and young

These nest on islands of the tropical and subtropical zones. Tropic-birds move with difficulty on land and the nest is usually on a ledge sheltered by an overhang, or in a cavity or crevice in the face of a cliff or steep rock face overlooking the water to allow an easy take-off, occasionally on flatter and more open sites. The nest is a bare hollow, sometimes with a few feathers, and the single egg is pale-shelled, rarely with dark blotches, but usually so heavily marked with very fine freckling of purple-brown as to appear dark in colour. Both birds incubate for 6–6½ weeks. The chick has thick buff or grey down from hatching. It is fed by both parents and leaves the nest at *c.* 12–15 weeks.

RED-BILLED TROPIC-BIRD *Phaethon aethereus* **Pl. 15**
Medium, 24 ins, 61 cm, including tail streamers 38 ins, 96 cm. Wing-span 44 ins, 112 cm. The general appearance is mainly white. Adults have white heads with a striking black band running before, over and through the eye. Whole upperparts are finely barred with black. Leading primaries black, appearing as a black band on outer wing tips. Bill stout, slightly curved downwards and pointed, coral red. The two central white tail feathers are extremely elongated. Legs usually greyish-white, webs of feet black. Immature birds have heavy black barrings over upperparts, the long central tails are absent or much reduced.
The tail possesses 14 tail feathers.
RANGE: Tropical and sub-tropical zones of Atlantic, Indian and Pacific Oceans. Map 119.

RED-TAILED TROPIC-BIRD *Phaethon rubricauda* **Pl. 15**
Medium, 18 in, 46 cm, including tail streamers, 36 ins, 91 cm. Wing-span 44 ins, 112 cm. The plumage of the adult Red-tailed Tropic-bird is a silky white sometimes diffused with a beautiful pink tinge. A broad black crescent passes before and through the eye. The shafts of the white primaries and tail feathers are black and some black feathers sometimes show in the flanks. In adult plumage the most outstanding feature is the addition of two long blood red central tail feathers or streamers, which are shed however in moult. The stout bill is coral red in adults; legs pale blue, feet black.
Young birds are white, lacking the pink flush, have upperparts broadly barred with black markings, and carry no elongated central tail feathers. Bill black changing to yellow and orange.
The flight is more leisurely than in other species, its wingbeats slower, and it is apt to sail between wingbeats. The Red-tailed Tropic-bird has 16 tail feathers.
RANGE: Tropical and sub-tropical Indian and Pacific Oceans; it does not occur in the Atlantic. Highly oceanic. Map 120.

WHITE-TAILED TROPIC-BIRD *Phaethon lepturus lepturus* **Pl. 15**
Medium, 16 ins, 41 cm including tail streamers 32 ins, 81 cm. Wing-span 36 ins, 92 cm. The general appearance is mainly white. Adults have white heads with a striking black band running before and over the eye. The whole upperparts are white except for a black band across the upperwings and black outer wing tips. Bill stout, slightly curved downwards and pointed, yellow. The two central white tail feathers are extremely elongated. Legs usually greyish-white, webs of feet black. Immature birds have black barring over upperparts but not as pronounced as other species. The long central tail feathers are absent or much reduced.

The tail possesses 12 tail feathers.
RANGE: Tropical and sub-tropical zones of Atlantic, Indian and Pacific Oceans. Map 121.
RACE:
 CHRISTMAS TROPIC-BIRD *Phaethon lepturus fulvus* **Pl. 15**
 This sub-species breeds on Christmas I. in the Indian Ocean and occurs only locally. Similar to the White-tailed Tropic-bird but distinguished by the golden tint of its plumage. Not mapped.

Eastern White Pelicans:
a breeding colony with young birds.

PELICANS Pelecanidae

Pelicans with their great size, heavy bodies, broad rounded wings, and huge bill carrying a large distensible pouch are quite unmistakable. Most species frequent inland lagoons and marshes. With the exception of the Chilean Pelican they will not occur on sea routes but may be seen by ships visiting harbours and ports and when passing close to islands. In flight they carry their necks tucked back into their shoulder and may often be seen in small parties flying low over the water in formation in a somewhat undulating flight with steady wingbeats and glides the birds keeping precise time with their leader. When fishing they fly with bills pointing downwards, suddenly checking their flight and plunging awkwardly into the sea with an enormous splash. At other times they will swim in formation until locating fish when they will all submerge in unison.

The maps show only coastal areas where they are most likely to be seen by ships.

Nesting and young

They nest in colonies, on sites providing some protection from predators and may desert *en masse* if badly disturbed. Nests are in coastal mangroves or other trees, on bare islands, or high rocks, or low islands and ridges in extensive estuarine or lakeside swamps. Nest material may be absent or large mounds assembled on the ground. Large twig platforms are built in trees. 2–4 eggs are laid. These are white with a chalk-like white outer layer of irregular thickness. Both adults incubate for *c*. 4 weeks. The young are naked at first and later covered with brown or blackish down. In colonies on level ground the larger young may assemble in huddled groups. They are fed by both parents, taking food from their gullets, and they fledge in *c*. 10 weeks.

WHITE PELICAN *Pelecanus onocrotalus* **Pl. 16**
Outsize, 55–70 ins, 140–178 cm. Wing-span 100 ins, 254 cm. Almost entirely white plumage with black primaries and secondaries, a small crest on the back of the

59

head, and a tuft of yellowish feathers on the breast. Naked skin on face is purplish or yellowish-white; bill grey with pink edges; pouch yellow; legs pink.

Young birds are buff coloured above with brown primaries, and have white underparts.

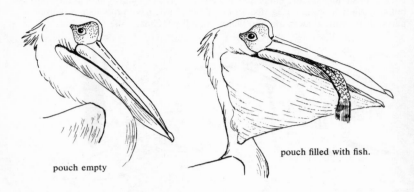

pouch filled with fish.

pouch empty

Eastern White Pelican (p.59)

Sometimes the white plumage in adults shows a pinkish flush. Distinguished from Pink-backed Pelican by its pink legs.

RANGE: Southern Europe, Africa, and central Asia. In winter to India, Malay Peninsula and adjacent islands. Occurs in Persian Gulf.   Map 122.

PINK-BACKED PELICAN *Pelecanus rufescens*   **Pl. 16**
Outsize, 55–60 ins, 138–152 cm. Wing-span 85 ins, 214 cm. The overall plumage is similar but somewhat greyer than that of the White Pelican, but the back, rump, flanks and under tail-coverts show a distinct pink flush. The crest on the back of the head is more evident, the feathers on the breast are longer shaggy plumes. The tail is grey. Bill yellowish-white with orange tip; pouch flesh-coloured; legs yellowish. Adults in winter plumage and young birds show brown wings and tails.

Distinguished from White Pelican by its grey tail and yellowish legs.

RANGE: Rarely in southern Africa but northwards to Gambia, Ethiopia, Madagascar (Malagasy) and southern Arabia. Liable to overlap with the White Pelican on coasts of Arabia.   Map 123.

GREY PELICAN *Pelecanus philippensis*   **Pl. 16**
Outsize, 50–60 ins, 127–152 cm. Head, neck and upperparts including upperwings grey. Underparts greyish-white, under tail-coverts mottled-brown. A crest of elongated brown feathers, tipped white on the back of the head. Bill pinkish; pouch purple; legs dark brown.

Easily distinguished by its overall grey appearance.

RANGE: Southern Asia from Persia to Ceylon, Malaysia, southern China and Philippines. Breeds on islands in Persian Gulf and inland waters in Ceylon and Burma. Rarely seen on sea coast.   Map 124.

DALMATIAN PELICAN *Pelecanus crispus* **Pl. 16**

Outsize, 60–70 ins, 152–177 cm. Wing-span 100 ins, 254 cm. Upperparts silvery-grey; wing quills blackish-brown, secondaries greyish-brown. Underparts dull greyish-white with large yellow patch on lower throat, absent in winter. Feathers on back of head only slightly elongated and curly. Eye pale yellow; skin of face pink; bill grey; pouch orange. Legs lead-grey. Young birds have brownish-grey upperparts, dirty white underparts and yellowish bill pouches.

Dalmatian Pelican   Eastern White Pelican (p.59)

In flight Dalmatian Pelican shows almost totally white underwing and grey legs compared with dark band of flight feathers and pink legs of Eastern White Pelican.

Easily confused with White Pelican except in flight where White Pelican shows dark underwing pattern of primaries while Dalmation Pelican shows an almost totally white underwing. Lead-grey legs of Dalmation compare with pink legs of White.

RANGE: Breeds on inland lakes and seas in S.E. Europe, Asia Minor, Persia eastwards to China. May be seen by ships in Persian Gulf but rarely seen on sea coast elsewhere. Map 125.

AUSTRALIAN PELICAN *Pelecanus conspicillatus* **Pl. 17**

Outsize, 60 ins, 152 cm. Wing-span 100 ins, 254 cm. A mainly white pelican with black wing quills, and black band on each side of lower back and above tail, scapulars and portions of upperwing-coverts. The foreneck and underparts are white, the feathers on the foreneck elongated, yellow, and a greyish crest at the back of the head. The large bill is flesh-coloured with blue sides; pouch flesh-coloured; legs slaty-blue; rump patch and tail-band black.

Young birds are similar but the black areas in adult plumage are brown and lack yellow plumes.

The only species of pelican in Australia and New Guinea. Most likely to be seen by ships in the Bass Strait. Breeds on inland lagoons and also off the coasts around Australia and in the Bass Strait and Tasmania. Map 126.

AMERICAN WHITE PELICAN *Pelecanus erythrorhynchus* **Pl. 17**

Outsize, 55–70 ins, 140–178 cm. Wing-span 110 ins, 269 cm. Plumage generally all

white with primaries and leading secondaries black. Elongated crest on back of head in breeding plumage white or very pale yellow with pale yellow shade on breast and wing-coverts. In winter the crest is replaced by a grey area. Bill, with horny knob, and pouch reddish-orange in summer, yellow in winter, horny knob absent. Naked skin on face orange, in winter yellow. Legs reddish-orange. Young birds are similar to adults in winter plumage.

RANGE: Outside the breeding season it tends to resort to salt water bays. Breeds inland in western N. America and migrates south in winter occurring chiefly off Florida, Cuba and coastal waters of Gulf of Mexico to the Panama Canal. Rarely seen in the W. Indies.   Map 127.

BROWN PELICAN
Pelecanus occidentalis   **Pl. 17**
Outsize, 40 ins, 110 cm. Wing-span 90 ins, 229 cm. In summer plumage back of head, neck and foreneck chestnut-brown; in winter whole head and neck whitish-yellow.

Head white, dirty yellow on crown, a white line continuing down each side of the brown neck. There is a crest on the back of the head and a tuft of elongated blackish-yellow feathers on the lower foreneck. The primary wing feathers are black, upperwing-coverts and tail grey. The facial skin is blue, the large bill

Brown Pelican diving.

yellowish, pouch dusky and legs greyish-black. Whole underparts dark greyish-brown.

Young birds have brownish upperparts and white underbodies.

The smallest of the pelicans. Seen regularly in bays, harbours and along coast-lines.

RANGE: Both coasts of U.S.A. from N. Carolina southwards through the W. Indies to tropical Brazil. On the west coast of U.S.A. from Washington to Peru. Breeds from S. Carolina to the Orinoco, from California to Ecuador, and on the Galapagos Is.   Map 128.

CHILEAN PELICAN *Pelecanus thagus*   **Pl. 17**
Outsize, 60 ins, 152 cm. Much larger but otherwise similar to the Brown Pelican, but a pale straw-coloured crest on the back of the head is more developed, and white flecking shows on underparts. Yellow feather tuft on foreneck. The bill is yellow with red sides and tip; pouch black with blue lines and legs slate-coloured.

Young birds are similar to young Brown Pelicans.

RANGE: Abundant in the coastal areas of the Humboldt Current off the coasts of Peru and Chile. Breeds on islands off the coast of Peru.   Map 129.

Brown Pelican
Chilean Pelican
Both in non-breeding plumage.
When found together, they
are only distinguishable in the
field by their difference in
size.

Australian Gannets fishing. The dark bird is an immature 1st year.

GANNETS and BOOBIES   Sulidae

Gannets and boobies are by our 'size definition' outsize birds of some 30 ins or more in length with cigar shaped bodies, long narrow wings, stout conical bills and long wedge-shaped tails. Those that live in the temperate latitude belts are gannets, the tropical species being known as boobies.

The flight of all the species is similar. At sea they may be seen flying in steady direct flight, sometimes at sea level, more usually at some 30 ft above the sea employing powerful rather rapid regular wingbeats with occasional glides. When in company they often fly in a ragged single line ahead formation. They obtain their food by rising to 50 ft or more above the sea and, when fish are located, checking their flight before hurtling in a headlong dive with wings partially closed into the sea. Boobies usually dive from lower levels at more slanting angles.

Boobies frequently perch on ships at sea, sometimes using a vantage point on the forecastle structure from which to dive upon flying fish skipping away from the bow wave. They may remain thus for several hours; indeed their name originated in the seafarers' term for them for they appear particularly stupid, often showing no concern on being approached and captured.

Nesting and young

These often nest in large colonies, and in some species the nests are closely packed together. Nesting may be on more level ground of flattish islands or cliff tops, on cliff ledges, on bushes or on trees. As with cormorants the nests may vary from a pile of seaweed and debris on the ground or a ledge, to a substantial stick nest in a tree. The eggs, 1–2 according to species, are pale blue, but with the colour almost entirely concealed by an irregular chalk-like white outer layer. During incubation, performed by both birds, warmth is conveyed to the eggs through the webs of the feet which cover them. Incubation lasts 42–47 days. The young hatch naked and dark-skinned and after about a week grow a thick white down. They are fed by both parents, taking regurgitated food from the adult gullet. They become very large and fat and starve for a week or so before leaving the nest. They fledge in 10–12 weeks in the gannets, but it may be up to 17 weeks in other species, possibly varying with the food supply.

NORTHERN GANNET *Sula bassana*   **Pl. 18**
Outsize, 36 ins, 92 cm. Wing-span 68 ins, 173 cm. Mainly white with primaries only blackish-brown. Tail feathers white. Head and nape pale straw-yellow; naked skin on face and throat bluish-black; bill pale horn-coloured; legs black.

Young birds have upperparts greyish-brown with white speckling; underparts whitish with brown mottling.

RANGE: N. Atlantic Ocean from Iceland southwards off west coasts of Europe and east coast of N. America and Canada reaching Canary Is. and N.W. coast of Africa. Breeds in Iceland, Norway, the Faroes, British Isles, Channel Is., Brittany, Newfoundland and Gulf of St. Lawrence.   Map 130.

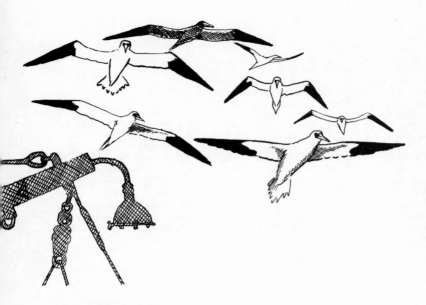

Gannets following a ship.

CAPE GANNET *Sula capensis*   **Pl. 18**

Outsize, 33–35 ins, 84–89 cm. Mainly white with primaries, secondaries and all twelve tail feathers brown. Crown and nape yellow; naked skin on face and throat black; bill pale bluish; legs brownish-black.

Young birds have greyish-brown upperparts with white speckling and whitish underparts with brown bars.

Known locally as the 'Malagas'.

RANGE: Both coasts of S. Africa from Cape of Good Hope to 20°S.   Map 131.

AUSTRALIAN GANNET *Sula serrator*   **Pl. 18**

Outsize, 36ins, 92 cm. Wing-span 68 ins, 172 cm. Mainly white with primaries and secondaries blackish-brown, and the majority of the central tail feathers blackish-brown, outer tail feathers white. The crown and nape are yellow; naked skin of face and throat slate-blue; bill bluish-grey; legs greyish-black with bright green lines running along top of the toes.

Young birds have upperparts brown with white speckling; underparts mainly white with some brown mottling on the throat and flanks.

RANGE: S. and E. coasts of Australia, the Bass Strait, Tasmania and New Zealand coastal waters. Breeds within the Bass Strait, in Tasmania and in New Zealand. Map 132.

BLUE-FOOTED BOOBY *Sula nebouxii*   **Pl. 19**

Outsize, 32–36 ins, 83–92 cm. Wing-span 60 ins, 152 cm. Head, neck and upper breast cinnamon-brown, with some white mottling, the back also being mottled white. The wings and tail are brown, the central tail feathers white. Lower breast and underparts white. The naked skin on face and throat slate-blue; bill olive-blue. Its most distinctive feature is its bright blue legs.

Young birds are very similar but their white underbodies show considerable dusky mottling.

In adult plumage it differs from other boobies by the brown and white appearance of its upperparts. Unless its bright blue legs are seen however it is liable to be mistaken for immature birds of the other species.

RANGE: West coast of tropical America. Breeds on islands off the coast of Mexico, Ecuador, northern Peru and the Galapagos Is. Map 133.

PERUVIAN BOOBY *Sula variegata* Pl. 19
Very large, 29 ins, 74 cm. The whole head, neck and upper back are white, the lower back, tail and flanks mottled black and white. Underparts white. Wings brownish-black. Bill blue; legs bluish-black.

Young birds are very similar but show mottled underparts.

Easily distinguished by its white and speckled plumage.

RANGE: West coast of S. America. Abundant off the coasts of Peru and Chile. Breeds on islands off coast of Peru. Map 134.

ABBOTT'S BOOBY *Sula abbotti* Pl. 19
Large, 28 ins, 71 cm. Adult. Head, neck, back and upper tail-coverts white. Black skin and dark orbital ring around brown eye conspicuous. Underbody white with black thigh patches evident when wings are raised. Underwing-coverts white. Upperwing-coverts black with some small indistinct white feathers. Wing quills black, the inner webs of some primaries white, showing in flight. Carpal joint feathers spotted with white extending to leading edge. Tail black with some white mottling. Bill large, deep at base, varies in male yellow or blue-grey tinged with pink, in female yellow or rosy, both sexes showing a broad black tip. Legs leaden-grey.

Immatures similar to adult males with indistinct buff edges to scapulars and upperwing-coverts. Bill greyish, broadly tipped black.

Note: Wings tend to bleach brown and may appear as such when immatures and adults are virtually indistinguishable.

RANGE: Breeds on Christmas I. (Indian Ocean), nesting high up in tall jungle trees in the central plateau inland. Not mapped.

BLUE-FACED BOOBY or MASKED BOOBY *Sula dactylatra* Pl. 18
Outsize, 32–36 ins, 81–92 cm. Wing-span 60 ins, 152 cm. Mainly white, with chocolate-brown primaries and secondaries forming a complete dark margin to the edge of the wing, and a chocolate-brown tail. The naked skin on face and throat is bluish-black giving it a 'masked' appearance from which it is also known as the Masked Booby. The stout bill varies in colour but is usually yellowish; legs usually greyish-blue but vary, sometimes orange.

Young birds in first plumage have the head and neck dark brown, the remainder of upperparts greyish-brown, second year birds having mainly white heads and mottled greyish-brown upperparts.

Distinguished from the adult Red-footed Booby in the light phase by having both primary and secondary flight feathers and the tail dark.

RANGE: Widespread throughout the tropical and sub-tropical belt of the oceans. Breeds throughout its range on islands in the Atlantic, Indian and Pacific Oceans. Map 135.

BROWN BOOBY *Sula leucogaster*   **Pl. 19**
Very large, 28–30 ins, 71–76 cm. Wing-span 57 ins, 145 cm. The whole head, neck, upperparts and breast are dark chocolate-brown, the remainder of its underbody and under tail-coverts white. Tail dark chocolate-brown. The axillaries and median underwing-coverts show white against the dark outer areas of the underwing.

A clear cut line divides the dark chocolate breast from the white underparts. Stout pointed bill usually bluish-white or greenish-yellow; legs yellow or bluish-green. The naked skin on face and throat varies from greenish-yellow to purple.

Young birds are dusky-brown above including breast, underparts below breast mottled-brown.

Unmistakable in adult plumage from all other boobies, but immature plumage may be confusing.

RANGE: The commonest booby throughout the tropical and sub-tropical belts of the oceans, but does not range far from land. Breeds throughout its range on islands in the Atlantic, Indian and Pacific Oceans.   Map 137.

RED-FOOTED BOOBY *Sula sula*   **Pl. 19**
Very large, 26–29 ins, 66–74 cm. Wing-span 38 ins, 97 cm. Adult birds may be in three plumage phases.

WHITE PHASE. Plumage mainly white, often with a golden-buff tint. Primaries and secondaries blackish-brown. Tail-coverts and tail white.

INTERMEDIATE PHASE. Head, neck and underparts dull white to pale buff, head and neck sometimes with golden tint. Back and wings chocolate-brown to greyish-brown. Tail-coverts and tail white.

DARK PHASE. Head, neck and underparts ashy-grey or ashy-brown, head and neck often with a golden-brown tint. Tail-coverts and tail white, sometimes pale grey.

Naked skin on face, blue. Gular sac, black. Bill, bright medium-blue, and base of both mandibles pink. A deep blue-black stripe extends below lower mandible towards junction with feathers. Legs and feet, coral-red. Eye ring and skin around eye, rich blue.

Young birds are generally brownish-grey with paler underparts. Facial skin dark blue. Bill blackish.

There is considerable variation in tones of plumage in the intermediate and dark phases and in colour of soft parts, but the red legs are quite distinctive.

RANGE: Tropical Atlantic, Indian and western and central Pacific Oceans, breeding in islands throughout its range including the Galapagos Is.   Map 136.

All Gannets and Boobies nest on the ground or on rock, except for Abbot's Booby and the Red-footed Booby. These two species, in their relatively safe nest sites in trees, lay only a single egg.

Common Cormorant nesting colony in trees. They also nest on cliffs.

CORMORANTS Phalacrocoracidae

Cormorants are heavy-bodied birds with long sinuous necks, long rounded wings and rather long wedge-shaped tails. Their bills are long, slender and sharply hooked at the tip; their legs and large webbed feet are set well aft in their bodies. In certain parts of the world some of the family are known as shags, a name frequently applied to the whole family by seafarers.

Cormorants are predominantly black in colour, those found in the northern hemisphere almost exclusively so, while in the southern hemisphere many have white underparts and in some cases pied plumage.

They are essentially coastal seabirds, sociable in habits, frequently seen in harbours but rarely on the sea routes. On the surface they swim low in the water, and when feeding gain their food by springing from the surface in a 'jack-knife' dive beneath the water in pursuit of fish, using both wings and legs for propulsion. Indeed when fishing they may often be seen with only their long necks appearing above the surface. When disturbed they usually dive at once.

In flight, usually low over the sea but on long journeys sometimes rising to a considerable height, they proceed with necks fully extended and steadily flapping wings interspersed with short glides, flocks in a '**V**' formation. Cormorants are extremely partial to perching on posts, beacons or rocks with wings extended in order to dry their body feathers in the air.

Nesting and young

These usually breed in colonies; on cliffs, rocky shores, islands and islets, and inland lakes and rivers. The nest site may be a ledge or level open site, or a tree in or near water. Material is carried to the site, and the nest is usually a bulky structure of seaweed or sticks according to site, with a finer lining. The clutch is usually of 2–4 eggs; the pale blue shell covered with a white, chalk-like layer of irregular thickness, wholly or partly concealing the underlying colour. Both birds incubate for c. 27–30 days. The young hatch naked, but later grow a coat of short dark down. They take their food from the gullet of the parents. They may leave the nest at 5–6 weeks and move about the colony, sometimes gathering into groups. They become independent in c. 10–12 weeks.

DOUBLE-CRESTED CORMORANT *Phalacrocorax auritus* Pl. 21
Very large, 29–35 ins, 74–89 cm. Wing-span 50 ins, 127 cm. General plumage glossy greenish-black, back, scapulars and upperwing-coverts bronze, feathers edged with black. In breeding plumage a tuft of black or black and white curly feathers shows on each side of the head.

A noticeable feature is the orange colour of the naked skin on the face and throat. Bill slate-grey, yellow at base; legs black. Young birds have greyish-brown upperparts, black rump, whitish breasts and blackish underbodies. Naked skin dull yellow.

A widespread N. and Central American species, considerably larger than the Bigua Cormorant. A number of different races occur.

RANGE: N. and Central America, W. Indies, and Pacific coast of N. America. Map 138.

BIGUA CORMORANT *Phalacrocorax olivaceus*   **Pl. 21**
Very large, 25–30 ins, 64–76 cm. Wing-span 40 ins, 102 cm. General plumage glossy
black. In breeding plumage the face and throat are edged white, and it carries a
white tuft of feathers on each side of the head. The bill is brown; naked skin on face
and throat a dull yellow and legs black. The tail is noticeably long.
   Young birds have brown upperparts and greyish-white underparts.
   Smaller than the Double-crested Cormorant with which it is liable to be confused.
RANGE: On both coasts of tropical and sub-tropical America, the W. Indies,
extending down the full length of the west coast of S. America.   Map 139.

LITTLE BLACK CORMORANT *Phalacrocorax sulcirostris*   **Pl. 23**
Large, 24–25 ins, 61–64 cm. Wing-span 32 ins, 82 cm. Plumage entirely black with
dull green gloss, ashy-grey on shoulders and upperwing-coverts. In breeding
plumage narrow white plumes occur on the sides of the head and about the eyes, not
noticeable at any distance. Pouch dull bluish-purple; bill rather long and dull lead
colour; iris green; legs black. Young birds generally duller brownish-black.
   Frequents lakes and estuaries but also occurs on the sea coast, birds tending to
keep in flocks.
RANGE: Malay Archipelago and E. Indies. Breed in E. Indies, Australia, Tasmania, New Zealand and Norfolk I.   Map 140.

COMMON CORMORANT *Phalacrocorax carbo*
(A) Outsize, 36 ins, 92 cm. Wing-span 60 ins, 152 cm; (B) Chin and sides of face
white; (C) General plumage glossy bluish-black, upperwing-coverts dull bronze;
(D) In breeding plumage some white filo plumes sprinkle head and neck, feathers on
back of head elongated but do not form a crest, and a large white patch shows on
each flank; in winter these are absent; (E) Naked skin on lores and throat-pouch
yellow; (F) Bill long, slender, lead-grey, tip hooked, legs black; (G) Immatures
brownish above, underparts whitish.
RANGE: Widespread throughout the world.
RACES:
   COMMON CORMORANT *Phalacrocorax c. carbo*   **Pls. 20, 23**
   Breeds in Labrador, Nova Scotia, Greenland, Iceland, Norway, Faroe Is.,
   Shetland Is., British Isles, France, Mediterranean, Spain, Australia and New
   Zealand.   Map 141.
   COMMON CORMORANT (continental race) *Phalacrocorax c. sinensis* **Pl. 20**
   Breeds in central and southern Europe, to central Asia, India, Japan and China.
   (B), (D), dark band from eye circles sides of face and throat; in breeding plumage
   nape and neck almost entirely white.   Map 142.

WHITE-NECKED CORMORANT *Phalacrocorax lucidus*   **Pl. 20**
Outsize, 36 ins, 92 cm. Wing-span 60 ins, 152 cm. Top of head, back of neck and
upperparts black, upperwings with bronze tint. Face, front of neck and breast
white; remainder of underparts black. White patch on flanks in breeding plumage.
Bill yellow; legs slate grey.
   Immatures have brown upperparts and wings, and whitish underparts. The
largest of the S. African cormorants.
RANGE: West, south and east coasts of S. Africa, extending to coasts of E. Africa.
Occurs both on coasts and inland on lakes and rivers.   Map 143.

INDIAN CORMORANT *Phalacrocorax fuscicollis*   **Pl. 23**
Large, 24–27 ins, 610–686 mm. General plumage metallic bronze-black with pale

brown cheeks and throat. In breeding plumage the male has a tuft of whitish feathers on each side of the head. Naked skin of face and throat pale green. Bill brown. Legs black. Young birds have brownish upperparts and brownish-white underparts.

Overlaps with the Javanese Cormorant in range, but may be distinguished by its paler cheeks, larger size and longer bill and tail.

RANGE: India, Sri Lanka, Burma. Breeds on lagoons and tanks, but also frequents the sea coast. Map 144.

CAPE CORMORANT *Phalacrocorax capensis* Pl. 20

Large, 25 ins, 64 cm. Wing-span 43 ins, 109 cm. General plumage black, foreneck and breast dark brown. Naked skin on face and throat yellow; bill slaty-black; legs black. Tail noticeably short.

Young birds have brownish upperparts and underparts, their forenecks and chests whitish.

The commonest cormorant of S. African coasts. Considerably smaller than both the Bank and white-necked Cormorant of S. Africa and distinguished by its overall dark plumage and yellow throat.

RANGE: Both coasts of S. Africa from southern Angola to Durban. Found only on salt water. Breeds in large numbers on guano islands. Map 145.

SOCOTRA CORMORANT *Phalacrocorax nigrogularis* Pl. 20

Very large, 30 ins, 76 cm. General plumage glossy-black overall, wing-coverts and scapulars tinged with bronze. Naked skin on face and throat black; bill greyish-black, greenish at base of lower mandible; legs black.

Young birds have brownish-black upperparts and paler brown underparts.

Distinguished from the Common Cormorant by lack of any white facial or flank patches.

RANGE: Persian Gulf, coastal on Arabian coasts, southern Red Sea and Socotra. Map 146.

BANK CORMORANT *Phalacrocorax neglectus* Pl. 20

Very large, 27–30 ins, 69–76 cm. Wing-span 52 ins, 132 cm. General plumage dark-glossy overall, slightly browner on the wings, showing white feathers in the form of a patch above the rump. In breeding plumage the feathers on the forehead are elongated to form a crest. The bill, naked skin on face and pouch are black; legs black.

Young birds are brownish-black overall.

Distinguished from White-necked Cormorant by its black as opposed to white breast, and from Cape Cormorant by its larger size and black as opposed to yellow pouch. More 'woolly' in appearance than other African cormorants.

RANGE: South and west coasts of S. Africa. Map 147.

JAPANESE CORMORANT *Phalacrocorax capillatus* Pl. 20

Very large, 32 ins, 81 cm. Wing-span 54 ins, 137 cm. Very similar to the Common Cormorant which also occurs in Japan. It differs only in the naked skin on the face being more orange in colour, and in breeding plumage by the head and neck being covered with white filo plumes, and throat feathers extend forward to lower mandible.

Young birds are similar to young Common Cormorants.

RANGE: Coasts of N.E. Asia, China and Japan. Breeds in Korea, Japan and Sakhalin I. Map 148.

BRANDT'S CORMORANT *Phalacrocorax penicillatus* **Pl. 21**
Very large, 30 ins, 76 cm. General plumage glossy greenish-black. The throat is fawn coloured. In breeding plumage fine white hair-like plumes are scattered over the neck and upper back, these feathers extending to a point on the throat. Tufts of white feathers show behind the ears. Naked skin on face and throat blue; bill grey; legs black.
Young birds have brown upperparts, paler underparts.
The commonest cormorant on the Pacific coast of the U.S.A. Considerably larger than the Pelagic Cormorant and never showing any white patch on the flanks.
RANGE: Pacific coast of N. America as far south as Lower California. Map 149.

SHAG or GREEN CORMORANT *Phalacrocorax aristotelis* **Pl. 21**
Very large, 26–30 ins, 66–76 cm. Wing-span 48 ins, 122 cm. General plumage glossy greenish-black overall. In breeding plumage the feathers on the crown are elongated forming a very noticeable crest curving forwards, and some white filo plumes occur here and there about the neck. The naked skin around the bill is yellow, on the throat black with yellow spots. Bill and legs are both black.
Young birds are brownish above and below.
Its more slender build, and lack of any white on the body serve to distinguish it from the Common Cormorant.
RANGE: Coastal along the western seaboard of Europe and northern Africa and throughout the Mediterranean. Map 150.

PELAGIC CORMORANT *Phalacrocorax pelagicus* **Pl. 21**
Very large, 28 ins, 71 cm. Wing-span 40 ins, 102 cm. General plumage glossy greenish-black overall. In breeding plumage tufts of bronze feathers on the crown and nape form two crests and a large white patch occurs on each flank. Naked skin on face dark greyish, throat and pouch coral-red. Bill very slender, blackish-brown; legs black.
Its small head, thin neck and bill and more agile rapid flight distinguish it from Brandt's Cormorant which never shows white flank patches and has a fawn coloured throat.
RANGE: Coastal on both eastern and western seaboards of N. Pacific from Alaska south to Mexico, from Siberia south to Japan and China in winter. A common species on the coast of British Columbia. Map 151.

RED-FACED CORMORANT *Phalacrocorax urile* **Pl. 21**
Very large, 28–30 ins, 71–76 cm. General plumage glossy greenish-black. In breeding plumage two tufts of bronze feathers show, one on the crown and another on the nape, and a white patch of feathers occurs on each flank. The forehead is bare and the naked skin on both forehead and face red, on throat blue with red wrinkles at the base. Bill blue; legs black.
Young birds are dark brown overall.
Distinguished by colour of skin on face. It differs from the Common and Japanese Cormorants by its black as opposed to white chin and throat. Larger but very similar to Pelagic Cormorant.
RANGE: Breeds on the coasts of Kamchatka, N.E. Siberia, Bering Sea, Aleutian Is., Kuril Is., south in winter to Hokkaido, rarely seen further south in Japan. Map 152.

MAGELLAN CORMORANT *Phalacrocorax magellanicus* **Pl. 22**
Large, 26 ins, 66 cm. Wing-span 36 ins, 92 cm. Head and neck black in summer; in winter chin, throat and foreneck white. Upperparts greenish-black; flanks and under tail-coverts black; remainder of underparts white. In breeding plumage long white plumes occur on head and neck and some white feathers on lower back and flanks. Naked skin on face and throat red; bill black; legs flesh-coloured.

Differs from Blue-eyed Cormorant in its red face and black neck in breeding plumage.

RANGE: Breeds on coasts and islands north to Chiloe I. on west coast of S. America, and to Point Tombo, 44°S., 65°20′W., on east coast, and Falkland Is. Map 153.

GUANAY CORMORANT *Phalacrocorax bougainvillei* **Pl. 22**
Very large, 30 ins, 76 cm. Head, neck and upper parts glossy greenish-black, the chin and underparts below the neck white. In breeding plumage the dark feathers on the head are elongated forming a crest, and a patch of white plumes shows above the eye. Naked skin on face red; bill horn-coloured with a red wattle at the base; legs pink.

Young birds are very similar but the foreneck is whitish.

Distinguished by its white throat and underparts and distinctive red face. Unlike many coastal cormorants it is often seen flying at a considerable height to locate shoals of fish from the air, diving from a height to capture them.

RANGE: Throughout the entire length of the west coast of S. America from Peru southwards where it occurs in enormous numbers. Extends northward in small numbers on east coast to Point Tombo, 44°S., 65°20′W. Breeds on coasts and islands. Map 154.

PIED CORMORANT *Phalacrocorax varius* **Pl. 22**
Very large, 28–32 ins, 71–81 cm. Top of head, hind-neck, upperparts and tail glossy greenish-black. Wing quills bronze-grey with greenish gloss, feathers bordered with black. Sides of face, front and sides of neck and underparts white. Iris sea-green. Naked skin in front of eye yellow, blue on face and pink on pouch. Bill dark horn colour, legs black. Dark eye shows below, separate from black crown.

Young birds are browner above, the pale underparts mottled-brown.

The commonest cormorant on Australian coasts.

RANGE: Coasts of Australia, and New Zealand. Map 155.

BLACK-FACED CORMORANT *Phalacrocorax fuscescens* **Pl. 22**
Very large, 28–30 ins, 71–76 cm. Top of head, hind-neck, upperparts, underwing-coverts and tail glossy blue-black. The sides of the face, throat, sides of neck and underparts white, terminating in blue-black thighs. Naked skin around eye and pouch black. Bill dark grey; legs black. Iris bright green. Young birds have brown upperparts and white underparts.

Very similar to Pied Cormorant but differs in having blue-black thighs and a mat of short white feathers on neck, rump and thighs.

RANGE: South coast of Australia and Tasmania. Map 156.

ROUGH-FACED CORMORANT *Phalacrocorax carunculatus*
(A) Very large, 30 ins, 76 cm. (B) No crest; whole head, back, sides of neck metallic bluish-green. (C) Upperwing coverts glossy green showing a white alar bar on inner median wing-coverts, usually a white patch on outer scapulars and a white patch on back, but extent of these varies. (D) Wings, tail, blackish-brown. (E) Underbody

white, thighs bluish-green. (F) Eye-ring bright blue. (G) Naked skin on face and throat reddish-brown, patch of yellow caruncles above base of bill. (H) Bill brown, legs pink. (K) Immatures dull brown above, underparts white.

RANGE: At no distance from coasts breeding on the principal islands in the New Zealand seas.

RACES:

ROUGH-FACED CORMORANT   *Phalacrocorax c. carunculatus*   **Pl. 22**
Islands and outlying rocks in the Cook Strait, New Zealand.   Map 157.

CAMPBELL ISLAND CORMORANT   *Phalacrocorax c. campbelli*   **Pl. 22**
Breeds only on Campbell I. and adjacent small islands. (A) Smaller, 25 ins. 64 cm; (B) and (C) Uniformly darker shade, white alar bar and white patches always absent; (E) Black throat band 3 ins wide; (F) Eye-ring purple; (G) Naked skin dark red; (K) Foreneck mottled brown. Breeds on Campbell I. and its adjacent islands.   Not mapped.

KERGUELEN CORMORANT   *Phalacrocorax verrucosus*

Large, 27 ins, 69 cm. Head, cheeks, sides of neck and upperparts metallic greenish-black. Throat, foreneck and underparts white, feathers of throat extending forwards to base of lower mandible. A crest occurs on the head in breeding plumage. Yellow caruncles at base of bill. Legs pink. Young birds are brown overall, underparts slightly paler and show a white throat. Very similar to Rough-faced and King Cormorants which breed in different areas.

RANGE: Breeds on Kerguelen Is.   Map 158.

RED-LEGGED CORMORANT   *Phalacrocorax gaimardi*   **Pl. 21**

Very large, 28 ins, 71 cm. Wing-span 35 ins, 89 cm. Head and neck dark grey with an elongated white patch on each side of the neck. Upperparts dark grey, wing coverts silvery-grey. Underparts pale grey. Naked skin on face red; bill bright yellow, orange-red at base; legs coral-red.

Young birds have upperparts dark brown showing white patches on the sides of the neck; wing-coverts and underparts brownish-white mottling.

Easily identified by the white patches on sides of neck and very noticeable bright red legs which can be seen as the bird dives under water.

Blue-eyed Cormorant   King Cormorant   Kerguelen Cormorant

All in breeding plumage.

King Cormorants nesting.

RANGE: Throughout the entire length of the west coast of S. America from Peru southwards. A small breeding colony is also known at Puerto Deseado, 48°S., on east coast.   Map 159.

SPOTTED CORMORANT *Phalacrocorax punctatus*
Handsome diversified plumage. (A) Very large, 29 ins, 74 cm. Breeding plumage: (B) Stripe from bill over crown, top of head to nape, and crests on forehead, back of neck, greyish-black; (C) Back of neck, lower back, rump glossy greenish-blue; (D) Sides of neck, throat black; (E) White curving band from above eye to shoulder dividing sides of neck from throat to shoulder; (F) Upperwings, scapulars, wing-coverts pale grey, black spots at ends of feathers; (G) Underparts silver-grey, thighs and under tail-coverts greenish-black; (H) Naked skin on face bluish-green, on pouch bright blue; (K) Bill pale brown-colour, gular pouch bright blue, legs bright orange-yellow; (L) Non breeding, white areas mottled; (M) Immatures dark grey above, whitish-grey underparts, legs brownish-pink.
RANGE: Coasts of New Zealand and Chatham Is., confined to salt water close to coasts.
RACES:

SPOTTED CORMORANT *Phalacrocorax p. punctatus*   **Pl. 22**
Uncommon in North Island, New Zealand, breeds at two localities; breeds abundantly in South Island.   Map 160.
PITT ISLAND CORMORANT *Phalacrocorax p. featherstoni*   **Pl. 22**
Breeds only at Chatham I. (A) Smaller, 25 ins, 64 cm; (B), (C), (D) Black with bluish tint; (E) White neck band absent; (F) Deep grey with greenish gloss, triangular black spots at end of feathers; (G) Dark silvery-grey; (H) Purple; (K) Legs orange; (M) Immatures brownish above, pale brown below. *Note:* Scapulars and upperwing-coverts resemble adults at (F).   Not mapped.

BLUE-EYED CORMORANT *Phalacrocorax atriceps*   **Pl. 22**
Very large, 27–29 ins, 69–74 cm. Wing-span 44 ins, 112 cm. Top of head, back of neck and upperparts glossy-black. Throat, cheeks, foreneck and underparts white. In breeding plumage a fine tuft of plumes forms a crest above each eye, a white bar extends across the upperwings and a white patch shows on the back. Bill brownish

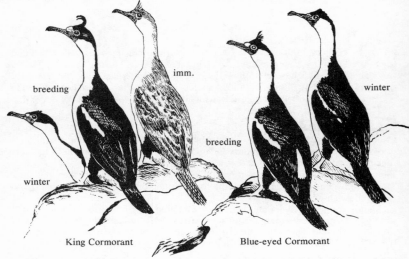

breeding

imm.

winter

winter

King Cormorant

breeding

Blue-eyed Cormorant

King Cormorant never show a white patch on the back; the dark area around the head extends lower on the cheeks than in Blue-eyed Cormorant (p.77).

with yellow excrescence at base of upper mandible. Ring around eyes bright blue; naked skin of face blue; legs flesh-coloured, webs black.

Distinguished from Magellan Cormorant by its blue naked skin of face (in Magellan Cormorant this is red). In breeding plumage also the neck of the Magellan Cormorant becomes entirely black.

RANGE: From islands adjacent to Antarctica northwards. Breeds on S. Shetlands, S. Orkneys, S. Sandwich Is., S. Georgia, off Cape Horn and Patagonia and at Heard I. Map 161.

KING CORMORANT *Phalacrocorax albiventer* **Page 76 and above**
Very large, 27–29 ins, 69–74 cm. Wing-span 40 ins, 102 cm. Similar in plumage to Blue-eyed Cormorant except that the glossy-black plumage on sides of head extends much lower on the cheeks below the line of the bill. At no time is there a white patch on the back.
RANGE: Breeds in the Falkland Is., on east coast of Patagonia, north to Point Tombo, Argentina, 44°S., 65°20′W., Crozet Is. and Macquarie I. Map 162.

LITTLE PIED CORMORANT *Phalacrocorax melanoleucus* **Pls. 22, 23**
Medium–large, 22–24 ins, 56–61 cm. Wing-span 29 ins, 74 cm. Compared with other cormorants the Little Pied Cormorant is considerably smaller and occurs in variable plumage.

In the light phase the top of the head, hind neck, upperparts and tail are glossy-black. A white line shows over the eye, and the sides of the face, throat, front and sides of neck and underparts are white. The underwing-coverts and under tail-coverts are black. The tail is unusually long in proportion. Naked skin on face and throat yellow; bill black above, yellow below; legs black. In breeding plumage the feathers on the crown are elongated forming a small crest.

In the dark phase in New Zealand, usually known as the Little Shag or White-throated Shag, only the sides of the face, chin and throat are white, the remainder of the underparts and whole of the upperparts glossy-black.

Young birds are dull brownish overall, showing a conspicuous yellow bill and face, the light phase race often dusky-white below.

RANGE: The dark phase predominates in New Zealand coastal waters. The light phase ranges widely throughout the E. Indies, islands in the western central Pacific Ocean, Australia and Tasmania. Breeds mainly in freshwater areas inland. Map 163.

REED CORMORANT *Halietor africanus* Pl. 23
Medium–large, 23 ins, 58 cm. Wing-span 35 ins, 89 cm. Breeding plumage is glossy-black with greyish scapulars and upperwing-coverts. A tuft of black feathers occurs on the forehead and a few white plumes on face and neck. The winter plumage is a dull brown with a greyish-white throat. Naked skin of face and gular pouch red. Legs black; tail noticeably long. Young birds have brown upperparts and yellowish-white underparts.

Mainly frequents rivers and lagoons, swimming very low in the water.

RANGE: Distributed widely throughout Africa, breeding and resorting largely to inland rivers and lakes. In southern Africa coastal birds are found only on west coast from Walvis Bay to Cape Agulhas where they breed also. Map 164.

JAVANESE CORMORANT *Halietor niger* Pl. 23
Medium–large, 22 ins, 56 cm. Plumage glossy-black, scapulars and upperwing coverts greyish, feathers with black edges. In winter throat is white. In breeding season feathers on nape are elongated with a few scattered white plumes on head and neck. Naked skin on face black. Bill purplish-brown. Legs black. Young birds have dark brown upperparts and whitish throats.

The Javanese Cormorant overlaps in range with the Indian Cormorant, but can be distinguished by its greyer wing-coverts, smaller size and shorter bill.

RANGE: From India through Sri Lanka, Burma, Java and Borneo. Map 165.

PIGMY CORMORANT *Halietor pygmaeus* Pl. 23
Medium size, 19–23 ins, 48–58 cm. General plumage glossy greenish black. Head and neck reddish-brown, scapulars and upperwing-coverts grey, feathers with black margins. A triangular patch on the head and a line through the eyes white. In breeding plumage a short crest occurs on the back of the head, and the neck, underparts and upper tail-coverts show small white spots. Bill brownish. Naked skin of face flesh-coloured. Feet dusky. Young birds have blackish-grey upperparts, whitish throats and abdomen, flanks and under tail-coverts black. Bills yellowish.

Its small size, reddish-brown head and neck and white markings readily distinguish it.

RANGE: Central and S.E. Europe, northern Africa, S.W. and central Asia. Breeds largely on lakes and rivers inland, and is unlikely to be seen on the sea coast. Map 166.

FLIGHTLESS CORMORANT *Nannopterum harrisi* Pl. 20
Outsize, 36–39 ins, 91–99 cm. Plumage generally brownish-black, paler on breast. Scapulars and upperwing-coverts dark grey, feathers with dark edges. A few plumes occur on head and neck. The wings are greatly reduced in size with few flight feathers, its breast bone is without a keel and it has lost all power of flight. Naked skin on face slate-coloured, on gular pouch flesh-coloured. The legs are black and a stiff flap of skin occurs on the tarsus.

RANGE: Confined to the Galapagos Is. Not mapped.

Frigate-birds.
Male courting display

FRIGATE-BIRDS   Fregatidae

As a family these large mainly black sinister-looking pirates of the tropical belt, known to seafarers as 'Man-o'-War Hawks', cannot fail to be recognised.

They spend much of their time soaring high in the air, their long wings motionless, their long slender sharply hooked bills, and extremely long deeply forked tails silhouetted against the blue sky. As they wheel or fight among themselves in the air their forked tails will be seen to open and close 'scissor fashion' to retain balance. At other times they fly with deep deliberate wingbeats. Never landing on the water they obtain their varied diet by snatching up surface marine food or scraps. They never miss a chance however of harrying neighbouring seabirds by vicious chases and, if need be, pecks from their hooked bills, forcing them to disgorge their catch and snatching it up before it reaches the water. During breeding seasons they range over nesting colonies snatching up chicks in low swoops without touching the ground.

Adult males are all black with bright red throat patches which they inflate into large balloons during display. Females have partly white underparts varying in each species, and immatures have white heads. The adult female Ascension Frigate-bird however has a completely dark underbody, and the male Christmas Frigate-bird a white abdomen.

Frigate-birds are seen frequently at a considerable distance from land.

Nesting and young

These nest on oceanic islands. The nests are built on top of low bushes, or in trees, or on the ground where vegetation is absent. They nest in colonies close to those of other breeding seabirds which they can harry for food and rob of chicks. The nests are untidy platforms of sticks, feathers and other debris, built by both birds, which incubate a single white egg for *c*. 7 weeks. The chick is naked at first and later covered in grey down. It may fly at 4–5 months but appears to have a much longer period of complete or partial dependence on the adults for food after fledging.

ASCENSION FRIGATE-BIRD *Fregata aquila*   Pl. 24
Outsize, 38 ins, 97 cm. Wing-span 85 ins, 165 cm. The adult male has black overall plumage with a glossy-green sheen on the back, red pouch and red legs. The female is similar but shows a dark brown breast.

Young birds have white heads and brownish-black plumage.

The female is the only species of female frigate-bird with totally dark underbody. A very rare form with white breast and abdomen may still occur.

RANGE: Disperses around Ascension I. where it breeds.   Not mapped.

CHRISTMAS FRIGATE-BIRD *Fregata andrewsi*   Pl. 24
Outsize, 35–40 ins, 89–100 cm. The adult male has black glossy-green upperparts, the foreneck and breast black, the abdomen white. Pouch bright red; bill black; legs black, feet with yellow soles. The female has head, neck and upperparts black. Throat black, breast and abdomen white. Bill reddish; legs white.

Young birds have brownish-black upperparts with a pale wing bar; head and neck rufous; abdomen white showing a dark band across the chest.

Immature Frigate-birds.

The male is the only species of male frigate-bird with a white abdomen.
RANGE: Local to Christmas I. in Indian Ocean and surrounding sea.   Not mapped.

MAGNIFICENT FRIGATE-BIRD *Fregata magnificens*   Pl. 24
Outsize, 38–40 ins, 97–100 cm. Wing-span 95 ins, 241 cm. The adult male is similar
to the adult Great Frigate-bird but its upperwings lack the brown band across the
wing-coverts. Its bill is usually bluish and legs black. The adult female differs from
the female Great Frigate-bird in having a whitish collar at the back of the neck, a
black throat and foreneck forming a contrast with the white underparts, the abdomen and flanks black. Its bill is horn-coloured and legs red. Young birds are similar
to young Great Frigate-birds but lack the rusty colouring.
The male cannot be distinguished at sea from the adult male Ascension Frigatebird. The female can be distinguished from the female Great Frigate-bird by its
black throat.
RANGE: In the Atlantic breeds throughout the W. Indies, Central America, Fernando Noronha I., Brazilian coastal islands and Cape Verde I. Also ranges into Gulf
of Panama and Galapagos Is.   Map 167.

GREAT FRIGATE-BIRD *Fregata minor*   Pl. 24
Outsize, 34–40 ins, 86–100 cm. Wing-span 90 ins, 229 cm. The adult male has
generally black upperparts with a greenish sheen and a brown band across the
median wing-coverts. Underparts brownish-black. Beneath its long slender black
hooked bill it carries a large bright red distensible pouch. Its legs are usually black,
sometimes pinkish. The female has similarly coloured upperparts with a brown
collar at the back of the neck. Its throat and foreneck are greyish, the lower neck,
breast and sides white, the rest of the abdomen and flanks black. Its bill is usually
horn-coloured but varies, and legs reddish or bluish.
Young birds have brownish upperparts, the head, neck and underparts whitish
rusty-coloured.
The adult female is the only species with a whitish throat immediately adjoining
its white underparts.
RANGE: In the S. Atlantic breeds on Trinidad and Martin Vas Is. Ranges widely
over the tropical Indian and Pacific Oceans, including Galapagos Is.   Map 168.

LESSER FRIGATE-BIRD *Fregata ariel*   Pl. 24
Very large, 31 ins, 79 cm. Wing-span 90 ins, 229 cm. Adults have generally black
upperparts with a deep blue purplish sheen on the back; underparts browner.
Adult males have grey bills, bright red pouches, a noticeable white patch on
either side of the dark abdomen under the wings and reddish-brown or black legs.
Adult females have a chestnut collar on the hindneck, not easily seen, and a
brownish patch on the upperwing-coverts. The throats of the females are black, the
breasts white and a white patch shows on each side of their dark abdomens. Their
bills are bluish, skin on the throat and legs red.
Young birds have brownish-black upperparts, the head, neck, breast and abdomen white with rusty streaks. Their heads are sometimes rufous.
Adults of both sexes differ from other frigate-birds by the white patch on each
side under the wings. They are considerably smaller than Great Frigate-birds.
RANGE: In the Atlantic breeds on Trinidad and Martin Vas Is. Ranges widely over
islands in the tropical Indian Ocean and W. Pacific. Breeds also on small islands in
N. Queensland, and N.W. Australia.   Map 169.

Phalaropes swim buoyantly, bobbing like corks on the water.

PHALAROPES Phalaropodidae

Phalaropes are a unique family of small dainty waders 'clothed and booted' specially to enable them to live for the greater part of their entire lives apart from the breeding season on the open ocean.

To this end their under plumage is thick, they possess underdown like ducks, and their toes are fitted with broad webbed fringes to assist them in swimming.

They feed at sea on plankton, congregating to 'winter' in certain favoured sea areas where surface plankton is rich.

They are extremely slender little birds, somewhat resembling sandpipers, swim buoyantly and usually collect in flocks at sea. When disturbed flocks fly with rapid jerky wingbeats for short distances to settle once again. When feeding they paddle and twirl in circles as they peck hurriedly for surface plankton.

On the sea routes they are, rather naturally, almost always seen in their pale winter plumage, vastly different from the brighter splashes of orange or red in breeding plumage, and are thus extremely difficult to identify positively by species.

Nesting and young

These tend to nest in loose sociable groups on tundra or grassy waterside sites. The sex roles are reversed, the larger, brighter females displaying and courting, the males incubating and tending the young alone. The females are probably polyandrous. The nest is a hollow on the ground, lined with vegetation to form a cup nest; and usually concealed in vegetation where possible. There is a clutch of 4 eggs, pyriform and cryptically coloured in olive-green with dark markings. The male incubates for *c*. 3 weeks. The young are downy and striped; feeding themselves, but brooded and guarded by the male. They become independent in *c*. 3 weeks.

GREY PHALAROPE *Phalaropus fulicarius* **Pl. 25**
Very small, 7.5–9 ins, 191–229 mm. Wing-span 15 ins, 38 cm. A somewhat sturdier little bird than the Red-necked Phalarope with a shorter more thick-set bill. *Winter plumage*: head, neck and underparts white, a dusky patch extending from below the eye backwards across the cheeks. The back of the head and hindneck are slaty-grey, the remainder of the upperparts lightish blue-grey, darker on wings and tail, with only pale streaking and a white wing bar conspicuous in flight. Bill relatively short, heavy and broad in comparison with that of the Red-necked Phalarope; bill yellow, tip black; legs horn-coloured. *Breeding plumage*: females have rich red throats, necks and underparts, white cheeks, crown and chin darkish and upperparts more richly streaked with buff and black. White wing bar. Underwings and sides of rump white. Bill yellow with black tip; legs yellowish. Males are less showy than females.
RANGE: See Map 170.

WILSON'S PHALAROPE *Steganopus tricolor* **Pl. 25**
Small, 8.5–10 ins, 216–254 mm. Wing-span 14 ins, 36 cm. Larger than the other two species with a slender neck and long slender black bill. *Winter plumage*: upperparts pale grey, wing quills darker grey. The upper tail-coverts, sides of the back, rump and underparts are white, and a broad white stripe shows above the eye. Bill black, long and slender; legs black. No white wing bar. *Breeding plumage*: the crown and middle of the back are bluish-grey, the wings and lower back greyish-brown, upper tail-coverts white and tail grey. The sides of the face are white and a black stripe extends through the eye to the side of the neck, continuing as a chestnut stripe along the side of the back. The throat and abdomen are white, the foreneck and breast pale rufous. Bills and legs black.
In winter plumage Wilson's Phalarope looks considerably whiter than the other two species, and shows no white wing bar in flight.
RANGE: See map 171.

RED-NECKED PHALAROPE *Lobipes lobatus* **Pl. 25**
Very small, 6.5–8 ins, 165–203 mm. Wing-span 14 ins, 36 cm. A rather smaller and daintier bird than the Grey Phalarope with a very slim neck and longer straight needle-like bill. *Winter plumage*: similar to Grey Phalarope but both back and wings darker and the back more conspicuously streaked. White wing bar is more conspicuous in flight. *Breeding plumage*: the crown and cheeks are slate-grey, and a white spot shows above the eye. The chin and throat are white and a rufous band stretches down the sides and front of the neck, the underparts thereafter being white. The upperparts and wings are slate-grey, the back with buff streaking. Bill and legs bluish-grey.
In winter plumage the shorter and broader yellow bill with a dark tip and the white forehead in the Grey Phalarope helps to distinguish it from the Red-necked Phalarope.
RANGE: See map 172.

Yellow-billed Sheathbills and Gentoo Penguin. Sheathbills scavenge for all kinds of offal, mixing with nesting colonies of other antarctic birds, sucking eggs and killing small chicks. White looks belie dirty habits.

SHEATHBILLS Chionididae

Sheathbills are something of a paradox being a connecting link between waders and gulls for they have only rudimentary webs between the three front toes and a well developed hind toe. When seen pecking about the shore line on the sub-antarctic and S. Indian Ocean islands scavenging amongst the most unpleasant offal, they look more like pigeons. Sheathbills are however able to swim in the sea, and may be seen occasionally out to sea on ice floes. They are not active birds, flying laboriously with a flapping flight on somewhat rounded wings.

The two separate species are very similar, those breeding in the sub-antarctic being distinguished by yellow bills, those breeding on islands in the southern area of the Indian Ocean by black bills.

Nesting and young

These nest in scattered pairs near an assured source of food such as a penguin colony. The nest is in a well-concealed site in a cavity or crevice among boulders. It consists of a collection of pebbles, bones, plant fragments and similar debris. The clutch of 2–4 eggs are creamy-yellowish, heavily spotted and blotched in purplish-brown. Incubation, shared by both birds, takes c. 4 weeks. The chicks have dull brownish down, becoming grey. Often only one of the brood is successfully reared. The young have no special juvenile plumage, moulting from down into the white adult plumage in c. 7–8 weeks.

YELLOW-BILLED SHEATHBILL *Chionis alba*　　　　　　　**Pl. 25**
Medium, 16 ins, 41 cm. Plumage white overall. The distinctive features are the bill and wattles. Bill short, stout and conical, black at tip shading to pinkish-yellow at base. The basal half of the upper mandible is covered by a horny sheath from which the bird derives its name. Beneath the eye is a bare pinkish crinkly wattle, and a second wattle on top of the base of the bill, giving the bird a 'scabby' appearance. Legs black; rudimentary webs between the three front toes; hind toe well developed.
RANGE: Confined to the Antarctic Peninsula and sub-antarctic islands. Breeds on Falkland Is. S. Georgia, S. Sandwich, S. Orkney and S. Shetland Is., and islands adjacent to Graham Land.　　Map 173.

BLACK-BILLED SHEATHBILL *Chionis minor*　　　　　　**Pl. 25**
Medium, 16 ins, 41 cm. General plumage white, similar to the Yellow-billed Sheathbill. Its bill however is black and legs vary in colour, usually black in those breeding in its northerly islands, and varying from brown to flesh-colour in those breeding further south.
RANGE: Breeds in Marion and Prince Edward Is., Kerguelen and Heard Is.　　Map 174.

Long-tailed Skua chasing a tern.

Great Skua

SKUAS Stercorariidae

Skuas are seen frequently by ships on the ocean routes for they remain largely at sea outside the breeding season when they undertake long oceanic migrations.

Three of the smaller skuas or 'jaegers' as they are often named, the Arctic Skua, the Pomarine Skua and the Long-tailed Skua breed in the arctic belt of the northern hemisphere and migrate southwards to winter in the far southern hemisphere.

The larger Great Skua of the northern hemisphere which breeds slightly south of the Arctic Circle and its counterpart of the southern hemisphere, the southern Great Skua, of which there are several races, resort to more temperate climates outside their breeding seasons and rarely cross the Equator. The southern Great Skua is almost identical with the Great Skua and the separate races in the southern hemisphere are closely similar, with the exception of McCormick's Skua, that their differences cannot normally be observed under sighting conditions at sea.

All four species are bold rapacious seabirds, betraying their profession as predators by the sharply hooked tip of the upper mandible, and their inveterate habit of harrying other seabirds to force them to jettison their food.

The Great Skua is a much larger and more heavily built brown bird with broad wings with pale wing patches, somewhat like a large brown gull. The smaller skuas are almost falcon-like in appearance with narrow sharply pointed wings and a strong rapid direct flight. The Long-tailed Skua very rarely occurs in a dark phase, but both the Arctic and Pomarine Skuas occur in both a light and a dark phase.

The Great Skua is quite a regular 'ship follower', often picking up a ship and remaining astern for several hours, waiting to harry other seabirds or land in the sea to gobble up refuse from the galley. The Pomarine Skua is also attracted to ships for short periods, but the Arctic and Long-tailed Skuas appear to pay little attention.

At sea the Arctic and Pomarine Skuas may easily be confused except in full adult plumage and then only if a clear sight of their protruding 'pin' tail feathers is possible.

Nesting and young

Nesting occurs on sea-coasts, offshore islands, tundra or moorland and mountain slopes. Although the Great Skua is a coastal nester and feeder, the smaller species often nest further inland and depend extensively on lemmings and small rodents for food while nesting. Nesting is often sociable, but the nests are well-spaced. The nest is a shallow hollow, usually in an exposed site on the ground commanding a good view around, and is unlined or sparsely lined with fragments of nearby vegetation. The clutch is usually of 2 eggs, which are dull olive, greenish or buff, with dark markings. Incubation is undertaken by both birds and lasts c. 4 weeks. The young are covered in dark brown down. They are fed by both parents and take 6–8 weeks to become independent.

GREAT SKUA *Catharacta skua* **Pl. 26**
Medium–large, 21–24 ins, 53–61 cm. Wing-span 59 ins, 150 cm. The Great Skua of the northern hemisphere can be distinguished from somewhat similar northern gulls in brown immature plumage by its heavier build and, in particular, by the large white patches which show at the base of the primaries. Its wings are broad and rounded. It has a stout blackish bill, hooked at the tip, black legs and a short

wedge-shaped tail. At leisure its flight appears ponderous and heavy, but when harrying seabirds it shows great agility and speed. Young birds are similar.

It obtains much of its food by pursuing other seabirds, causing them to disgorge their food, or by scavenging for offal, and frequently follows ships.

RANGE: Breeds in Iceland, the Faroes, Shetland and Orkney Is., and ranges widely across the N. Atlantic as far as Newfoundland and Nova Scotia. Outside the breeding season it disperses southwards, and has been observed as far south as the Equator. Map 175.

GREAT SKUA ('Southern Skua', southern form of Great Skua)   Pl. 26
Catharacta skua

Medium–large, 21–24 ins, 53–61 cm. In the southern hemisphere, the Great Skua is represented by the Southern Skua showing similar plumage and characteristics. The southern Great Skua, of which a number of sub-species have been named but cannot be distinguished at sea, breeds on the Antarctic Peninsula, adjacent sub-antarctic islands, S. Shetlands, S. Orkneys, S. Sandwich Is., Marion I., Crozet, Kerguelen and Heard Is., S. Georgia, Falkland Is., Bouvet I. Tristan da Cunha, Gough, eastwards to the islands south and east of New Zealand. Map 176.

McCORMICK'S SKUA   *Catharacta maccormicki*   Pl. 26

Medium–large, 21 ins, 53 cm. This antarctic skua is similar but much lighter in colour than the Great Skua. The crown and upperparts are brown, the neck feathers partly straw-coloured, the forehead, sides of head and underparts pale brown, almost whitish, but normally browner on the abdomen. Bill stout and black, hooked at tip; legs black; tail short and round.

RANGE: Occurs on the antarctic continent and S. Shetlands. Unlikely to be seen on the sea routes. Map 177.

POMARINE SKUA   *Stercorarius pomarinus*   Pl. 26

Medium–large, 21–22 ins, 53–56 cm. Wing-span 48 ins, 122 cm. Noticeably smaller than the Great Skua, yet more stoutly built than the Arctic and Long-tailed Skuas, it occurs in both light and dark phases. *Light phase*: The top of the head is sooty-black contrasting with the straw-coloured sides of the head and collar. The neck and breast are white the remainder of the underbody whitish, flanks and under tail-coverts dusky or barred. Underwing and remainder of upperparts and upperwings dusky-brown. A rather faint white band appears at the base of the primaries, and a dusky band usually shows across the breast. Bill brown with black hooked tip; legs black. The most distinctive feature is its long dark wedge-shaped tail which in full adult plumage, carries projecting central tail feathers extending to 2 ins with broad rounded and vertically twisted tips. *Dark phase*: In the dark phase the entire underparts are dark of the same tone as the upperparts.

Occasionally follows ships.

RANGE: Breeds in high arctic latitudes. Migrates to wintering areas through all oceans as far as 50°S. Map 178.

ARCTIC SKUA   *Stercorarius parasiticus*   Pl. 26

Medium size, 17–20 ins, 43–51 cm. Wing-span 40 ins, 102 cm. Smaller and more falcon-like than the Pomarine Skua but very similar in plumage pattern to the Pomarine both in its light and dark phases. *Light phase*: top of head, back, wings and tail ashy-brown, sides of head and neck yellowish, breast white, remainder of underbody whitish, under tail-coverts and underwing ashy-brown. A faint white band appears at the base of the primaries. Bill brown, hooked at tip; legs black. The tail is long and wedge-shaped and, in full adult plumage, carries two sharply pointed

Arctic Skua

Pomarine Skua

Long-tailed Skua

narrow tail feathers about 3 ins long. *Dark phase*: neck and underparts sooty-brown, slightly paler than upperparts. *Intermediate phase*: whitish-buff sides of head. Pale brown below.

RANGE: Breeds in high northern latitudes. Migrates to wintering areas as far as 60°S. Map 179.

POMARINE and ARCTIC SKUAS – IMMATURE PLUMAGE –
MOULT IN ADULTS

Immatures of both species are indistinguishable at sea, having brown heads, necks and wings and buffish-brown underparts, the underparts showing varying degrees of barring. In immatures the elongated central tail feathers have not developed.

Adults in moult lose their distinguishing elongated tail feathers, and at other times they may become broken. At such times differentiation between species at sea is almost impossible.

LONG-TAILED SKUA *Stercorarius longicaudus* **Pl. 26**

Medium–large, 21–23 ins, including 6–8 ins tail and streamers, 53–58 cm. Wingspan 30 ins, 76 cm. The smallest and slenderest of the smaller skuas or jaegers and does not appear to occur in a dark phase. The top of the head is brownish-black, remainder of the upperparts greyish-brown with black primaries. The sides of the head and entire neck are yellowish, breast and underbody white, duskier on the flanks, underwings greyish-brown. No white band is noticeable on the upperwings, and no dark breast band is ever present. Bill brown with black hooked tip; legs bluish-grey. In adult plumage the very distinctive feature is the presence of two greatly elongated narrow pointed central tail streamers.

Young birds have greyer ashy-brown upperparts, and paler greyish-white underparts, slightly barred, in comparison with young Pomarine and Arctic Skuas.

Tail streamers are not present in immatures.

RANGE: Breeds in arctic latitudes. Migrates to wintering areas south of the Equator. Map 180.

GULLS   Laridae

Gulls are primarily coastal seabirds, obtaining their food from the coastlines and inshore. They swim buoyantly however, and in certain areas they will follow fishing fleets far from land living off the refuse thrown overboard. They rarely dive below the surface. Many gulls disperse from their breeding areas to winter in warmer climates, some from the northern hemisphere undertaking long migrations and crossing the Equator. In general however, with the notable exception of the kittiwake they are not oceanic as a family and are seen rarely at sea far from land.

In adult plumage, with few exceptions, gulls have white wings, bodies and square tails, their upperwings varying from pearl grey to sooty-black. Males and females appear alike. Some however acquire dark hoods in the breeding season, and bills and legs vary in colour. In the majority of species the immature plumage is entirely different, being of a dark streaked and mottled brown, with dark bills and frequently dark bands on tails. The gradual change to adult plumage may take two to four years, and during this period specific identification often presents considerable difficulty.

Their flight is buoyant and elegant, sometimes circling and planing in updraughts of air currents, hovering over food or turning and twisting sharply. At eventide they are often seen winging their way gracefully to their night roosts.

Nesting and young

These nest colonially, or more rarely in single pairs, on a variety of sites – cliff ledges, or small projections built up with nest material, rock stacks, islands, cliff-tops, sandbanks and shingle banks on coasts and lakes, inland marshes and moors, and in some instances in trees. Nest material is carried to the site and the nest may be a substantial structure of plant material, sticks or seaweed. The clutch is usually 2–3 eggs, variable in colour but usually ranging from creamy to olive or buff, with dark markings. Both birds incubate for *c.* 3–4 weeks. The chicks are downy, grey or buffish with dark spots or mottling. They remain at or near the nest site. They are fed by both parents on regurgitated food, and become independent in *c.* 4–6 weeks. The cycle is usually annual, but may vary since the Silver Gull has six-month cycles in W. Australia and S. Africa.

PACIFIC GULL   *Larus pacificus*   **Pls. 27, 34, 40**
Large, 25 ins, 64 cm. Wing-span 54 ins, 137 cm. This is a noticeably large black-backed gull with white head, neck and underparts. Mantle and upperwing-coverts black. The primaries and secondaries are also black, broadly tipped white. The large sturdy bill is deep-yellow with a red spot at the angle; legs yellow. Tail white, a distinctive feature being the presence of a sub-terminal black band.

Young birds are brown, the feathers with paler edges, primaries and tail brownish-black. Bill flesh-coloured with a black sub-terminal band; legs brown.

Distinguished from the Dominican Gull by its large bill and black band on tail.
RANGE: S. Australian and Tasmanian coasts.   Map 181.

Gulls are seldom found far from land. They like to look out over the sea for food from cliffs or any high vantage point.

MAGELLAN GULL *Gabianus scoresbyi*   **Pls. 30, 38**
Medium, 18 ins, 46 cm. Wing-span 40 ins, 102 cm. In adult southern summer
plumage the head, neck and underparts pale grey. Upperparts and upperwings
slaty-black; under-surface of wings dark grey. Primaries and secondaries show
white tips. Tail white; bill stout, red; legs red. Young birds have head, neck and
upper breast palish-brown; upperwings brown; upper tail-coverts, lower breast and
abdomen white; tail white with broad black sub-terminal band. Bill brown with
black tip; legs brown.
    Mainly confined inshore and on the shore line.
RANGE: Breeds in the Falkland Is., Tierra del Fuego, and on east coast of
S. America northwards to Point Tombo, 44°S., 65°20′W.   Map 182.

IVORY GULL *Pagophila eburnea*   **Pls. 33, 39**
Medium, 16–18 ins, 41–46 cm. The adult plumage is entirely white. Eye large and
black showing a distinct red eye-ring. Bill rather short, dark at base shading to
yellow with a reddish tip. Legs short and black.
    Its short legs and habit of standing with tail depressed and head raised gives it an
awkward appearance. On the wing however its flight is buoyant and graceful.
Young birds show grey smudges on face and chin, the upperparts finely spotted
with black, wing quills tipped black and tail showing a narrow sub-terminal black
band.
RANGE: A species of the high arctic frequenting open leads in the pack ice outside
the breeding season. Wanders southwards in small numbers in autumn and winter
to Iceland, rarely further south, Alaska, Hudson Bay, Labrador and Bering Sea.
Breeds on islands across the high arctic oceans.   Map 183.

DUSKY GULL *Larus fuliginosus*   **Pls. 30, 33, 38**
Small–medium, 15–17 ins, 39–43 cm. Adults have black heads with white eyelids,
dark grey upperparts with grey rump and tail. Underparts grey, paler on abdomen.
Bill dark, tip red. Legs black. Young birds are dark sooty-brown above, head, wing
quills and tail blackish, and underparts grey. Bill and legs black.
RANGE: Local to Galapagos Is.   Not mapped.

GREY GULL *Larus modestus*   **Pls. 30, 38**
Medium, 18 ins, 46 cm. The gull in adult plumage is easily identified for with the
exception of its head which is white in summer and palish-brown in winter, the
whole plumage is leaden-grey, darker on the wing quills. The dark secondaries
however have broad white tips which show a white band along the trailing edge of
the wings in flight. The grey tail carries a broad black band. Bill and legs reddish-
black.
    Young birds are generally brown with pale edges to feathers, the wings and tail
darker. Bill and legs black.
    The contrast between the white head in summer, grey body and white band on the
trailing edge of wings in flight is very noticeable.
RANGE: West coast of S. America. Breeds inland in the deserts of Peru and
Chile.   Map 184.

HEERMANN'S GULL *Larus heermanni*   **Pls. 30, 38**
Medium size, 17 ins, 43 cm. Adults in summer plumage have head and upper neck
white; in winter greyish-brown. Upperparts and upperwings slate-grey, wing quills
tipped white. Lower neck, underparts and upper tail-coverts pale grey. Underwing
brownish-grey. Bill red; legs black; tail dark, almost black with white tip. Young

birds are dark brown overall with some buff flecking; bill and legs black.

Easily distinguished by its grey colouring and white or greyish head.

RANGE: Pacific coast of N. America from Vancouver to southern Mexico. Breeds on Mexican coast. Map 185.

RED SEA BLACK-HEADED GULL or WHITE-EYED GULL
Larus leucophthalmus **Pls. 32, 37, 40**

Small–medium size, 15.5 ins, 39 cm. In breeding plumage, head, nape, throat and neck deep black. Eyelids white. No white ring around neck. Mantle and upperwing-coverts slate-grey, in winter brownish-black. Primaries and secondaries black, secondaries tipped white. Underparts of sides of breast slate-grey, remainder of underparts white. Underwings greyish. In winter head and throat pale mottled-white and neck grizzled. Bill dusky-red, tip black. Legs yellowish. Immatures are brown above, underparts whitish, rump white, black band on tail, bills greenish.

See Aden Gull (p. 95) for comparison.

RANGE: From Gulf of Suez south through Red Sea, Gulf of Aden and Somaliland coast. Breeds in southern Red Sea. Map 186.

ADEN GULL *Larus hemprichi* **Pls. 32, 37, 40**

Medium, 17.5–18.5 ins, 44–47 cm. In breeding plumage head, nape and throat coffee-brown. Eyelids white. A white ring shows around neck. Mantle and upperwing-coverts greyish-brown. Primaries and secondaries brownish-black, secondaries tipped white. Breast pale brown, abdomen and tail white. Underwings greyish. In winter, head and throat mottled-brown and indistinct collar brownish-grey. Bill greenish with sub-terminal black band and red tip. Legs yellowish. Immatures are brown above, underparts whitish, tail black and bill greenish.

Aden Gulls and Red Sea Black-headed Gulls are very similar. When seen together the Aden Gull looks decidedly larger.

A detailed comparison should be made.

RANGE: Southern Red Sea, coasts of S. Yemen, Oman and Persian Gulf, southwards from Somaliland to Zanzibar. Breeds throughout range. Map 187.

SIMEON GULL *Larus belcheri* **Pls. 30, 34, 38**

Medium, 20 ins, 51 cm. In adult summer plumage the head, neck, underparts and rump are white; in winter the head becomes brownish-black showing white eyelids. Mantle and upperwing-coverts sooty-black; primaries black, secondaries grey with broad white tips. Bill yellow with a black band and red tip; legs yellow. Tail white with a broad central black band.

Young birds have pale mottled-brown upperparts, black primaries, whitish underparts, yellow bills with a black tip and greyish legs. The tail is black showing a white tip.

Somewhat similar to the Dominican Gull but smaller and distinguished in adult plumage by the black bar on the tail and black band on bill.

RANGE: West coast of S. America from Peru south to Coquimbo in Chile, breedingly chiefly on rocky islands along coast of Peru. On east coast, the lesser well-known Atlantic form ranges further south from Buenos Aires possibly to Patagonia; breeding in 1963 established only on small low-lying island of San Blas, south of Bahia Blanca. Map 188.

JAPANESE GULL *Larus crassirostris* **Pls. 27, 34**
Medium, 19 ins, 48 cm. In adult summer plumage the head and underparts are white, the upperparts slate-grey. The first two primaries are grey, remaining primaries and secondaries black, all showing white tips. The tail is white with a distinctive black sub-terminal central band. Bill yellow with a black cross-band and red tip; legs yellow. In winter the head becomes greyish-brown.

Young birds have dark brown upperparts with pale edges to feathers, darker brown wings and tail, paler upperparts. Bills flesh-coloured with black tip; legs flesh-coloured.

The black band on the white tail is distinctive.

RANGE: Coasts of eastern Asia. Breeds on coasts of Japan and China. Map 189.

AUDOUIN'S GULL *Larus audouinii* **Pls. 29, 35**
Medium–large, 20 ins, 51 cm. In adult summer plumage head, neck, underparts and tail white; in winter head shows greyish streaks. Upperparts and upperwings very pale grey; outer primaries black with white spot; inner primaries and secondaries grey with white tips. Eye-ring red. Bill coral red with sub-terminal black band and yellow tip; legs dark olive-green. Young birds have streaked whitish-grey heads with dark spot behind eye, greyish-brown upperparts and upperwings, whitish underparts, and are very similar but smaller than immature Lesser Black-backed Gulls.

In size it is midway between the Common Gull *Larus canus* and the Herring Gull *Larus argentatus*. The colour of its stout red bill and eye-rim helps to distinguish the adult.

RANGE: Mediterranean Sea. It appears to cling to rocky coastlines mainly along the northern shore. A relatively rare species not yet reported on the main sea route from Gibraltar to Port Said. Map 190.

RING-BILLED GULL *Larus delawarensis* **Pls. 28, 35, 40**
Medium, 18.5 ins, 47 cm. Wing-span 48 ins, 122 cm. In adult plumage the Ring-billed Gull closely resembles a Herring Gull but is distinctly smaller in size. It is distinguished by the colour of the bill which is greenish-yellow and crossed by a black band towards the tip. Its legs also are yellow or greenish in colour.

Young birds have head and neck whitish-grey with some brown mottling, mantle and upperwing-coverts brownish-grey with paler edging to feathers; underparts and tail mottled whitish-brown; tail with narrow dark sub-terminal band; bill brown with dark sub-terminal band; legs pinkish or flesh-grey.

In flight the Ring-billed Gull is more buoyant than the Herring Gull, and shows more black on the underside of the primaries. Young birds look much whiter than young Herring Gulls.

RANGE: Breeds in central U.S.A. Occurs on both coasts of U.S.A. south to Texas and Gulf of Mexico. Map 191.

COMMON or MEW GULL *Larus canus* **Pls. 28, 35, 40**
Medium, 18 ins, 46 cm. Wing-span 48 ins, 122 cm. Head, neck, underparts and tail white; in winter the head shows grey streaking. Upperparts pale grey; outer primaries black with broad white tips, remainder of primaries and secondaries grey with white tips. Bill and legs greenish-yellow.

Young birds have greyish-white heads, remainder of upperparts mottled greyish-brown, underparts whitish-brown mottling; bill brown with a black sub-terminal bar; legs flesh-coloured. Tail whitish, mottled brown with dusky sub-terminal band.

Adults differ from Ring-billed Gulls by greater amount of white on wing tips and lack of black band on bill.

RANGE: Widespread throughout global temperate N. latitude belts.   Map 192.

HERRING GULL   *Larus argentatus*   Pls. 28, 35, 40
Medium–large, 22–24 ins, 56–61 cm. Wing-span 52 ins, 132 cm. In adult breeding plumage head and neck white, in winter showing pale grey streakings. Underparts and tail white. Mantle and upperwing-coverts grey. Primaries and secondaries black, tips white. Outermost primaries have white sub-terminal spots. Bill yellow with red spot at angle. Legs pinkish flesh-coloured. Immatures in first year are coarsely mottled-brown overall with brownish-black wing quills and tail, the latter barred. Bill black. As they grow older head, underparts and rump become progressively paler. Second year birds show tail with broad dark terminal band, the bill has semblance of a dark tip (compare second year Ring-billed Gull, p. 96).

First year immatures are virtually indistinguishable from similar immature Lesser Black-backed Gulls, which however grow darker as they grow older during transition to adult plumage. Through geographical distribution certain adult Herring Gulls show a somewhat darker mantle and yellow legs, and are best referred to as yellow-legged Herring Gulls.

RANGE: Widespread across the whole northern hemisphere, breeding throughout range.   Map 193.

THAYER'S GULL   *Larus thayeri*   Pls. 28, 35
Medium–large, 22–24 ins, 56–61 cm. Very similar to Herring Gull, and Kumlien's Gull. Chief differences lie in the primaries usually grey compared to the black primaries of Herring Gull, but the white mirrors in wing tips show. The primaries are always darker than those of Kumlien's Gull.

RANGE: Arctic coasts of Canada and arctic islands to Baffin I.   Map 194.

LESSER BLACK-BACKED GULL   *Larus fuscus*
(A) Medium–large, 20–24 ins, 51–61 cm. Wing-span 50 ins, 127 cm; (B) Adult breeding, head, neck, underparts and tail white; (C) Mantle and upperwing-coverts slate-grey, primaries black, first primary with a sub-terminal white spot, remainder white, secondaries and tertials grey, broad white tips; (D) Bill yellowish, red spot at angle; (E) legs yellowish; (F) Immatures in first winter have coarsely brown upperparts, mottled underparts, dark bills, tails blackish-brown. In second winter, head freckled, underparts white, tail white with black terminal band.

RANGE: N. Russia, Norway, Baltic, Germany, Holland, France, British Isles, Shetlands, Faroes, extending range to Iceland. A number disperse southwards in winter to Mediterranean, Atlantic coasts of Europe, N. Africa and E. Atlantic Is.

RACES:

LESSER BLACK-BACKED GULL   *Larus f. fuscus*   Pls. 27, 34, 40
Scandinavia and Baltic. (C) Mantle and upperwing-coverts slaty-black, often look black at sea; (E) Bright yellow.   Map 195.

LESSER BLACK-BACKED GULL   *Larus f. graellsii*   Pls. 27, 35, 40
British Isles, Germany, Holland, France, Shetlands, Faroes. (C) Mantle and upperwing-coverts dark slaty-grey; (E) Yellow.   Map 196.

Note: First winter immatures are virtually indistinguishable from similar immature Herring Gulls *Larus argentatus*; second year immatures appear darker than second year Herring Gulls.

CALIFORNIA GULL *Larus californicus*   Pls. 28, 35
Medium, 20 ins, 51 cm. Wing-span 49 ins, 125 cm. For adult plumage see similar
Herring Gull (p. 97). The California Gull is slightly smaller and differs only in
showing a partially dusky sub-terminal band on its yellow bill and in its greenish, as
opposed to flesh-coloured, legs.

Young birds cannot normally be distinguished from young Herring Gulls.

RANGE: Winters on Pacific coast of N. America from British Columbia to California. Breeds on inland lakes in western N. America.   Map 197.

WESTERN GULL *Larus occidentalis*   Pls. 27, 34
Medium–large, 21–22 ins, 53–56 cm. Wing-span 54 ins, 137 cm. In adult plumage
the head, neck, underparts and tail are white. In winter the head and neck may carry
grey streaks. Mantle and upperwing-coverts leaden-grey. The wing quite grey with
white tips, the first four primaries however having black outer webs, and the leading
primary a white sub-terminal spot. Bill yellow with a red spot at angle; legs
flesh-coloured.

Young birds have brownish-grey plumage, the upperparts with white mottling;
wing quills and tail black; legs brown.

Distinguished from the California Gull by its darker mantle and flesh-coloured as
opposed to greenish-yellow legs.

RANGE: West coast of N. America, from British Columbia to California. Breeds on
coasts and islands.   Map 198.

SOUTHERN BLACK-BACKED GULL *Larus dominicanus* Pls. 27, 34, 40
Medium–large, 23 ins, 58 cm. Wing-span 50 ins, 127 cm. A large gull. In adult
plumage the head, neck, underparts and tail are white; mantle and upperwings
sooty-black. The primaries and secondaries are black, the four outer primaries
tipped white, secondaries broadly tipped white. The leading primary has an additional white sub-terminal patch. The tertials are also tipped white so that two white
bands are seen on the upperparts when the wings are closed. Bill yellow with a red
spot at angle; legs yellow or olive-green.

Young birds do not attain adult plumage until their third winter. Early plumage is
brown all over the buff-edged feathers on upperparts, mottled brown on underparts, barred brown and white on rump and tail coverts. Tail is brown; bill blackish;
legs greenish-yellow.

Known locally as the 'kelp gull'. The only large black-backed gull in the southern
hemisphere with an entirely white tail.

RANGE: Both coasts of S. America, S. Africa, in New Zealand and many islands in
the southern ocean belt. Recently extended northwards to New South Wales.
Map 199.

SLATY-BACKED GULL *Larus schistisagus*   Pls. 27, 34
Medium–large, 24 ins, 61 cm. Wing-span 53 ins, 135 cm. See Herring Gull (p. 97).
This gull can be distinguished from the otherwise similar Herring Gull by its much
darker slate-coloured mantle and upperwing-coverts and larger size.

Young birds have noticeably paler light-brown upperparts than the Herring Gull,
a conspicuous dark bar on the wing, underparts greyish, dark brown tail; bill black;
legs brown.

RANGE: Coasts of N.E. Asia dispersing south to China and Japan. Breeds on
coasts of Sea of Okhotsk, Kamchatka, Kuril Is. and northern Japan.   Map 200.

GREAT BLACK-BACKED GULL *Larus marinus* **Pls. 27, 34, 40**
Very large, 27–30 ins, 69–76 cm. Wing-span 65 ins, 165 cm. The largest black-backed gull.

In adult plumage the head, neck, underparts and tail are pure white; mantle and upperwings sooty-black, the primaries and secondaries tipped white. In winter some dusky streaks appear on the head and neck. The powerful massive bill is yellow with a red spot at angle; legs flesh-coloured.

Young birds are paler than the mottled brown young of Herring and Lesser Black-backed Gulls, and have whitish underparts. Their upperparts are brownish, primaries brownish-black; tail white with black mottling; bill brownish-black; legs pale flesh-coloured.

Its much greater size, almost black upperparts and slow deliberate flight distinguish it from smaller black-backed gulls.

RANGE: East and west coasts of N. Atlantic, some dispersing southwards in winter to Mediterranean and N. Atlantic Is. and on the east coast of N. America to Virginia. Map 201.

GLAUCOUS-WINGED GULL *Larus glaucescens* **Pls. 29, 35**
Large, 25 ins, 64 cm. Wing-span 53 ins, 135 cm. Similar to the Herring Gull but with a paler grey mantle and upperwings, and dark grey (as opposed to black), primaries with white sub-terminal spots; secondaries grey with white tips. Bill yellow with red spots at angle; legs flesh-coloured.

Young birds in second winter are unusual in being grey overall with a darker grey tail, the throat and vent alone white. Bill dark; legs brown.

RANGE: Breeds on the N.E. coasts of Siberia and the N.W. coasts of Alaska and Aleutian Is., ranging southwards in winter to northern Japan and California. Map 202.

GLAUCOUS GULL *Larus hyperboreus* **Pls. 29, 35, 40**
Very large, 28 ins, 71 cm. Wing-span 53 ins, 135 cm. An outstandingly large, stoutly built, pale winged gull with a stouter and longer bill than the similar and smaller Iceland Gull. Head and neck white in summer, in winter showing grey streaking. Remainder of body and tail white. Upperwings pale grey, wing quills white, wings broader than in Iceland Gull. Bill stout, yellow with red spot at angle. In breeding plumage eye ring is lemon yellow. Legs pink.

Immatures in first year are creamy-brown with some barring with flesh-coloured bills and dark tips. Tail shows no dark band. Second year birds are white overall, the upperparts gradually becoming pale grey.

See also Iceland Gull for comparison (p. 99).

RANGE: Arctic seas dispersing southwards in winter into the N. Atlantic and N. Pacific Oceans. Map 203.

ICELAND GULL *Larus leucopterus*
(A) Medium–large, 22 ins, 56 cm. Adult. (B) Summer head, neck white, in winter streaked, upper tail-coverts and tail white; (C) mantle, upperwing; coverts and wing quills pale grey with white tips; (D) in summer eye-ring red; (E) bill yellow, red spot at angle, legs pinkish-flesh colour; (F) Immatures first winter finely mottled overall pale brown, bill dusky with dark band towards tip. Second winter birds are almost pure white, bill yellowish, tip dark; (G) Flight: more buoyant and with faster wing-beats than Glaucous Gull *Larus hyperboreus*.

Smaller and slimmer, with relatively longer wings and a more slender bill than the larger Glaucous Gull which has a yellow eye-ring in the breeding season. Observed on the water its wing tips will be seen to project well beyond its tail.

RANGE: Breeds in Greenland, arctic Siberia and arctic Canada dispersing southwards in autumn and winter, occasionally as far south as Latitude of New York, rarely to the British Isles.

RACES:

ICELAND GULL   *Larus l. leucopterus*   **Pls. 29, 33, 35, 40**
Map 204.

KUMLIEN'S GULL   *Larus l. kumlieni*

Breeds in Baffin I. and vicinity. Probably ranges eastwards and has been observed in the Belle I. Strait. (C) Wing quills slightly darker grey than Iceland Gull and shows grey spots towards white wingtips, but difficult to identify between the two, Kumlien's Gull being rarely seen.   Map 205.

Iceland Gull (p.99)   Kumlien's Gull.

These two species are very similar. Iceland Gull shows red eye-ring in summer. Kumlien's Gull shows slightly darker wing quills with grey spots towards white tips.

GREAT BLACK-HEADED GULL   *Larus ichthyaetus* **Page 104; Pls. 32, 37**
Large, 27 ins, 69 cm. Readily noticeable by its exceptionally large size in comparison with any other dark-hooded gull.

In adult summer plumage the head is deep black, and white crescentic patches show above and below the eye. The mantle and upperwings are grey; primaries white, outer primaries with sub-terminal black bars; inner primaries and secondaries grey, tipped white. Underparts and tail white. In winter the black head becomes white with some streaking. The bill is distinctive, yellow with a sub-terminal black band and broad red tip; legs greenish-yellow.

Young birds have mottled white heads, dark brown mantle and upperparts with buff streaking and paler wing feathers. Underparts and tail are white, the tail showing a broad sub-terminal black band; bill and legs greyish.

RANGE: Breeds in inland seas and lakes in southeastern Russia and central Asia. Winters on coasts in southern Red Sea, Persian Gulf, India, Sri Lanka, Bangladesh and Burma.   Map 206.

LAUGHING GULL *Larus atricilla* **Pls. 31, 36**
Medium, 16.5 ins, 42 cm. Wing-span 41 ins, 104 cm. In adult summer plumage the whole head and upper neck is greyish-black, showing white eyelids above the eye; the upperparts bluish-grey, the first five outer primaries black, inner primaries and secondaries grey, all with white tips. Lower neck and remainder of underparts and tail white. Bill in summer red, in winter blackish; legs reddish-brown. In winter the crown and sides of head and neck become white with some mottling.

Young birds have pale greyish-brown upperparts, with much darker primaries and secondaries, the latter tipped white. Tail grey with broad black sub-terminal band; breast brown, rump and remainder of underparts and under tail-coverts white. Bill black; legs brown.

In flight the white border on the trailing edge of the wings is conspicuous. In immatures the brown breast and white at base of tail is noticeable.

RANGE: Breeds on Atlantic coast of N. America from Nova Scotia to Texas and Caribbean, dispersing southwards in winter to Brazil, to Gulf of Panama and coast of Ecuador. Map 207.

INDIAN BLACK-HEADED GULL *Larus brunnicephalus*
Page 104 and Pls. 32, 37
Medium, 16–17 ins, 41–43 cm. In adult plumage the hood is brown, paler on forehead and blacker at neck. Mantle and upperwing-coverts blue-grey, wing-coverts at edge and bend of wing white. Outer primaries black, leading two with white patches near tips, inner primaries and secondaries grey. Underbody and tail white, underwing-coverts blue-grey. Bill and legs deep-red. In winter the hood disappears and head becomes white; dark patch behind eye.

Immature birds have head greyish-brown, mantle brownish, outer primaries brown; bill yellowish; legs orange.

Very similar to Northern Black-headed Gull but paler hood and can be distinguished by the large white patches near the tips of its black outer primaries.

RANGE: Coastal from Aden eastwards through India to Burma. Breeds in central Asia from Turkestan to Tibet. Map 208.

GREY-HEADED GULL *Larus cirrocephalus* **Pls. 30, 36, 38**
Small-medium, 16 ins, 41 cm. Wing-span, 40 ins, 102 cm. In adult summer plumage the head and throat to the middle of the nape is lavender-grey showing a clear cut white neck; in winter only a pale-grey half hood remains. The mantle and upperwing-coverts are grey; primaries black with a white sub-terminal patch on the outer two, the inner primaries and secondaries grey. Neck, underbody and tail white; underwing-coverts grey; bill and legs deep crimson-red. At rest the folded wings are seen to extend beyond the tail.

Young birds have mottled white heads, mottled grey-brown upperparts, outer primaries black, inner primaries and secondaries brown. Tail white with a dark terminal band. Bill yellow with dark tip; legs brown or yellowish.

In flight it is distinguished by its grey head and back, large white mirror on black outer primaries and distinct white fore edge to wing.

RANGE: Coasts of Peru, Southern Brazil, Argentine, W. and S.E. coasts of Africa. Breeds inland in tropical Africa and eastern S. America. Map 209.

ANDEAN GULL *Larus serranus* **Pls. 30, 36**
Medium, 19 ins, 48 cm. In adult plumage the head in summer is black, a white semi-circle behind the eye; in winter streaked white with a greyish smudge behind

the eye, and a square headed appearance due to a rather flat crown. The mantle and upperwing-coverts are pale pearl-grey, primaries black, leading primaries with large white sub-terminal patches, posterior ones with white tips, secondaries grey. The underwing-coverts are grey, pale at the axillaries, and the large white patch shows clearly on the underwing in flight. The neck, underbody and tail are white, the breast showing a rosy tint. Bill and legs dark red.

Young birds have the crown, neck and mantle mottled-brown, secondaries brown, underparts white, tail with a sub-terminal black band. Bill and legs brown.

In flight the gull appears to have a large wing spread. At a distance it looks rather like a large pale Northern Black-headed Gull, or Laughing Gull, the wings showing a distinct white leading edge. The broad white wing patches are distinctive.
RANGE: In winter to coasts of Peru and Chile south to Valparaiso. Breeds on lakes in the Andes.   Map 210.

FRANKLIN'S GULL   *Larus pipixcan*   **Pls. 30, 31, 36**
Small–medium, 13.5–14 ins, 34–36 cm. Wing-span 35 ins, 89 cm. A small lightly built gull. In adult summer plumage the hood is deep black with white rim above and below the eye; in winter the hood recedes leaving only a dull black crown and forehead. Underparts and tail white. The upperparts are bluish-grey. First five primaries black with white tips, remaining primaries and secondaries grey tipped white. A white window separates the black primaries from the grey upperwing-coverts on each wing. Bill dark red; legs reddish-brown.

Young birds have white foreheads, crowns and sides of head dusky, upperparts greyish-brown, wing-tips white, underparts white; tail grey with a broad sub-terminal black band; bill and legs brown.

Smaller but rather similar to Laughing Gull but with paler upperparts and distinguished in flight by the sharply divided black and white wing-tips. Immatures are very similar to immature Laughing Gulls, but young Laughing Gulls normally have all-brown heads and brown breasts as opposed to the pale foreheads and white underparts of young Franklin's Gulls.
RANGE: Breeds in interior of N. America and Canada and migrates southwards to Gulf coasts of Louisiana and Texas, wintering largely along the west coast of S. America.   Map 211.

SILVER GULL   *Larus novaehollandiae*   **Pls. 29, 38, 40**
Small–medium, 14–15 ins, 36–38 cm. Wing-span 36 ins, 92 cm. In adult plumage the head, neck, underparts and tail are white; mantle, upperwing-coverts and underwing-coverts pearl-grey. The primaries are mainly black, white tipped, having basal areas white, the two outer black primaries having broad sub-terminal white bands. Bill, eyelids and legs scarlet.

Young birds have pale buff tips on the mantle and brown patches on the secondaries forming a dark band on the wing; tail white with narrow sub-terminal brown band; bill and legs brownish-black.

There are several forms, the Australian gull known as the Silver Gull; the New Zealand form, the Red-billed Gull; the S. African form, the Hartlaub's Gull. In Australia it is the only small gull. The outer and inner white flashes on the black primaries are noticeable in flight.
RANGE: Western, southern and all round coasts of Australia, coasts of New Zealand, western and southern coasts of southern Africa; also in New Caledonia.   Map 212.

BLACK-BILLED or BULLER'S GULL *Larus bulleri* **Pls. 29, 38**
Small–medium, 14.5 ins, 37 cm. A delicately built gull. Head, neck, underparts and tail white, eyelid dark red; mantle and upperwing-coverts very pale pearly-grey. The first four outer primaries are white with black points and white tips, the remaining primaries and secondaries grey, thus a very broad white triangle, tipped black, appears on the forewing in flight. Bill black; legs dark reddish-black.

Young birds show buff mottling on upperparts, primaries with small white tips, bill reddish, tip black and legs pinkish-brown. In 2nd year bill becomes red causing confusion with Red-billed Gull (see Silver Gull).

Largely an inland gull of lakes and rivers, but occurs in small numbers occasionally in harbours and coasts in winter. Adults distinguished from Silver Gulls by black bills; immatures difficult to distinguish from immature Silver Gulls.
RANGE: New Zealand. Map 213.

MEDITERRANEAN BLACK-HEADED GULL **Pls. 32, 37**
Larus melanocephalus
Medium, 15.5–17 ins, 39–43 cm. Wing-span 36 ins, 92 cm. A medium sized black-headed gull resembling the Northern Black-headed Gull but distinguished from it in adult summer plumage by its black as opposed to coffee-brown head, in winter white streaked blackish. Small white crescentric patches show above and below the eye. Upperparts pale pearl-grey as opposed to blue-grey. Entirely pale wing quills with white tips, as opposed to the black tips in the Northern Black-headed Gull. Its bill is very stout, coral red with a black sub-terminal band; legs dark red.

Young birds are similar to young Northern Black-headed Gulls but show a brown band along the leading edge of the wing and dark band on tail.

In adult plumage a white band is noticeable along the leading edge of the pearl-grey wings.
RANGE: Mediterranean. Map 214.

PATAGONIAN BLACK-HEADED GULL **Pls. 31, 36**
Larus maculipennis
Small–medium, 14–15 ins, 36–38 cm. See Northern Black-headed Gull (below).

Somewhat smaller and more slightly built but in other respects both adult and immature plumage are very similar to the Northern Black-headed Gull. Outer primaries white at ends. The white underbody in adults sometimes show a rosy tint.

In view of its limited range on the coasts of S. America it cannot be confused with the northern species.
RANGE: Both coasts of S. America southward from southern Brazil, and from about 30°S. on the west coast. Breeds in Falkland Is., Patagonia, southern Chile, Argentine and Uruguay. Map 215.

NORTHERN BLACK-HEADED GULL **Pls. 28, 31, 32, 37, 40**
Larus ridibundus
Medium, 15–17 ins, 38–43 cm. Wing-span 36 ins, 92 cm. In adult summer plumage the head is coffee-brown with a narrow white eye-ring, white neck, underbody and tail. Mantle and upperwing-coverts blue-grey, the wing-coverts at the edge and bend of wing white. The outer primaries are mainly white with black tips, inner primaries and secondaries grey; underwing-coverts dark grey. Bill and legs deep-red. In winter the head becomes white with a dusky mark behind the eye.

Young birds have head greyish-brown, mottled brownish-grey upperparts, outer primaries black with white centres; tail white with sub-terminal blackish band; bill yellowish with dark tip; legs dull red.

The broad white leading edge of the leading black primaries and the slender red bill and red legs are noticeable in adults.

RANGE: Breeds inland from British Isles eastward through Europe to eastern Asia. Disperses southwards to winter to the Mediterranean, Red Sea, Persian Gulf, coasts of India, China and Japan.　Map 216.

Indian Black-headed Gull (p.101)

Mongolian Gull (below)　　　　　　　　　　　　　　　Great Black-headed Gull (p.100).

MONGOLIAN GULL　*Larus relictus*　　　　　　　**Drawing above**
Small numbers of this hitherto lost species of black-headed gull have been discovered recently breeding on Lake Alakul on the eastern border of Kazakstan (U.S.S.R.).

RANGE: Its range and distribution are as yet uncertain.　Not mapped.

BONAPARTE'S GULL　*Larus philadelphia*　　　　　　**Pls. 31, 36**
Small–medium, 14 ins, 36 cm. Wing-span 32 ins, 82 cm. A small tern-like gull. In adult summer plumage the head is black, mantle and upperwing-coverts pearl-grey. Outer primaries black at tip with large white areas on inner webs, which show as a long white triangle at the front edge of the wing. Underparts, underwing-coverts and tail white; bill black; legs red. In winter plumage the head becomes white with a conspicuous black spot behind the eye, and the bill appears black.

Young birds have greyish-brown upperparts; forehead, neck and underparts white, dusky patch on side of head, and a dark sub-terminal band on the white tail; bill and legs dusky.

Distinguished by its black bill and reddish feet, pale upperparts, and in flight by the long triangle of white at the front edge of the wing.

RANGE: From breeding area migrates southwards along east and west coasts of N. America to Caribbean area and Gulf of Panama. Breeds in N.W. Canada. Map 217.

SLENDER-BILLED GULL *Larus genei* **Pls. 29, 37**
Medium, 15.5–18.5 ins, 39–47 cm. Wing-span 37 ins, 94 cm. In adult plumage the whole head, neck, underbody and tail are white, showing rosy tint except on head. The mantle and upperwing-coverts are pearl-grey. First four primaries white, tipped black, the leading primary with a black outer web; inner primaries and secondaries grey. Axillaries and underwing-coverts grey. The bill is noticeably slender and red; legs red.

Young birds are rather similar to adults but with grey markings on crown and nape; ashy-brown upperparts and white underbody; bill orange-yellow; legs yellow; lacks rosy tint. The white tail carries a black terminal band.

Always has a white head, is larger but somewhat similar to a Northern Black-headed Gull in winter plumage.

RANGE: Coasts of N.W. Africa, Mediterranean, Black Sea, Red Sea, Persian Gulf and Mekran coast. Breeds in Spain, Asia Minor, on coasts of Black, Azov and Caspian Seas, and in Persia and Baluchistan. Map 218.

LITTLE GULL *Larus minutus* **Pls. 31, 32, 37**
Small, 10–12 ins, 25–31 cm. Wing-span 25 ins, 64 cm. Much smaller than any other gull.

In adult summer plumage the head and upper neck are black, the lower neck, underbody and tail white. The mantle and upperwing-coverts are pale grey, wing quills grey, with no trace of black, and with broad white tips. The underbody sometimes shows a rosy tinge. The underwings are dark smoky-grey. Bill and legs deep red in summer. In winter plumage the head becomes white, the crown and nape shows a greyish-black patch; bill black.

Immatures in first plumage have a basically white head with dark brown markings on the crown, also through or near the eye and down the back of the neck. The mantle is dark brown, the central upperwing-coverts dark brown with pale edging, the forward triangle of the inner wing darker forming a dark zig-zag pattern across the wing resembling young kittiwakes. The underbody and underwing are white; tail white with a broad sub-terminal dark band; bill brownish; legs dull flesh-coloured.

Little Gulls appear very neat and compact. The head and tail appear to project less beyond the wings than other gulls; this is accentuated by the head being rounded rather than tapering into the short fine bill. In flight the wings appear broader and shorter from the carpal joint to the tip than in most gulls. On the ground the Little Gull's very short legs distinguish it, closely resembling the posture of a tern. The untidy dark markings about the head are a useful recognition feature in all plumages except full breeding plumage, and the dark slate-grey underwings in adults.

RANGE: Breeds in northern Europe from Holland and Denmark eastwards, and in Siberia to the Sea of Okhotsk. Disperses southwards in winter passing through British Isles to winter in the Mediterranean, Black Sea and Japan Sea. Map 219.

CHINESE BLACK-HEADED GULL *Larus saundersi* **Pls. 31, 37**
Small–medium, 12.5 ins, 32 cm. In adult summer plumage the head is bluish-black and a narrow white ring surrounds the eye, interrupted at the back. In winter the head is white with dusky patches. Neck, underparts and tail white. Upperparts dark pearl-grey; flight feathers mainly white, the first primary with a narrow black edge on outer web, other primaries with black inner webs and black sub-terminal bars.

Underwing-coverts grey. Bill black; legs red. Young birds have upperparts mottled brownish-grey, the first two primaries with black outer webs, remainder with black tips. Tail white with sub-terminal black band. Bill black; legs brownish.

Distinguished from Northern Black-headed Gull by its black as opposed to brown head in summer, darker mantle, black bill and large amount of white on primaries. Very similar to Bonaparte's Gull.

RANGE: Breeds inland in N. China and Mongolia and occurs on coasts of eastern Siberia, Korea and China, Japan and Taiwan. Map 220.

SABINE'S GULL *Xema sabini*   Pls. 33, 39

Small–medium, 13–14 ins, 33–36 cm. Wing-span 34 ins, 86 cm. In adult summer plumage the head and throat are slate-grey, the neck, underparts and forked tail pure white. In winter the head and throat become white leaving some dusky marking. The appearance of the upperparts in flight ismost striking. The grey mantle and wing-coverts form one triangle with its apex at the bend of the wing; the first four black primaries form a second triangle with its apex at the bend of the wing; the remaining very pale inner primaries and secondaries form a third white triangle between the grey mantle and black outer primaries, which show white tips. The tail is forked; bill black with yellow tip; legs dark.

Young birds have the whole upperparts ashy-brown, with a white forehead; underparts and tail white, a broad black terminal band across the forked tail; bill and legs brown.

The only gull with a forked tail except the Swallow-tailed Gull which is much larger and has a deeply forked tail. Both gulls occur off Ecuador and might be confused.

RANGE: Breeds in the high arctic and migrates south to winter off W. African coast and the west coast of S. America. Map 221.

ROSS'S GULL *Rhodostethia rosea*   Pls. 33, 39

Small–medium, 13–14 ins, 33–36 cm. Adults in summer plumage have head and neck whitish with a narrow black collar round the neck; in winter head and neck pale bluish grey. Eyelids red. Upperparts and upperwings pearl-grey, outer web of first primary black, secondaries with rosy-white tips. Underbody, rump and wedge-shaped tail rosy-white; underwing-coverts grey. Bill black; legs red.

Young birds have crown, neck and mantle brownish-grey; forehead and sides of head dull white; outer primaries black, inner primaries and secondaries white. A dark band shows on upperwing-coverts. Underparts white; bill black; legs dark flesh-coloured; tail with broad black terminal band on central feathers. Immatures recall immature Sabine's Gull.

A rare small gull distinguished by its black collar, red eyelids, grey underwing and red legs.

RANGE: High arctic regions rarely wandering south of Arctic Circle. Map 222.

COMMON KITTIWAKE *Rissa tridactyla*   Pls. 33, 39

Medium, 15.5–16 ins, 39–41 cm. Wing-span 36 ins, 92 cm. This lightly built, largely oceanic gull can be distinguished in adult summer plumage by its white head and neck, white underparts, under surface of wings and white tail, and its pearl-grey upperparts. The tips of the outer four primaries are black, remaining primaries and secondaries grey. At close range its dark eye, slender greenish-yellow bill and dark legs are noticeable. In winter plumage the crown and sides of the head have dark grey streaking.

Young birds, known as 'tarrocks', are distinctive, having a dark band at the back of the neck, a conspicuous dark diagonal band across each upperwing, forming a '**W**' pattern, and a black band across the tail. Bill black.

The flight is light and buoyant, more often than not low over the sea. Outside the breeding season kittiwakes keep to the open ocean, and frequently pick up and follow ships in small flocks.

The solid black wing tips form a point in identification in flight.

RANGE: Arctic seas, N. Atlantic and N. Pacific Oceans. Map 223.

RED-LEGGED KITTIWAKE *Rissa brevirostris* **Pls. 33, 39**
Small–medium, 15 ins, 38 cm. Wing-span 36 ins, 92 cm. Adults are similar to the Common Kittiwake but differ in having a darker mantle and upperwing coverts, and red legs.

Young birds are similar to adults but upperparts are browner and a broad dark band shows across the nape; lack black diagonal band on upperwings and have plain white tails. Bills dark; legs brown.

RANGE: Ranges in high latitudes of N. Pacific Ocean and southern Bering Sea and only likely to be seen by ships undertaking extremely northerly passages. Breeds in Aleutian Is. and islands in the Bering Sea. Map 224.

SWALLOW-TAILED GULL *Creagrus furcatus* **Pls. 33, 39**
Medium–large, 20 ins, 51 cm. This rather large gull is unusual in that it looks more like a tern in flight on account of its long wings, long white forked tail and distinctive upper surface plumage.

In adult summer plumage the head and neck are dark grey with a white stripe on each side of the forehead. In winter the head becomes white with a dark ring round the eye and greyish collar. The eyelids are crimson. The mantle is grey; outer webs of outer primaries black, inner primaries and first few secondaries grey, remaining secondaries white, the wing-coverts also white. The effect in flight from above is to show a wide triangular white patch on the upperwings, against the outer black primaries.

The white throat and breast show a rosy tinge, the remainder of the underparts, tail and upper tail-coverts white. Bill dark greenish with a pale tip; legs pinkish-red. The tail is deeply forked.

Young birds have white mottled head, neck and upperparts mottled and barred brown and white; bill dark; legs greyish-white; tail white with black terminal band.

Much larger than Sabine's Gull, which occurs in the same area, but can be distinguished by the large white triangular patch on the upperwings and more deeply forked tail.

RANGE: Breeds only on the Galapagos Is. and ranges southwards along coasts of Ecuador and northern Peru. Not mapped.

Like many seabirds, terns and noddies breed in large colonies – terns on the ground, noddies often in trees or shrubs.

TERNS and NODDIES   Sternidae

TERNS

Terns with their graceful bodies, long pointed wings, finely tapering bills, deeply forked tails and buoyant flight have acquired the name of sea swallows. With the exception of one or two species such as the Sooty Tern and to a lesser extent the Brown-winged and Crested Terns which range often well out into the ocean, terns are seen by ships close to the coastlines and harbours, frequently hovering over shoals of small fish with bills pointing downwards, and plunging one after the other with a splash as they capture their sand eels or fry. Some species resort almost entirely to inland swamps, lagoons and rivers remote from the coasts.

The majority favour the warm water belts of the globe where great numbers colonise tropical islands. Certain species however that breed in the north temperate latitude belt are migratory, forsaking their breeding areas and migrating to warmer climates north and south of the Equator to winter. At such times, notably off the bulge of N. Africa, large numbers of different species may be seen. The Arctic Tern undertakes an enormous annual migration, leaving its breeding areas north of the Arctic Circle in late summer or early autumn and wintering as far south as sub-antarctic latitudes.

Nesting and young

Most species nest in colonies, often large, on open sites such as stretches of sand or shingle, or small islets, by the coast or on large lakes or marshes. The nests are often very close together and may be simply bare hollows, or may be lined with varying amounts of plant material if this is available close at hand. Marsh terns build shallow nests on floating marsh vegetation. Inca Terns nest in crevices or holes in rocks. Noddy Terns nest on trees, shrubs, rock ledges or rocky islets, carrying material to the site and building quite substantial nests. White Terns lay single eggs on tiny ledges or small level surfaces of rocks or trees where they seem precariously balanced. The clutch may be of 1–3 eggs, varying with different species, and the eggs are usually pale, creamy, yellowish or buffish, or sometimes olive or deep buff, and variably and cryptically patterned with dark markings. Both adults incubate for *c.* 3 weeks in most species and up to 5 weeks in Noddy and White Terns

The young are downy, usually pale in colour with dark spotting and mottling, the down sometimes in spiky tufts; but young noddies have dark brown down with whitish crowns. They may remain and hide near the nest site, but larger young of some species flock by the water's edge. Young White Terns have well-developed claws for clinging to their circumscribed sites. Young terns are fed by both parents and may fly at 4–5 weeks, but take much longer to become fully independent. There is evidence in some places of breeding of Sooty Terns occurring at nine-month and possibly six-month intervals. Six-month intervals in nest site occupation are known for some other species but it is not certain that the same individuals are involved each time.

WHISKERED TERN *Chlidonias hybrida* Pl. 44

Small–medium, 13 ins, 33 cm. Wing-span 27 ins, 69 cm. In adult summer plumage the top of the head is deep black level with the top of the eye. A conspicuous white streak extends from the base of the bill backwards below the black cap on each side. Upperparts slate-grey, primaries darker grey, inner webs of outermost primaries pale. Throat white, darkening to slate-grey on breast to deep blue-grey on flanks and abdomen. In winter the forehead and whole underbody become white, the crown streaked with black, darkest on nape. Upper tail-coverts and tail grey, outer feathers with white outer webs. Tail short, slightly forked, outer feathers rounded. Underwing-coverts and under tail-coverts white. Bill deep red, legs vermilion. Young birds similar to adults in winter, but upperparts and tail mottled-brown.

The winter plumage is hard to distinguish from the White-winged Black Tern in winter plumage.

RANGE: Widely spread throughout the warmer parts of eastern Europe and Asia, E. Indies, Australia and S. Africa. Frequents swamps and lagoons and rarely visits coasts. Map 225.

WHITE-WINGED BLACK TERN *Chlidonias leucoptera* Pl. 44

Small, 8.5–9.5 ins, 216–242 mm. Wing-span 26 ins, 66 cm. In adult summer plumage the head, neck, upper back and underparts black. Underwing linings also black (white in Black Tern *Chlidonias nigra*). Tail white (grey in Black Tern). The outstanding feature in flight is the broad white 'shoulder' or lesser upperwing-coverts, forming a distinctive pattern against the greyish-black primaries and secondaries.

In winter plumage the head is white, mottled black on crown. The upperparts including upperwings and tail slate-grey, the underparts and underwing linings white (similar to Black Tern). Bill red in summer, black in winter; legs orange. Young birds similar to adults in winter but upperparts have brown mottling. Tail grey, upper tail-coverts white.

Largely an inshore tern but sometimes seen in harbours.

RANGE: Ranges and breeds widely across central and southern Europe, extending to eastern Asia. Migrates southwards in winter and has been seen by ships at Aden, Persian Gulf, Malaysia and Borneo. Reaches S. Africa and Australia and occasionally to New Zealand. Map 226.

BLACK TERN *Chlidonias nigra* **Pl. 44**

Small, 9.5–10 ins, 242–254 mm. Wing-span 26 ins, 66 cm. In adult summer plumage head and neck are black; mantle, upperwings, and tail slate grey; the breast and underbody black; under tail-coverts white. The underwings are light grey. In winter plumage head and neck become mottled-white, the crown and nape appearing grey; the chin, throat and underbody become white. A noticeable feature is the thin white margin at the bend of the wing. Bill black; legs purplish-brown. The tail is only slightly forked.

Young birds are similar to adults in winter but head and mantle mottled-brown and flanks greyer.

RANGE: Breeds mainly in inland swamps in Europe and N. America migrating southwards to winter where it is seen frequently off the coasts in certain favoured areas. Map 227.

LARGE-BILLED TERN *Phaetusa simplex* **Pl. 45**

Small–medium, 14.5 ins, 37 cm. Wing-span 36 ins, 92 cm. Top of head glossy-black. A narrow white line shows above the bill. Mantle and tail slate-grey. Upperwing-coverts white. Primaries dark brown, secondaries white. Underparts white. Bill very stout, chrome-yellow. Legs olive, webs yellow. Tail short, nearly square. Young birds have greyish upperparts mottled with brown, and white underparts.

Distinguished by its stout yellow bill and square tail.

RANGE: Tropical S. America, breeding on rivers and estuaries in northern and north-east S. America from Bolivia to southern Brazil and Argentine. Unlikely to be seen at sea. Map 228.

GULL-BILLED TERN *Gelochelidon nilotica* **Pl. 43**

Medium, 15–16 ins, 38–41 cm. Wing-span 34 ins, 86 cm. In adult summer plumage crown and sides of head deep glossy black; in winter forehead and crown white with dark streaks, a black ear patch showing behind the eye. Upperparts and tail pale grey. The tail is only partially forked. Underparts including under surface of wings white. The stout bill is gull-like and black; legs blackish.

Young birds are similar to adults in winter but head duller white with dusky streaks, back and scapulars spotted-brown, stout bill and legs reddish-brown.

Chiefly noticeable for its gull-like appearance, stout black bill and lightly forked grey tail.

RANGE: South-east coast of N. America, California, Gulf of Mexico, W. Indies and S. America, western and southern coasts of Europe, N. Africa. E. to Indo China, Australia. Chiefly inland on lakes, marshes and estuaries. Breeds throughout range. Map 229.

CASPIAN TERN *Hydroprogne caspia* **Pl. 41**

Medium–large, 19–22 ins, 48–56 cm. Wing-span 53 ins, 135 cm. The largest of the terns, almost the size of a Herring Gull.

In adult summer plumage forehead, sides of head to below eye, crown and nape black, the feathers at the nape elongated. In winter the forehead is streaked and crown greyish. Upperparts ash-grey, upper tail-coverts white, tail grey and only slightly forked. The inner webs of primaries slate-grey. Underparts white. Bill very stout, heavy and coral-red; legs black.

Young birds are similar to adults in winter but with upperparts lightly mottled brownish; bill dull orange; legs blackish-brown. The flight is powerful, somewhat gull-like and frequently at a considerable height.

The large size and very large red bill distinguish it. In flight when viewed from below the ends of the primaries look conspicuously dark.

RANGE: N. America, Europe, Africa, Asia, Australia and New Zealand. Map 230.

INDIAN RIVER TERN *Sterna aurantia*   Pl. 45

Medium, 15–17 ins, 38–43 cm. In adult breeding plumage top of head and circle around eye greenish-black; in winter crown grey and forehead white. Upperparts and tail dark pearl-grey. Outer primaries pale brown. Throat, underwing-coverts and under tail-coverts white, breast and abdomen pale pearl-grey. Bill stout, orange-yellow with a dusky tip in winter. Legs orange-red. Tail very long and deeply forked. Immatures have forehead, crown and head buffish with brown flecking, and dull yellow bills.

Its deeply forked tail and stout orange-yellow bill assists identification. Resorts chiefly to rivers and estuaries, sometimes seen off coasts.

RANGE: Tropical Asia from Persia through India, Sri Lanka, and Burma to Singapore. Breeds on islands on lakes and rivers.   Map 231.

SOUTH AMERICAN TERN *Sterna hirundinacea*   Pl. 42

Medium, 16 ins, 41 cm. Wing-span 33 ins, 84 cm. See Arctic Tern (below). Except for its larger size and very slightly curved bill the plumage and characteristics of the South American Tern are entirely similar to the Arctic Tern. Its upperwings are distinctly paler.

RANGE: East and west coast of S. America.   Map 232.

COMMON TERN *Sterna hirundo*   Pls. 42, 43

Small–medium, 12.5–15 ins, 32–38 cm. Wing-span 31 ins, 79 cm. In adult summer plumage the top of the head is black, in winter brown and forehead streaked with white. Mantle and upperwings French-grey, outer primaries with black outer web. Forked tail grey. Throat, rump, under tail-coverts and underwings white; breast and abdomen pale grey, white in winter. Bill scarlet with black tip; legs coral-red. In winter the bill becomes mainly black but always retains some red, legs duller red.

Young birds have forehead and front of crown white, remainder of crown streaked, the mantle mottled ashy-brown showing a dark band in the region of the shoulder. Underparts white; bill brownish; legs flesh-coloured.

Very similar to Arctic Tern and almost impossible to distinguish at sea, doubtful sightings usually quoted as 'comic' tern. Eastern races of Common Tern are darker with a dark bill.

RANGE: Eastern N. America, temperate Europe and Asia. Breeds widely throughout range, and extends southwards from many breeding areas as far as southern Africa and Australia.   Map 233.

ARCTIC TERN *Sterna paradisea*   Pls. 41, 42

Small–medium, 13–15 ins, 33–38 cm. Wing-span 31 ins, 79 cm. Top of head black showing a narrow white streak running from the base of the bill to the nape below the black cap. In winter plumage the crown and forehead are mottled white. Upperparts pearl-grey, secondaries with white margins. Throat, breast and underbody French-grey. Tail deeply forked, outermost tail feathers very long with dark grey outer webs. Bill blood-red; legs very short and coral-red. In winter bill and legs change by stages to black.

Young birds similar to adults in winter plumage but with ashy-brown mantle, and black bill and legs.

Distinguished from Common Tern by red bill without black tip, longer outer tail feathers and darker grey underparts. It is however extremely difficult to distinguish between Common and Arctic Terns at sea and in their winter or juvenile plumage.

Whether Arctic Terns during their great trans-global migrations pass along the east coast of S. America may not yet be established owing to confusion between the extremely similar South American Tern.

RANGE: Breeds from arctic coasts of Alaska, Canada, Greenland, Europe, Siberia, including British Isles. Migrates to winter in extreme southern continental latitudes, reaching the antarctic ice edge.   Map 234.

1 Common Tern (p.111). Tail not extending beyond wing-tips.
2 Arctic Tern (p.111). Tail slightly larger than Common Tern's.
3 Roseate Tern (p.113). Tail streamers extending well beyond wing-tips.

ANTARCTIC or WREATHED TERN *Sterna vittata*   Pl. 42

Small–medium, 16 ins, 41 cm. Wing-span 31 ins, 79 cm. In adult southern summer plumage forehead, crown and nape black; a broad white stripe extends from the gape below the eye to the nape. In winter plumage forehead and crown white. Upperparts and upperwings pale bluish-grey, outer webs of outermost primaries black. Rump and tail white, outer webs of tail feathers pale grey; tail deeply forked. Throat and underparts pearl-grey; under tail-coverts white. Bill coral red; legs orange-red. Young birds similar to adults in winter but have pure white underparts. Flight undulating.

RANGE: Southern oceans and antarctic seas. Breeds at Tristan da Cunha, Gough, Kerguelen, St. Paul and Amsterdam Is., S. Georgia, S. Sandwich Is., S. Orkneys, S. Shetlands, the antarctic continent and the sub-antarctic islands of New Zealand.   Map 235.

KERGUELEN TERN *Sterna virgata*   Pl. 42

Small–medium, 13 ins, 33 cm. Wing-span 31 ins, 79 cm. In adult plumage the top of head black with a broad white moustachial streak between the black crown and grey throat on each side. Upperparts, underparts and tail pearl-grey. Bill red; legs orange. Young birds are similar but forehead brownish, crown, nape and upperparts mottled brownish.

RANGE: Breeds at Marion, Crozet Is., Kerguelen and Heard Is. in S. Indian Ocean.   Map 236.

FORSTER'S TERN *Sterna forsteri*   Pl. 42

Small, 10–11 ins, 25–28 cm. Wing-span 30 ins, 76 cm. Top of head black in summer, whitish in winter with large black patch on each side of face. Upperparts and upperwings pearl-grey; primaries silvery-grey, inner border of inner web of outer primary white. Rump and underparts white; tail pale grey. Bill orange with black tip; legs orange; tail deeply forked. In winter the bill becomes black. Young birds have browner upperparts, shorter tails and a dark patch through eye and ear.

Very similar to Common Tern. From above however the primaries of Forster's Tern are lighter than rest of wing in contrast to Common Tern, and the tail of the Common Tern is whiter contrasting with the grey of its back.

RANGE: Breeds in marshes along east coast of U.S.A. from Maryland to Texas migrating southwards in winter when it may be seen in Panama zone and western California.   Map 237.

TRUDEAU'S TERN   *Sterna trudeaui*   Pl. 43

Small, 10–11 ins, 25–28 cm. Wing-span 30 ins, 76 cm. Top of the head, sides and chin white. A noticeable black streak runs through the eye. Upperparts and upperwings pale pearl-grey, shading into white above rump. Primaries and secondaries grey, secondaries showing broad white edges. Breast and underbody grey. Under-surface of wings white. Bill yellow with broad sub-terminal black band; legs orange; forked tail grey; outer tail feathers white. Young birds are similar but crown greyish; upperparts with some brown mottling; tail dark grey with white outer edges; bill dusky; legs yellowish.

RANGE: S. American coasts from Rio de Janeiro to northern Patagonia on the east; coast of Chile on the west. Breeds inland in Argentina. Occasionally resorts to coasts and harbours.   Map 238.

ROSEATE TERN   *Sterna dougalli*   Pl. 42

Small–medium, 15 ins, 38 cm. Wing-span 30 ins, 76 cm. In adult summer plumage forehead, crown and nape black; in winter forehead and crown speckled white. The mantle and upperparts are very pale pearl-grey, primaries slightly darker, the outer web of the outer primary noticeably darker. Underparts, rump and long deeply forked tail white. In summer the underparts show a distinct rosy tint. Bill varies from dark red to red at base with dark tip, and is often black in winter; legs dark red.

Young birds similar to adults in winter but upperparts mottled ashy-brown showing a dark band on the upperwing coverts. Bill and legs dark.

In appearance it looks much whiter than the Common and Arctic Terns and its very long forked tail is conspicuous. At rest the tail extends well beyond the wing tips.

RANGE: Breeds on east coast of U.S.A. southwards through W. Indies to Venezuela, Azores, Madeira, British Isles, southern Europe, northern Africa, islands in Indian Ocean eastwards, western and northern Australia, and New Caledonia.   Map 239.

WHITE-FRONTED TERN   *Sterna striata*   Pl. 43

Medium, 16–17 ins, 41–43 cm. In adult plumage the forehead is white, the crown and nape black. In winter the white on the forehead is extended and the crown mottled. Upperparts pearl-grey, outer web of outer primary brownish-black, inner webs of primaries with white edges to the tips. Underparts, including under-surface of wings white, the breast sometimes showing a pink tint. Bill black; legs reddish-brown. Tail white, deeply forked.

Young birds have crown and nape streaked and spotted with white, black and buff, upperparts barred and mottled, a broad band of dark brown on the shoulders of the wings and a dusky edging to the fork of the tail.

Distinguished in adult plumage from the Black-fronted Tern by its white forehead. The commonest tern around the New Zealand coast, many dispersing during the southern autumn (see below). Marine in habits.

RANGE: Breeds in New Zealand, Chatham and Auckland Is. In the autumn large numbers migrate to coasts of Tasmania, Victoria and New South Wales, being plentiful between May and November.   Map 240.

WHITE-CHEEKED TERN *Sterna repressa*   **Pl. 42**
Small–medium, 12.5–14.5 ins, 32–37 cm. In adult summer plumage forehead, crown and nape black. Upperparts and tail darkish-grey, secondaries smoky-grey. Underparts grey, much darker than in Common Tern. Underwing-coverts and under tail-coverts pale grey. A white area shows between the dark cap and the grey underparts. Tail forked, bill slender, coral-red with dark tip, legs red. In winter forehead and crown become mottled and streaked white. Young birds similar but forehead and crown grey and a dark band on upperwing-coverts. Underparts white. Bill blackish, legs dusky-yellow.

Similar but darker than Common Tern.

RANGE: Red Sea, Persian Gulf to west coast of India. Breeds on coast of N.E. Africa, southern Arabia, Persian Gulf and Laccadive Is.   Map 241.

BLACK-NAPED TERN *Sterna sumatrana*   **Pl. 43**
Small–medium, 13.5–14.5 ins, 34–37 cm. Wing-span 24 ins, 61 cm. Head and neck white with a triangular black spot in front of the eye and a black band round the nape. Mantle, upperwings and rump pale pearl-grey. Underparts white, sometimes showing a rosy flush. The white tail is long and deeply forked, the central tail feathers grey. Bill black with yellow tip; legs black.

Young birds have the top of the head grey-brown mottling, with a black patch on the nape. Upperparts barred greyish-brown; primaries grey with inner margins white. Bill yellow; legs yellowish-brown.

Favours lagoons and usually keeps close inshore. The black band round the nape is distinctive.

RANGE: Tropical islands in Indian and Pacific Oceans and off northern Australia and the Great Barrier Reef. Breeds throughout range.   Map 242.

BLACK-BELLIED TERN *Sterna melanogastra*   **Pl. 45**
Small–medium, 12–13 ins, 31–33 cm. In adult breeding plumage top of head black; in winter crown and forehead greyish with dark streaking, showing a dark patch round eye. Upperparts and tail pearl-grey. Throat and underwings white. Foreneck and breast pearl-grey. Abdomen and under tail-coverts brownish-black, in winter greyish. Bill orange-yellow. Legs red. Tail deeply forked, outer tail feathers white.

Smaller than Indian River Tern with more slender bill, and can be confused when in winter plumage. An inland species resorting to rivers and marshes, and unlikely to be seen on coasts.

RANGE: Similar to Indian River Tern (p. 111).   Map 231.

ALEUTIAN TERN *Sterna aleutica*   **Pl. 44**
Small–medium, 13.5 ins, 34 cm. Forehead white. Crown and nape black, a line from bill to eye black. Upperparts and upperwings medium grey, primaries dark grey, outer primary black, remainder of wing quills grey with white inner webs. Tail white. Foreneck, breast and abdomen pale grey; underwing and under tail-coverts

white. Bill and legs black. Young birds have greyish-brown head and upperparts, dark grey wing quills and grey rump and tail; underparts white. Bill dusky; legs reddish-yellow.

Distinguished from Common and Arctic Terns by its white forehead and darker overall colour contrasting with white underwings and black bill and legs.

RANGE: Breeds on coasts of Alaska and eastern Siberia. A rare straggler to Japan. Map 243.

SPECTACLED TERN *Sterna lunata* **Pl. 44**

Small–medium, 14–15 ins, 36–38 cm. Wing-span 29 ins, 74 cm. See Brown-winged or Bridled Tern (below). The characteristic plumage of the Brown-winged Tern is repeated in the Spectacled Tern which can be distinguished however apart from its black crown, nape and stripe from bill to eye, by its grey upperparts and tail as opposed to the dark brownish-grey upperparts and tail of the Brown-winged Tern. Its outer tail feathers are white.

Young birds have mottled grey-brown crowns and upperparts; underparts white.

RANGE: Tropical Pacific Ocean, more abundant in the central Pacific and relatively rare in the western Pacific where the Brown-winged Tern is the common species. Map 244.

BROWN-WINGED or BRIDLED TERN *Sterna anaethetus* **Pl. 44**

Small–medium, 14–15 ins, 36–38 cm. Wing-span 30 ins, 76 cm. Liable to be confused with the Sooty Tern.

Crown and nape black and a black band extends on each side from bill to eye. Between the bands a narrow white patch on the forehead (narrower than in Sooty Tern) extends beyond the level of the eyes, giving it a 'bridled' appearance. Upperparts brownish-grey, a whitish band showing around the nape. White piping on leading margin of wing. Underparts and under tail-coverts white. Tail deeply forked, greyish-brown. Bill and legs black. Flight similar but more graceful than Sooty Tern with a quicker wing-beat. Immatures have mottled-brown heads and mantles and greyish underparts.

See Sooty Tern for comparison (below).

RANGE: Widespread throughout the tropical and sub-tropical zones of the Atlantic, Indian and Pacific Oceans, west and north coasts of Australia. Breeds throughout range. Map 245.

SOOTY TERN *Sterna fuscata* **Pl. 44**

Medium, 17 ins, 43 cm. Wing-span 34 ins, 86 cm. The first impression is of a tern with black upperparts and white underparts. Crown and nape black and a black band extends on each side from bill to eye. Between the bands the forehead is white, terminating at the eye. Upperparts dark brownish-black, a white piping showing clearly in flight at close range along the leading margin of the wing. Underparts and under tail-coverts greyish-white. Tail dark, deeply forked, outer webs of outer tail feathers white, showing as a white piping. Bill and legs black. Flight buoyant and undulating, steady wing-beats appearing to pause on completion of down stroke. Capable of soaring in updraughts on motionless wings. Immatures are sooty-brown overall with white tips to feathers on mantle.

See Brown-winged or Bridled Tern for comparison (above). The Sooty Tern is the most truly oceanic of all terns, and frequently follows ships at night.

RANGE: Widespread throughout the tropical zones of the Atlantic, Indian and Pacific Oceans. Breeds throughout range.   Map 246.

Sooty Terns fishing. This species is one of the few terns to be found at sea far from land.

FAIRY TERN   *Sterna nereis*   Pl. 43
Small, 10 ins, 25 cm. Wing-span 21 ins, 53 cm. Crown and nape black; forehead white with a black band extending forward from the eye and just short of the bill. Upperparts very pale pearl-grey; underparts and tail white, outer tail feathers not markedly elongated. Bill wholly yellow; legs orange. In winter bill tip black.
    Young birds very similar with dusky bills and legs.
    Differs from Little Tern in larger size, much paler upperparts and in adults totally bright yellow bill. Young birds are virtually impossible to distinguish from young Little Terns.
RANGE: Breeds on southern and western coasts of Australia and New Caledonia, and a few pairs in North Island, New Zealand.   Map 247.

BLACK-FRONTED TERN   *Chlidonias albostriata*   Pl. 43
Small–medium, 12 ins, 31 cm. In adult summer plumage forehead, top of head and nape deep velvety-black, a broad white stripe showing beneath the black head and nape. Mantle, upperwings and tail blue-grey. The rump and under tail-coverts are white, the breast and abdomen blue-grey. The white rump is noticeable in flight. Bill and legs bright orange-red. In winter the top of the head and nape become pale grey.
    Young birds are similar to adults in winter plumage but show some brown mottling on upperwings and tail. Bill yellowish with dark tip; legs bright orange-red.
RANGE: Largely an inland tern breeding in the South Island of New Zealand but moves north during the southern autumn and occurs off the west coast of North Island at this period. Confined to New Zealand.   Map 248.

AMAZON TERN   *Sterna superciliaris*   Pl. 45
Small, 9 ins, 23 cm. In breeding plumage, crown, nape and a band from bill to eye black. Forehead white. In winter, crown and nape become white with dark speck-

ling. Mantle and upperparts grey; four outer primaries greyish-black. Underparts white. Bill wholly greenish-yellow. Legs dull yellow. Tail white, forked. Young birds have dusky crowns, darker around back of head, upperparts mottled greyish-brown. Bills and legs dull yellow.

A fresh water tern extending far inland up S. American rivers.

RANGE: Breeds on sandbanks of rivers of eastern S. America from the Orinoco to the La Plata rivers. Map 249.

DAMARA TERN   *Sterna balaenarum*   Pl. 43

Small, 8.5–9 ins, 216–229 mm. Wing-span 20 ins, 51 cm. In adult summer plumage the top of the head is black, in winter the forehead and crown mottled-white. Mantle and upperparts pale-grey; underparts white, slightly grey on breast. Tail grey; bill black with yellow base; legs yellow.

Young birds are similar to adults in winter but upperwings darker grey.

Very similar to the Little Tern but distinguished by its black forehead and black bill. Its range does not overlap with that of the Little Tern.

RANGE: Confined to the western coast of southern Africa.   Map 250.

CHILEAN TERN   *Sterna lorata*   Pl. 43

Small, 9.5 ins, 24 cm. In adult plumage this little tern has the crown and nape black, a white forehead and a black band from the eye to the bill narrowing towards the bill. Mantle, upperwings, rump and forked tail slate-grey, the outer web of the leading primary black. Throat and underwing-coverts white; breast and abdomen pale grey. Bill greenish-yellow with black tip; legs brown.

This is a small very grey looking tern, darker and slightly larger but which might be confused with the Little Tern which occasionally overlaps its northern range in winter months.

RANGE: Breeds on the coasts of Peru, ranging southward to northern Chile.   Map 251.

LITTLE TERN   *Sterna albifrons*   Pl. 43

Small, 8–11 ins, 205–280 mm. Wing-span 20 ins, 51 cm. In adult summer plumage crown, nape and a band from the bill to the eye black; forehead white. In winter the crown and nape become white with dark speckling. Mantle and upperparts pale pearl-grey; underparts and forked tail white. Bill yellow with black tip; legs yellow. In winter the bill tends to become black.

Young birds have whitish-buff crowns with a darker patch from the eye around the back of the head, upperparts greyish, mottled with buff and dark areas on the fore edge of the wings; bills black; legs dull yellow.

Distinguished by its small size, narrow wings, yellow bill with black tip, yellow legs and white forehead. Its light buoyant flight with quicker wingbeats than other terns is noticeable at a distance.

RANGE: Widespread throughout temperate and tropical parts of the world.   Map 252.

CRESTED TERN   *Thalasseus bergii*   Pl. 41

Medium, 18–19 ins, 46–48 cm. Wing-span 43 ins, 109 cm. In adult summer plumage the forehead is white, crown and nape black with elongated feathers which can be raised to form a crest. In winter the crown is mainly white. Upperparts and tail pearl-grey, secondaries with white tips; sides of head, neck and underparts white.

Bill powerful, greenish-yellow; legs brownish-black; tail deeply forked.

Young birds are similar but forehead and crown white with brownish-black mottling; mantle and upperparts with buffish-white mottling; bill greenish-yellow; tail darker grey than in adults.

One of the largest terns, distinguished from the Lesser-crested Tern by its larger size, darker grey colour, white forehead (the Lesser-crested Tern's forehead is black), and greenish-yellow bill (the Lesser-crested Tern's bill is bright orange). RANGE: Ranges throughout islands and coasts of the Indian Ocean, Persian Gulf, tropical Pacific, coasts of Australia, Tasmania and S. Africa. Map 253.

ROYAL TERN *Thalasseus maximus* **Pl. 41**

Medium, 19 ins, 48 cm. Wing-span 43 ins, 109 cm. In adult summer plumage, crown and nape are black, feathers on the nape noticeably elongated forming a partial crest. The forehead may be black but frequently white. In winter the forehead is white, crown streaked. Upperparts pale grey, outer primary darker grey. Underparts, rump, edge of wing and deeply forked tail white. Bill large, red; legs black.

Young birds are similar to adults in winter but upperparts show dusky spotting, tail feathers dusky-white, bill and legs yellow.

The more heavily built Caspian Tern is similar but has an even stouter bright red bill, and a much less deeply forked tail. The Royal Tern is the commonest tern in the W. Indies.

RANGE: Coasts of N. and S. America from Virginia to Peru, from West Indies southwards on east coast of S. America to Point Tombo, Argentine, 44°S., 65°20'W. Also on N.W. coast of Africa. Breeds from Virginia to Mexico, West Indies, and in N.W. Africa. Map 254.

LESSER-CRESTED TERN *Thalasseus bengalensis* **Pl. 41**

Small—medium, 15–16 ins, 39–41 cm. Wing-span 35 ins, 89 cm. See Crested Tern, p. 117 – very similar but smaller than Crested Tern. In adult summer plumage the Lesser-crested Tern's forehead is black (white in Crested Tern), and the upperparts are a paler grey. The colour of their bills is different, the Lesser-crested Tern's being orange (greenish-yellow in Crested Tern). In both cases the legs are black.

In flight both species have a steady measured wing-action, slightly hesitant on completion of the down stroke, giving the appearance of a powerful and yet graceful flight.

RANGE: Red Sea, east coast of Africa, Arabian Sea, Persian Gulf, islands in Indian Ocean, coasts of India, islands in E. Indies and northern Australia. Map 255.

CHINESE CRESTED TERN *Thalasseus zimmermanni* **Pl. 41**

Small—medium, 15 ins, 38 cm. Forehead, crown and nape black, feathers on nape elongated; hindneck white. Upperpart and upperwings very pale grey; first five primaries very dark grey with white wedges on inner webs. Underparts and tail white. Bill yellow with broad black tip; legs black.

Distinguished from Lesser-crested Tern by its heavier yellow bill with broad black tip. A little known species.

RANGE: Coasts of China. Map 256.

CAYENNE TERN *Thalasseus eurygnatha* **Pl. 41**

Medium, 17 ins, 43 cm. Wing-span 37 ins, 94 cm. Similar to Royal Tern but distinguished from it by its long pale yellow bill and black legs. Tail deeply forked. Young birds similar to young Royal Terns but bill black.

The only tern in S. America with a pale yellow bill.

RANGE: From Colombia eastwards, Lesser Antilles, and east coast of S. America. Breeds throughout range as far south as Santa Cruz, Argentine, 44°S., 65°20′W. Map 257.

ELEGANT TERN *Thalasseus elegans* Pl. 41

Medium size, 16.5 ins, 42 cm. Similar to Royal Tern but distinctly smaller. Bill longer and more slender. Upperparts and upperwings pale grey (darker than Royal Tern); tail deeply forked (whiter than Royal Tern); bill orange-red; legs black. Young birds similar to young Royal Terns but bills blackish and shorter than in adults.

RANGE: West coast of Americas from Lower California to Chile. Breeds on coasts of lower California. Map 258.

SANDWICH TERN *Thalasseus sandvicensis* Pls. 41, 43

Medium, 16–18 ins, 41–46 cm. Wing-span 37 ins, 94 cm. In adult summer plumage forehead, crown and nape black, the feathers on the back of the crown elongated and erected as a crest at times. In winter the forehead and crown become streaked white. The upperparts are pale pearl-grey, primaries with white margins on inner webs, the outer primary dark slate-grey on the outer web. Underparts and tail white. The bill is long, slender, black with a yellow tip; legs comparatively long and black; tail less deeply forked than normal in terns. The flight is more gull-like than in other common terns.

Young birds have brownish foreheads, crown white, heavily streaked, upperparts with black and white mottling and slate-grey tails. Underparts white; bill and legs dark.

The crested effect of the elongated feathers on the crown and the long black bill with its yellow tip help to identify it.

RANGE: Coasts of N. and S. America from Carolina to Peru and Argentina. Coasts of S. Africa, Persian Gulf. British Isles, west and southern Europe to Black Sea. Map 259.

INCA TERN *Larosterna inca* Pl. 44

Medium, 16 ins, 41 cm. A most distinctive species with an overall dark slate-blue plumage, darker on crown and nape and paler and bluer on the throat, breast and underwing-coverts. The four outer primaries and the secondaries are broadly tipped white. The stout bill which curves slightly downwards is scarlet, and fleshy yellow wattles occur on each side at the base of the gape. A striking narrow white feathered 'handlebar' moustache leads back and down from the wattles, curving upwards like a ram's horn at the bend of the wing. Legs bright red; tail medium-forked.

Young birds are similar, but somewhat browner with duller coloured bills and legs.

RANGE: West coast of S. America. Map 260.

WHITE TERN *Gygis alba* Pl. 43

Small, 10.5–13 ins, 27–33 cm. Wing-span 28 ins, 71 cm. Adult snow white overall with a black ring round the eye. Bill black, blue at base, legs vary between black and pale blue, webs whitish-yellow. Tail slightly forked. Young birds similar but show a black spot behind the eye and black shafts to wing quills and tail feathers. Its flight is light, often rising and sinking, and erratic, diving to surface to catch fish but never submerging.

Quite closely related to the noddies (see below), this beautiful tern is often called the White Noddy. It lays a single egg either on a bare branch or ridge of rock and appears exceptionally tame and confiding at its breeding quarters.

RANGE: Distributed throughout tropical islands in the Atlantic, Indian and Pacific Oceans. Breeds throughout range.   Map 261.

NODDIES

The brown plumaged noddies, one species of which is however blue-grey, are distributed throughout islands in the tropical and sub-tropical belts of the oceans but behave somewhat differently from most other terns. They nest amongst the branches of trees and bushes making crude nests of sticks and seaweed. They rarely dive below the surface but feed largely on small fry skipping above the water, and may often be observed in large flocks where fish are jumping under attack from tuna, bonito and other large game fish. In courtship the noddy displays by nodding the head vigorously towards the female from which its name has doubtless been derived. Unlike other terns noddies have wedge-shaped tails, the outer tail feathers becoming progressively shorter, with only a shallow 'V' shaped cut in the centre. Flight is swift, erratic and normally low over the sea. Noddies do not range far from the coast.

BLUE-GREY NODDY *Procelsterna cerulea*   **Pl. 44**
Small, 10–11 ins, 25–28 cm. Wing-span 24 ins, 61 cm. Forehead and throat pale grey; crown and nape grey; a narrow black ring around eye. Upperparts smoky-grey, secondaries with white tips. Underparts and tail grey, tail slightly forked. Some paler birds have paler underparts and underwings. Bill black; legs black with yellow webs to feet.

Young birds are darker grey with dark primaries.

Easily recognised by its grey appearance.

RANGE: Confined to central and southern Pacific Ocean. Breeds throughout range.   Map 262.

COMMON or BROWN NODDY *Anous stolidus*   **Pl. 44**
Small–medium, 14.5–16 ins, 37–41 cm. Wing-span 33 ins, 84 cm. Top of head lavender-grey, paler on forehead. White arc above and below eyes. Upperparts dark brown, primaries and tail almost black. Underparts dark brown, underwings paler. Bill black; legs brownish-black; tail rather long, wedge-shaped with shallow 'V' cut in centre. Young birds lighter brown with greyish cap.

Larger and not so dark as White-capped Noddy which also has a white cap. Bill stouter than other noddies. Ranges up to 50 miles from land.

RANGE: Widely distributed in tropical and sub-tropical Atlantic, Indian and Pacific Oceans, west and north coasts of Australia. Breeds throughout range.   Map 263.

WHITE-CAPPED NODDY *Anous minutus*   **Pl. 44**
Small–medium, 13–14 ins, 33–36 cm. Wing-span 28 ins, 71 cm. Smaller than Common Noddy with top of head white and overall plumage almost black. White

arc above and below eyes. Bill black, legs brown. Tail wedge-shaped, slightly forked. Top of head is whiter than either Lesser or Common Noddy.
RANGE: Distributed widely through Caribbean, tropical Atlantic and tropical Pacific Oceans. Less numerous than Common Noddy throughout its range.   Map 264.

LESSER NODDY *Anous tenuirostris*   **Pl. 44**
Small–medium, 12–13 ins, 31–33 cm. Wing-span 28 ins, 71 cm. Top of head greyish-white. White arc below eyes. Overall plumage sooty-brown, primaries darker. Bill black, legs blackish-brown. Tail wedge-shaped slightly forked. Top of head is paler than that of Common Noddy. White-capped Noddy has almost pure white at top of head.
RANGE: Indian Ocean. Breeds on Maldives, Chagos, Cargados Carajos, Mauritius, Seychelles, Abrolhos (W. Australia) and possibly other islands.   Map 265.

Black Skimmers. Adults in breeding plumage.
These birds collect food by skimming the water
with their lower mandibles while on the wing.

SKIMMERS Rynchopidae

Skimmers, with their long narrow wings, black or dark brown upperparts, white
foreheads and underparts, short legs and short forked tails, superficially resemble
dark terns. Their structural peculiarities however, adapted to their remarkable
method of fishing, places them in a family of their own.

When feeding they fly with steady wing-beats very close to the surface, their
longer lower mandible cutting the water. To achieve this their wing strokes terminate above the horizontal. When the lower mandible strikes a fish the upper
mandible snaps shut like a trap door. Their bills are so constructed that the outer

edges of both mandibles are compressed to knife-like edges, broader towards the mouth, the edges of the lower mandible closing into grooves within the upper mandible. When a fish is caught it is usually tossed in the air and swallowed on the wing, the lower bill returning immediately to scoop through the water.

Skimmers usually feed in the evenings or by moonlight, when shrimps and fish rise to the surface, and rest in flocks on sandbanks by day. Their usual habitats are lakes and rivers, but they also resort to the coast and are occasionally seen at sea.

Nesting and young

These nest sociably on coastal and river sandbanks, but although large numbers may be present the nests are well-spaced. The nest is a bare, shallow hollow with 2–4 eggs, cryptically coloured and similar to those of terns. The young are downy, with a finely mottled pattern for concealment on a sandy background. They are precocial, leaving the nest soon after hatching and can swim well at an early age. They are fed at first on regurgitated, and later on whole fish, brought by the parents. The bill is unspecialised at first and the elongated lower mandible does not develop until the chick is well-grown.

BLACK SKIMMER *Rynchops nigra* Pl. 45

Medium, 19 ins, 48 cm. Wing-span 45 ins, 114 cm. Crown, nape, upperparts and upperwings black; in winter a whitish collar around the neck. Secondaries have broad white tips. Forehead and underbody white. Underwings and under tail-coverts whitish-grey. Bill long, lower mandible extending beyond upper mandible, bright red at base, merging into black at forward end. Legs short, red. Tail slightly forked, brown with white edges, outer tail feathers white. Young birds mottled brown above, underparts mottled-grey. Bills shorter, brown. Legs dusky red.
RANGE: Rivers, lakes and coasts of the Americas from Massachusetts to Buenos Aires and from Ecuador to Chile. Breeds from Massachusetts to Texas, in winter from S. Carolina to the Gulf of Mexico. From Columbia southwards to the Argentine. Map 266.

AFRICAN SKIMMER *Rynchops flavirostris* Pl. 45

Small–medium, 14 ins, 36 cm. Wing-span 42 ins, 107 cm. Crown, nape and upper-wings brown, feathers with buff edges; in winter a whitish collar around the neck. Secondaries have broad white tips. Forehead and underbody white. Underwings dusky-brown. Bill long, upper mandible orange-red, lower mandible orange at base merging into yellow at forward end. Legs short, red. Tail slightly forked, greyish. Young birds similar but forehead streaked grey. Bill yellowish, with dark tip.
RANGE: Rivers, lakes and coasts throughout tropical Africa, from Senegal to the Orange River across Africa, and from the Nile to the Zambesi. Map 267.

INDIAN SKIMMER *Rynchops albicollis* Pl. 45

Small–medium, 16 ins, 41 cm. Wing-span 43 ins, 109 cm. Crown and nape dark brown. Hindneck, rump and tail white. Remainder of upperparts dark brown, primaries blackish. Secondaries have broad white edges. Forehead and underparts white, underwings grey. Bill orange, tip yellow. Legs red. Young birds have streaked foreheads, paler brown upperparts with paler mottled feathering and a brown tip to tail feathers.
RANGE: Rivers and lakes in India and Burma. Breeds on sandbanks. Map 268.

A breeding colony of Auks and Guillemot. Killiwakes.

ALCIDS Alcidae

The family *Alcidae*, auks, guillemots, razorbills, auklets, puffins and murrelets, are all seabirds of the high latitudes in the colder water of the northern hemisphere where they replace the penguins and diving-petrels of the southern hemisphere.

They are rather stoutish-bodied, medium to small sized birds; in colouring mostly black above and white below, some dark with white wing patches and with varying shaped and coloured bills and legs. Outside the breeding season they spend much of their time in flocks at sea at no great distance from the land, diving below water using their wings to propel them in search of fish. They swim high in the water and when taking wing fly with rapid 'whirring' wingbeats for short distances low over the sea. When disturbed they will often splash along the surface before diving.

Most species breed in colonies on ledges or clefts in cliffs, making no nest and laying their eggs on the bare rock. Puffins however nest in burrows scraped out of springy turf along cliffs making a sparse nest of grasses and feathers.

It is by no means easy to identify individual species at sea.

Nesting and young

The nesting habits vary, but most species are sociable in their nesting. Nest material may be accumulated if it is available close to the nest site. Only one or two eggs are laid, large for the size of the birds, and both parents take a share in incubating eggs and caring for the young. The young usually have thick, soft and dark coloured down. Guillemots and razorbills tend to crowd on open rock ledges and niches of cliffs, and on flat-topped stacks. The large single pear-shaped egg is very varied in colour and pattern. It is laid on a bare ledge often crowded with birds and the considerable variation may enable birds to recognise their own eggs. The young leave for sea at 2–3 weeks, only partly grown, and accompanied by the parents. The other species nest in rock crevices, cavities or burrows dug by the birds. These are usually on islands, or boulder-beaches, cliff-tops and screes on the coast, exceptionally on higher ground further inland. Black Guillemots have two heavily spotted eggs in a rock crevice, puffins and auklets have a single faintly marked or unmarked egg, and the Little Auk has an unmarked blue egg. The young of these remain in the nest until fledged, at about 3–4 weeks for the Little Auk, 5–6 for the Black Guillemot, and *c*. 7 for the Atlantic Puffin.

Most murrelets and auklets nest in burrows, the former having speckled eggs and those of the latter being plain and whitish. The young of Ancient and Crested Murrelets are exceptionally precocious, leaving the burrow for the sea within two days of hatching. Kittlitz's Murrelet nests on bare rocky slopes high on mountains near the sea, while the Marbled Murrelet nests on platforms of twigs, moss or old nests in coastal forests.

LITTLE AUK or DOVEKIE *Plautus alle*   **Pl. 46**
Very small, 8 ins, 203 mm. Wing-span 12 ins, 31 cm. Head, neck, upper breast and upperparts black; in winter the throat and ear-coverts become white. Secondaries and scapulars show white streaks visible at short range. Lower breast and under-parts white. Bill very short, thick, black, yellow inside mouth; legs flesh-coloured.

Young birds similar to adults in winter but have browner upperparts.

Distinguished by its very small stubby appearance and short stout bill. Swims very low in the water and dives when alarmed. Frequently seen in the N. Atlantic on the routes from the British Isles to the Gulf of St. Lawrence, and has been seen off New York in winter.

RANGE: N. Atlantic and adjacent arctic seas. Disperses southwards in winter to the latitude of the British Isles and New York. Occasionally driven ashore or further south during gales.   Map 269.

RAZORBILL   *Alca torda*   Pl. 46
Medium, 16.5 ins, 42 cm. Wing-span 26 ins, 66 cm. Head, neck and upperparts black with a somewhat 'bull-necked' appearance. A narrow white line extends from bill to eye. In winter the cheeks and foreneck become white; underparts and underwing-coverts white. Secondaries tipped white, showing a white line when the bird is on the water. Bill stout, compressed, black and crossed by a conspicuous white band; legs black.

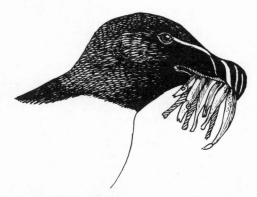

Razor-billed Auk with bill full of food for young.

Young birds similar to adults in winter but with a smaller black bill lacking the white line.

When on the water it carries its tail cocked in the air.

RANGE: N. Atlantic and adjacent arctic seas. Some disperse southwards in winter to latitude of New York and Straits of Gibraltar.   Map 270.

BRUNNICH'S GUILLEMOT or THICK-BILLED MURRE   Pl. 46
Uria lomvia
Medium, 18 ins, 46 cm. In breeding plumage head, neck and upperparts black, the whole head dark. Breast and underbody white. In winter it retains the sides of the face below the ear-coverts black, the throat and neck white like the rest of the underbody. The tips of the secondaries are white forming a thin white line. Bill noticeably stouter than Common Guillemot, pointed, a pale streak running back along the base of the upper mandible. Legs yellow in front, black behind. Tail short and round.

Young birds similar to adults but browner and bills shorter.
See also Common Guillemot or Murre (below) for comparison.
RANGE: Similar to Common Guillemot or Murre but confined to higher arctic latitudes.   Map 271.

COMMON GUILLEMOT or MURRE *Uria aalge* Pls. 46, 48
Medium, 17 ins, 43 cm. Wing-span 42 ins, 107 cm. In breeding plumage head, neck and upperparts dark chocolate-brown. Some birds known as 'Bridled Guillemots' have a white ring round the eye and a white stripe running back from the eye. Breast and underbody white. In winter the ear-coverts, throat and front of neck are white like the rest of the underbody, and a black streak runs backwards from the eye over the ear-coverts. The tips of the secondaries are white forming a thin white line. Bill black, long, fine and pointed. Legs brownish to yellowish. Tail short and round.

Birds in the higher northern latitudes have black as opposed to the browner plumage of birds further south. Young birds similar to adults but underparts dusky-white, bills shorter and legs paler.

The neck is rather long and slender in comparison with other auks. See also Brunnich's Guillemot for comparison (above).
RANGE: N. Atlantic and N. Pacific Oceans and adjacent arctic seas, dispersing southwards in winter to the Straits of Gibraltar, Maine, California, northern Japan.   Map 272.

BLACK GUILLEMOT *Cepphus grylle* Pl. 46
Small–medium, 12–14 ins, 30–36 cm. Adults in summer are uniformly black except for a conspicuous broad white patch on the wing. Axillaries and underwing-coverts white. In winter the crown, hindneck, back and upperparts are white with dark speckling; primaries and secondaries black; wing patch and underparts white. Bill pointed, black outside, inside vermilion; legs red.

Young birds similar to adults in winter but with black mottling on wing patch and underparts.
RANGE: N. Atlantic and adjacent arctic seas. Southwards to Massachusetts, and the latitude of the British Isles. Breeds in Greenland, arctic coasts of Canada, Gulf of St. Lawrence south to Maine, arctic coasts of Europe, Siberia, Norway, Baltic, Iceland and British Isles.   Map 273.

PIGEON GUILLEMOT *Cepphus columba* Pl. 46
Small–medium, 14.5 ins, 37 cm. The Pacific representative of the Black Guillemot with a very similar summer and winter plumage. The white wing patch is divided into two or three black transverse patches. In winter the wings are sometimes entirely black. Underwing-coverts and axillaries brownish-grey (white in Black Guillemot). Bill black, legs bright red. Young birds similar to young Black Guillemots in winter plumage, but the white feathers are tipped black, sometimes making young birds look almost black.
RANGE: N. Pacific and Bering Sea extending from Wrangel I. southward to the Kuril Is., eastwards to the Aleutian Is. and southwards to Sta. Barbara Is., California. In winter to Japan and Lower California.   Map 274.

SPECTACLED GUILLEMOT *Cepphus carbo* Pl. 46
Small–medium, 14.5 ins, 37 cm. In summer the overall plumage is slaty-black, the shoulders and underwing-coverts brownish. A conspicuous white ring surrounds

the eyes. In winter the chin, throat and underbody white; underwing-coverts brownish. Bill black; legs red.

Young birds similar to adults in winter plumage but with grey forenecks. Resident in Japan.

RANGE: Western N. Pacific. Okhotsk Sea and Sea of Japan to Bering Sea.   Map 275.

MARBLED MURRELET   *Brachyramphus marmoratus*   Pl. 48
Small, 9.5–10 ins, 24–25 cm. Head, neck and upperparts dark brown, the back, rump and upper tail-coverts with buff barring in summer plumage. Scapulars white. Underparts white with greyish-black patches and barring in summer; underwing-coverts greyish-black. In winter a white ring shows around the eye and a white band across the nape. Bill slender, black; legs flesh-coloured.

Young birds have dusky upperparts; white on nape and scapulars, and dusky-white underparts.

When on the water the white band on each side above the wings is noticeable and it carries its bill and tail cocked up. Has been observed off Vancouver I. and north Japan.

RANGE: N. Pacific. Breeds in Kamchatka and the Kuril Is. in the western Pacific and on the west coast of N. America from Unalaska to Vancouver I.   Map 276.

KITTLITZ'S MURRELET   *Brachyramphus brevirostris*   Pl. 48
Small, 9.5 ins, 24 cm. In summer plumage cheeks, chin and neck pale buff. Upperparts dusky with buff streaking. Underparts whitish with black bars on chest and sides. Axillaries and underwing-coverts dark brownish-grey. In winter upperparts slate-grey spotted white, a white collar on nape, sides of head and underparts white. A grey crescent in front of eye and grey bars on sides of breast. Bill black; legs pale brown. Tail edged and tipped white.

RANGE: N. Pacific and Bering Sea extending from arctic coasts of Siberia and the Kuril Is., eastwards to the Aleutian Is. and Alaska. In winter to Japan.   Map 277.

XANTUS'S MURRELET   *Brachyramphus hypoleucus*   Pl. 48
Small, 8.5 ins, 216 mm. Upperparts and flanks slate-grey, darker on wings. Underparts and underwings white. Bill small, slender, black, bluish at base. Legs pale blue. Tail short, round. Young birds similar.

Distinguished from Craveri's Murrelet by white underwings.

RANGE: West coast of U.S.A. from San Francisco to southern lower California. Breeds on Sta. Barbara and Los Coronados Is.   Map 278.

CRAVERI'S MURRELET   *Brachyramphus craveri*   Pl. 48
Small, 8.5 ins, 216 mm. Upperparts slaty-black. Underparts white with brownish-grey flanks. Underwings brownish-grey. Bill small, slender, black. Tail short and round. Young birds similar but sides and breasts with blackish spots.

Distinguished from Xantus' Murrelet by darker upperparts and underwings.

RANGE: Both coasts of Lower California. Breeds on islands in the Gulf of California.   Map 278.

ANCIENT MURRELET   *Synthliboramphus antiquus*   Pl. 48
Small, 10.5 ins, 27 cm. Wing-span 17 ins, 43 cm. In breeding plumage throat, face, head and hindneck black. A white stripe shows on each side of the crown. Sides of neck white. Upperparts slaty-blue, tail and wings black. Underparts and

underwing-coverts white, sides and flanks black. Bill short, stout, whitish; feet grey. In winter the throat becomes white and chin greyish.

Young birds similar to adults in winter plumage.

Distinguished by the blue appearance of upperparts and sharply defined white sides to neck and stripe on crown.

RANGE: N. Pacific and Bering Sea. A common winter visitor to north Japan and reaches the coast of California in winter.   Map 279.

CRESTED MURRELET *Synthliboramphus wumizusume*   **Pl. 48**

Small, 10.5 ins, 27 cm. Forehead, crown and nape slaty-black, cheeks and throat slate-grey. In summer a crest of loose feathers curving back from crown; a broad white stripe of feathers running back from eye and meeting at back of head. Upperparts blue-grey; underparts white. Bill very short, stout, yellow; legs yellow. Young birds are similar to adults in winter but head and upperparts brownish-grey.

Distinguished by its grey upperparts and, in summer plumage, by its black crest and white stripe along the side of head.

RANGE: Breeds only in Japan.   Map 280.

CASSIN'S AUKLET *Ptychoramphus aleuticus*   **Pl. 48**

Small, 9 ins, 230 mm. This very small Pacific Ocean auklet has dusky-grey upperparts; chin, throat and foreneck brownish; sides and flanks grey, remainder of underbody white. Underwing-coverts greyish-brown. It shows white spots above and below the eye. Bill pointed, black; legs bluish. Young birds similar.

RANGE: West coast of U.S.A. from Aleutian Is. to Lower California.   Map 281.

PARAKEET AUKLET *Cyclorrhynchus psittacula*   **Pl. 48**

Small, 10.5 ins, 27 cm. Wing-span 18 ins, 46 cm. Upperparts slaty-black. Chin, throat, foreneck, sides and flanks greyish-brown in summer, in winter all white. In breeding plumage only elongated white plumes extend from behind the eye downwards across the black cheeks. Bill very stubby, small and deep, orange-red, the lower mandible curving upwards. Legs pale bluish. Young birds similar to adults in winter without plumes, and with a smaller brownish bill.

Its flight is reported as stronger and usually higher above the sea than other species.

RANGE: N. Pacific and Bering Sea from N.E. Siberia, Kuril Is. eastwards to Aleutian Is. In winter to northern Japan and California.   Map 282.

CRESTED AUKLET *Aethia cristatella*   **Pl. 47**

Small, 10.5 ins, 27 cm. Upperparts slaty-black. A distinctive forward curving brown crest of plumes projects from forehead, and elongated white plumes extend backwards and downwards from behind the eye. Underparts, forehead and underwings brownish-grey. Bill short, deep, compressed, orange-red with pale tip. Legs bluish-grey. Young birds similar but without crest or plumes, and with smaller dull brown bills.

RANGE: N. Pacific, Bering Sea and adjacent arctic sea. In winter to Japan and Kodiak I.   Map 283.

LEAST AUKLET *Aethia pusilla*   **Pl. 47**

Very small, 6.5 ins, 165 mm. Smaller than any other auk. In summer, upperparts slaty-black, scapulars partly white, secondaries tipped white. Throat white, underparts white with dark blotches which sometimes appear as a dusky band around the foreneck. Underwing-coverts white. A row of elongated white plumes stretches from behind the eye extending downwards across the dark cheeks, and another row from the corner of the gape. In summer also some white pointed feathers occur on the forehead. Bill small, stubby, red; legs brown. Winter, lacks white plumes; bill black.

Young birds similar to adults in winters.

RANGE: Bering Sea and adjacent parts of N. Pacific. Reported to occur in flocks in the northern quarter of the N. Pacific in winter, and a regular winter visitor to north Japan. Map 282.

WHISKERED AUKLET   *Aethia pygmaea*   Pl. 47

Very small, 7.5 ins, 191 mm. Upperparts dusky-grey. A blackish forward curving crest projects from forehead. Two elongated white plumes on each side in front of eye, one extending upwards and curving forwards, another extending backwards and downwards. Chest grey, lower underbody and under tail-coverts white. Underwing-coverts brown. Bill short, bright red with a pale tip and blunt horny knob at base. Legs bluish. Young birds similar but without crest, plumes, or knob on smaller dusky bill.

Differs from Crested Auklet by smaller size, differing white plumes, by knob on bill in summer and white under tail-coverts.

RANGE: N. Pacific and southern Bering Sea from Kamchatka and Kuril Is. eastward to Aleutian Is. and coast of Alaska. Map 283.

RHINOCEROS AUKLET   *Cerorhinca monocerata*   Pl. 47

Small–medium, 14 ins, 36 cm. Upperparts sooty-black. Underparts white with brownish-grey chin, throat, chest, sides and flanks. Underwings brownish-grey. A line of white elongated straight plumes extends from the eye across the cheeks, and another from the bill below the eye. Bill rather long, orange-yellow with a horny projection on the top of the base of the upper mandible in the breeding season. Legs yellow. Young birds similar to adults in winter without the white plumes, and with a smaller duller bill.

RANGE: N. Pacific Ocean from the coast of Kamchatka and the Kuril Is. Also from the west coast of Alaska south to Washington. In winter to Japan and Lower California. Map 284.

ATLANTIC PUFFIN   *Fratercula arctica*   Pl. 47

Small–medium, 11.5–14 ins, 29–36 cm. Wing-span 18 ins, 46 cm. In adult summer plumage the crown, nape and upperparts black, cheeks and throat white with a darker streak behind the eye, a blue horny triangle above eye, and narrow rectangle below eye, eye-ring red. Underparts white. The remarkable laterally-compressed parrot-like triangular bill is pale blue at base, bright red at tip and crossed by yellow bands. Legs bright red. In summer a yellow wattle patch occurs at base of gape. After the breeding season the face becomes grey, basal part of the bill sheath is shed and the bill becomes smaller and yellower, and the wattle shrivels.

Young birds are similar to adults in winter plumage, with browner upperparts and more 'normal' slender bills.

In the N. Atlantic, while the guillemot and razorbill have been observed well out at sea, the Puffin appears usually to remain closer to the coast.

RANGE: Both sides of the N. Atlantic and adjacent arctic seas. Some disperse southwards in winter to the Straits of Gibraltar and Massachusetts. Map 285.

HORNED PUFFIN   *Fratercula corniculata*   Pl. 47

Small–medium, 14–16 ins, 36–41 cm. Wing-span 22 ins, 56 cm. Chin and crown greyish-brown, neck and upperparts black. Cheeks and underbody white; a fleshy excrescence occurs over the eye. Underwing-coverts greyish-brown. The very large triangular bill is red at tip, yellow at base; legs red. In winter cheeks grey; bill reduced, red at tip, dusky at base.

Young birds are similar to adults with grey cheeks and much reduced brownish bills.

A common winter visitor to north Japan.

RANGE: N. Pacific and Bering Sea from arctic coasts of Siberia eastwards to Aleutian Is. and S.E. Alaska. Disperses southwards to Kuril Is. and British Columbia.   Map 286.

Atlantic Puffins inspecting nesting burrows.

TUFTED PUFFIN *Lunda cirrhata*   **Pl. 47**
Medium, 16 ins, 41 cm. In adult summer plumage the forehead and cheeks are white and long yellow drooping tufts extend behind the eye down the sides of the head. Eye-ring red. Upperparts black; underparts greyish brown. In winter chin, throat and foreneck sooty-brown. The very large laterally compressed triangular bill is greenish-yellow at the base and bright red at the forward end; a red wattle patch occurs at the base of the gape. Legs bright red. In winter the overall plumage is duller, the bill reduced, bluish at base and red at tip, the plumes are not present and the whole head and face dark. Young birds have yellowish bills.

RANGE: N. Pacific and Bering Sea from north coasts of Siberia and Kuril Is., eastwards to Aleutian Is., Alaska and west coast of America to Sta. Barbara Is., California.   Map 287.

Plate 1　　　　　　　　PENGUINS

Flightless birds, confined to the southern oceans except for the Galapagos Penguin. May be seen swimming far from land.

1 EMPEROR PENGUIN *Aptenodytes forsteri*　　　　　　page 7
Very large; orange-yellow neck band; red slash lower mandible; long bill. Map 2.

2 KING PENGUIN *Aptenodytes patagonica*　　　　　　　　7
Large; orange neck band extends to foreneck; orange-reddish slash lower mandible; long bill. Map 1.

3 GENTOO PENGUIN *Pygoscelis papua*　　　　　　　　　　7
White band over back of head; bill red, tip black; legs orange. Map 3.

4 ADELIE PENGUIN *Pygoscelis adeliae*　　　　　　　　　7
White eyelids; bill stubby, brick-red, tip dark; legs pinkish-white. Map 4.

5 CHIN-STRAP or BEARDED PENGUIN　　　　　　　　　　8
Pygoscelis antarctica
Black line surrounds white throat; bill black; legs pinkish-white. Map 5.

6 JACKASS PENGUIN *Spheniscus demersus*　　　　　　　11
Single black horseshoe band; bill black, grey band; legs black.　Map 14.

7 HUMBOLDT PENGUIN *Spheniscus humboldti*　　　　　　11
Single black horseshoe band; bill stout, blackish, base flesh-colour; legs blackish. Map 15.

8 MAGELLAN PENGUIN *Spheniscus magellanicus*　　　　　11
Black band around foreneck; black horseshoe band below; bill blackish; legs mottled blackish. Map 16.

9 GALAPAGOS PENGUIN *Spheniscus mendiculus*　　　　　11
Small; black band around foreneck; black horseshoe band below; bill black above, yellow below; legs black, mottled white. Confined to Galapagos Is.

Plate 2   PENGUINS

1 **ROCK-HOPPER PENGUIN** *Eudyptes crestatus*   page 9
Yellow plumes from each side behind nostrils; iris red; bill orange
red; legs flesh-colour. In the background, a Rock-hopper group with
one young.   Map 9.

2 **MACARONI PENGUIN** *Eudyptes chrysolophus*   9
Golden plumes from centre of forehead; bill black, tip red; legs
pinkish.   Map 10.

3 **SNARES CRESTED PENGUIN** *Eudyptes robustus*   8
Narrow yellow crest, end bushy; bill reddish-brown; legs flesh-
colour.   Map 7.

4 **FIORDLAND CRESTED PENGUIN**   8
Eudyptes pachyrhynchus
Similar to Snares Crested Penguin; yellow plumes straight, shorter;
bill reddish-brown; legs pale flesh-colour.   Map 6.

5 **ERECT-CRESTED or BIG-CRESTED PENGUIN**   8
Eudyptes sclateri
Bright yellow crest curves upwards; iris red; bill reddish-brown; legs
pale-flesh colour.   Map 8.

6 **ROYAL PENGUIN** *Eudyptes schlegeli*   9
Side of face white; long orange plumes curve downwards; iris red; bill
pale reddish-brown; legs flesh-colour. Breeds only on Macquarie I.

7 **YELLOW-EYED PENGUIN** *Megadyptes antipodes*   10
Crown and face pale golden; pale yellow band circles crown; bill
flesh-colour, dull brown on culmen and tips of lower mandible; legs
flesh-colour.   Map 11.

8 **LITTLE or BLUE PENGUIN** *Eudyptula minor*   10
Upperparts slate-blue; iris silver-grey; bill black; legs pale flesh-
colour.   Map 12.

9 **WHITE-FLIPPERED PENGUIN** *Eudyptula albosignata*   10
Upperparts pale slate-grey; iris silver-grey; bill black; legs pale flesh
colour.   Map 13.

Plate 3   **ALBATROSSES**

Oceanic birds of great size and wing-span. Often follow ships, alighting briefly astern to feed on garbage.

1   SHORT-TAILED ALBATROSS *Diomedea albatrus*   page 17
  a Adult above. Mainly white above and below; wing quills, leading wing-coverts and tail band dark; bill and legs flesh-colour; under-wings white.   Map 20.

  b Immature below. Sooty-brown overall; bill and legs flesh-colour.

2   ROYAL ALBATROSS *Diomedea epomophora epomophora*   17
  a Adult above. Always mostly white; primaries black; thin dark margin to trailing edge of underwing; black cutting edge to both mandibles; bill faintly pink; legs bluish-white.   Map 18.

  b Northern race   *Diomedea e. sandfordi*   17
  Adult above. Slightly smaller than 2a. Upperwings show less white, sometimes entirely dark.   Map 18.

3   WANDERING ALBATROSS *Diomedea exulans*   16
  a Adult above. Slight speckling on back and shoulders; bill and legs pale flesh-colour.   Map 17.

  b Adult below. Thin dark margin to trailing edge of underwing often shows.

  c Immature above. Bill whitish; tail brown.

  d Immature below. Face and throat white; central linings of underwings white; underbody and tail brown.

Plate 4   ALBATROSSES

Plate 5   **ALBATROSSES**

1   BLACK-BROWED ALBATROSS *Diomedea melanophris*   page 18
  a Adult above. Dark streak around eye; bill stout, yellow, pink tip; legs
      bluish-white; tail slaty-black.   Map 23.

  b Adult below. Broad dark margins to leading and trailing edges of
      underwing.

  c Immature below. Crown and hindneck greyish, merging into white;
      broad smudgy margins to underwing; bill greyish-black.

2   GREY-HEADED ALBATROSS *Diomedea chrysostoma*   20
  a Adult above. Whole head and neck dusky-grey; white around back of
      eye; yellow bands above and below bill, tip bright pink.   Map 27.

  b Adult below. Dark margins to underwing, wider from bend of wing on
      leading edge.

3   YELLOW-NOSED ALBATROSS *Diomedea chlororhynchos*   19
  a Adult above. Dark patch at eye; bill slender, black, yellow band on
      ridge of upper mandible, tip bright orange; legs flesh-colour.   Map
      26.

  b Adult below. Clearly defined thin dark margins to underwing, leading
      margin broader.

Plate 6   **ALBATROSSES**

1 SOOTY ALBATROSS *Phoebetria fusca*   page 20
Adult above. White ring around eye; yellow groove along side of
lower mandible; tail long, wedge-shaped. Map 28.

2 LIGHT-MANTLED SOOTY ALBATROSS   21
Phoebetria palpebrata
Adult above. Paler, greyer than Sooty Albatross; white ring around
eye; pale blue groove along side of lower mandible; tail long,
wedgeshaped. Map 29.

3 BLACK-FOOTED ALBATROSS *Diomedea nigripes*   17
  a Adult above. White area around bill; bill dark brown; legs black.
  Map 21.

  b Immature above. Broad whitish area around and above bill; upper
  tail-coverts whitish.

4 NORTHERN GIANT PETREL *Macronectes halli*   24
Above for size comparison. See also Pl. 7. Map 31.

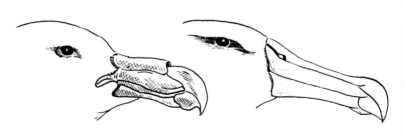

GIANT PETRELS   SHY ALBATROSS

The large, squat, plated bill of the Giant Petrels immediately distinguishes them from any Albatross. In flight the Giant Petrels appear
ungainly, with awkward flapping or rather stiff-winged gliding.

Plate 7   PETRELS and SHEARWATERS

Oceanic birds, smaller than albatrosses with which they share a tube-nose (see p. 13). Generally seen flying close over the sea surface.

1 WHITE-CHINNED PETREL *Procellaria aequinoctialis*   page 29
  a Above. Heavy build; white on chin noticeable; long massive yellowish bill. Map 45.

  b White on chin frequently much reduced in birds breeding on New Zealand islands.

  c, d Variable heads. Peculiar to birds breeding on Tristan da Cunha; sometimes seen in South Atlantic.

2 PARKINSON'S PETREL *Procellaria parkinsoni*   29
  Dark blackish-brown overall; bill bluish-horn, tip black; legs black. Map 46.

3 WESTLAND PETREL *Procellaria westlandica*   29
  See Parkinson's Petrel. Bill yellowish. Map 47.

4 WEDGE-TAILED SHEARWATER *Puffinus pacificus*   31
  a Above, dark phase. Dark chocolate-brown overall; bill long, slender, grey; tail long, wedge-shaped; legs flesh colour. Map 53.

  b Below, pale phase. Slightly paler above than 4a; dark margins to underwings; bill and legs flesh-colour.

5 CHRISTMAS SHEARWATER *Puffinus nativitatis*   32
  Above. Smaller, paler chocolate-brown than 4a; bill long, slender, dark; legs brown; tail rounded. Map 57.

6 NORTHERN GIANT PETREL *Macronectes halli*   24
  Below. Outsize; darker body and head than 7a, darker yellowish-brown bill. See also Pl. 6. Map 31.

7 SOUTHERN GIANT PETREL *Macronectes giganteus*   24
  a Below. Outsize; very large plated bill; dark feathers around pale eye; legs sooty-black. Map 30.

  b Immature above. Rich dark chocolate-brown; eye dark.

  c White phase with chick. Occasional in southerly breeding colonies.

Plate 8   **SHEARWATERS**

1 SHORT-TAILED SHEARWATER *Puffinus tenuirostris*   page 32
a Below. Greyish lining to underwing; bill slender, dark; legs bluish-grey; tail short, round.   Map 56.

b Above.

2 SOOTY SHEARWATER *Puffinus griseus*   32
a Below. Larger than 1. Silvery lining to underwing; pale under chin. Map 55.

b Above.

3 PALE-FOOTED SHEARWATER *Puffinus carneipes*   30
a Below. Underbody and wings chocolate-brown; bill straw-colour, tip brown; legs yellowish-flesh-colour; tail short, round.   Map 51.

b Above.

4 PINK-FOOTED SHEARWATER *Puffinus creatopus*   30
a Below. Underbody whitish, underwing mottled-white; bill pink, tip black; legs pink.   Map 50.

b Above.

5 GREY-BACKED SHEARWATER *Puffinus bulleri*   31
a Below. All white underparts; bill long, bluish; legs flesh-colour. Map 54.

b Above. Dark '**W**' pattern; dark wedge-shaped tail.

6 WHITE-FACED or STREAKED SHEARWATER   29
Calonectris leucomelas
a Below. Underwing linings white, darker streaked margins; legs flesh-colour; tail brown.   Map 48.

b Above.

Plate 9   PETRELS and SHEARWATERS

1 **BULWER'S PETREL** *Bulweria bulwerii*
Above. Paler band on upperwing.   Map 94.

2 **JOUANIN'S PETREL** *Bulweria fallax*
Above. Larger than 1. Short thick black bill.   Map 93.

3 **GREAT SHEARWATER** *Puffinus gravis*
a Below. White neck under dark cap.   Map 52.

b Above. Dark cap; white band across rump.

4 **CORY'S SHEARWATER** *Calonectris diomedea*
a Below. Bill stout, yellow; legs pinkish.   Map 49.

b Above.

5 **LITTLE SHEARWATER** *Puffinus assimilis assimilis*
a Below. Small; white extends into head; legs bluish. Map 66.

b Madeiran race.   *Puffinus a. baroli*
Below. More white in front of eye.   Map 66.

c Cape Verde Is. race.   *Puffinus a. boydi*
Below. Darker under tail.   Map 66.

d Little Shearwaters are sharply black and white. They often fly with dropping legs like storm-petrels.

6 **MANX SHEARWATER** *Puffinus puffinus puffinus*
a Below. Dark of head extends below eye; legs pinkish.   Map 58.

b **Levantine Shearwater** *Puffinus p. yelkouan*
Below. Dark area further below eye.   Map 59.

c **Balearic Shearwater** *Puffinus p. mauretanicus*
Below. Underparts mottled brown.   Map 60.

d **Black-vented Shearwater** *Puffinus p. opisthomelas*
Below. Under tail-coverts and flanks dark.   Map 63.

e **Manx Shearwater** Above.

f **Manx Shearwater** Swimming.
Townsend's and Newell's Shearwaters (see p. 33) are similar.

7 **AUDUBON'S SHEARWATER** *Puffinus l'herminieri l'herminieri*
Below. Compare Pl. 10, No. 9.   Map 67.

8 **HEINROTH'S SHEARWATER** *Puffinus heinrothi*
Below. Known only from single specimen near New Britain.

Plate 10　　PETRELS and SHEARWATERS

Plate 11　　　　　　　　　**PETRELS**

1 NORTHERN FULMAR *Fulmarus glacialis*　　　　　page 25
  a Pale phase.

  b Dark phase. There is also a rare all-white phase. Map 32.

2 SOUTHERN FULMAR or SILVER-GREY PETREL　　　25
  Fulmarus glacialoides
  Paler than 1a. No dark phase.　Map 33.

3 SNOW PETREL *Pagadroma nivea*　　　　　　　25
  All white; black bill; dark grey legs.　Map 35.

4 WHITE-NECKED PETREL *Pterodroma externa*　　　38
  a Above. Upperparts medium-grey; dark '**W**' pattern across wings;
  white collar round neck.　Map 84.

  b Below. Dark margin between bend of wing and leading primary.

5 WHITE-HEADED PETREL *Pterodroma lessoni*　　　35
  a Above. Hindneck pale grey; dark patch at eye.　Map 70.

  b Below. Underwing grey; legs flesh-colour.

6 KERGUELEN PETREL *Pterodroma brevirostris*　　　36
  Map 75.

7 BLUE PETREL *Halobaena caerulea*　　　　　　26
  Small; dark '**W**' pattern across wings; legs blue; tail square, white
  tips.　Map 37.

8 DOVE PRION *Pachyptila desolata*　　　　　　28
  a Above. Small; black patch at eye; black terminal band on tail; tail
  wedge-shaped.　Map 40.

  b Below. Underparts and underwings white.

  The following are not illustrated separately, as being indistinguishable in the field from Dove Prion:
    Broad-billed Prion *Pachyptila vittata* Page 28, Map 38.
    Salvin's Prion *Pachyptila salvini* Page 28, Map 39.
    Thin-billed Prion *Pachyptila belcheri* Page 28, Map 41.
    Fairy Prion *Pachyptila turtur* Page 28, Map 42.
    Fulmar or **Thick-billed Prion** *Pachyptila crassirostris* Page 28,
    Map 43.

9 CAPE PIGEON or PINTADO PETREL *Daption capensis*　25
  a Above. Typically piebald black and white.　Map 34.

  b Below.

  c Swimming.

10 ANTARCTIC PETREL *Talassoica antarctica*　　　26
  Underwing-coverts white.　Map 36.

Plate 12   **PETRELS**

Plate 13   STORM-PETRELS

Small oceanic birds. Flight close to the sea and fluttering; they sometimes follow ships.

Plate 14   STORM-PETRELS and
                     DIVING-PETRELS

Diving-petrels are small, stubby oceanic birds; flight is whirring and close above the sea, with frequent dives below the surface.

Plate 15   **TROPIC-BIRDS**

Unmistakable white-looking oceanic birds, with long streaming tail-feathers. Flight strong and steady at some height above the sea. All swim with their tails cocked.

1 RED-BILLED TROPIC-BIRD *Phaethon aethereus*   page 57
 a Adult above. Black band over and beyond eye; upperparts finely barred black; bill coral red.   Map 119.

 b Adult below. Legs dull yellow, feet black; webs black.

 c Immature above. Upperparts barred black; indistinct band through eye; bill yellow; tail streamers absent or short.

2 RED-TAILED TROPIC-BIRD *Phaethon rubricauda*   57
 a Adult. Black crescent before and over eye; totally white upperparts; bill usually orange-red; legs blue; tail streamers very long, deep red. Map 120.

 b Immature. Upperparts thickly barred; indistinct eye stripe; bill black; tail streamers absent or short.

 c Adult in rosy plumage.

 d Adult swimming.

3 WHITE-TAILED TROPIC-BIRD *Phaethon lepturus lepturus*   57
 a Adult. Black crescent over and beyond eye; upperparts white with black band across upperwings; bill yellow; tail streamers very long, white.   Map 121.

 b Immature. Upperparts more lightly barred; dark eye stripe; bill yellow; tail streamers absent or short.

 c **Christmas Tropic-bird** *Phaethon l. fulvus*   57
 Adult. Sub-species of 3a distinguished by golden tinted plumage. Breeds only on Christmas I., Indian Ocean; limited range.

Plate 16   **PELICANS**

Very large inshore birds of the tropics, with unmistakable pouched bill.

1 DALMATIAN PELICAN *Pelecanus crispus*   page 61
 a Adult breeding. Grey bill; pouch orange; legs lead-grey. Yellow on
    breast absent in winter.   Map 125.

 b Immature. Greyish-brown, wings paler; pouch yellowish.

 c In flight below. Black tips of primaries only visible; compare 2c.

2 WHITE PELICAN *Pelecanus onocrotalus*   59
 a Adult. Grey bill; pouch yellow; legs pink. Sometimes shows rosy tint
    on white feathers.   Map 122.

 b Immature. Upperparts, neck and wings brown; underparts whitish;
    bill dull greyish-blue.

 c In flight below. Black primaries and secondaries very evident; legs
    pink.

3 PINK-BACKED PELICAN *Pelecanus rufescens*   60
    Adult. Overall plumage similar but a little greyer than 2a, pink tints
    showing; bill pale yellow; pouch flesh-colour; legs pale flesh-
    colour.   Map 123.

4 GREY PELICAN *Pelecanus philippensis*   60
    Adult. Overall plumage grey, paler below; bill pink; pouch purple;
    legs dark brown.   Map 124.

Plate 17   **PELICANS**

Plate 18   **GANNETS and BOOBIES**

Large offshore birds, cigar-shaped, with long narrow wings and long dagger-shaped bills.

1 NORTHERN GANNET *Sula bassana*   page 65
a Adult. Map 130.

b Adult with gular stripe.

c Immature in flight. Upperparts greyish-brown, white speckling; underparts white, brown speckling.

d Sub-adult.

e Adult in flight. Primaries only blackish-brown; tail white.

f Juvenile in flight

2 CAPE GANNET *Sula capensis*   66
a Adult. Map 131.

b Adult with gular stripe.

c In flight. Primaries, secondaries and all tail feathers brown.

3 AUSTRALIAN GANNET *Sula serrator*   66
a Adult. Map 132.

b Adult in flight. Tail: central feathers blackish-brown, outer feathers white; primaries and secondaries blackish-brown.

c Immature diving.

4 BLUE-FACED or MASKED BOOBY *Sula dactylatra*   67
a Adult.   Form with legs blue, bill blue-grey.   Map 135.

b Adult. Form with legs orange; bill yellow.

c In flight. Primary, secondaries and tail chocolate-brown.

d Juvenile.

e Sub-adult.

Plate 19   **BOOBIES**

1 RED-FOOTED BOOBY *Sula sula*   page 68
a Adult, white phase. Mainly white, wing quills blackish-brown; tail white; legs coral red; bill blue, base pink, black stripe below lower mandible. Eye ring and skin around eye bright blue.   Map 136.

b Intermediate phase. Variable, but red legs are diagnostic.

c Intermediate phase in flight.

d Adult, white phase in flight.

e Brown phase, diving.

f Juvenile. Legs greenish-yellow; bill dark.

2 ABBOTT'S BOOBY *Sula abbotti*   67
a Adult female. Black thigh patches on underbody; black skin around eye conspicuous; bill: male blue-grey, female rosy; broad black tips. Breeds only on Christmas I., Indian Ocean; limited range.

b Adult above. Upperwing-coverts show white speckling.

c Adult in flight below. Black thigh patch.

3 PERUVIAN BOOBY *Sula variegata*   67
a Adult.   Bill blue; legs bluish-black.   Map 134.

b Adult in flight.

4 BLUE-FOOTED BOOBY *Sula nebouxii*   66
a Adult.   Bright blue legs; blue bill; brown tail.   Map 133.

b Adult in flight.

5 BROWN BOOBY *Sula leucogaster*   68
a Adult.   Map 137.

b Variable colours of bills and legs; chocolate-brown upperparts.

c With grey on head.

d Adult above, in flight.

e Adult below, in flight. Clear cut line between brown breast and white underparts.

f Immature below. Dark underneath.

Plate 20 CORMORANTS

Long-necked inshore birds often seen perched on buoys with wings extended to dry, or swimming and diving from the surface.

Plate 21   CORMORANTS

1 DOUBLE-CRESTED CORMORANT   page 71
  Phalacrocorax auritus
  a Adult breeding. Crest each side of head; naked skin on throat
      orange.   Map 138.

  b Immature.

  c Submerged. Adult breeding with white on crest.

2 BIGUA CORMORANT *Phalacrocorax olivaceus*   72
  a Adult breeding. White tuft of feathers each side of head; naked skin
      on face and throat yellow; tail noticeably long.   Map 139.

  b Immature.

3 RED-FACED CORMORANT *Phalacrocorax urile*   74
  a Adult breeding. Tufts on crown and nape; forehead bare; skin
      forehead and face red; bill blue.   Map 152.

  b Immature.

  c Adult. White patch on flank in breeding plumage.

4 PELAGIC CORMORANT *Phalacrocorax pelagicus*   74
  a Adult breeding. Smaller but similar to 3a; large white patch on flank;
      bill very slender, blackish-brown.   Map 151.

  b Immature.

  c Adult in flight.

5 SHAG or GREEN CORMORANT *Phalacrocorax aristotelis*   74
  a Adult breeding. Crest on crown noticeable; naked skin around bill
      yellow.   Map 150.

  b Immature.

6 BRANDT'S CORMORANT *Phalacrocorax penicillatus*   74
  a Very large; white hair-like plumes on sides of face and back; naked
      skin of face and throat blue. Throat fawn-coloured.   Map 149.

  b Immature.

7 RED-LEGGED CORMORANT *Phalacrocorax gaimardi*   76
  a Adult. White patch on side of neck; bright red legs noticeable; bright
      yellow bill.   Map 159.

  b Immature. White patches on sides of neck.

Plate 22 CORMORANTS

Plate 23   **CORMORANTS**

1 JAVANESE CORMORANT   *Halieter niger*   page 79
  a Adult breeding. Scapulars greyish; naked skin throat and face black; legs black.   Map 165.

  b Winter.

2 PIGMY CORMORANT   *Halietor pygmaeus*   79
  a Adult breeding. Head and neck brown, scapulars and wing-coverts greyish.   Map 166.

  b Adult winter.

  c In flight.

  d Immature.

3 INDIAN CORMORANT   *Phalacrocorax fuscicollis*   72
  a Adult breeding. Tuft of white feathers at side of head; naked skin of face green.   Map 144.

  b Immature.

4 COMMON CORMORANT   *Phalacrocorax carbo carbo*   72
Adult winter for size comparison. See also Pl.20.   Map 141.

5 LITTLE PIED CORMORANT   *Phalacrocorax melanoleucus*   78
  a Adult. White throat. See also Pl.22.   Map 163.

  b Immature for size comparison.

6 REED CORMORANT   *Halietor africanus*   Adult breeding   79
  a Tuft on forehead; long tail; back and wing often very pale; red skin on face and pouch.   Map 164.

  b Sub-adult.

  c Immature.

7 LITTLE BLACK CORMORANT   *Phalacrocorax sulcirostris*   72
  a Adult breeding. Indistinct white plumes on side of head and eye.   Map 140.

  b Immature. Similar to 7a but duller brownish-black; plumes absent.

Plate 24   FRIGATE-BIRDS

Large black birds, with long forked tails, usually seen high overhead, in harbours and at sea.

1 CHRISTMAS FRIGATE-BIRD *Fregeta andrewsi*   page 81
  a Adult male. Foreneck and breast back; pouch bright red; bill black. Not mapped. Breeds only on Christmas I., Indian Ocean; limited range.

  b Adult female. Throat black; bill reddish; legs white.

2 LESSER FRIGATE-BIRD *Fregata ariel*   83
  a Adult male. White patches under wings; bill grey; pouch bright red. Map 169.

  b Adult female. Throat black; chestnut collar on hindneck; bill bluish; red under throat; legs red.

3 MAGNIFICENT FRIGATE-BIRD *Fregata magnificens*   83
  a Adult male in courtship display
    Similar to 5a, 5b, but lacks brown band across upperwing-coverts. Map 167.

  b Adult female. White collar around neck; foreneck and throat dark; underparts white; abdomen and flanks black; bill horn-colour.

4 ASCENSION FRIGATE-BIRD *Fregata aquila*   81
  a Adult male. Black overall; red pouch; red legs. Breeds only on Ascension I.; limited range.

  b Adult female. Black; breast dark brown; legs red.

  c Male and female, very rare form with white breast and abdomen.

5 GREAT FRIGATE-BIRD *Fregata minor*   83
  a Adult male. Red pouch only seen on display. Map 168.

  b In flight. Brown band across upperwings.

  c Adult female. Throat and foreneck greyish; lower neck, breast and sides white; legs reddish or bluish.

Plate 25   PHALAROPES and SHEATHBILLS

Phalaropes: Small delicate waders, breeding in the high tundra but wintering in flocks at sea.

Sheathbills: White, pigeon-like birds, confined to sub-antarctica; usually inshore but also on ice-floes.

1 WILSON'S PHALAROPE *Steganopus tricolor*   page 85
 a Adult winter. No white wing bar.   Map 171.

 b Adult winter. Long needle-like bill.

 c Adult male breeding.

 d Adult female breeding. Black stripe eye to side of neck; chestnut stripe on side of back.

2 GREY PHALAROPE *Phalaropus fulicarius*   85
 a Adult winter. White wing bar; bill much shorter than 1a.   Map 170.

 b Adult winter. Dark stripe through eye; patch on cheek; bill yellow, tip black.

 c Adult male breeding.

 d Adult female breeding. Richer colour than males; legs yellowish.

3 RED-NECKED PHALAROPE *Lobipes lobatus*   85
 a Adult winter. White wing bar conspicuous.   Map 172.

 b Adult winter. Dark stripe through eye; patch on cheek; upperparts darker than 2b, more streaked; bill finger than 2b, bluish-grey.

 c Adult male breeding.

 d Adult female breeding. Chin and throat white; rufous band down sides and front of neck.

4 YELLOW-BILLED SHEATHBILL *Chionis alba*   87
 Bill pinkish-yellow, tip black; legs black.   Map 173.

5 BLACK-BILLED SHEATHBILL *Chionis minor*   87
 Bill black; legs flesh-colour.   Map 174.

Plate 26   SKUAS

Migratory hawk-like birds; flight high and swift, harrying other sea-birds for food. White flash on wings.

1 **ARCTIC SKUA** *Stercorarius parasiticus*   page 90
  a Adult, dark phase. Sharply pointed protruding tail feathers; tail wedge-shaped. Map 179.

  b Adult, pale phase. Dark top of head, yellow sides and neck, white patch on primaries.

  c Adult, intermediate phase. Chasing an immature Ivory Gull.

2 **POMARINE SKUA** *Stercorarius pomarinus*   90
  a Adult, dark phase. Blunt-twisted protruding tail feathers; tail wedge-shaped. Map 178.

  b Adult, pale phase. Dark band on breast; flanks dusky.

3 **LONG-TAILED SKUA** *Stercorarius longicaudus*   91
  a Adult. Smaller, paler above than other skuas; very long pointed central tail feathers. Map 180.

4 Immature of Arctic, Pomarine and Long-tailed Skua; but Long-tailed Skua has paler upperparts and greyish-white slightly barred underparts. Central tail feathers undeveloped.

5 **GREAT SKUA** (Southern Skua in Southern Hemisphere)   90
  Catharacta skua
  Adult below. Large, stoutly built; white patches on wings; bill stout. Maps 175 and 176.

6 **McCORMICK'S SKUA** *Catharacta maccormicki*   90
  Paler and smaller than 5. Forehead, sides of head and underparts pale brown. Map 177.

Plate 27   GULLS

Inshore birds with white underparts and grey or black upperwings and square tails; stance upright. Immatures speckled brown (see also Pl.40). For gulls in flight see Pls. 34–40.

1   PACIFIC GULL   *Larus pacificus*   page 93
Adult. Large bill; black tail band. See also Pls.34, 40.   Map 181.

2   GREAT BLACK-BACKED GULL   *Larus marinus*   99
a Adult. Large; pink legs. See also Pls.34, 40.   Map 201.

b 2nd year.

3   LESSER BLACK-BACKED GULL   *Larus fuscus fuscus*   97
a Adult. Scandinavian race. Bright yellow legs. See also Pls.34, 40.   Map 195.

b *Larus fuscus graellsii*   97
Adult. British race. Paler on back; yellow legs. See also Pls.35, 40. Map 196.

c 2nd year, *Larus fuscus graellsii*

4   WESTERN GULL   *Larus occidentalis*   98
Adult. Slate-grey back; pinkish legs. See also Pl.34.   Map 198.

5   SLATY-BACKED GULL   *Larus schistisagus*   98
Adult. Dark-grey back; pink legs. See also Pl.34.   Map 200.

6   JAPANESE GULL   *Larus crassirostris*   96
Adult. Black band on yellow bill, tip red; pale yellow legs; black band on tail. See also Pl.34.   Map 189.

7   SOUTHERN BLACK-BACKED GULL   *Larus dominicanus*   98
Adult. Greenish-yellow legs; white tail. See also Pls.34, 40.   Map 199.

Plate 28   **GULLS**

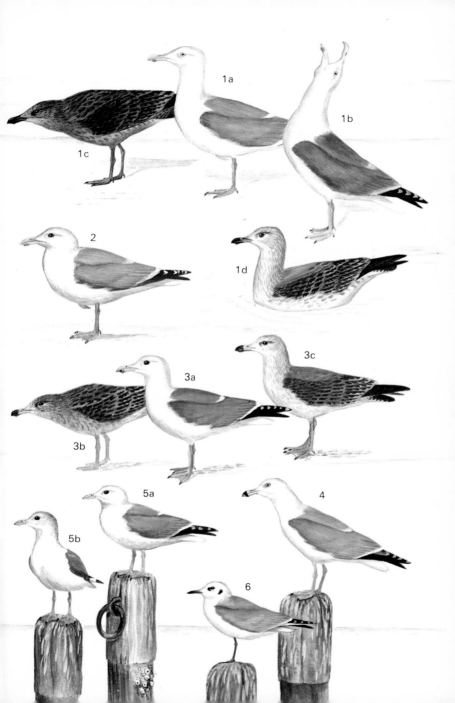

Plate 29   **GULLS**

1 GLAUCOUS-WINGED GULL *Larus glaucescens*   page 99
a Adult breeding. Larger but similar to Herring Gull (Pl.28) except dark grey primaries, white spots, grey secondaries, white tips. See also Pl.35. Map 202.

b Immature 1st winter.

2 ICELAND GULL *Larus leucopterus leucopterus*   99
a Adult breeding. Smaller than 3a; white tips to wing quills; red eye ring; very pink legs. See also Pls.33, 35, 40. Map 204.

b Immature 2nd winter. Almost pure white; bill pale, tip dark; legs dusky pink; tail white.

3 GLAUCOUS GULL *Larus hyperboreus*   99
a Adult breeding. Very large, stoutly built; stout bill; wings broader than 2a; yellow eye-ring; compare 2a. See also Pls.35, 40. Map 203.

b Immature 2nd winter. White over all; bill yellow, tip black.

4 SLENDER-BILLED GULL *Larus genei*   105
a Adult breeding. Rosy tint on underbody; bill slender, red; legs red. See also Pl.37. Map 218.

b Immature. Crown and nape grey; upperparts ashy-brown; bill orange-yellow; legs yellow; lacks any rosy tint.

5 AUDOUIN'S GULL *Larus audouinii*   96
a Adult breeding. Eye-ring red; upperparts very pale grey; bill coral-red, black sub-terminal band; legs dark olive-green. See also Pl.35. Map 190.

b Immature. Greyish-brown upperparts; greyish-white underparts; bill dusky yellow; black sub-terminal band; black tail band.

6 SILVER GULL *Larus novaehollandiae*   102
a Adult breeding. Outer and inner white flashes on primaries in flight; bill, eyelids and legs scarlet. See also Pls.38, 40. Map 212.

b Immature. Buff markings on mantle; secondaries form dark band on wings; bill and legs brownish-black.

c South African form. Adult breeding.

7 BLACK-BILLED or BULLER'S Gull *Larus bulleri*   103
a Adult breeding. Broad white triangle tipped black on forewing shows in flight; bill and legs black. See also Pl.38. Map 213.

b Immature 2nd year. Bill reddish, tip black; legs pinkish.

Plate 30   **GULLS**

1 MAGELLAN GULL *Gabianus scoresbyi*   page 94
  a Adult breeding. White tips to wings; head, neck and underbody pale grey; bill stout, red; legs red; tail white. See also Pl.38.   Map 182.

  b Immature. Bill brown, tip black; lower breast, abdomen, upper tail-coverts and tail white, sub-terminal black band.

2 GREY GULL *Larus modestus*   94
  a Adult breeding. Head white; white band on trailing edge of wings seen in flight; broad black band on tail. See also Pl.38.   Map 184.

  b Adult winter. Head dark greyish-brown.

  c Immature.

3 HEERMANN'S GULL *Larus heermanni*   94
  a Adult breeding. Head and upper neck white; bill red; legs black; white tip to tail. See also Pl.38.   Map 185.

  b Adult winter.

  c Immature.

4 GREY-HEADED GULL *Larus cirrocephalus*   101
  a Adult breeding. Grey head and throat; white neck; bill and legs crimson-red; in flight large white area on primaries, white fore edge to wing, white mirror on outer primaries. See also Pls.36, 38.   Map 209.

  b Immature. Bill yellow, tip black; dark tail band.

5 DUSKY GULL *Larus fuliginosus*   94
  Adult breeding. White eyelids; bill red; legs black. See also Pls.33, 38. Not mapped. Breeds only on Galapagos Is.

6 ANDEAN GULL *Larus serranus*   101
  a Adult breeding. Rosy tint on breast; bill and legs dark red; broad white wing patches and white leading edge show in flight. See also Pl.36.   Map 210.

  b Adult winter. Dusky smudge at eye; forehead and crown streaked white.

  c Immature. Sub-terminal black band on tail; bill yellow.

7 SIMEON GULL *Larus belcheri*   95
  a Adult breeding. Bill yellow; black band, tip red; tail black, tip white; legs yellow. See also Pls.34, 38.   Map 188.

  b Adult winter. Brownish-black head; eyelids white.

  c Immature 2nd year. Bill yellow, tip black; legs greyish.

8 FRANKLIN'S GULL *Larus pipixcan*   102
  Adult winter. For comparison. See also Pls.31, 36.   Map 211.

Plate 31   **GULLS**

1 NORTHERN BLACK-HEADED GULL *Larus ridibundus*   page 103
  a Adult breeding. Head coffee-brown; white eye-ring; bill and legs deep red. See also Pls.28, 32, 37, 40.   Map 216.

  b Juvenile. Bill yellow, tip black.

  c Immature 1st winter. Bill yellow, tip black; black band on tail.

  d Sub-adult 1st summer. Bill dull reddish-black; black band on tail.

  e Adult winter. Dusky patch behind eye.

2 PATAGONIAN BLACK-HEADED GULL   103
Larus maculipennis
  a Adult breeding. Similar to 1a; sometimes shows rosy tint; outer primaries white at ends; bill dark red. See also Pl.36.   Map 215.

  b Immature 1st winter.

3 BONAPARTE'S GULL *Larus philadelphia*   104
  a Adult breeding. Head black; bill black; legs red. In flight long triangle of white at front edge of wing. See also Pl.36.   Map 217.

  b Adult winter. Black patch behind eye.

  c Immature. Bill and legs dusky; black sub-terminal band on tail.

4 CHINESE BLACK-HEADED GULL *Larus saundersi*   105
  a Adult breeding. Similar to 3a; much white shows on primaries. See also Pl.37.   Map 220.

  b Adult winter.

  c Immature. Black sub-terminal band on tail.

5 FRANKLIN'S GULL *Larus pipixcan*   102
  a Adult breeding. Small, light build; deep hood; white eye rims; in flight, white area between black wing-quills and grey coverts; bill and legs dark red. See also Pls.30, 36.   Map 211.

  b Adult winter.

  c Immature. Whitish forehead; dusky crown; broad black tail band.

6 LAUGHING GULL *Larus atricilla*   101
  a Adult breeding. Head and neck dark greyish-black; in flight white border on trailing edge of wing conspicuous; bill red; legs reddish-brown. See also Pl.36.   Map 207.

  b Adult winter.   Crown and sides of head mottled; bill blackish.

  c Immature.   Black sub-terminal band.

  d Immature 2nd winter.

7 LITTLE GULL *Larus minutus*   105
  Immature. For comparison. See also Pls.32, 37.   Map 219.

Plate 32 GULLS

1 MEDITERRANEAN BLACK-HEADED GULL page 103
Larus melanocephalus
a Adult breeding. Entirely pale wing quills, tips white; bill coral red; black sub-terminal band; legs dark red. See also Pl.37. Map 214.
b Adult winter. Dark patch behind eye.
c Immature. Bill and legs dusky; black sub-terminal band on tail.

2 NORTHERN BLACK-HEADED GULL *Larus ridibundus* 103
Adult breeding. Coffee-brown head; outer primaries white, tips black. See also Pls.28, 31, 37, 40. Map 216.

3 INDIAN BLACK-HEADED GULL *Larus brunnicephalus* 101
a Adult breeding. Brown hood, blacker at neck; large white patches near tips of black primaries. See also Pl.37. Map 208.
b Adult winter. White head, dark patch behind eye.
c Immature. Bill yellowish; legs orange; black band on tail.

4 LITTLE GULL *Larus minutus* 105
a Adult breeding. Very small; entirely pale wing quills, tips white; underwings dark grey; bill and legs deep red. See also Pls.31, 37. Map 219.
b Adult winter. Greyish-black patch on crown; bill black.
c Juvenile. Dark zig-zag pattern across upperwing in flight; black band on tail.
d 1st winter.

5 GREAT BLACK-HEADED GULL *Larus ichthyaetus* 100
a Adult breeding. Very large size; primaries white, outer quills, black bars; bill yellow, black band, red tip; legs greenish. See also Pl.37. Map 206.
b Adult winter. Head white, streaked; bill yellow, black band.
c Juvenile. Broad black band on tail; bills and legs greyish.

6 RED SEA BLACK-HEADED or WHITE-EYED GULL 95
Larus leucopthalmus
a Adult breeding. Deep black hood; eyelids white; sides of breast slate-grey; bill red, tip black. See also Pls.37, 40. Map 186.
b Adult winter. Head and neck grizzled.
c Immature. Rump white; tail black band.

7 ADEN GULL *Larus hemprichi* 95
a Adult breeding. Coffee-brown hood; white ring around neck; bill greenish, sub-terminal black band, red tip; eyelids white. See also Pls.37, 40. Map 187.
b Adult winter. Neck brownish-grey.
c Immature. Brown above; underparts white; tail black.

Plate 33   **GULLS**

1 IVORY GULL   *Pagophila eburnea*   page 94
  a Adult breeding. Entirely white; red eye-ring; bill short, dark at base, shading yellow, reddish tip; legs short, black. See, Pl.39.   Map 183.

  b Immature. Upperparts finely speckled black; black band on tail.

2 ICELAND GULL   *Larus leucopterus leucopteras*   99
Immature 2nd year. Compare 1a. See also Pls.29, 35, 40.   Map 204.

3 COMMON KITTIWAKE   *Rissa tridactyla*   106
  a Adult breeding. Lightly built, black wing tips; slender greenish-yellow bill; dark legs. See also Pl.39.   Map 223.

  b Immature. Dark band at back of neck; bill black; dark diagonal band across upperwings; black band on tail; bill black.

4 RED-LEGGED KITTIWAKE   *Rissa brevirostris*   107
  a Adult breeding. Similar to 3a; mantle darker; legs red. See also Pl.39.   Map 224.

  b Immature. Broad dark band across nape; upperwings show no diagonal bands; legs dark brown.

5 ROSS'S GULL   *Rhodostethia rosea*   106
  a Adult breeding. Black collar around neck; very short black bill; legs red; rosy tint often absent. See also Pl.39.   Map 222.

  b Adult winter. Black collar indistinct.

  c Immature. Dark band on upperwing-coverts shows in flight; bill black; black band on central tail feathers.

6 SABINE'S GULL   *Xena sabini*   106
  a Adult breeding. Head and throat slate-grey; bill black, tip yellow; tail white, forked. Three triangular patches, grey, black and white show on upperparts in flight. See also Pl.39.   Map 221.

  b Adult winter.

  c Immature. Upperparts ashy-brown; black band across forked tail.

7 SWALLOW-TAILED GULL   *Creagrus furcatus*   107
  a Adult breeding. White patch on forehead; bill dark greenish, tip pale; tail white, forked; legs pinkish-red; white triangular patch on upperwings in flight; very large eyes. See also Pl.39. Breeds only on Galapagos Is.

  b Immature. Mottled brown and white above; black band across tail.

8 DUSKY GULL   *Larus fuliginosus*   94
Immature. All dark brown; compare 7b. See also Pls.30, 38. Breeds only on Galapagos Is.

Plate 34   ADULT GULLS IN FLIGHT

Plate 35   ADULT GULLS IN FLIGHT –
WINTER PLUMAGE

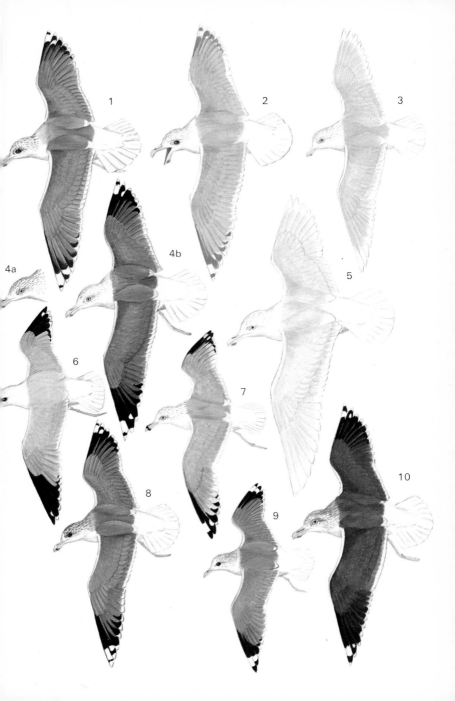

Plate 36   GULLS IN FLIGHT

1 LAUGHING GULL *Larus atricilla*   page 101
a Breeding head. See also Pl.31.   Map 207.

b Adult winter. White border on trailing edge of wings.

c Immature. Black band on tail.

2 FRANKLIN'S GULL *Larus pipixcan*   102
a Breeding head. See also Pls.30, 31.   Map 211.

b Adult winter. Divided black/white wing tips.

3 BONAPARTE'S GULL *Larus philadelphia*   104
a Breeding head. See also Pl.31.   Map 217.

b Adult winter. White triangle front edge of wings.

c Immature. Black tail band.

4 PATAGONIAN BLACK-HEADED GULL *Larus maculipennis*   103
a Breeding head. See also Pl.31.   Map 215.

b Adult winter. Broad white leading edge of wings.

5 GREY-HEADED GULL *Larus cirrocephalus*   101
a Breeding head. See also Pl.30, 38.   Map 209.

b Winter above. Broad white patch on wings; head variable.

c Winter below. Grey underwing-coverts.

6 ANDEAN GULL *Larus serranus*   101
a Breeding head. See also Pl.30.   Map 210.

b Winter. White patches on forewings.

Plate 37   **GULLS IN FLIGHT**

1 NORTHERN BLACK-HEADED GULL *Larus ridibundus*   page 103
  a Breeding head. See also Pls.28, 31, 32, 40.   Map 216.

  b Winter. Conspicuous white leading edge to wings.

2 INDIAN BLACK-HEADED GULL *Larus brunnicephalus*   101
  a Breeding head. See also Pl.32.   Map 208.

  b Winter. Large white patches show on forewing and wing tips.

3 MEDITERRANEAN BLACK-HEADED GULL   103
  Larus melanocephalus
  a Breeding head. See also Pl.32.   Map 214.

  b Winter. Entirely pale upper and underwings.

4 SLENDER-BILLED GULL *Larus genei*   105
  Winter. White leading edge to wings; legs yellow in summer. See
  Pl.29.   Map 218.

5 LITTLE GULL *Larnus minutus*   105
  a Breeding head. See also Pls.31, 32.   Map 219.

  b Winter below. Sooty-grey underwings.

  c Immature above. '**W**' pattern on upperparts; black band on tail.

6 GREAT BLACK-HEADED GULL *Larus ichthyaetus*   100
  a Breeding head. See also Pl.32.   Map 206.

  b Winter. Broad white area on forewing; black band on bill; bill and legs
  greenish-yellow.

7 CHINESE BLACK-HEADED GULL *Larus saundersi*   105
  a Breeding head. See also Pl.31.   Map 220.

  b Winter. White leading edge to wings.

8 RED SEA BLACK-HEADED or WHITE-EYED GULL   95
  Larus leucopthalmus
  a Breeding head. Deep black hood; bill red, tip black. See also Pls.32,
  40.   Map 186.

  b Winter. Sides of breast dusky.

9 ADEN GULL *Larus hemprichi*   95
  a Breeding head. Coffee-brown hood, white band around neck; bill
  greenish, with black band, red tip. See also Pls.32, 40.   Map 187.

  b Winter. Indistinct band around neck; breast brown.

Plate 38   **GULLS IN FLIGHT**

1 **SILVER GULL** *Larus novaehollandiae*   page 102
a Breeding head, South African form. Lavender ring sometimes
encircles neck. See also Pls.29, 40. Map 212.

b Winter. Broad white area on forewing.

2 **GREY-HEADED GULL** *Larus cirrocephalus*   101
Breeding head. For comparison. See also Pls.30, 36.   Map 209.

3 **BLACK-BILLED or BULLER'S GULL** *Larus bulleri*   103
Winter. Bill black; outer primaries white, small black border. See also
Pl.29.   Map 213.

4 **DUSKY GULL** *Larus fuliginosus*   94
Winter. See also Pls.30, 33. Breeds only on Galapagos Is.

5 **GREY GULL** *Larus modestus*   94
a Breeding head. See also Pl.30.   Map 184.

b Winter.

6 **MAGELLAN GULL** *Gabianus scoresbyi*   94
a Immature. Head, neck and upper breast brown; broad black sub-
terminal band on tail; bill and legs dark. See also Pl.30.   Map 182.

b Winter above. Head dusky; bill and legs red.

c Summer below. Underwing coverts grey.

7 **SIMEON GULL** *Larus belcheri*   95
a Immature head (Pacific). Yellow bill, dark tip. See also Pls.30, 34.
Map 188.

b Immature head (Atlantic).

c Summer head. Yellow bill, black band, red tip.

8 **HEERMANN'S GULL** *Larus heermanni*   94
a Breeding head. See also Pl.30.   Map 185.

b Adult winter. Dark wings and tail.

c Immature.

Plate 39　　　　　GULLS IN FLIGHT

1　SABINE'S GULL　*Xema sabini*　　　　　　　page 106
a Adult winter. See also Pl.33.　Map 221.

b Breeding head.

c Immature. Ashy-brown above; similar wing pattern to 1a; black band on forked tail.

2　ROSS'S GULL　*Rhodostethia rosea*　　　　　　106
a Adult winter. Wedge tail. See also Pl.33.　Map 222.

b Breeding head. Also occurs without rosy tint.

c Immature.

d Adult breeding.

3　SWALLOW-TAILED GULL　*Creagrus furcatus*　　　107
a Adult winter. Compare upperwing pattern with 1a; tail forked. See also Pl.33. Breeds only on Galapagos Is.

b Breeding head.

4　RED-LEGGED KITTIWAKE　*Rissa brevirostris*　　　107
a Adult breeding. Red legs. See also Pl.33.　Map 224.

b Immature. Black band on neck; no dark bands across wings; bill and legs dark.

5　COMMON KITTIWAKE　*Rissa tridactyla*　　　　106
a Adult breeding. See also Pl.33.　Map 223.

b Immature. Black band on neck; diagonal dark bands over wings; bill and legs dark; black band on tail.

c Adult below. White underwing, black tips.

6　IVORY GULL　*Pagophila eburnea*　　　　　　94
a Adult breeding. See also Pl.33.　Map 183.

b Immature.

Plate 40   GULLS IN FLIGHT: 1ST YEAR WINTER

Plate 41   **TERNS**

Sometimes called "sea swallows" for their slender build, dipping flight and deeply forked tails. Mainly inshore birds when not migrating. They hover and dive steeply for food.

1 CASPIAN TERN *Hydroprogne caspia*   page 110
a Adult breeding. Very large tern; bill very stout, coral red; legs black; tail only slightly forked.   Map 230.

b Adult winter head.   **c** Immature.   **d** Adult breeding in flight.

2 ARCTIC TERN *Sterna paradisea*   111
Size comparison. See also Pl.42.   Map 234.

3 ROYAL TERN *Thalasseus maximus*   118
a Adult breeding. Crested head; white front to cap.   Map 254.

b As 3a but white front to cap absent.   **c** Winter head.   **d** In flight. Pale underwing.

4 ELEGANT TERN *Thalasseus elegans*   119
a Adult breeding. Smaller than 3a, upperparts darker; bill long, slender, orange-red.   Map 258.

b Winter head.

5 CRESTED TERN *Thalasseus bergii*   117
a Adult breeding. Large; forehead white; crested head; bill greenish-yellow; legs dark.   Map 253.

b Autumn head.   **c** Winter head.

6 Immatures on *Thalasseus* terns. For varying bill colours, see the individual species.

7 LESSER-CRESTED TERN *Thalasseus bengalensis*   118
a Adult breeding. Forehead black; bill orange. Compare 5a.   Map 255.

b Winter head. Compare 5c.

8 CHINESE CRESTED TERN *Thalasseus zimmermanni*   118
a Adult breeding. Upperparts very pale grey. Note bill.   Map 256.

b Winter head.

9 CAYENNE TERN *Thalasseus eurygnatha*   118
a Adult breeding. Similar to 3a except bill long, slender, pale yellow.   Map 257.

b Winter head.

10 SANDWICH TERN *Thalasseus sandvicensis*   119
Adult breeding summer head. See also Pl.43.   Map 259.

11 A *Thalasseus* tern with crown feathers erect in display.

Plate 42   **TERNS**

1 ROSEATE TERN *Sterna dougalli*   page 113
  a Adult breeding. Much whiter than 2a, 3a; rosy tint on underparts;
     long deeply forked tail.   Map 239.
  b Winter head.
  c At rest. Tail projects beyond wings; legs red.

2 COMMON TERN *Sterno hirundo*   111
  a Adult breeding. Bill scarlet, tip black; legs red. See also Pl.43.   Map
     233.
  b Winter head, bill mainly black.
  c At rest. Wing tip and tail equal length.

3 ARCTIC TERN *Sterna paradisea*   111
  a Adult breeding. Bill and legs red; legs very short. See also Pl.41.
     Map 234.
  b Winter head. Bill blackish.
  c At rest. Short red legs; tail a little longer than wing tip.

4 ANTARCTIC or WREATHED TERN *Sterna vittata*   112
  a Adult breeding. White stripe from gape to nape; deeply forked tail;
     bill and legs red.   Map 235.
  b Winter head.
  c At rest.

5 FORSTER'S TERN *Sterna forsteri*   112
  a Adult breeding. Very pale; bill orange, black tip; deeply forked tail.
     Map 237.
  b Winter head.
  c At rest.

6 SOUTH AMERICAN TERN *Sterna hirundinacea*   111
  a Adult breeding. Pale upperwings.   Map 232.
  b Winter head.
  c At rest.

7 WHITE-CHEEKED TERN *Sterna repressa*   114
  a Adult breeding. Upperparts darkish-grey; underparts and tail grey;
     white area below cap.   Map 241.
  b Winter head.
  c At rest.

8 KERGUELEN TERN *Sterna virgata*   112
     Adult breeding. Map 236.
  b Winter head.
  c At rest.

Plate 43   TERNS

1 BLACK-FRONTED TERN *Chlidonias albostriata*   page 116
  a Adult breeding. Broad white stripe beneath cap; white rump seen in
  flight; bill and legs orange-red. **b** Winter head.   Map 248.

2 TRUDEAU'S TERN *Sterna trudeaui*   113
  a Adult breeding. Small, pale pearl-grey; black streak through eye; bill
  yellow, broad black central band; forked tail grey. **b** Winter head.
  Map 238.

3 WHITE-FRONTED TERN *Sterna striata*   113
  a Adult breeding. White forehead; black bill; legs reddish-brown.
  b Winter head.   Map 240.

4 BLACK-NAPED TERN *Sterna sumatrana*   114
  a Adult breeding. Very pale; black spot at eye; black band around
  nape; bill black, tip yellow; legs black. **b** Juvenile head.   Map 242.

5 FAIRY TERN *Sterna nereis*   116
  a Adult breeding. Small, pale; white forehead; bill yellow; tail lightly
  forked.   Map 247.

6 LITTLE TERN *Sterna albifrons*   117
  a Adult breeding. Smaller than 5; white forehead, black band bill to
  eye; bill yellow, tip black; legs yellow. Compare Pl.45, No.3.
  b Immature.   Map 252.

7 CHILEAN TERN *Sterna lorata*   117
  a Adult breeding. Very small; white forehead, black band bill to eye;
  appears slate-grey; white throat; legs brown. Compare 6a.   Map
  251.

8 Winter plumage.

9 DAMARA TERN *Sterna balaenarum*   117
  a Adult breeding. Very small; black forehead; black bill. Compare 6a.
  b Winter head.   Map 250.

10 GULL-BILLED TERN *Gelochelidon nilotica*   110
  a Adult breeding. Bill stout, gull-like, black; legs blackish; tail lightly
  forked, pale grey.   Map 229. **b** Winter head. **c** Adult. Long legs;
  gull-like appearance. **d** Immature.

11 SANDWICH TERN *Thalasseus sandvicensis*   119
  a Adult breeding. Crest on crown; bill long, slender, black, tip yellow;
  legs black. See also Pl.41. Map 259. **b** Winter head. **c** At
  rest. **d** Immature.

12 COMMON TERN *Sterna hirundo*   111
  Immature for size comparison. See also Pl.42.   Map 233.

13 WHITE TERN *Gygis alba*   119
  a Adult breeding.   Map 261. **b** Immature. Fawn speckled on head,
  back and wings. **c** At nest on bare branch.

Plate 44   **TERNS and NODDIES**

Noddies are inshore tropical birds. Brown plumage with whitish caps and notched (not forked, except for Blue-grey Noddy) tails. Flight low over the water, dipping for food.

Plate 45   INLAND TERNS and SKIMMERS

Inland Terns overfly marshes, lagoons and rivers.
Skimmers have same habitat but distinctive feeding flight (usually at dark or on moonlit nights) with lower mandible skimming the surface.

1 INDIAN RIVER TERN *Sterna aurantia*   page 111
 a Adult breeding. Bill stout, yellow; tail very long, deeply forked.   Map 231.

 b Adult winter in flight. Crown grey, forehead white, winter, dusky tip on bill.

2 BLACK-BELLIED TERN *Sterna melanogastra*   114
 a Adult winter. Smaller than 1b; bill slender.   Map 231.

 b Adult breeding. Black abdomen.

3 AMAZON TERN *Sterna superciliaris*   116
 Adult breeding. Very small; white forehead; bill yellow, no black tip; almost identical with Little Tern (Pl.43).   Map 249.

4 LARGE-BILLED TERN *Phaetusa simplex*   110
 a Adult breeding. Bill very stout; tail short, nearly square.   Map 228.

 b Adult winter in flight.

 c Adult breeding in flight.

5 INDIAN SKIMMER *Rynchops albicollis*   123
 a Adult breeding. Back of neck white; upperparts dark brown.   Map 268.

6 Skimmers in flight

7 AFRICAN SKIMMER *Rynchops flavirostris*   123
 Adult breeding. Back of neck brown; upperparts brown.   Map 267.

8 BLACK SKIMMER *Rynchops nigra*   123
 a Immature.   Map 266.

 b Adult breeding. Back of neck black; upperparts black.

9 Skimmers
 Winter head, adults. All have whitish collars in winter.

Plate 46   **AUKS and GUILLEMOTS**

The Auk Family (Auks, Guillemots, Puffins, Auklets and Murrelets – Pls.46–48) are offshore and oceanic, black-and-white looking birds; confined to the northern hemisphere. Short stubby wings, fast whirring flight, diving from the surface to pursue their food under water.

1   COMMON GUILLEMOT or MURRE   *Uria aalge*   page 127
  a Adult breeding. Dark chocolate-brown above; neck long; bill long, pointed. See also Pl.48.   Map 272.

  b Bridled form. White ring at eye; white stripe from eye.

  c Adult winter. Throat and front of neck white.

  d Adult in flight.

2   BRUNNICH'S GUILLEMOT or THICK-BILLED MURRE   126
    Uria lomvia
  a Adult breeding. Black above; bill stouter than 1a, pale streak backwards from base of bill.   Map 271.

  b Adult winter. Black sides of face lower than 1c, otherwise similar.

3   RAZORBILL   *Alca torda*   126
  a Adult breeding. Thick neck; white line bill to eye; white band across stout flattened bill.   Map 270.

  b Adult winter. Cheeks and foreneck white; tail cocked, swimming.

  c Immature 1st winter. Bill smaller; white line and bill band absent.

4   LITTLE AUK or DOVEKIE   *Plautus alle*   125
  a Adult breeding. Very small, stubby; bill very short; dives freely; head, neck, upper breast black.   Map 269.

  b Adult winter. Throat and ear-coverts white; underparts white.

5   BLACK GUILLEMOT   *Cepphus grylle*   127
  a Adult breeding. Map 273.

  b Adult winter.

  c Adult in flight. White underwing-linings.

6   Black and **Pigeon Guillemots**
    Immature plumage. Both species similar.

7   PIGEON GUILLEMOT   *Cepphus columba*   127
  a Adult breeding. Similar to 5a, except black transverse bars on white area.   Map 274.

  b Adult winter.

8   SPECTACLED GUILLEMOT   *Cepphus carbo*   127
  a Adult breeding. Conspicuous white eye-ring.   Map 275.

  b Adult winter.

Plate 47   **PUFFINS and AUKLETS**
See notes on Plate 46

1 ATLANTIC PUFFIN *Fratercula arctica*   page 130
a Adult breeding. Large parrot-like bill; face white.   Map 285.

b Adult winter. Duller bill without sheath; face greyish.

c Immature. Bill more slender, dark; face darker.

d Adult in flight.

2 HORNED PUFFIN *Fratercula corniculata*   130
a Adult breeding. Very triangular yellow-red bill; cheeks white.   Map 286.

b Adult winter. Reduced bill, blue-red; head dark; indistinct eye patch.

c Immature. Bill more slender, dark.

3 TUFTED PUFFIN *Lunda cirrhata*   131
a Adult breeding. Huge bill, greenish-red; long yellow drooping plumes.   Map 287.

b Adult winter. Bill reduced, greyish-red; head and face dark; plumes absent.

c Immature. Bill yellowish.

d Adult in flight.

4 RHINOCEROS AUKLET *Cerorhinca monocerata*   130
a Adult breeding. White plumes across cheeks; yellow horn on orange bill.   Map 284.

b Adult winter. Plumes absent; bill yellow.

5 WHISKERED AUKLET *Aethia pygmaea*   130
a Adult breeding. Very small; groups of drooping white plumes adorn head; bill bright red.   Map 283.

b Immature. Plumes absent; bill dusky-yellow.

6 CRESTED AUKLET *Aethia cristatella*   130
a Adult breeding. Dark crest curves forward over red, deeply compressed bill; white plumes behind eye.   Map 283.

b Adult winter. Crests much reduced; bill yellow.

c Immature. Slaty-black; crest absent.

7 LEAST AUKLET *Aethia pusilla*   129
Adult breeding. Very small; black above; white throat; white plume behind eye; speckled underparts. See also Pl.48.   Map 282.

Plate 48   **AUKLETS and MURRELETS**
                      See notes on Plate 46

1 **CASSIN'S AUKLET** *Ptychoramphus aleuticus*   page 129
   a Adult breeding. Small; dusky; whitish central underparts. Map
   281. **b** Winter in flight. Light throat.

2 **LEAST AUKLET** *Aethia pusilla*   129
   a Adult breeding. Very small; black above; white plume behind eye;
   white throat; speckled underparts; bill red. See also Pl.47. Map
   282. **b** Adult winter. Black bill **c** Winter in flight. Scapulars
   white.

3 **MARBLED MURRELET** *Brachyramphus marmoratus*   128
   a Adult breeding. Dark brown above, speckled below; whitish
   scapulars. Map 276. **b** Adult winter. White eye-ring; white side
   of neck; scapulars white; white underparts. **c** Adult in flight,
   winter.

4 **KITTLITZ'S MURRELET** *Brachyramphus brevirostris*   128
   a Adult breeding. Dusky above, barred brown below; bill stumpy,
   black. Map 277. **b** Adult winter. Slate-grey above, spotted white;
   white face and collar; white underparts. **c** Winter in flight. Note
   white spots on upperparts.

5 **XANTUS'S MURRELET** *Brachyramphus hypoleucus*   128
   a Adult breeding. Underparts white. Map 278. **b** Adult in flight
   below. White underwing linings.

6 **Xantus's** and **Craveri's Murrelets**
   In flight above.

7 **CRAVERI'S MURRELET** *Brachyramphus craveri*   128
   a Adult breeding. Similar to 5a, 5b, except underwing linings dark.
   Map 278. **b** Adult in flight below. Underwing linings dark.

8 **CRESTED MURRELET** *Synthliboramphus wumizusume*   129
   Adult breeding. Black crest; white stripe on head below black
   crest. Map 280.

9 **ANCIENT MURRELET** *Synthliboramphus antiquus*   128
   a Adult breeding. Upperparts slate-blue; white stripe across crown;
   white sides of neck; bill whitish. Map 279. **b** Adult winter.
   Throat white; white stripe absent. **c** Adult winter in flight.

10 **PARAKEET AUKLET** *Cyclorrhynchus psittacula*   129
   a Adult breeding. Bill very stubby, compressed, bright red; white
   plumes across cheeks; chin, throat, foreneck brownish. Map
   282. **b** Adult winter. White chin, throat. **c** Adult winter in flight
   above. White throat. **d** Adult summer in flight below. Dark throat

11 **COMMON GUILLEMOT or MURRE** *Uria aalge*   127
   For size comparison. See also Pl.46. Adult winter. Map 272.

WORLD DISTRIBUTION MAPS

On the following two pages are mapped the 104 principal groups of islands on which seabirds breed. Then follow the distribution maps for individual species. Here **solid red** indicates principal breeding areas and the shaded areas of **light red** the oceanic (non-breeding) distribution. Red lines indicate migratory or dispersal routes. On certain maps figures indicate months of the year in areas where migratory species may be expected. E.g. 6–8=June–August inclusive.

The maps have all been drawn to show the mean distribution areas. They do not take account of occasional sightings of a bird far outside its normal range.

MAP CAPTIONS. The figures following each bird's map number and common name are references: in normal type to its text description, in **bold** type to its colour plate.

Under each map is given: the map number (referred to in the main text and in the index); the bird's common name; and references to its text description (in normal type) and its colour plate (in **bold** type).

BIRDS NOT MAPPED are listed below. These are either species whose status is uncertain or birds whose breeding is confined to a single island and whose oceanic range normally extends at no great distance to seaward.

ROYAL PENGUIN *Eudyptes schlegeli*, p.9   Macquarie I, New Zealand Seas
GALAPAGOS PENGUIN *Spheniscus mendiculus*, p.11   Galapagos Is, tropical East Pacific
HEINROTH'S SHEARWATER *Puffinus heinrothi*, p.34   One specimen only known from coast of New Britain, West S. Pacific
BECK'S PETREL *Pterodroma rostrata becki*, p.37   Two specimens only known off Solomon Is. West S. Pacific
REUNION PETREL *Pterodroma aterrima*, p.37   Reunion I, West Indian Ocean
JAMAICA PETREL *Pterodroma hasitata caribbaea*, p.39   Status in doubt, formerly bred on Jamaica
BERMUDA PETREL *Pterodroma cahow*, p.39   Bermuda Is, West N. Atlantic
CHATHAM ISLAND PETREL *Pterodroma axillaris*, p.40   Chatham I, New Zealand Seas
MACGILLIVRAY'S PETREL *Bulweria macgillivrayi*, p.44   One specimen only known from Fiji Is, S. Pacific
GUADALOUPE STORM-PETREL *Oceanodroma macrodactyla*, p.49   Possibly extinct. Bred on Guadaloupe I, East N. Pacific
CHRISTMAS TROPIC-BIRD *Phaethon lepturus fulvus*, p.57   Christmas I, East Indian Ocean
ABBOTT'S BOOBY *Sula abbotti*, p.67   Christmas I, East Indian Ocean
CAMPBELL ISLAND CORMORANT *Phalacrocorax carunculatus campbelli*, p.76   Campbell I, New Zealand Seas
PITT ISLAND CORMORANT *Phalacrocorax punctatus featherstoni*, p.77   Chatham I, New Zealand Seas
FLIGHTLESS CORMORANT *Nannopterum harrisi*, p.79   Galapagos Is, tropical East Pacific
ASCENSION FRIGATE-BIRD *Fregata aquila*, p.81   Ascension I, S. Atlantic
CHRISTMAS FRIGATE-BIRD *Fregata andrewsi*, p.81   Christmas I, East Indian Ocean
DUSKY GULL *Larus fuliginosus*, p.94   Galapagos Is, tropical East Pacific
MONGOLIAN GULL *Larus relictus*, p.104   Status in Mongolia uncertain
SWALLOW-TAILED GULL *Creagrus furcatus*, p.107   Galapagos Is, tropical East Pacific

Key to principal islands

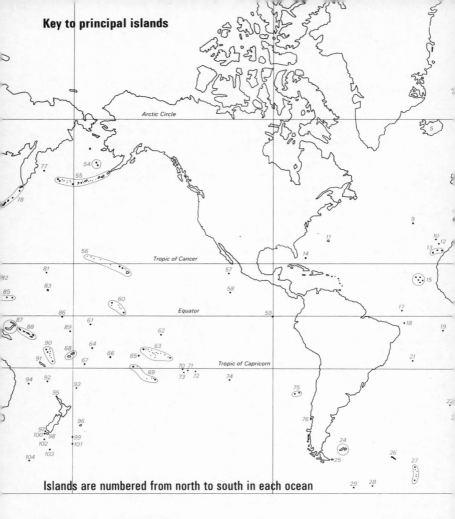

Arctic Circle

Tropic of Cancer

Equator

Tropic of Capricorn

Islands are numbered from north to south in each ocean

Arctic and N. Atlantic
1 Franz Joseph Land
2 Spitsbergen
3 Bear I
4 Jan Mayen
5 Iceland
6 Faroes
7 Shetland Is
8 Balearic Is
9 Azores
10 Madeira
11 Bermuda
12 Salvage Is
13 Canary Is
14 Bahama Is
15 Cape Verde Is
16 Sao Tome I
17 St Paul Rocks

S. Atlantic
18 Fernando de Noronha
19 Ascension I
20 St Helena
21 Trinidad – Martin Vas
22 Tristan da Cunha
23 Gough I
24 Falkland Is
25 Staten I
26 South Georgia
27 South Sandwich Is
28 South Orkney Is
29 South Shetland Is
30 Bouvet I

N. Indian Ocean
31 Kuria Muria Is
32 Socotra I
33 Laccadive Is
34 Andaman Is
35 Maldive Is

S. Indian Ocean
36 Seychelles
37 Amirantes
38 Chagos Arch
39 Cocos Keeling Is
40 Christmas I
41 Alegela I
42 Providence I
43 Aldabra Is
44 Comoro Is
45 Cargados Carajos Is
46 Mauritius
47 Reunion I
48 Amsterdam
49 St Paul
50 Crozet Is
51 Marion Is
52 Kerguelen Is
53 Heard Is

N. Pacific east of 180°
54 Pribilof I

5	Aleutian Is	69	Austral Is
6	Hawaiian Is	70	Oeno I
7	Revilla Gigedo I	71	Henderson I
8	Clipperton I	72	Ducie I
9	Galapagos Is	73	Pitcairn I
10	Line Is – Christmas I	74	Easter I
. Pacific east of 180°		75	Juan Fernandez Is
1	Phoenix Is	76	Mocha I
2	Marquesas Is	**N. Pacific west of 180°**	
3	Tuamotu Arch	77	Kommandu I
4	Samoan Is	78	Kuril Is
5	Society Is	79	Bonin Is
6	Cook Is	80	Volcano I
7	Tonga Is	81	Wake I
8	Fiji Is	82	Mariana Is – Guam

83	Marshall Is
84	Palau I
85	Caroline Is
86	Gilbert Is
S. Pacific west of 180°	
87	New Britain
88	Solomon Is
89	Ellice Is
90	New Hebrides
91	New Caledonia Is
92	Norfolk I
93	Kermadec Is
94	Lord Howe I

New Zealand Seas

95	Three Kings Is
96	Chatham Is
97	Solander I
98	Stewart I
99	Bounty Is
100	Snares Is
101	Antipodes Is
102	Aukland Is
103	Campbell I
104	Macquarie Is

231

232

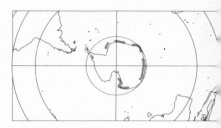

1. King Penguin, 7.1

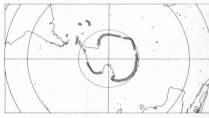

2. Emperor Penguin, 7.1

3. Gentoo Penguin, 7.1

4. Adelie Penguin, 7.1

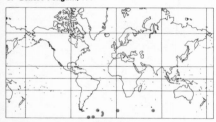

5. Chin-strap or **Bearded Penguin, 8.1**

6. Fiordland Crested Penguin, 8.2

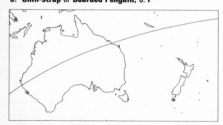

7. Snares Crested Penguin, 8.2

8. Erect-crested or **Big-crested Penguin, 8.2**

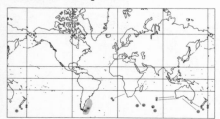

9. Rock-hopper Penguin, 9.2

10. Macaroni Penguin, 9.2

11. Yellow-eyed Penguin, 10.2

12. Little or Blue Penguin, 10.2

13. White-flippered Penguin, 10.2

14. Jackass Penguin, 11.1

15. Humboldt Penguin, 11.1

16. Magellan Penguin, 11.1

17. Wandering Albatross, 16.3

18. Royal Albatross, 17.3

19. Waved Albatross, 17.4

20. Short-tailed Albatross, 17.3

234

21. Black-footed Albatross, 17.6

22. Laysan Albatross, 18.4

23. Black-browed Albatross, 18.5

24. Buller's Albatross, 19.4

25. Shy or **White-capped Albatross,** 19.4

26. Yellow-nosed Albatross, 19.5

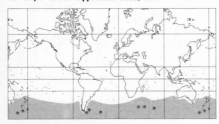

27. Grey-headed Albatross, 20.5

28. Sooty Albatross, 20.6

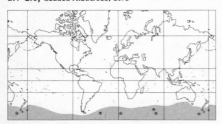

29. Light-mantled Sooty Albatross, 21.6

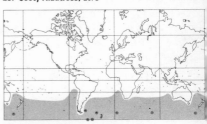

30. Southern Giant Petrel, 24.7

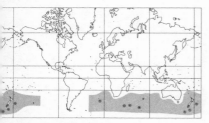

Northern Giant Petrel, 24.6,7

32. Northern Fulmar, 25.11

Southern Fulmar or Silver-grey Petrel, 25.11

34. Cape Pigeon or Pintado Petrel, 25.11

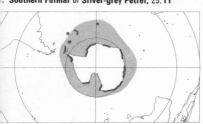

Snow Petrel, 25.11

36. Antarctic Petrel, 26.11

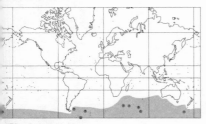

Blue Petrel, 26.11

38. Broad-billed Prion, 28

Salvin's Prion, 28

40. Dove Prion, 28

236

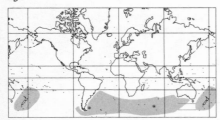

41. Thin-billed Prion, 28

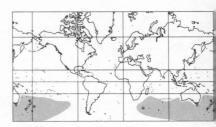

42. Fairy Prion, 28

43. Fulmar Prion or **Thick-billed Prion**, 28

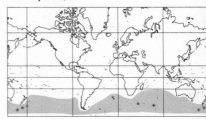

44. Brown Petrel, 28.**10**

45. White-chinned Petrel, 29.**7**

46. Parkinson's Petrel, 29.**7**

47. Westland Petrel, 29.**7**

48. White-faced or **Streaked Shearwater**, 29.**8**

49. Cory's Shearwater, 30.**9**

50. Pink-footed Shearwater, 30.**8**

51. Pale-footed Shearwater, 30.8

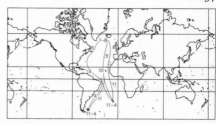

52. Great Shearwater, 31.9

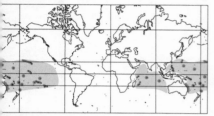

53. Wedge-tailed Shearwater, 31.7

54. Grey-backed Shearwater, 31.8

55. Sooty Shearwater, 31.8

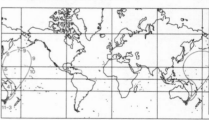

56. Short-tailed Shearwater, 32.8

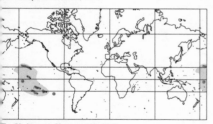

57. Christmas Shearwater, 32.7

58. Manx Shearwater, 32.9

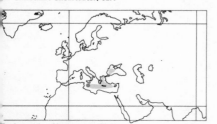

59. Levantine Shearwater, 33.9

60. Balearic Shearwater, 33.9

238

61. Townsend's Shearwater, 33

62. Newell's Shearwater, 33

63. Black-vented Shearwater, 33.**9**

64. Fluttering Shearwater, 33.**10**

65. Hutton's Shearwater, 33.**10**

66. Little Shearwater, 33.**9**

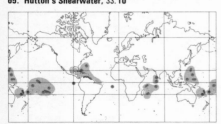

67. Audubon's Shearwater, 34.**9**

68. Persian Shearwater, 34.**10**

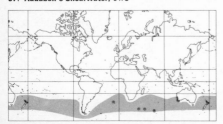

69. Great-winged or **Grey-faced Petrel**, 34.**10**

70. White-headed Petrel, 35.**11**

239

. Schlegel's Petrel, 35.10

72. Solander's Petrel, 35.12

. Murphy's Petrel, 35.12

74. Peale's Petrel or Mottled Petrel, 36.12

. Kerguelen Petrel, 36.11

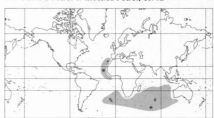

76. Soft-plumaged Petrel, 36.10

. Tahiti Petrel, 37.12

78. Phoenix Petrel, 37.12

. Kermadec Petrel, 37.12

80. Trinidade Petrel, 38.10

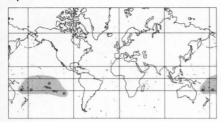

81. Herald Petrel, 38.10

82. Black-capped Petrel, 39.10

83. Hawaiian Petrel, 39.12

84. White-necked Petrel, 38.11

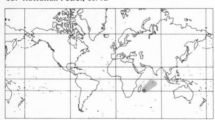

85. Barau's Petrel, 39.10

86. Bonin Petrel, 40.12

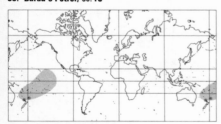

87. Black-winged Petrel, 40.12

88. Cook's Petrel, 42.12

89. Stejneger's Petrel, 42.12

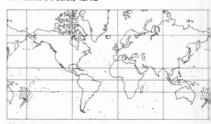

90. Pycroft's Petrel, 43

241

. Gould's Petrel, 43.12

92. Collared Petrel, 43.12

. Jouanin's Petrel, 43.9

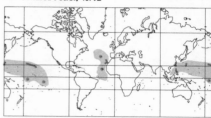

94. Bulwer's Petrel, 44.9

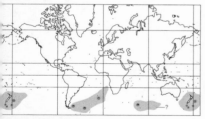

. Wilson's Storm-petrel, 46.13

96. Elliot's Storm-petrel, 46.13

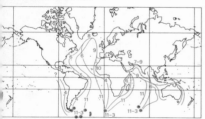

Grey-backed Storm-petrel, 46.14

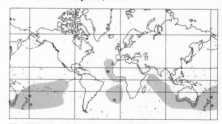

98. White-faced Storm-petrel, 47.13

White-bellied Storm-petrel, 47.13

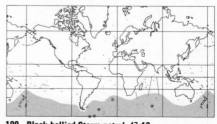

100. Black-bellied Storm-petrel, 47.13

101. White-throated Storm-petrel, 48.13

102. British Storm-petrel, 48.13

103. Least Storm-petrel, 48.14

104. Galapagos Storm-petrel, 48.13

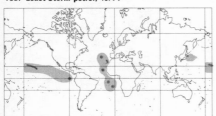

105. Madeiran Storm-petrel, 49.13

106. Leach's Storm-petrel, 49.13

107. Swinhoe's Storm-petrel, 50.14

108. Tristram's Storm-petrel, 50.14

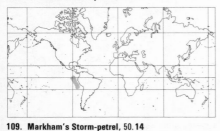

109. Markham's Storm-petrel, 50.14

110. Matsudaira's Storm-petrel, 50.14

. Black Storm-petrel, 51.14

112. Ashy Storm-petrel, 51.14

3. Hornby's Storm-petrel, 51.14

114. Fork-tailed Storm-petrel, 51.14

. Peruvian Diving-petrel, 54.14

116. Magellan Diving-petrel, 54.14

. Georgian Diving-petrel, 54.14

118. Common Diving-petrel, 54.14

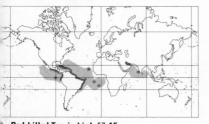

. Red-billed Tropic-bird, 57.15

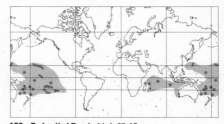

120. Red-tailed Tropic-bird, 57.15

244

121. White-tailed Tropic-bird, 57.15

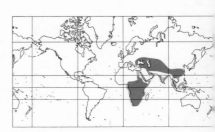

122. White Pelican, 59.16

123. Pink-backed Pelican, 60.16

124. Grey Pelican, 60.16

125. Dalmatian Pelican, 61.16

126. Australian Pelican, 61.17

127. American White Pelican, 61.17

128. Brown Pelican, 62.17

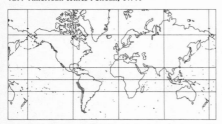

129. Chilean Pelican, 63.17

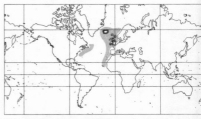

130. Northern Gannet, 65.18

131. Cape Gannet, 66.18

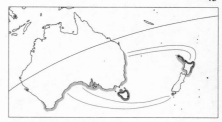

132. Australian Gannet, 66.18

133. Blue-footed Booby, 66.19

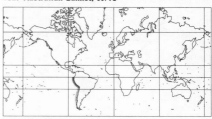

134. Peruvian Booby, 67.19

135. Blue-faced or Masked Booby, 67.18

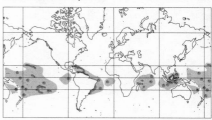

136. Red-footed Booby, 68.19

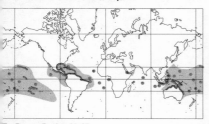

137. Brown Booby, 68.19

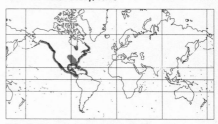

138. Double-crested Cormorant, 71.21

139. Bigua Cormorant, 72.21

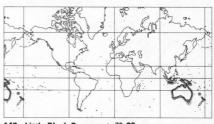

140. Little Black Cormorant, 72.23

246

141. Common Cormorant, 72.20,23

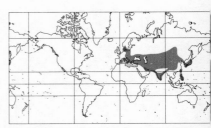

142. Common Cormorant (Continental race), 72.20

143. White-necked Cormorant, 72.20

144. Indian Cormorant, 72.23

145. Cape Cormorant, 73.20

146. Socotra Cormorant, 73.20

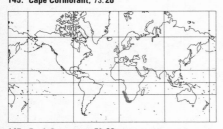

147. Bank Cormorant, 73.20

148. Japanese Cormorant, 73.20

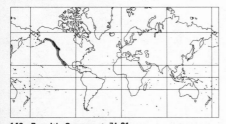

149. Brandt's Cormorant, 74.21

150. Shag or Green Cormorant, 74.21

1. Pelagic Cormorant, 74.21

152. Red-faced Cormorant, 74.21

3. Magellan Cormorant, 75.22

154. Guanay Cormorant, 75.22

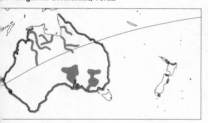

5. Pied Cormorant, 75.22

156. Black-faced Cormorant, 75.22

7. Rough-faced Cormorant, 75.22

158. Kerguelen Cormorant, 76

9. Red-legged Cormorant, 76.21

160. Spotted Cormorant, 77.22

248

161. Blue-eyed Cormorant, 77.**22**

162. King Cormorant, 78

163. Little Pied Cormorant, 78.**22,23**

164. Reed Cormorant, 79.**23**

165. Javanese Cormorant, 79.**23**

166. Pigmy Cormorant, 79.**23**

167. Magnificent Frigate-bird, 83.**24**

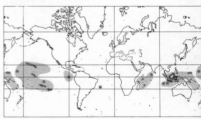

168. Great Frigate-bird, 83.**24**

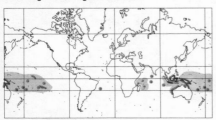

169. Lesser Frigate-bird, 83.**24**

170. Grey Phalarope, 85.**25**

171. Wilson's Phalarope, 85.25

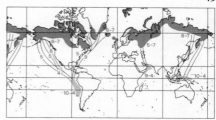

172. Red-necked Phalarope, 85.25

173. Yellow-billed Sheathbill, 87.25

174. Black-billed Sheathbill, 87.25

175. Great Skua, 89.26

176. Southern Skua, 90.26

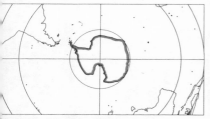

177. McCormick's Skua, 90.26

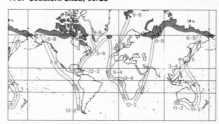

178. Pomarine Skua, 90.26

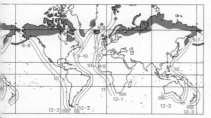

179. Arctic Skua, 90.26

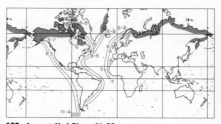

180. Long-tailed Skua, 91.26

181. Pacific Gull, 93. **27,34,40**

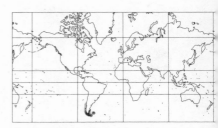

182. Magellan Gull, 94. **30,38**

183. Ivory Gull, 94. **33,39**

184. Grey Gull, 94. **30,38**

185. Heermann's Gull, 94. **30,38**

186. Red Sea Black-headed or White-eyed Gull, 95. **32,37,40**

187. Aden Gull, 95. **32,37,40**

188. Simeon Gull, 95. **30,34,38**

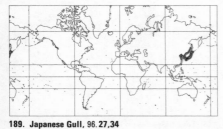

189. Japanese Gull, 96. **27,34**

190. Audouin's Gull, 96. **29,35**

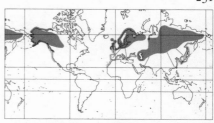

191. Ring-billed Gull, 96.**28,35,40**

192. Common or **Mew Gull**, 96.**28,35,40**

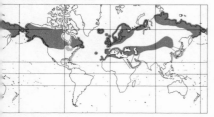

193. Herring Gull, 97.**28,35,40**

194. Thayer's Gull, 97.**28,35**

195. Lesser Black-backed Gull (Scandinavian race),
197.**27,34,40**

196. Lesser Black-backed Gull (British race), 97.**27,35,40**

197. California Gull, 98.**28,35**

198. Western Gull, 98.**27,34**

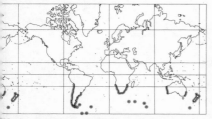

199. Southern Black-backed Gull, 98.**27,34,40**

200. Slaty-backed Gull, 98.**27,34**

201. Great Black-backed Gull, 99.27,34,40

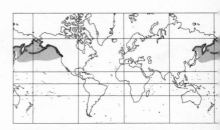

202. Glaucous-winged Gull, 99.29,35

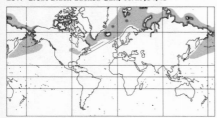

203. Glaucous Gull, 99.29,35,40

204. Iceland Gull, 99.29,33,35,40

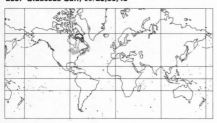

205. Kumlien's Gull, 100

206. Great Black-headed Gull, 100.32,37

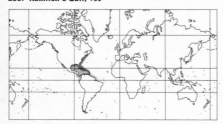

207. Laughing Gull, 101.31,36

208. Indian Black-headed Gull, 101.32,37

209. Grey-headed Gull, 101.30,36,38

210. Andean Gull, 101.30,36

253

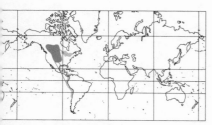

211. Franklin's Gull, 102.30,31,36

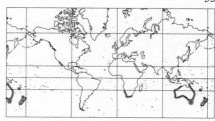

212. Silver Gull, 102.29,38,40

213. Black-billed or **Buller's Gull, 103.29,38**

214. Mediterranean Black-headed Gull, 103.32,37

215. Patagonian Black-headed Gull, 103.31,36

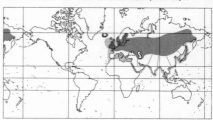

216. Northern Black-headed Gull, 103.28,31,32,37,40

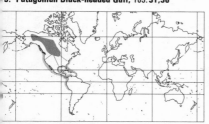

217. Bonaparte's Gull, 104.31,36

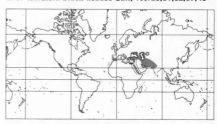

218. Slender-billed Gull, 105.29,37

219. Little Gull, 105.31,32,37

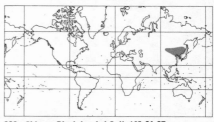

220. Chinese Black-headed Gull, 105.31,37

254

221. Sabine's Gull, 106.**33,39**

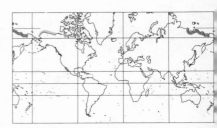

222. Ross's Gull, 106.**33,39**

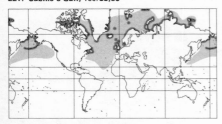

223. Common Kittiwake, 106.**33,39**

224. Red-legged Kittiwake, 107.**33,39**

225. Whiskered Tern, 109.**44**

226. White-winged Black Tern, 109.**44**

227. Black Tern, 110.**44**

228. Large-billed Tern, 110.**45**

229. Gull-billed Tern, 110.**43**

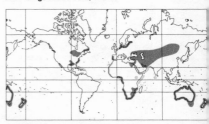

230. Caspian Tern, 110.**41**

231. Indian River Tern, 111.45
Black-bellied Tern, 114.45

232. South American Tern, 111.42

233. Common Tern, 111.42,43

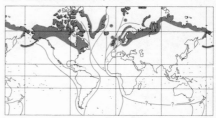

234. Arctic Tern, 111.41,42

235. Antarctic or Wreathed Tern, 112.42

236. Kerguelen Tern, 112.42

237. Forster's Tern, 112.42

238. Trudeau's Tern, 113.43

239. Roseate Tern, 113.42

240. White-fronted Tern, 113.43

256

241. White-cheeked Tern, 114. 42

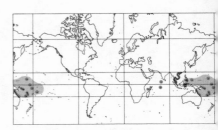

242. Black-naped Tern, 114. 43

243. Aleutian Tern, 114. 44

244. Spectacled Tern, 115. 44

245. Brown-winged or **Bridled Tern, 115. 44**

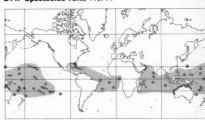

246. Sooty Tern, 115. 44

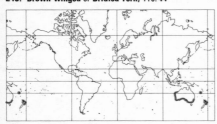

247. Fairy Tern, 116. 43

248. Black-fronted Tern, 116. 43

249. Amazon Tern, 116. 45

250. Damara Tern, 117. 43

51. Chilean Tern, 117.43

252. Little Tern, 117.43

53. Crested Tern, 117.41

254. Royal Tern, 118.41

55. Lesser-crested Tern, 118.41

256. Chinese Crested Tern, 118.41

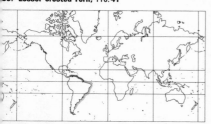

57. Cayenne Tern, 118.41

258. Elegant Tern, 119.41

59. Sandwich Tern, 119.41,43

260. Inca Tern, 119.44

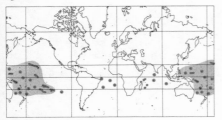

261. White Tern, 119. **43**

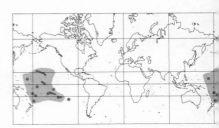

262. Blue-grey Noddy, 120. **44**

263. Common or **Brown Noddy**, 120. **44**

264. White-capped Noddy, 120. **44**

265. Lesser Noddy, 121. **44**

266. Black Skimmer, 123. **45**

267. African Skimmer, 123. **45**

268. Indian Skimmer, 123. **45**

269. Little Auk or **Dovekie**, 125. **46**

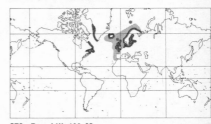

270. Razorbill, 126. **46**

259

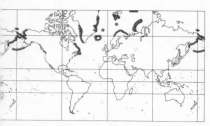

271. **Brunnich's Guillemot** or **Thick-billed Murre**, 126.46

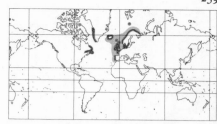

272. **Common Guillemot** or **Murre**, 127.46,48

273. **Black Guillemot**, 127.46

274. **Pigeon Guillemot**, 127.46

275. **Spectacled Guillemot**, 127.46

276. **Marbled Murrelet**, 128.48

277. **Kittlitz's Murrelet**, 128.48

278. **Xantus' and Craveri's Murrelets**, 128.48

279. **Ancient Murrelet**, 128.48

280. **Crested Murrelet**, 129.48

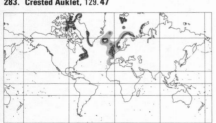

281. Cassin's Auklet, 129.48

282. Parakeet Auklet, 129.48
Least Auklet, 129.47,48

283. Crested Auklet, 129.47

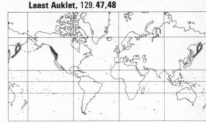

284. Rhinoceros Auklet, 130.47

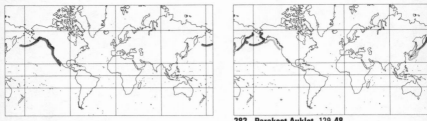

285. Atlantic Puffin, 130.47

286. Horned Puffin, 130.47

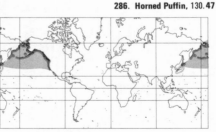

287. Tufted Puffin, 131.47

SEABIRDS OF THE BRITISH ISLES

INTRODUCTION

About 200 species of birds nest in the British Isles. Internationally, the most important part of the avifauna is the two-dozen or so breeding seabird species – more, and for many species in greater numbers, than in any other European country.

The reasons for this varied and abundant seabird fauna are not difficult to find. The long coastline provides a great variety of different nesting habitats: rocky cliffs for Guillemots, Razorbills and Kittiwakes, rocky stacks and islands for Shags, Cormorants and storm-petrels, vegetated islands for Puffins, Manx Shearwaters and Great Black-backed Gulls, sand-dunes and beaches for terns, salt-marshes for Black-headed Gulls, coastal moorlands for skuas, and so on.

More important still, the coastal waters are equally varied, being generally shallow (though in the west the deeper waters beyond the Continental Shelf are not that far distant) and rich in fish. Many areas contain abundant populations of small fish such as sand-eels, sprats and the young stages of herrings, which form the main diet of so many British seabirds. These fish are particularly abundant in the surface layers of inshore waters during the summer months, when they are joined by the young stages of several species whose adults spend most of their lives on the sea floor. In winter, the amount of surface living zooplankton, and the fish which prey on it, are considerably reduced, and those seabirds, notably the terns, which catch their food by means of a shallow dive, migrate south to areas where food resources are more reliable.

In general, except for the coastal feeding gulls and terns, the majority of British and Irish seabirds breed most commonly in northern Scotland and western Ireland. The sites of their breeding colonies are determined not only by the availability of suitable nesting sites but also by the availability of rich food resources close inshore. Particularly in the case of the auks, which pursue their prey under water, the colonies are situated frequently on (or on islands just off) major promontories and headlands, where strong tidal currents bring large numbers of surface living fish close inshore.

The geographical position of the British Isles is such that nearly all the seabird species of the temperate eastern North Atlantic breed here; the only ones nesting in similar latitudes in Europe that are absent are the Little Gull and Caspian and Gull-billed Terns. Three species (Leach's Storm-petrel, Great and Arctic Skuas) are confined to northern Scotland, and three more (Red-necked Phalarope, Black Guillemot and Common Gull) are virtually confined to Scotland and Ireland. The remainder breed throughout almost the entire latitudinal range of the British Isles. As mentioned earlier, most tend to be more numerous in the north, the only exceptions being the Manx Shearwater, Lesser Black-backed Gull and Common, Roseate, Little and Sandwich Terns which have their largest colonies in England and Wales rather than Scotland.

A marked feature of seabird breeding populations in the British Isles is that most species have increased during the present century. The few exceptions are the Little Tern, now one of the scarcest of all our seabirds, whose nesting beaches have become increasingly disturbed by man, and three of the auks, the Guillemot, Razorbill and Puffin. Various reasons have been put forward to account for these declines in auk numbers which have been particularly marked at their southernmost colonies; in the early 1970s Puffins in northwest Scotland decreased markedly too.

One important mortality factor, particularly for the Guillemot, has been oil pollution, which kills many thousands of individuals every year. Other more insidious kinds of marine pollution, in the form of various persistent toxic substances used in industry and agriculture and dumped or discharged indiscriminately into the sea, have been recognised in recent years. When more than 12,000 Guillemots were washed ashore dead in the Irish Sea in autumn 1969, several of the bodies examined were found to contain high concentrations of various industrial pollutants, including polychlorinated biphenyls (PCB's) and various toxic metals. While the deaths of the birds could not be attributed with certainty to poisoning (other stress factors such as moult, gales and possible food shortage were also at work), it is possible that these toxic substances are having sublethal (and occasionally lethal) effects on the birds. It is already clear that of all sea areas around the British Isles, the Irish Sea is the most heavily contaminated with toxic materials such as the PCB's and mercury. These materials are highly persistent and can accumulate in fish and seabirds to reach relatively high levels in their body tissues. They reach the Irish Sea from factories in industrialised north-west England through the direct discharge of effluents and from toxic wastes and sewage sludge dumped at sea. The slow rate of exchange of seawater within the partly enclosed Irish Sea does not facilitate the rapid dilution of these stable materials in the infinitely larger water mass of the open Atlantic. Levels of both mercury and PCB's in, for example, Guillemot eggs from some colonies in the Irish Sea average some twenty-five times higher than in similar samples from colonies remote from manufacturing industry, such as those in the Faeroes.

Yet, apart from the Little Tern, the auks and the Roseate Tern (which has slumped from 3500 to 600 pairs in the last few years) most British seabirds have increased over the last 70 years and appear still to be increasing despite increased pollution. Some increases, such as those of the Fulmar, Gannet, Shag and the larger gulls, have been spectacular. Many of the changes appear to have been due in one way or another to man's activities: in the cases of the larger gulls and the Fulmar to the provision of additional sources of food; in the case of the Gannet, and perhaps some other species, to the relaxation of persecution which was persistent and heavy at some colonies until towards the end of the 19th century. On the other hand, in the cases of marked changes among some other seabirds human factors do not seem to have played a major role, and the primary causes are often not known.

THE BREEDING SEABIRDS – GENERAL

Of the 'Primary Seabirds' included in this book, and defined in its Introduction (p. xiii), 25 species nest regularly in the British Isles. These species are all listed in the Table opposite which sets out the type of habitat they occupy for nesting. All are colonial (though the 'colonies' of two species, the Red-necked Phalarope and Black Guillemot, tend to be rather loosely knit), and, as can be seen from the Table, most nest exclusively on the coast, where their distributions are determined primarily by two factors: the availability of suitable and safe places in which to nest, and the proximity of an abundant food supply within the optimum feeding range of the species in question. A few species, however, also nest inland in small numbers, for example Common Tern, Lesser Black-backed Gull, Herring Gull and Cormorant. A few others, for example the Red-necked Phalarope and Common and Black-headed Gulls have exclusively or mainly inland, or at least fresh-water, breeding distributions in the British Isles, though in winter they are wholly marine (absent from the British Isles in the case of the phalarope) or partly marine (the gulls).

Breeding species

STORM-PETRELS

Two species of these our smallest seabirds nest in the British Isles, the **British Storm-petrel** (p. 48; Pl. 13) and the much rarer and more localised **Leach's Storm-petrel** (p. 49; Pl. 13). They share a number of common ecological features. Both feed on small planktonic organisms obtained from the surface of the sea as the birds hover just above it. Both are migratory, wintering mainly in the Atlantic in tropical or more southerly latitudes (Storm-petrels ringed at colonies in Britain have been recovered off the coasts of west and south Africa), although there have been a few winter records of both species in British waters. Both choose to nest on remote and usually uninhabited marine islands lacking mammalian predators such as foxes, cats and rats, while to further escape the attention of avian predators, they arrive at and depart from their nesting burrows only during the hours of darkness. Both nest mainly in natural crevices among rocks or in cliff face scree, favourite sites of Storm-petrels being among the boulders of storm beaches (where in such places on Annet, Isles of Scilly, many hundreds attain a nesting density as high as one pair to the square metre) or among the remnants of old drystone walls on islands on which farming was abandoned many years ago (e.g. Skokholm, Pembrokeshire, and in Shetland).

Both species arrive back at their breeding quarters in April, lay single eggs in late May or June after a long period of nocturnal courtship at and over the colony, and have protracted incubation and fledging periods so that the chicks do not fledge until September or October.

The two species are hardly ever seen in any numbers in daylight around British and Irish coasts, and those that are observed are usually off western coasts rather than eastern ones. Periodically, as in 1881, 1891, 1899, 1908, 1917 and 1952, weather 'wrecks' of Leach's Storm-petrels have occurred in late autumn, when large numbers were found close inshore and many others were blown inland in a moribund condition.

Leach's Storm-petrel is one of the most localised of all British breeding birds, and is largely restricted to four remote island groups off north-west Scotland: St. Kilda,

	Bare/rocky islands	Islands with soil/vegetation	Mainland seacliffs	Sand dunes	Shingle beaches	Coastal lagoons	Salt marshes	Coastal buildings	Paramaritime moors	Freshwater marshes, lakes
Fulmar	●	O	●					O		
Storm Petrel	●	O								
Leach's Petrel	●	O								
Manx Shearwater		●								
Gannet	●	O	O							
Cormorant	●	O	●							O
Shag	●		●							
Razorbill	●		●							
Guillemot	●		●							
Black Guillemot	●		●							
Puffin	O	●	O							
Kittiwake	●		●					O		
Great Black-backed Gull	●	●	O		●				●	O
Lesser Black-backed Gull	O	●	O	O	●				●	O
Herring Gull	●	●	●	●	●	O		O	O	O
Common Gull					O					●
Black-headed Gull					●	●	●			●
Sandwich Tern	O	●		●	●		O			
Common Tern	O	●		●	●	O	O			O
Arctic Tern	●	●		O	O				●	O
Roseate Tern	●	●								
Little Tern					●					
Great Skua									●	
Arctic Skua									●	
Red-necked Phalarope										●

TABLE: Nesting habitats of seabirds in the British Isles. Under each habitat type, ● denotes main habitat(s) of the species, O denotes less important habitats.

the Flannans, Sula Sgeir and North Rona. Being nocturnal the species is extremely difficult to census and the size of the total population, which is probably in excess of 2,000 pairs, can only be guessed at. Small numbers may breed on a few other remote north Scottish islands, for example on Foula (Shetland) and Sule Skerry (Orkney) where eggs have been found occasionally in the past. There are also a few old breeding records from western Ireland, but no positive ones more recently than 1906.

The British Storm-petrel has a much wider breeding distribution – mainly on western marine islands from the Isles of Scilly north to Shetland. As with Leach's Storm-petrel, the inaccessibility of the colonies and the problems of counting a nocturnal species make it impossible to assess the size of the total population, though it must run into tens of thousands. There is some evidence that the predation of adults by Great Black-backed Gulls has caused local population declines at some colonies, for example in the Isles of Scilly and in the Minch.

MANX SHEARWATER

This is a migratory species which, as has been shown by extensive ringing at British colonies, winters mainly off the Atlantic coast of Brazil, which is reached by an extremely rapid migratory passage in September-October. Birds return to the vicinity of their breeding colonies in early spring, some as early as late February, but come ashore only intermittently until breeding begins in earnest in late April. A single egg is laid and there are long incubation and fledging periods, most chicks departing in late August and September having been deserted by their parents about a week beforehand.

Manx Shearwaters (p. 32; Pl. 9) feed mainly on small fish – pilchards are especially important – which they obtain by shallow dives. During the early part of the breeding season off-duty parents may travel considerable distances to feed, those from colonies off the Pembrokeshire coast travelling even as far as the Bay of Biscay.

Most colonies are situated on soil-covered uninhabited islands off western and northern coasts. The birds excavate their own burrows or, more usually, occupy or renovate one excavated in a previous year. Like the two storm-petrels, arrivals and departures from the breeding colonies take place only at night, but even so at many colonies considerable numbers are killed and eaten by Great Black-backed Gulls. The species is, however, seen at sea much more often than the two storm-petrels. Around sunset, large rafts of shearwaters gather on the sea close to their breeding colonies waiting for dusk to fall, while their feeding movements often bring them close inshore where they can be watched passing by from suitable headlands in various parts of western Britain and Ireland.

Some colonies are very large – in all there are probably 130,000 breeding pairs on the Pembrokeshire islands of Skokholm and Skomer – but no assessment has been made of the total British population. Nor is it known whether the population as a whole is increasing or decreasing, though some smaller Scottish colonies and the one on Annet, Isles of Scilly, are known to have declined during the present century.

FULMAR

During the last 100 years and more the numbers of **Fulmars** (p. 25; Pl. 11) breeding in the British Isles, indeed in the North Atlantic generally, have increased enormously. Until 1878 the only British breeding station was St. Kilda, but in that year Foula (Shetland) was colonised and by the end of the century the species had begun nesting at other sites in Shetland and the Outer Hebrides. Since then it has spread steadily southwards and now, though the main population remains in the north, it breeds on nearly all suitable cliff bound coasts of the British Isles. Nest sites are typically on the higher parts of steep cliffs, often where the ledges have a covering of soil and vegetation.

Like the other petrels, the Fulmar is primarily a plankton feeder and is largely pelagic outside the breeding season. Over the years, fish offal and other waste thrown overboard from trawlers has become an increasingly important source of food for the species, and with the growth of the fishing industry it is this increased food supply which is believed to have enabled the Fulmar to expand its numbers so dramatically.

Although British Fulmars are known to range widely over the North Atlantic outside the breeding season (ringed birds commonly reach Greenland and New-foundland as well as northwest Europe), the cliffs on which they nest are visited by some birds in nearly all months of the year. Indeed a feature of the species is the numbers of pre-breeders which occupy nest-sites for many hours at a time, and many new sites are prospected by these birds for several years before they actually breed. Fulmars do not lay eggs until they are at least seven years old.

GANNET

By far the greatest proportion of the North Atlantic **Gannet** (p. 65; Pl. 18) population breeds in the British Isles, where the total now numbers well over 100,000 nesting pairs. These are distributed among 14 island and one mainland breeding stations, the largest of which is the St. Kilda group, which at the last count held a total of 52,000 pairs. Four other colonies exceed 10,000 pairs – on Grassholm (Pembrokeshire), Ailsa Craig (Ayrshire), Little Skellig (Co. Kerry) and Bass Rock (East Lothian). Only three contain fewer than 100 pairs – the single mainland and English colony at Bempton Cliffs (Yorkshire) and recently established ones on the Flannans (Outer Hebrides) and Fair Isle (Shetland).

The whole North Atlantic population has undergone a steady growth in numbers during the present century, this growth being attributed to the almost complete cessation of the Gannet's exploitation by man as a source of food; during the 19th century man's persecution reduced the world population by about two-thirds. The only British colony which is still harvested is Sula Sgeir (Outer Hebrides), and here the numbers of young taken are now controlled.

Gannets lay a single egg in April and have long incubation and fledging periods, most chicks leaving the nest in August or September. Although many adults remain in British waters throughout the winter, a number together with juveniles are migratory, most of them spending the first year or two of their life off the coasts of west Africa.

Feeding, weather and migratory movements of Gannets can be seen off all coasts of the British Isles, though they are commonest off headlands on western coasts of Britain and in Ireland (especially during strong north-west winds in autumn) and least common in south-east England

COMMON CORMORANT AND SHAG

Both species are widely distributed on rocky western and northern coasts of Britain and Ireland, though they are much scarcer on eastern and southern ones, particularly in England between Yorkshire and the Isle of Wight. **Cormorant** (p. 72; Pls. 20, 23) colonies tend to be more discrete and localised than **Shags'** (p. 74; Pl. 21), and are usually situated in the open – on the top of rocky islands or on broad ledges high up steep cliffs – whereas Shags usually (though not invariably) choose to nest lower down on cliffs in rock cavities, amidst boulders or in caves. While Shags nest exclusively on the coast, there are single Cormorant colonies a few miles inland in Wales (Merionethshire) and Scotland (Wigtownshire) and there are also a few well inland on islands in lakes in Ireland. Unlike in the Netherlands and some other parts of Europe, however, there are no tree-nest colonies in Britain.

Both species feed mainly in inshore waters, the Shag mainly on small non-commercial fish such as sand-eels, the Cormorant on a wide variety of larger fish species, including flat fish, and, from estuaries and fresh-water, eels and trout. Because of this, it is an unpopular bird with fishermen and in many areas is heavily persecuted. Both species are relatively sedentary, some birds dispersing outside the breeding season to other parts of the British coast (and a few Cormorants to inland waters); young birds from Britain may move as far as the adjacent parts of the Continental coast, while some young Cormorants migrate south as far as Portugal. Every few years, during periods of winter gales and food shortage, numbers of Shags are blown inland and may be seen on lakes, reservoirs and other fresh water even in the middle of England. The Shag has been increasing in numbers in Britain in recent years, particularly on the North Sea coasts of northern England and southern Scotland.

Cormorants and Shags normally build bulky seaweed nests and lay clutches of three eggs. The breeding season varies from place to place (and not necessarily with latitude: Shags in Shetland nest earlier than do those in the Isles of Scilly, though the reverse is true for Cormorants) but eggs are usually laid about April.

SKUAS

Two species breed, the **Arctic Skua** (p. 90; Pl. 26) and **Great Skua** (p. 89; Pl. 26), both of which are confined to northern Scotland where they have increased in numbers during the present century. The increase in Great Skuas has been especially marked. Towards the end of the last century it was confined to Foula and Unst (Shetland), but since about 1920 it has spread to many other parts of Shetland and south to Orkney, Caithness and Lewis (Outer Hebrides) and in the last few years to Sutherland and St. Kilda. Arctic Skuas have increased somewhat less dramatically, though they are still slowly expanding their range; this is similar to the Great Skua's but extends slightly farther south to include Coll and Jura in the Inner Hebrides. Both species lay clutches of two eggs and nest in rather loose colonies on moorland, usually close to the sea but sometimes a few miles inland.

Skuas characteristically obtain much of their food by chasing other seabirds in flight and forcing them to disgorge their food. Great Skuas, in addition, frequently take the eggs and young of other seabirds, and they also feed on waste thrown overboard from fishing boats. Both species are migratory (a few Great Skuas, however, occur in British waters even in mid-winter): Arctic Skuas winter mainly in the Atlantic south of the equator (one Shetland-ringed immature having been found as far away as Brazil), while Great Skuas disperse widely over the North Atlantic (one ringed bird having reached as far as the Caribbean). In autumn there is a well marked passage of Arctic Skuas down both sides of the British Isles, but many fewer are seen passing north in spring, when the species is particularly scarce along North Sea coasts. Great Skuas are regularly noted on migration (usually in March-April and August-October) along the North Sea, Irish Sea and Atlantic coasts of the British Isles, but their numbers are usually small except off western Ireland where there is a substantial southwards autumn passage.

GULLS

This familiar and highly successful seabird family numbers six regular breeding species in the British Isles, or seven if one includes the Mediterranean Gull, a pair or two of which have nested in southern England during the last few years. Without exception, all have increased in recent years, in several cases spectacularly and to the detriment of other seabirds.

For the present purpose, they can be divided into three groups: the two smaller *Larus* gulls, **Black-headed** (p. 103; Pls. 28, 31–2, 37, 40) and **Common** (p. 96; Pls. 28, 35, 40); the three larger *Larus* species, **Herring** (p. 97; Pls. 28, 35, 40), **Lesser Black-backed** (p. 97; Pls. 27, 35, 40) and **Great Black-backed** (p. 99; Pls. 27, 34, 40); and the single member of the genus *Rissa,* the **Kittiwake** (p. 106; Pls. 33, 39).

Although there are several large coastal colonies of **Black-headed Gulls**, this species and the **Common Gull** breed mainly inland and indeed many must spend most of their lives away from salt water. Characteristically, Black-headed Gulls – by far the more numerous and widespread of the two – nest in dense colonies among aquatic vegetation growing in eutrophic shallow lochs and peat bogs; increasingly, large numbers now also nest on coastal salt marshes, particularly in south-east England and Hampshire. Common Gulls, on the other hand, are much more local, being restricted mainly to Scotland and Ireland, and nest in small groups, typically on small rocky islands in deeper fresh-water lochs.

Both species feed extensively on farmland on worms and other terrestrial invertebrates, while in winter they also feed in or near large towns (rubbish dumps being especially favoured) and roost at night on large lakes and reservoirs. Marine feeders tend to be restricted to littoral waters. The British populations of both species are relatively sedentary (though numbers of Black-headed Gulls, particularly young birds, do migrate as far south as Spain and Portugal) and their numbers are augmented in winter by tens of thousands of immigrants from many parts of northern Europe.

Of the larger *Larus* gulls, the **Herring Gull** is the most abundant and widespread. As in many other parts of its range, its numbers have increased enormously in the British Isles in recent years, and some colonies are now very large indeed. Three number 15,000 or more breeding pairs: Walney Island (Lancashire), first established in 1928 and where only 120 pairs nested as recently as 1947; the Isle of May (Fife), first colonised in 1907 but holding only 455 pairs as recently as 1936; and Puffin Island (Anglesey), where numbers appear to have reached saturation point by about 1960, and have begun to decline again during the past decade. Colonies are found in many types of coastal habitats and in the last 30 years the species has increasingly nested on buildings, particularly among the chimney pots of coastal towns and villages in south-west and north-east England. Herring Gulls feed mainly by scavenging, and an important factor in the species' general increase and expansion has been its ability to exploit the abundance of edible refuse now provided by man at rubbish dumps, fishing ports and harbours, especially in winter.

Lesser Black-backed Gulls have increased less dramatically, and in parts of northern Scotland have even decreased. Nevertheless several large new colonies exist, notably among the Herring Gulls on Walney Island where there are now over 17,000 nesting Lesser Black-back pairs. Several large colonies also exist on inland moors, notably in Lancashire and Perthshire. Unlike the two other large gulls, this species is mainly migratory, British birds wintering along the coasts of Portugal and north-west Africa, though a small but increasing proportion of the population remains in southern England. It is also less of a scavenger, a greater part of its diet in the breeding season consisting of invertebrates obtained from the shore or from arable land, as well as fish caught in inshore waters.

The third member of this trio, the **Great Black-backed Gull**, has an almost exclusively coastal breeding distribution in most parts of Britain and Ireland, though some colonies in Orkney and the Outer Hebrides are situated a few miles inland. It breeds chiefly on western and northern coasts but is gradually extending its range and has recently colonised parts of north-east Scotland, while a pair or two occasionally attempts to nest on the English east coast and in Dorset. The species has increased enormously during the present century in all parts of the British Isles. In England and Wales it now numbers about 3,000 breeding pairs, compared with about 2,000 in 1956, 1,200 in 1930 and under 100 in 1900. The largest colonies (or groups of colonies) at the present time are those in the Isles of Scilly (over 1,500 pairs), on North Rona, Outer Hebrides (1,500 pairs) and on Hoy, Orkney (over 2,000 pairs).

Great Black-backs take a variety of mainly vertebrate foods and at many colonies some individuals prey almost exclusively on rabbits and seabirds such as Manx Shearwaters and Puffins and also young gulls; the last named may include those of its own species, especially in colonies where the density of nests is particularly great. Many others obtain most of their food by scavenging around fish docks and fishing fleets, often going far out to sea to seek out the latter.

The increase of the three large gulls has caused various problems The predation by Great Black-backs of other seabird species, notably adult Puffins and Storm-petrels and the fledging chicks of Razorbills and Guillemots, has almost certainly caused population declines among these species at certain colonies, although it is known, in the case of the Manx Shearwater, that if a breeding colony is large enough and flourishing it can survive a considerable amount of gull predation. Aside from predation, gulls can, by sheer weight of numbers, crowd out other ground-nesting species. Thus the disappearance of terns from the Isle of May and Annet (Isles of Scilly) seems to be due to the fact that today all available nesting territory is occupied by gulls (Herring Gulls on the former island, Lesser Black-backeds on the latter) so that no room is available for the terns by the time they arrive back from Africa in late April. For these reasons, attempts to control the numbers of breeding gulls have been made on a number of island nature reserves, including Skokholm and Skomer (Pembrokeshire) and the Isle of May.

Unlike the other gulls, the **Kittiwake** is a maritime species, occurring inshore only when breeding or on weather movements, and inland only accidentally when sick or storm-driven. While the bulk of the population breeds on the North Sea coasts of Scotland and northern England, colonies are found on all suitable cliff-bound coasts of the British Isles. Nests are usually situated on tiny ledges on cliff faces, but in recent years, following a 70-year period of continuous expansion in its numbers, a few colonies have been established in north-east England on man made structures such as harbour walls and the window ledges of water-side warehouses. The only colony on the southern part of the English east coast was established on a pier pavilion at Lowestoft (Suffolk) in 1958, while even more remarkable has been the nesting since 1962 of a few pairs on a building overlooking the River Tyne at Gateshead (Co. Durham), more than nine miles from the sea.

Kittiwakes live almost exclusively on small fish and zooplankton taken from or just beneath the surface of the sea. Outside the breeding season it disperses widely over the North Atlantic, many British-ringed birds having reached Newfoundland and Greenland. Dispersive, weather or feeding movements occur off nearly all parts of the coast of the British Isles, especially during onshore winds in spring and autumn, but also on a smaller scale in other months of the year.

TERNS

Excluding the inland nesting **Black Tern** (p. 110; Pl. 44), which has made a few recent attempts to re-establish itself as a British breeding bird on the Ouse Washes (Cambridgeshire), and the **Gull-billed Tern** (p. 110; Pl. 43), which has nested in Britain on only one occasion (in Essex in 1950) five species of terns breed in the British Isles. All tend to nest on flat ground on low-lying, often sandy, coasts where inlets and estuaries provide shallow and relatively undisturbed waters in which small fish and crustacea living near the surface can be caught by means of an air to sea plunging dive. All except the Little Tern usually nest in large, dense colonies often with other tern species; all have clutches of two or three eggs laid in May or June; and all are highly migratory, wintering south of the equator, one of them, the Arctic Tern, going as far south as the Antarctic Ocean.

Sandwich Terns (p. 119; Pls. 41, 43) are the first to arrive back in spring (the first birds in mid-March). In Britain they nest entirely on the coast, but in Ireland there are a few colonies in the west of the country inland on lakes. Thanks to protection at many breeding sites, such as Scolt Head and Blakeney Point (Norfolk) and the Farne Islands (Northumberland), they have increased in recent years and the total population in Britain and Ireland now exceeds 10,000 pairs.

Roseate Terns (p. 113; Pl. 42) are the latest to arrive in spring (late April) and are entirely coastal. There are about 20 colonies, mostly on the coasts of the Irish Sea. The British Isles form the European headquarters of the species. Roseate Terns increased considerably during 1900–50, but have decreased again recently, from 3500 pairs in the mid-1960s to 600 pairs in 1977.

Arctic and Common Terns, while mainly coastal, do also breed inland, the **Arctic Tern** (p. 111; Pls. 41–2) now only in northern Scotland (on riverain shingle banks and on islands in lochs), the **Common Tern** (p. 111; Pls. 42–3) in small numbers in Scotland and, increasingly, on islands in gravel pits and other fresh-water in England. Less is known about their population sizes and status trends than for other terns. Common Terns number about 6,000 pairs in England and there are perhaps as many again in Scotland and Ireland together, with a few in north Wales. Arctic Terns are most abundant in northern Scottand, the bulk of the population probably being found in Orkney, but there is also a large colony on the Farne Islands (Northumberland). Both species may have decreased slightly in the last few decades.

Little Terns (p. 117; Pl. 43) nest only on the coast, usually on shinle beaches. Although there are over 100 colonies most of them are small and the total population is only 1,600 pairs. This is one of the few British seabirds known to be decreasing at the present time, this decrease being almost entirely due to disturbance at the breeding sites by holidaymakers. In reserves and other areas where the species is protected its numbers are being maintained.

AUKS

Excluding the flightless Great Auk, which became extinct in the middle of the 19th century, there are four breeding species, the **Guillemot** (p. 127; Pls. 46, 48), **Razorbill** (p. 126; Pl. 46), **Black Guillemot** (p. 127; Pl. 46) and **Puffin** (p. 130; Pl. 47). All except the Black Guillemot have decreased in the British Isles in recent decades. The decrease in the Guillemot population, particularly in the southern half of the country has been a cause of concern, as was a recent heavy decrease in Puffin numbers at several large colonies in north-west Scotland.

The one auk species which has not decreased is the Black Guillemot, which differs from the other three in several respects. It lives almost entirely in inshore waters; it has a more varied diet including a greater proportion of crustacea; it is almost entirely sedentary, being found only rarely in winter outside its breeding range; it is only loosely colonial, nesting individually in crevices amongst boulders low down near the sea; and it lays two eggs (not one). The bulk of the population is found in north and north-west Scotland (especially in the Northern Isles) and there are small numbers around most parts of the Irish coast. A recent gradual expansion in breeding range has occurred in the Irish Sea region, a small number of pairs having become established as far south as Anglesey since about 1962.

The other three auks feed almost entirely on fish, especially sand-eels, sprats and young herrings, which they obtain by means of a dive from the surface and an under-water chase in which the wings provide the main propulsion. All are highly colonial, and each shows a preference for a particular nest site (though some Guillemot and Puffin sites overlap with Razorbills'): Guillemots nest on narrow cliff ledges, Razorbills in rock crevices and beneath boulders, while Puffins burrow into soil. All lay eggs in May, but while some Guillemots and Razorbills intermittently land at their breeding sites from November or December onwards, Puffins, which are more pelagic in winter, do not return until March or even April. All incubate their eggs for periods of 32–42 days, but while the chicks of Guillemots and Razorbills leave their cliff sites for the sea after only 15–23 days (when flightless and weighing less than a third of their eventual adult weight), Puffin chicks remain in the nest burrow for seven weeks, during the last of which they have been deserted by their parents and live off their accumulated body fat. The chicks of Guillemots and Razorbills are accompanied out to sea by one of their parents, usually the male which then attends them for an unknown period of time, probably several weeks. In September-October the adults undergo a complete wing and tail moult, during which time they are briefly flightless. Adult Puffins, on the other hand, usually have their wing and tail moult in late winter or early spring.

Outside the breeding season, Guillemots and Razorbills disperse out to sea (though not normally into the pelagic zone), many birds reaching the coasts of continental Europe from Norway south to the Bay of Biscay, with some Razorbills going even farther south to west Morocco and into the Mediterranean. However, since Guillemots come ashore at their breeding colonies as early as November-December many adults must be relatively sedentary and remain at sea off our coasts throughout the year. Puffins are rarely seen from shore during the winter and presumably disperse well out to sea: birds ringed in Britain have reached New-foundland, Greenland, the western Mediterranean, and many parts of the Atlantic coast of continental Europe, particularly southern Norway.

The breeding distributions of Guillemot and Razorbill are very similar, though the former is much the more numerous of the two. Both species have declined during the last 30 years, particularly the Guillemot for which the numbers have been most heavily reduced at its southernmost colonies. Many thousands of Guillemots and Razorbills are killed by oil pollution every year and it seems probable that this has been the main cause of their declines in the south, where some colonies have been reduced by 90% since the 1930s.

The numbers of Puffins breeding at many southern colonies also declined markedly during the period 1920–50. Several colonies that once held many thousands of breeding birds now have fewer than 100 pairs (e.g. Annet, Isles of Scilly; Lundy, Devon; Ailsa Craig, Ayrshire) or none at all (e.g. St. Tudwal's Islands, Caernarvonshire). Around 1970, sharp decreases were noted in north-west Scotland, including on St. Kilda, the Shiants and the Clo Mor cliffs in Sutherland. The accidental introduction of rats was almost certainly the cause of the earlier declines at some island colonies, while at others oil pollution or increased predation by Great Black-backed Gulls may have contributed. But the chief reasons for the recent decline in north-west Scotland are unknown and for the time being it fortunately appears to have ceased.

RED-NECKED PHALAROPE

This rare summer migrant has a very limited breeding range in the British Isles and is restricted to a few small, shallow fresh-water pools and lakes in northern Scotland (notably Shetland) and Co. Mayo, Ireland. The total breeding population is only about 50 pairs, and even on passage it is rarely seen at sea around the coasts of the British Isles.

NON-BREEDING VISITORS

In addition to the breeding birds already mentioned, a further 13 species of seabirds are annual visitors to the British Isles, while 23 more (listed on pp. 274–5) have been recorded as accidental vagrants.

PROCELLARIIDAE

Two species which nest in the southern hemisphere, the **Sooty Shearwater** (p. 32; Pl. 8) and **Great Shearwater** (p. 31; Pl. 9), occur regularly in British and Irish waters, mainly in July-October, during their non-breeding season. Both species occur quite widely in the Atlantic just north-west of the British Isles in July-August and then move southwards down the west coast of Ireland and, during on-shore winds, southwest England, between August and early October. Small numbers, particularly Sooty Shearwaters, enter the North Sea. Another species, **Cory's Shearwater** (p. 30; Pl. 9) of the Mediterranean and Atlantic Islands, regularly disperses north in late summer as far as the entrance to the English Channel, and in certain years occurs in some numbers off south-west Ireland and south-west England; a few have been recorded as far north as Shetland. The **Balearic Shearwater** (p. 33; Pl. 9), the distinctive western Mediterranean race of the Manx Shearwater, also occurs regularly in the English Channel in autumn, a few passing north into the North and Irish Seas and sometimes reaching as far as Scotland.

PHALAROPES

Grey Phalaropes (p. 85; Pl. 25) occur annually on autumn passage, between late August and November, though their numbers are extremely variable. At irregular intervals, when strong westerly gales coincide with their south-easterly migration across the North Atlantic in September, large flocks numbering hundreds of birds occur off the coasts of south-west England and western Ireland; the largest flock recorded was one of 1,000 birds in the Isles of Scilly in September 1960. But in most years only very small numbers are seen, including ones and twos on parts of the English east and south coasts.

SKUAS

As well as the two breeding species, two other skuas – **Pomarine Skua** (p. 90; Pl. 26) and **Long-tailed Skua** (p. 91; Pl. 26) – are scarce but regular migrants in the British Isles. Pomarine Skuas occur in small numbers (rarely more than ten together) in spring and autumn off most coasts, though they are recorded most frequently off north Norfolk, Cornwall and around Ireland. Long-tailed Skuas are even more uncommon, and are usually recorded as single birds in autumn off the coasts of Norfolk and Northumberland, though there are records from many other parts of the country. In recent years odd birds have sometimes remained for a few weeks in summer at the Arctic Skua colony on Fair Isle.

GULLS

Two northern species, **Iceland Gull** (p. 99; Pls. 29, 33, 35, 40) and **Glaucous Gull** (p. 99; Pls. 29, 35, 40), are regular winter visitors, particularly to fishing ports in the northern half of the British Isles. Glaucous is the more common, some birds reaching southern England in most winters. Immatures of both species sometimes remain in Britain in summer. Another northern gull, the highly migratory **Sabine's Gull** (p. 106; Pls. 33, 39), occurs regularly in very small numbers off south-west England and south-west Ireland, mainly during strong westerly winds in autumn.

Two other gulls are regular visitors. The **Mediterranean Black-headed Gull** (p. 103; Pls. 32, 37), a pair or two of which have nested in recent years in southern England, occurs in very small numbers, chiefly on the east and south coasts of England. It has been identified in all months of the year, and individuals sometimes overwinter in the same locality for several years in succession. The **Little Gull** (p. 105; Pls. 31, 32, 37) has bred just once in Britain (on the Ouse Washes in 1976), and though others often oversummer here, it appears mainly as a passage and winter visitor, being generally most common and widespread in September-October. It occurs mainly singly or in small flocks (in the south often with migrant Black Terns) but occasionally in flocks of up to 100 and more, especially on the coast of Fife in late summer. Though most frequent on the English east and south coasts it is also recorded fairly frequently elsewhere in the British Isles, including inland.

AUKS

The arctic breeding **Little Auk** (p. 125; Pl. 46) is a winter visitor, occurring regularly and often in some numbers off northern Scotland during the months of November to February. Variable, but usually small numbers occur annually in the North Sea as far south as Norfolk, and periodically winter 'wrecks' occur, when moribund Little Auks may be found widely inland in Britain.

RARE VISITORS

The following seabird species have also been recorded in the British Isles as vagrants. A few, such as the Little Shearwater and White-winged Black Tern, have been seen almost annually in recent years, but the majority have been recorded on fewer than ten occasions, some, such as the Black-capped Petrel and White-faced Storm-petrel, only once.

Black-browed Albatross	Bulwer's Petrel
Black-capped Petrel	Little Shearwater

Wilson's Storm-petrel	Bonaparte's Gull
White-faced Storm-petrel	Ross's Gull
Madeiran Storm-petrel	Whiskered Tern
Magnificent Frigate-bird	White-winged Black Tern
Wilson's Phalarope	Caspian Tern
Ivory Gull	Bridled Tern
Great Black-headed Gull	Sooty Tern
Laughing Gull	Royal Tern
Franklin's Gull	Brunnich's Guillemot
Slender-billed Gull	

WATCHING SEABIRDS

Seabird-watching in the British Isles takes two main forms: first, observation at the breeding colonies, and second, observation from coastal headlands or islands where large numbers of seabirds pass by on migration or on feeding or weather movements. Since Britain and Ireland, together with their offshore islands, have over 10,000 km of coastline and numerous places where seabirds can be observed *en masse*, it is beyond the scope of this section to list each and every important seabird site. Many of the biggest breeding colonies, including the largest of them all – St. Kilda – are remote and inaccessible. The purpose of the map which follows on page 20, therefore, is to show a selection of diverse sites which are reasonably accessible to the public or at which 'bird observatories' provide accommodation for visiting bird-watchers staying overnight.

Two kinds of site are shown. Breeding colonies (marked ●) are generally best visited during the months of May, June and July – for most species the main breeding season. August is too late for many species (virtually all auks, for example, have gone to sea again by the end of July), though some, such as the Gannet and petrels, having long fledging periods, are still about until early September or later. Sea-watching sites (marked x) are mainly composed of headlands, where under the right weather conditions at appropriate times of the year, large numbers of seabirds can be seen moving past relatively close to the coast, or at least at distances at which they can be identified with binoculars or telescope. In general, strong onshore winds in autumn (and to a lesser extent at other seasons), especially if coupled with poor visibility at sea, provide the best conditions for large coastal movements of seabirds.

Finally, it should not be forgotten that cross-channel ferries across, for example, the English Channel and Irish Sea, and between Cornwall and the Isles of Scilly, often provide excellent opportunities for seeing seabirds in their natural environment – at sea.

DISTRIBUTION MAPS

Immediately after the map of sites are 24 individual maps showing the breeding distributions of the 25 species which nest in Britain and Ireland. (The maps for Guillemot and Razorbill are combined since their distributions are virtually identical.) No attempt has been made to map non-breeding distribution, but the captions indicate the time of the year when each species is present in British and Irish waters, and the coasts on which they appear.

BRITISH SEABIRD SITES

1 Hermaness, Unst, Shetland. Large sea-bird colonies on cliffs, including gannetry; large puffinry on cliff top, and Arctic and Great Skuas breeding on blanket moorland.

2 Noss, Shetland. Has Shetland's largest gannetry, both skuas, and a large variety of cliff-nesting seabirds. Can be viewed best by tourist boats from Lerwick.

3 Fair Isle, Shetland (bird observatory). Best known for rare terrestrial migrant birds, but has fine seabird colonies including both skuas, all auks and the storm-petrel.

4 Isle of May, Fife (bird observatory). Huge Herring Gull colony (15,000 pairs), also auks, including large puffinry.

5 Bass Rock, East Lothian. Large gannetry (10,000 pairs) at which a single Black-browed Albatross has over-summered in recent years.

6 Farne Islands, Northumberland. Large and varied seabird populations including Sandwich, Roseate, Common and Arctic Terns, Puffins, Guillemots, Kittiwakes, Fulmars, Shags, etc. Arctic Skuas frequent offshore in autumn. Reached by frequent day-trip boats from Seahouses.

7 Northumberland coast. Good autumn sea-watching from several headlands, including Cullernose Point and St. Mary's Island, with numbers of gannets, kittiwakes, skuas, shearwaters, etc., passing close inshore, especially during cyclonic northeast winds.

8 Flamborough Head and Bempton Cliffs, Yorkshire. England's only gannetry, but also large numbers of Kittiwakes, Fulmars, Razorbills and Guillemots. The headland provides a good vantage point for migrant seabirds in spring and autumn.

9 Scolt Head, Norfolk, and
10 Blakeney Point, Norfolk. Best known for their terns, including Sandwich and Common and two of Britain's largest Little Tern colonies.

11 Cley, Norfolk. Autumn seabird movements, notably of skuas (including Pomarine and occasional Long-tailed), small numbers of Sooty Shearwaters, and in November Little Auks not infrequently.

12 Dungeness, Kent (bird observatory). England's only established breeding Common Gulls, also Little and Common Terns, Herring Gulls. Offshore passage movements of terns (including Roseate and Black), Little Gulls, Arctic Skuas, Gannets, etc. Mediterranean Black-headed Gulls are annual visitors.

13 Selsey Bill, Sussex. Various seabirds offshore, especially terns, including Gull-billed almost annually.

14 Portland Bill, Dorset (bird observatory). Small numbers of breeding auks and other seabirds. Autumn movements offshore include shearwaters (especially Balearic), skuas, gannets, kittiwakes and terns.

15 Isles of Scilly. Great variety of breeding seabirds, including England's only Storm-petrels and Manx Shearwaters, Puffins, Razorbills, Guillemots, Fulmars, Roseate Tern and Common Terns, and huge Great Black-backed Gull colonies. Landing is prohibited on many seabird islands, but there are frequent boat trips around them in summer. Autumn sea-watching regularly produces skuas (including Pomarine), rarer shearwaters, Grey Phalaropes and Sabine's Gulls.

16 St. Ives, Cornwall. Excellent autumn seawatching during strong northwest winds, when large numbers of auks, Gannets, Kittiwakes and shearwaters and skuas pass very close inshore under the 'island'. Local sewage outfall has attracted rare gulls including Bonaparte's, Mediterranean, Black-headed, Sabine's and Little.

17 Lundy, Devon. Auk colonies, including Puffins, now much reduced, plus other common cliff-breeding seabirds.

18 Pembrokeshire Islands. Skokholm and Skomer (daily boat trips, weather providing, in summer from Martinshaven) famed for huge Manx Shearwater colonies; Puffins, Razorbills, Guillemots, Kittiwakes, Fulmars, etc.; large Storm-petrel colony on Skokholm. Grassholm, further offshore, has very large gannetry.

19 South Stack, Anglesey. Colonies of Guillemots and other cliff-nesting seabirds seen easily from lighthouse steps.

20 Walney Island, Lancashire. Site of Britain's largest gull colony – altogether over 30,000 pairs of Herring and Lesser Black-backs.

21 Ailsa Craig, Ayrshire. Large gannetry and many other cliff-nesting seabirds, though Guillemot, Razorbill and Puffin numbers now much reduced.

22 Rhum, Inner Hebrides. Various cliff-nesting seabirds, but chiefly noted for large Manx Shearwater colony near mountain top at 2,500 feet.

23 Handa, Sutherland. Huge Guillemot colonies (30,000 pairs) and large numbers of other cliff-nesting seabirds, including Puffins. Recently colonised by Great and Arctic Skuas.

24 Cape Clear, Co. Cork (bird observatory). Sea-watching site *par excellence*; often huge movements of shearwaters (including Great, Sooty, Cory's and occasional Little Shearwaters) and many commoner seabirds; even albatrosses are not unknown. Many other headlands in Ireland provide excellent opportunities for sea-watching.

NOTE: *Bird Observatories* Addresses of those providing accommodation can be obtained from the British Trust for Ornithology, Beech Grove, Tring, Hertfordshire, England.

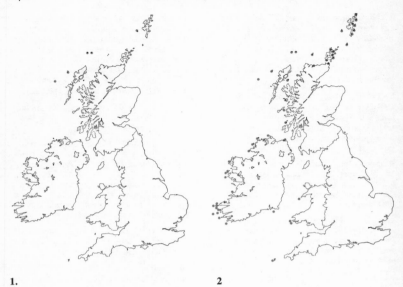

1.   2

1. Leach's Storm-petrel Summer visitor (April–October). On autumn passage most frequent off W. Ireland and S.W. Cornwall; annual in Liverpool Bay and off N. Norfolk; infrequent elsewhere.

2. Storm Petrel Summer visitor (April–October). Uncommon off British east and south coasts.

3. Manx Shearwater Summer visitor (March–October). Relatively uncommon off east and south coasts. Mediterranean race (Balearic Shearwater) reaches English Channel in autumn. Largest colonies are shown ■.

4. Fulmar Present all year. Bulk of the population is in N. Scotland.

5. Gannet Present all year, though young birds and some adults migrate south in winter. Fifteen colonies, of which five number over 10,000 pairs ⊡, five over 1,000 pairs ⊙ and five under 1,000 pairs ●.

6. Cormorant Present all year. Occurs off all coasts (also inland, especially in N. Britain) outside the breeding season.

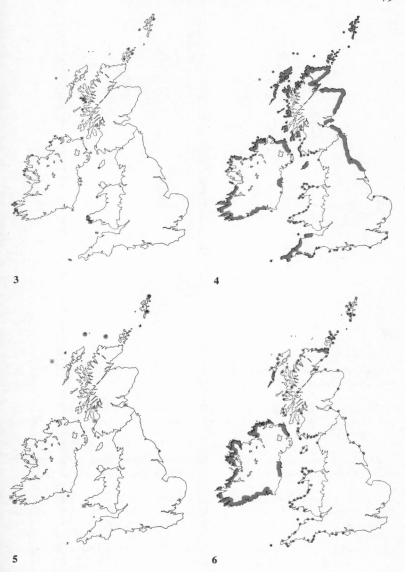

3

4

5

6

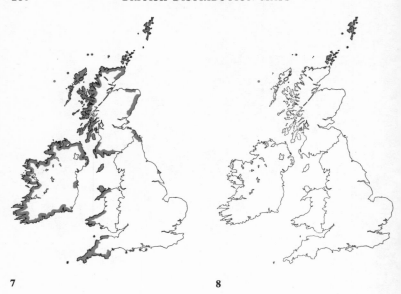

7   8

7. Shag Present all year. In winter occurs in small numbers off S.E. Britain, but only accidentally inland.

8. Great Skua Mainly summer visitor (March–November). All coasts on passage, usually small numbers, most frequent and numerous off S.W. Ireland and W. Cornwall.

9. Arctic Skua Summer visitor (April–October). Southward passage down North Sea and Atlantic coasts in autumn; less numerous and frequent in spring.

10. Black-headed Gull Present all year, in winter including many immigrants from northern and central Europe. An inland as much as coastal species in summer and winter, being widespread in S. England at the latter season.

11. Common Gull Present all year, including continental immigrants. Widespread (inland and coasts) on passage and in winter.

12. Herring Gull Present all year. Widespread in winter.

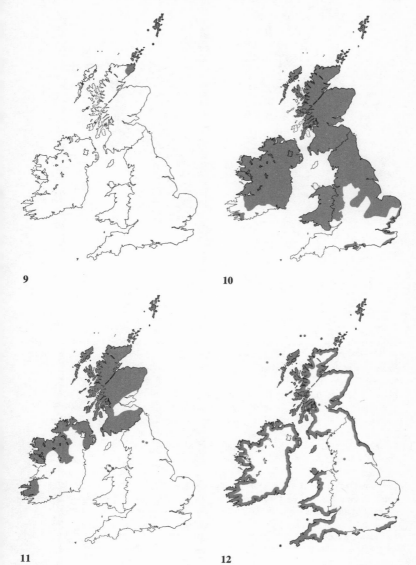

9

10

11

12

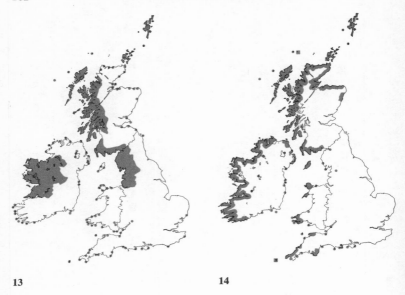

13   14

13. Lesser Black-backed Gull Mainly summer (February–October) visitor, but increasing numbers over-winter, especially in S. England. Breeds mainly on coasts but there are some inland colonies in areas shown in solid colour. Widespread, coasts and inland, on passage.

14. Great Black-backed Gull Present all year. Largest breeding concentrations (all over 1,000 pairs) at Scilly, North Rona and Hoy (Orkney) are shown ■. Widespread, all coasts and inland, in winter.

15. Kittiwake Present all year. Disperses at sea (but visits all coasts) outside breeding season.

16. Sandwich Tern Summer visitor (March–October). Largest colonies (over 1,000 pairs) at Scolt Head and Stiffkey (Norfolk) and Farne Islands and Coquet Island (Northumberland) shown ■. All coasts on passage.

17. Roseate Tern Summer visitor (April–September). Small numbers on passage on North Sea, English Channel and St George's Channel coasts.

18. Common Tern Summer visitor (April–October). All coasts (also inland) on passage.

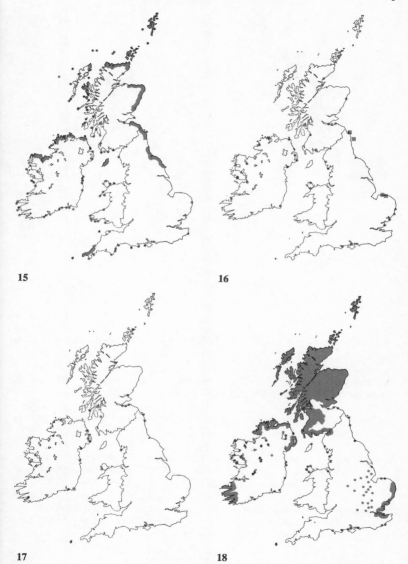

15

16

17

18

19   20

19. Arctic Tern Summer visitor (April–September). All coasts (also inland) on passage.

20. Little Tern Summer visitor (April–September). All coasts on passage though scarce in S.W. Wales and S.W. England.

21. Black Guillemot Present all year. Sedentary, inshore; rarely seen away from breeding areas.

22 Guillemot and **Razorbill** Present all year. Breeding distributions of the two species are similar. At cliff colonies Guillemots nearly always outnumber Razorbills. Present off all coasts in winter though most common in the west.

23. Puffin Mainly summer visitor (April–August) to inshore waters, though present out at sea throughout year. Largest colonies (over 20,000 pairs), on St Kilda, Shiants, Clo Mor and Sule Skerry, shown ■.

24. Red-necked Phalarope Summer visitor (April–September). Rare everywhere on passage though very small numbers are annual in autumn on East Anglian coasts.

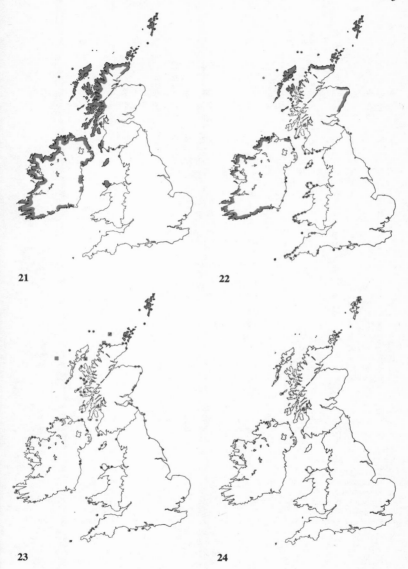

21

22

23

24

INDEX OF ENGLISH NAMES

References in Roman (normal) type are to text pages where the bird is described; in **bold** type they are to **colour plate numbers**; in *italic* type to *map numbers*.

INDEX OF SCIENTIFIC NAMES

References in Roman (normal) type are to text pages where the bird is described; in **bold** type they are to **colour plates**; in *italic* type to *map numbers*. Different subspecies are only indexed where their page, plate or map numbers differ.

STORK: Sowing Season

Book I

Brian Patrick Edwards

ROGUS ARDENS

BIRMINGHAM, ALABAMA

Brian Patrick Edwards/Rogus Ardens
Birmingham, Alabama
Email: Brianpedwards@yahoo.com
Instagram: @cathoholicism

Book Layout © 2017 BookDesignTemplates.com

Edited by Samantha Gluck

Cover Art & Design by Chris Lewis (www.BaritusCatholic.com)

STORK: Sowing Season/ Brian Patrick Edwards. -- 1st ed.
ISBN 978-0-578-67513-8

This book is dedicated to Lyla, Kristen, and the Blessed Mother. I'm increasingly thankful for you all every passing day.

I'd also like to give special thanks to Samantha Gluck for all of the incredible help and work you put into this project with me. It would have been in the trashcan without you!

The family is the test of freedom; because the family is the only thing that the free man makes for himself and by himself.

—GILBERT K. CHESTERTON

CONTENTS

PROLOGUE

"How did it come to this?" This is the question asked by those few with whom morals and objective truths still resonate. It is a mystery -- a scandal, actually -- that despite such magnificent advancements in technology, the innate barbarism of humanity was never truly quenched.

Instead of becoming more humane, we remain savages inhabiting a sleek and modern world. We are yet wicked in these times, which pull tomorrow into the present at an increasingly rapid pace. Immorality has made us its slaves. Its deceptive brand of false freedom forces us to live within a beautiful lie. Now, many have forgotten what was stolen from us right before our eyes. Sacrifice, slaughter, offering our own before the gods of this mean, new era; all done in the name of convenience, fear, success, and prosperity. At what point does mankind stop moving forward, to pause, to turn back and behold all that we have left behind?

The citizens of the Earth now live under a singular leader, a god of modern times. His mercy and benevolence extends to those most obedient; and, the disobedient suffer his wrath, which visits and stings quietly in the night. His name is Unity and he is the answer - for most. Unity, a tireless, ever-working artificial intelligence that reigns with cold calculated data. If the earth becomes hungry, he feeds it. If the earth becomes full, he empties it. The people spend their days wishing and praying to this singular provider, and he listens. He hears all, but he only answers his most obedient.

Religion has been slain, eradicated; the churches stand empty. Countries previously known as the most devoted are now populated with corpses of the past -- a people with no sense of the transcendent. Waves of famine and disease – some raising suspicion and giving birth to myriad conspiracy theories – serendipitously resolved many of the overpopulation concerns reported by a global consortium of scientists. Rather than draw on our incredible imaginations to innovate solutions for these and other modern fears, we allowed our primordial barbarism to drive our decisions.

The skeptics -- and those much maligned conspiracy theorists -- claim these supposed natural events were not natural at all, but synthesized. They believe Unity developed a new and powerful way to execute swift solutions to global problems, while protecting the naivety of Earth's citizens:

Indeed, all life between both tropic lines, around the globe, went dark. No heartbeat of light could be seen from the heavens, no traffic moving people to and fro, no humanity remained between those two imaginary lines.

This ushered forth a new era -- one in which an unprecedented manipulation of mankind began. Rights were taken from us and we watched without protest. Looking back, it was all quite easy, really. The blueprints for this new global world had already been drawn. For nearly a century, most women of the world were already on board with the idea that to prevent and terminate pregnancies gave them power and freedom. As with one shrill battle cry, women demanded freedom from what they believed to be an insufferable burden -- childbearing.

In order to convince women to abandon their innermost longings and their true purpose, the status of human life must be demoted. News, magazines, books, movies -- all forms of media -- promoted a new definition of what was once considered sacred and precious. That a pregnancy amounts to a clump of cells, a parasite, a non-human became the ubiquitous belief for most.

In this way, human life became increasingly unimportant in the minds of the masses. Suddenly, due to one of those mysterious natural events, all human females became infertile -- the ancient world called it barren -- and, thus, free of natural pregnancies. The great majority of people barely cared at all, so blind were they.

The claim that this global infertility came about from an act of nature was taken as fact. No one questioned it, certainly not the media. Out of this *crisis* was born a company, STORK, a new, safer pathway for those wishing to raise a child. Babies produced through STORK were all lab-grown, perfectly healthy, and free of detestable genetic and physical flaws. What else would anyone want in the new age of health and overall perfection?

Though this solution to the infertility problem may seem wonderful on its face, the reality is that only the most obedient can afford the high cost of a STORK child. Citizens of the Earth who refuse to pay taxes due to their strongly held moral beliefs will never have access to an income capable of covering STORK's fees. Only the elite and obedient are capable of experiencing the joy of parenting.

So, for some, the question is no longer, "How did it come to this," but rather, "How do we put an end to this?" Some people are awake and are pausing to turn back and behold all they have left behind. And what they see makes them long to return down that path. They desire to reclaim those stolen natural rights and the freedom to enjoy living. A new generation is rising and they seek to rule themselves for better or worse, until the last breath from the very last human fades.

CHAPTER ONE

Michael woke with a startle as a clamor of harsh sound erupted directly into his ears. His high cheeks lifted to meet the enormous eyebrows lowering as he winced in pain. He'd been in another place, within his resting mind, soaking his feet in the sandy and gritty surf of a beach far away. The disconnect between heaven and earth lurched forward, right as he was ready to dive into the waves as they met the beach. The realization that his feet were no longer wet and the sun no longer burned on his back brought him quickly back to reality and he knew he was in his bed.

"Well, off to work we go." Peace followed once he deactivated the device embedded within his ear, the Auris, with a quick pinch to his earlobe. He glared over at the curtain caught up in a light breeze, momentarily letting sunlight bleed through. His pupils shrank until all that could be seen in his eyes were brightly lit fields of hazel and green. Michael sat up, tied his unruly long black, greasy hair behind his head and let his eyes run along his wife's curves, as she laid turned away from him, completely covered in sheets. Today was an off day for her and he didn't want to disturb her. The fog of sleep lifted rapidly as he sprang from bed and grabbed his scrunched-up jeans and a shirt from the floor.

Now fully alert, he quietly got ready and listened intently to the news his Auris implant, a device that along with the Visum contacts had replaced the traditional phone. The Auris implants were for sound and listening, and were quite nice in audio quality. The Visum, contacts that changed in opacity for the viewer to read and watch whatever they desired. The contacts watched for whatever gestures their users made, changing from page to page or even typing at times when they didn't want to speak whatever private message they wanted to compose. Most everyone had them, some like Michael and his family used bootlegged versions. They have nearly all the same features, but retain a certain privacy when it comes to anonymity, something which is quite important to those who live outside the laws and taxations declared by Unity. Yes, technology had become great and evermore powerful, but there were still limits, and men still had means to remain secretive, even in a world that is ruled by the supreme Artificial Intelligence. The bootlegged versions were, of course, illegal and some had many defects, but no one was going from ear to ear checking them.

The Auris read to him, *"Protests in Southside, last night, in the wake of the failed bombing attempt on*

Birmingham's STORK clinic last week. The demonstrators were assembled, petitioning the Unity to finally put an end to the radica-" His mood changed quickly after hearing the opening details, prompting him to switch the news off. Silence would be better, although his thoughts were already filled with conflicting ideas and emotions that further bottled themselves up for a later time. He hated STORK and the atrocities he believed they and Unity guilty of committing, but he had an even greater disgust for the radicals these days. The radicals -- people who championed familiar dogmas, who had been holy and devoted at one time -- had allowed themselves to become corrupted with seething hatred.

Numerous factions from across the globe make up the group commonly referred to as *radicals*. A diverse variety of gods and ideologies feed the group's common desire to control and destroy. The two major factions comprise the bulk of the radical presence in the North American provinces -- the Retrogrades and the self-proclaimed Zealots. Numbers for both groups continue to grow rapidly as hatred for Unity deepens and spreads.

The Retrogrades want to send all of humanity back to the Dark Ages, simply desiring a more natural world, empty of advanced technologies. The Zealots, whose adherents largely consist of fallen-away Catholics and various protestant Christian denominations, seek to end the practices of STORK and eventually overthrow Unity altogether. They are more destructive than the

Retrogrades, often carrying out violent attacks because they believe that without engaging in a holy crusade, the end of their kind will surely be upon them. Even with the Church's excommunication of the Zealots' leaders, they continue to make excuses and vehemently claim that the violence is necessary and their fight a holy one.

He allowed thoughts about all of this to swirl in his mind while vigorously brushing his teeth. Drying his hands, he quickly glanced at the mirror to make sure his hair was at least passably neat and smoothed back. *To Hell with these old wooden stairs!* Almost every step creaked as he finally made his way down to the living room. There he found Cole, already awake. Cole is the younger of two cousins living with Michael and his wife. Their mother is an addict and when Michael found her strung out in an alleyway, something he learned happened daily, he invited Cole and Stone to live with them. The father vanished just before Cole's birth and no one seemed to know his name. Michael believes their father introduced his aunt to opioids early on in the relationship, but it's entirely possible the two boys come from different men.

Cole stands quite a bit taller than his older brother, his light complexion and curly brown hair contrast sharply with Stone's short, stocky build, dark hair, and dark complexion. Their personalities differ as much as their appearances. Stone goes out often and typically ends up partying, fighting, and chasing skirts. Cole is reserved, keeps to himself, and has no problem following rules.

Cole sipped from his steaming mug of coffee, peering at Michael above his fogged-over glasses, his boney, hairless face hidden behind the cup.

"Mornin' Mikey. Left some bacon and eggs on the counter."

"Thanks, bud. You still up for the move today?"

"Yup, think I'd be up before eight on a Saturday otherwise?" Cole's chipped snaggled-teeth revealed themselves through his smile. "How'd they get evicted, anyway? I don't think you ever told me."

"Too expensive -- even for a studio, especially with John being out of work." His response was muffled as he quickly scarfed down the remaining scrambled eggs. "Really appreciate the breakfast, but maybe next time you could leave out the shells." Michael pushed the crunchy bits out with his tongue, plucking them up with calloused fingers.

"Maybe next time you could get your lazy romp out of bed and make 'em yourself," Cole retorted, flipping him off.

"Speaking of lazy, where's that brother of yours? He said he'd be here."

"Um...I remember him leaving last night. Must've stayed over somewhere," he said, placing his empty mug in the sink.

"What for? You didn't think to ask?" Cole didn't respond. "Whatever, I'll talk to him later about it. We gotta get moving though. Grab us some water."

...

Within ten minutes, the moving truck they ordered arrived. The vehicle, like most others, was self-driven and fully electric. Michael and Cole climbed into the front seats, and commanded the vehicle to its destination. The truck took off quickly, weaving in and out of traffic with ease, using perfectly calculated speed and merges. Michael often wondered what it must have been like to be the one controlling such a large truck. To grip a wheel between your hands and press on the pedals, all of which this truck, along with many other vehicles, didn't have. Like any of them, this one takes verbal commands only and has a touch screen, which allows the rider to select parking spaces and alternate routes. It was a good thing that people no longer drove, Michael knew that for sure. After all, it was a car accident that killed his father many years ago.

He and Amelia were left now to care for the family and keep the house in which he and his sister, Maria, grew up. When he turned twenty-one, his mother said her goodbyes and moved to the gulf, where she cared for her father who couldn't afford hospice or the treatment for his cancer. The merciless disease ravaged him, leaving him bedridden in his last days. Once he passed, she never returned, and visiting her was very expensive, making it nearly impossible for them.

As they traveled along, Michael's eyes stared at the road and sidewalks, watching the proud people and families of Birmingham stroll outdoors in their fancy outfits for their breakfast and day of fun-filled activities. His excitement over seeing his sister and brother-in-law grew as they got closer to their home, but he desperately wanted a day free of obligations for once. Michael hadn't had a single day off work over the entire summer and the sight of all these people irritated him. He could tell they were really close now. He could see the short, weathered brick building Maria and her husband were living in. It stood just halfway up the Iron Mountain from Five Points, neatly tucked between the ugliest buildings in the entire city. Window air-conditioning units hung from its walls as if they were about to fall out and constantly rang and rattled throughout the day and night.

The truck parked and a feeling of eagerness came over him, making him forget his longing for rest. He hadn't seen his sister in months, but at last she appeared over the stairs carrying a box of chattering dinnerware. Her long mahogany-colored hair danced along in the wind as if each strand were waving to them. Nearly tripping at the sight of the moving truck, an enormous smile broke forth, stretching all across her slim face.

Michael wasted no time jumping from his seat to yell, "Maria!"

"A sight for sore eyes!" she cried out cheerily with a giggle, while setting down the heavily taped box.

"Missed you, sis," Michael said as he leaned in to give her a tight hug. He felt the bones sticking out of her back as she gasped for air.

She peeked over his shoulder at Cole's skeleton-like frame. "Have you not been feeding this boy?" She grabbed her cousin and hugged him as well, saying, "I'm going to have to cook a feast for y'all tonight. Amelia at work?"

"No, I let her sleep-in a while longer. She spent a little extra time last night cleaning out the room you'll stay in. As for Stone, the punk went out last night and I haven't heard from him this morning, Cole says he must have stayed over somewhere."

"That's fine. I think we'll get this knocked out real fast anyway, especially since you two got here so quickly. John's upstairs in the apartment breaking down the bed, but hopefully not actually breaking it. Go help him out with that and Cole and I will load up some of the boxes."

"Sounds good. Maybe he hasn't done any damage yet," Michael joked. Friends and family knew John's clumsiness and short-fused temper quite well.

...

The apartment building was an extremely inexpensive place to live. Anyone just walking by along the block could see that. The corridor floors inside were concrete, but had cracked over the past century and a half. Dirt, turned black with time packed into the cracks. Amelia would have had a fit if she'd ever visited. Paint chipped off of the warped, wobbly walls and littered the floors. Michael's nose filled with the many aromas that flowed from each tenant's apartment. On the first floor, he smelled curry and once he reached the second flight of stairs he noticed a haziness to the air; marijuana was popular among many of the apartment building residents. Finally, he was on the third and top floor -- the one Maria and John lived on. He could see the door wide open and heard John fidgeting with things from within. He quietly snuck into the studio and walked up on his crouching brother-in-law. The wooden floors groaned and startled John, catching him completely off-guard. John turned, his arms and legs stammered and buckled, as he warily looked at his intruder, a smiling Michael.

"Bastard!" John shouted, before getting to his feet to hug Michael, "Dangerous, sneaking up on a man..."

"Who were you expecting? A burglar?" Michael laughed loudly at the stumpy man, just before finding a spare ratchet to take apart the round table a few feet away in the kitchen area.

"The neighbors here are a bit...unpredictable." John itched his thick beard in thought, his deep, loud, and heavily accented voice filled the air. "It'll be nice not having to worry about them any longer. Last night there must've been an all-out brawl just down the street."

"Could've been the protest. I'm sure it got out of hand at some point."

"Likely so." After wiping away some sweat, John started back on unscrewing the bolts that held his bed together. The two of them spent some time talking politics and the state of the world. John loved to grumble about all things under the sun and Michael never knew a time that he didn't like to make himself heard.

"Worthless protesters," John started, after several quiet and busy minutes, "could barely make it through the crowd on my beer run."

"Beer run, huh?"

"Hell yeah, my wallet may go dry, but I don't plan on doing the same." John poked out his belly as he rubbed it.

"Well, we got plenty of beer and wine back at the house." Michael paused just after he finished taking the dresser apart. "As for the wallet, I may be able to find a place for you on the crew. Boss has many *undesirables* employed, myself included." John walked over to him with a freshly opened beer that dripped with condensation. The two of them sat on the mattress that laid on the floor.

"Thanks, brother, really means a lot. It's been dang near impossible these days. Everyone's got their radar cranked to ten, with Unity cracking down and what not. If you ain't payin' those damnable taxes then good luck, ya know? Not many payin' under the table these days."

"Yeah, my boss is a real good guy and there's actually a few of us Catholics on the site, several STORK opposing evangelicals too."

"Well, I ain't got much experience hammerin' and what have you, and you saw how I struggled with this bed. But I'll definitely take you up on that offer-" Just then, the door creaked open, interrupting John mid-speech, as Maria and Cole entered.

"Some new scratches on the furniture, huh?" Maria critiqued.

"Honey, we ain't even carried it down the stairs yet, just you wait." John smiled over at Michael. "Plus, the more scratches a piece of furniture has, the less noticeable it is." He laughed. "And pretty perfect timing really, we'd just sat down for a brew."

John reached into the ice-filled cooler and pulled out two more beers, opened them and handed them to Maria and Cole. Cole, after taking the beer and joining everyone in a toast to moving day, looked shocked and uncomfortable about drinking. He waited to take his first sip when no one was looking.

"Better start working on that a bit faster, brother," John teased, chuckling at Cole. After hearing this Cole chugged his entire beer, something he had never done before in front of adults. He blushed as everyone laughed at the spectacle.

...

After their break, the four of them got right back to work with the move. They carried the furniture down the three treacherous flights of stairs per Maria's instructions. She made sure to watch them closely as they maneuvered the bed and pivoted around the railing. Luckily, for John, the bed received no additional damage and he was off the hook for the time being, something they all laughed about in the cramped ride over to the house.

It wasn't common for people to own vehicles, so they all rode together in the truck's front seat. Michael was pressed against the left door, Maria sat in John's lap, and Cole sandwiched between everyone in a sideways manner with his neck bent against the ceiling of the truck.

"What's for dinner?" John asked as he rolled down his window. By holding his arm against the outside of the door he made a little more room for the other occupants.

"Well, Amelia told me last night that she was working on a feast of lasagna. We'll probably have salad and bread as well." Michael also lowered his window. A cool breeze flushed through the truck's cabin. "And, of course, Father Burns will be there holding Mass before dinner."

"Father Burns?" Maria interrupted, finally joining the conversation. "Thought he moved south. How long has he been back?"

"Well, he's back. He's been back for a couple of weeks now. Holds Mass at our house twice a week. He was only gone for a short while to meet with some clergy, I think he's said."

"Do you know what for?"

"I never asked."

The road grew much darker due to the massive solar panels that draped across much of the outskirts of the city. There were even areas that had streetlights employed all hours of the day. For many people, even the inhabitants of these artificially darkened regions, the massive structures were awe-inspiring, though the lack of natural light filled them with a bit of gloomy somberness. Stars, clouds, and the moon were forgotten faces to the houses and streets there; only the rain and occasional wind made its way through the cracks. When she was younger, Maria commonly remarked how she detested the sight of them. It was much of the reason she and John decided to leave for the city once they married.

"I miss dad," she said suddenly. "He'd drive us down past the edge to see the trees and animals, or take us over to Ruffner Mountain. We always pretended that we were time traveling." John rubbed her back as she spoke. "We'll have to go sometime soon, Mikey. It's been way too long."

"Absolutely!"

"What is there to do out there?" Cole asked.

"You've never been? Not even to Ruffner? You live just a mile away from it." Maria's eyebrows raised.

"No," Cole answered, having always been a child of the indoors. He was more fascinated by the perfection of virtual reality than the grimy natural outdoors. Who could blame him, when within the comfort of his home, he could be adventuring in a fantastical land.

"I can't believe this, Mikey. How have you not taken this boy? You oughta be ashamed of yourself."

"I'm always too busy!"

"Well, you're gonna have to make time!"

Amelia's slender figure towered over the soapy dish water in her sink. Her shoulder-length hair was wrapped up on top of her head in a messy, sort of half bun. Wispy, dirty blonde hairs poked in every direction, barely tamed by her elastic hairband. Everything from the warmth of the water and the wonderful aroma of cooking lasagna brought great joy to her. The house may be old and need some updating, such as the fifty-year-old cabinets and out of style blue and green tiles that Michael's grandparents had installed, but there wasn't a speck of dust on anything. She plunged her hands into the water and grabbed the nearest glass, scrubbing it relentlessly with her rag. Whenever she cooked, she cleaned before, during, and after. Amelia brought her head up momentarily to gaze outside the window, just as a reflection from the approaching truck caught her attention. She quickly wiped her hands dry with an out of season Christmas-themed towel hanging near the sink and darted out the front door.

"Wow, y'all got that done a lot faster than I thought you would've!" She shouted excitedly, hugging them as they exited the vehicle one by one.

"Have you seen Stone today?" Cole asked.

"I'm sure I heard him go in his room earlier. Haven't seen him though. Guess somebody had a late night."

"Wake him up, Cole. I want to unload this truck before Father Burns gets here," Michael ordered as he climbed into the back of the truck and turned on the light. It wasn't yet nighttime, but the overshadowing solar panels made it much darker in their neighborhood.

...

Cole entered the bedroom he shared with his brother. He saw Stone stretched across the lower half of a bunk bed, but he wasn't asleep, Cole could see the glow of a screen illuminating his brother's face.

"Sup?" he asked the intruder, turning on the light next to him.

"Mikey wants you to help us finish up the move before the priest gets here." Cole cleaned his glasses, even though there wasn't anything on them.

"Kill me," Stone sighed just before placing a pillow over his shaved head.

"What?"

"Maush wnd relemd fimnshi shighe...," he replied, his words muffled and incomprehensible.

"Please. Mikey will pitch a fit if you don't come down. He's already sorta pissed about you not showing up this morning." Cole watched his brother remove the pillow covering his face. "What happened last night, anyway?"

"It was amazing. Me and the boys went out to see that protest." He reached for the laptop on his nightstand and opened it up to show his brother the footage he recorded the night before with his camera. "I've already put a video together. Close the door quick."

Cole watched the video with his brother. The opening scene displayed a crowd of hundreds, holding their signs and shouting chants. They were assembled in front of the waterless Storyteller fountain, some hanging off of the statue of a ram, shouting and crying out in the cool night air. Seconds later, a fight broke out, for which Stone was, evidently, one of the instigators.

He and his friends approached, armed with nothing more than their fists, and started to rip signs out of the protesters' hands, then tearing them to pieces. Stone and his buddies had their faces covered in a variety of ways to conceal each person's identity. The only apparent uniformity was that many of them sported hastily painted crosses on the backs of their jackets and hoodies.

Cole recognized the symbol from the news. He never wanted to bring it up to his brother, whom he loved very much. It pained him greatly to imagine what Stone must be getting involved in. His mind drifted as the montage played, trying to find an excuse for his brother's behavior.

Maybe he isn't a part of the really bad stuff. He could just be screwing around, Cole thought. His spirit lifted briefly only to fall away again. He hid his sadness beneath a slight smile, trying to sell that the video entertained him. *Or maybe he doesn't know what he's involved with.* Images of the recent bombings and crying and bloodied people from the news flashed in his mind.

"Check this out. It's the best part. I can't believe I got it on camera." Stone nudged his younger brother.

Some of the larger protesters emerged from the gathering and struck Stone's camera out of his hand as they attacked. The camera flipped multiple times before landing on the ground, capturing video of debris and streamers floating by. The footage displayed a perspective that gazed out across the street. Cole saw strobing red and blue lights as the loud wail of sirens drowned out the screams and cursing of those engaged in an all-out brawl.

After a few moments of loud thuds and the snapping of wooden signs, canisters hurled from down the street landed nearby and gas sputtered from them. Stone's bloody hand came into view as he grabbed the camera, his masked face looked over the lens while he dusted it off. After a brief retreat, he continued to record the dispersing of the protesters and rioters alike, darting into the alleys and behind buildings, vanishing into the midnight.

"Cole!" Michael shouted as his footsteps led up the stairs to their room. Stone quickly closed his archaic laptop and placed it under his pillow just before the door swung open.

"We're on our way down. He was just telling me the game plan," Stone responded calmly, without the slightest bit of guilt on his face.

"Where the hell've you been all day?"

"I completely forgot about the move. I stayed over at Jeremy's house last night after we all went into the city."

"Right, so you just forgot our entire conversation from the night before," Michael growled, as the last of his patience drained away. "Just get your asses downstairs and help with what we've got left. We'll talk later, after dinner." He stopped abruptly as he caught a glimpse of a red knit ski mask poking out just below Stone's mattress. A hand-painted white cross just above the eye holes shone brightly against the red fabric, the symbol was used only by the lower ranking Zealots; however, it made no difference to Michael -- trouble is trouble, no matter what stage it's at.

Cole walked out of the room with Stone following him, but Michael stopped Stone by pressing his hand against his chest. Michael's eyes glittered, ablaze with anger. Blood rushed to his face, flushing it a deep red. He pushed Stone back into the room and slammed the door.

Stone, shocked, backed himself into a corner of the room, knocking over a lamp.

"What the hell is your deal?"

Michael bent down and grabbed the mask, gripping it tightly in his hands. Looking down at it he shook his head, his teeth were fully gritted, and his lips tightly pinched together.

"I know you've been out," he began, speaking in a hushed, but harsh tone. "At first I thought it was just the typical parties, but then I began to suspect you were up to something. I never would have guessed this. This symbol here isn't something to take lightly, Stone." He looked up at him, his finger on the cross.

"It's nothing." Stone tried to laugh it off, scratching his forehead.

"No, there is nothing excusable about this. I don't care if you're a poser or trying to fit in with the other kids. This clique you've mixed yourself up with are terrorists. They're honest to God terrorists and nothing more. I won't tolerate even a hint of it here." He folded the mask in his hand and placed it into his back pocket.

"I haven't done anything like that, Mikey. My friends and I just wear that when we go out screwing with the protesters." Stone looked out the bedroom window. He could see Cole and the others unloading the truck, so he cautiously drew closer to Michael. "They call all of us terrorists when referring to anyone associated with our faith. They make signs with the pope's image in league with tyrants of the past. They literally chant and call for the heads of the Faithful."

"And when you go out to pick fights with them, you're only stoking the fire." Michael looked directly at Stone, disgusted and no less enraged than before. "If I find that you haven't stopped this after today, then you'll be out." Michael turned and opened the door with no further words.

With the two of them working angrily, they finished the job quickly. The others could see clearly that there had been a disagreement. John tried multiple times, in vain, to crack jokes, but only received laughs from Amelia and Cole. Nothing he said had lightened the mood and nothing changed, even after the truck pulled away to return to its home lot.

...

All of Maria and John's belongings sat in their room, the same room she painted green in her late teen years. The couple unpacked and arranged their stuff. All things considered, they were happy and feeling excited about the change. Amelia continued to work in the kitchen, she lowered the temperature on the oven and prepared the table for her guests. Cole and Stone sat upon their bunks, resting from all of the lifting they did, as if it had been so brutal on them. Their faces were lit with screens and grungy music filled their room.

But Michael sat quietly on the front porch, enjoying one of the few personal pleasures he knew. The crackling sound brought him peace as the cigar burned, his face made orange by the hot end. He watched the lights along the streets flicker and glow underneath the dark solar panels that stretched over all the houses. No grass, no trees, no flowers, nothing grew in the yards, only concrete and gravel lots with decaying homes sitting upon them. He could hear the neighbors arguing and sirens wailing on a nearby street. Even so, Michael's bliss only grew deeper as the smoke twirled and curled around him. The sweet scent of the cigar masked the reek emanating from the nearby trash bins stacked along the sidewalks.

As he flicked the ash from the end of his cigar, his eye caught a movement in the outer darkness, just beyond the nearest streetlight. He had been waiting for that movement. An older man, tall and taking long strides entered the flood of light before him. His silver hair shone brightly as did the spectacles clenched against his bearded face. It was Father Burns, the priest who visited twice a week to hold Mass and eat dinner. Michael raised from his chair, shuffled down the stone steps and along the sidewalk to meet Burns by the street.

"Care if I have a puff?" Father Burns smiled, reaching his hand out greedily to receive the cigar.

"Be my guest," he responded in monotone. His mind in another place.

"Mmm, this one's quite sweet. Thank you, Michael." Michael didn't respond and stood quietly next to him.

"Something seems to be troubling you," he said bluntly. Michael clearly wasn't his normal self.

"I'm not sure if it's my place to share, Father. Maybe you'll hear of it in someone's confession tonight." Michael pulled the mask from his back pocket and presented it to the priest.

"Perhaps my homily will speak to its owner tonight," Burns replied, his surprise dying quickly. This wasn't the first time he had seen such things.

"I surely hope so, Father."

"Well," he said, standing in front of the house, "let those sinners know I've arrived and that I'll be in the backyard for the forgiveness of their sins." Burns laughed as he placed his collar around his neck and his stole over his shoulders. "And come to me, if you need to talk."

"Yes sir," Michael answered as he snatched the cigar from the priest's lips. "Maria and John are crashing here for a while as well. They may come down for confession shortly."

Members of the family and the neighbors who joined them took turns, running from their rooms to the chairs that sat in the nearly pitch-black yard for confession. Amelia took the longest, as usual, and as always returned crying, even though she was the purest of them all. John's was quick and everyone could hear roaring laughter from the back lot.

It disappointed Michael that he didn't see Stone come around for confession. He struggled with the anger, which raged boiled within him as he sat on the living room couch. But he donned a smile for the group when they entered the room and picked their seats for the Mass. Amelia sat next to him, gripping his hand tightly as she smiled. John and Cole both arrived and closed the curtains tightly along the windows, so that no outsiders could see inside the room. Maria turned off every light, and lit two candles for the celebration. The neighbors that came for Mass stood bordering the walls and darkening doorways into the room; it was the usual crowd, about fifteen in total, most of them very old and frail. The older women were given seats. They clung to their rosaries, their eyes glazed with age.

Father Burns stood before them, in front of the blackened fireplace at the end of the living room. The air was empty of noise and the ceiling and walls flickered with the dancing flames emanating from the candles.

They all rose to their feet and made the Sign of the Cross as the priest began to pray in Latin, *"In nómine Patris, et Fílii, et Spíritus Sancti."*

"Amen," they all replied.

And so, the Mass followed with recitations of Latin prayers and incantations that the faithful had spoken billions of times over centuries past in countries and kingdoms that no longer existed. These words passed down from their ancestors and, in this room, they still echoed along the walls. Few in this world know the significance and meaning of these holy words. The priest began to speak in English for a short while during his homily. He spoke of the martyrdom of Saint Stephen and the witness of it by Saul of Tarsus, who, after this account, saw a vision and subsequently gave his life forever to the Lord. Michael glanced over to Stone to see if he was listening, only to find that his cousin found picking at his nails and looking at his hands more entertaining and edifying than the Mass.

Burns concluded his homily saying, "We, the faithful are called to love our enemies, even when they offer us up to the dead. Because there is always hope that they may come to our Lord for salvation, we must keep our hearts open for them, even in persecution, just as Saint Stephen did."

After the Apostle's Creed and a few additional prayers, the priest consecrated the host, praying, "*Accípite et manducáte ex hoc omnes: hoc est enim corpus meum, quod pro vobis tradétur,*" and it became the flesh of Christ. One by one they went forward, kneeling as they received the Body of Christ on their tongues. Once a person took Communion he departed from the priest, crossing his chest before the crucifix that hung upon the wall.

...

At the priest's dismissal, the group gradually made their way to the kitchen where the source of their salivation sat, spreading its savory aroma all around. The neighbors received their portions of vegetarian lasagna and bread from Amelia and took their dinners home; there wasn't enough space or dinnerware to host them there.

Michael's blood sugar approached a dangerously low level and he knew that if he didn't eat soon he would be at his cousin's throat. Finally, the family sat down at the table, all seven of them, shoveling food into their mouths and talking about all things from the homily to the upcoming football season. Michael, however, had nothing to say of the Crimson Tide and their chances for a win tonight, he felt better with food in his stomach, but still carefully avoided looking Stone's way.

Clearing his throat, he spoke up, "Father, what do you think about the Zealots?"

The sudden shift to such a dismal topic nearly set him aback, until he remembered the mask. "They're excommunicated from the Church. Why do you ask?" His face brightened with a smile. "Hope you're not thinking of enlisting." He let out lighthearted laughter, as he went for another fork full of food.

"What church?" Stone mumbled tearing apart a slice of bread.

"Hm?" the priest probed, unsure of what the young man said.

"What church are you talking about?" his voice rattled quickly and breathlessly with irritation. "You said that the Zealots are not in accordance. I'm asking you with what church, exactly?"

"Stone!" Michael scolded, gritting his teeth.

"No, I want to know what church he is speaking of," Stone responded, whipping his head towards Michael. "Pardon me if I don't understand, having had Masses in living rooms my entire life. What church is there?" he questioned louder, this time, for everyone at the table. Maria gasped.

"The people that were here earlier. The very people at this table -- we are the Church, son. But, there must be millions out there, holding mass in their own homes with their own priest just as we have. And believe it or not, we still have a pope and bishops, although they're all in hiding."

"You know, I've never even once stepped foot inside a cathedral or parish for Mass. They've all been destroyed and the ones that remain have been made into places of blasphemy. There's no visible Church and with the absentee we have as a pope, I'm not sure what sort of accordance anyone has at all. Our faith is dwindling and the only people who seem to give a damn are the Zealots -- the terrorists -- so y'all call them." He threw his silverware down on the table and the silence filled the room like a giant. Michael nearly popped, gripping his napkin tightly. The only reason he hadn't had pounced on Stone already was wearing a collar and sitting across from him. All, except for Michael, Stone, and Father Burns left the table; the three of them remained quiet, gathering their thoughts.

"Son, you can't lose hope. And, don't think for a second that terrorism is the answer. Zealots haven't done anything, but further disgrace the Church and the message of Christ."

"It is a just war, that Zealots fight," Stone retorted.

Father Burns looked at him, his heart ached for the weary young man.

"How's it any different from what our ancient saints and heroes have done? They were killers, 'zealots' -- they were the terrorists of their times. If it weren't for their bloodshed, we wouldn't have any knowledge of Christ. We'd have even less hope than we have tonight."

"'The gates of hell, shall never prevail' and they never have, son. History books are filled to the brim with man's hatred for God and his people. Yet we always rise more powerful than ever. He protects us." Michael nodded his head in agreement with the priest.

"But you are disregarding the very things that kept hell at bay...the vigilante...the knight...the crusader." Stone laughed at the two men sitting with him. "All of Europe would have been named Mohammed long ago if something hadn't been done. Why do you still fail to understand this?"

"Stone," Michael said, trying to reason with him, "I promise you, if they came for us, if they slaughtered our people in the streets, I would be the first to join you in the fight. As of now, however, there hasn't been anything quite so violent. We've been taxed, that's all; and, so we now meet secretly."

Stone fumed in his seat, twiddling his thumbs and tearing at the ends of his nails.

"They have murdered us," Stone started to rebut. "Haven't you ever read about the plague that wreaked havoc just forty years ago?" Looking to the priest, he continued, "Have you forgotten? Everything between both Tropics was decimated. Billions died. You think this was an accident? It just so happened that the nations that supposedly contributed most to climate change were scrubbed from the earth. Not to mention, that the majority of the Church lived within those regions."

Michael considered the thought momentarily, looking to the priest for a response. The old man remembered it all very well. His eyes covered with sadness, thinking back to the horrific things that he had seen in those days, and the countless prayers that he made without answers. He thought back to a time when he stood just beyond the quarantine line that separated the healthy nation from the starved and contaminated people, unable to escape their fate. Father Burns had led a team down to the gate one summer, when the plague was at its peak of destruction. The congregation stood as close to the gate as allowed, only a mile from the plagued masses. From that distance, they could easily hear their cries and wailing. It sounded like the torment deep in the pits of Hell. He stayed there for many weeks, watching the bodies pile and children sitting next to their deceased parents.

"I cannot condemn what I do not know." The priest's voice cracked with tears forming in his eyes.

"I think it's very clear, sir," Stone responded coldly to the water dripping from the priest's eyes. "Are you also going to withhold judgement on them for sterilizing us? No one's been able to conceive naturally, for what? Fifteen years?"

"That's enough, Stone," Michael barked.

"You must not have been paying attention, old man," Stone continued, completely disregarding Michael's warning. "It's just a matter of time before they actually choke the life out of us. Those whores and bastards are in the streets at this very hour calling for the heads of you and yours."

It was at that moment that an already riled Michael leapt towards his cousin and brought him to the ground. Many curses rang out through the house as they scuffled along the dining room floor. Michael pressed his weight into his cousin, gaining the advantage and began swinging his fists in a blur. Again and again heavy hands landed against Stone's face, spilling blood over his brow.

Father Burns, shocked, attempted to stop them in vain. He watched them tumble, crying out, "Someone...John...help me!" He shouted beyond the dining room doorway. John quickly descended from the stairs, having heard the commotion. Confused, he sprinted towards the two men fighting upon the floor and forcefully placed his arms around Michael, dragging him off of the young man lying bloodied on the floor. John held Michael back as Stone scurried from the ground, running directly out the backdoor and into the inky darkness of the night.

CHAPTER TWO

The STORK building overlooked the entire city, it was the highest and most beautifully structured skyscraper in all of Birmingham. Since STORK was founded in that city, it provided a great deal of economic dynamics to it. Just a century before STORK's grand opening, the city had been all but abandoned. Now, the monolithic tower reflected everything from the ground up in its gloriously shining blue glass. Its massive presence nearly disappeared into the cloudless sky.

Isaac's eyes followed it from its base until he could no longer see beyond the countless windows that rose above him. He, a man of considerable height, was filled with abundant humility at that moment. He marveled at the near-miraculous feat wrought by the faceless structural engineers who had designed it. Isaac quickly combed his hand through his hair after catching his own gaze in the ground floor entrance while opening the door for his wife, Susan.

She stepped through the entrance, her long, well-toned legs carrying her at a fast pace in sparkling white stilettos. Everyone's eyes were drawn to her and the lush red curls that tumbled past her shoulders, bringing to attention, to the porcelain beauty of her face. She had striking green eyes with a strangely catlike character to them and pupils as small as pinholes. She glanced about the kiosk, never showing too much interest in anyone who greeted her. Isaac, handsome as he was from his well-groomed, flaxen hair to his chillingly blue eyes, never received much notice from anyone at all when he followed her.

"Welcome to STORK, Mrs. Lewis," said a young effeminate man from behind the marbled desk. "If you'll take the elevator to the fortieth floor, your consultant will be there to greet you."

Susan quickly stepped away from him without any words, her face tilted up high towards the open air. Isaac thanked the young man before grabbing several mints from the bowl and scurrying off after his wife who had already stepped onto the opening elevator. She had no problem entering before the leaving parties exited the elevator either. After all, they had already finished their business and hers was much more important.

"Pick up your pace, love," she demanded quietly to Isaac. "We haven't got all day. I want to make an excellent first impression." She had an almost imperceptible fierceness to her quiet tone as she reminded him of this. The ride in the sleek, gold-trimmed elevator seemed to take forever. Susan puckered her lips and fixed the crimson lipstick with a handkerchief she pulled from her bag.

"It's gonna be fine."

"Please, remove that mint from your mouth. Your speech will sound peculiar and I can't bear the sound of it rattling against your teeth." Her words sliced at him constantly, never without complaint. "Spit it out now." Her eyes darted in his direction.

"I don't have anything to spit into, honey," he told her, trying to savor his last moments with the sweet wintergreen sensation that covered his tongue.

"Spit it out on the floor, for all I care," she commanded, waiting to hear the thud of the mint landing on the ground. Isaac did as told, shamed and secretly enraged, biting his tongue as always.

The elevator door opened and, as promised, a woman with bluish tinted hair stood waiting. The consultant smiled, reached her hand out to Susan, and said, "Welcome, Lewis family!" She exploded with enthusiasm, catching Isaac completely off guard. "I'm Jocelyn, I'll be your guide on this journey. If you follow me to my office, we'll get things started."

Cubicles, constructed of bamboo and glass, occupied most of the floor space. Brilliantly colored lights in hues of orange and red mixed with the usual white lights to give the area a warm atmosphere. Office plants cast shadows along the walls and ceiling. It reminded Isaac of a jungle, void of wild animals and dirt -- an office space paradise, ringing phones and computer beeps replacing the bird songs and insect chirps.

...

"Here we are," she said, guiding them with her hand into her office. The sun lit the area with its bright, golden light. Through the window, Isaac could view the entire city -- from the iron Vulcan upon the hill to the historical northside that glimmered in rustic radiance.

Isaac and Susan took their seats promptly. "Would either of you like a beverage? Water, seltzer, or coke?"

"We will have two waters, thank you," Susan answered for them both, letting out a smile. Isaac liked the sound of a fizzling and chilled coke, but wouldn't dare change his wife's order. Within moments, a man appeared to place two glasses of water and a pitcher on the table that sat between their chairs. He poured both glasses and bowed out as he left, closing the translucent door behind him.

The consultant took a seat at her desk. A few cheesy family photos of her, another woman, and a set of toddlers sat in frames on top of her workspace. The office walls displayed artwork depicting storks piercing through cumulus clouds and delivering children to giddy recipients. The subjects in the paintings appeared androgynous, even the babies -- no pinks or blues -- only a harmonious mixture of the two. Isaac chewed the side of his cheek, studying them momentarily. The stork seemed to exude a perpetual joy or bliss, as he did his job, delivering these children. Isaac never had the opportunity to take care of an infant before, but he was well read and watched many films. which never made the pretense that traveling with a child is painless or easy. Susan, on the other hand, usually the more pragmatic of the two, soaked up the reality portrayed in the paintings. Isaac could see she bought into the idea of tearless babies and an infinity of smiles and wonder.

"So, Susan and Isaac, I hear y'all are thinking of having a baby?" Jocelyn smiled, as her biometrics unlocked her desktop. The display was only a sheet of glass, colored with images and words on the viewer's side, but completely transparent from the visitor's perspective.

"Yes, we've been waiting for quite a while, getting our finances in order and remodeling the house. It has been a very busy few years for us," Susan replied, reaching out to Isaac for the first time that day, rubbing the top of his forearm.

"Yes, we're very excited."

"Have y'all browsed online for anything in particular?"

"Browsed?" asked Isaac, realizing he was quite unprepared for the meeting. Susan was the one who studied the options and day-dreamed, perpetually, of her future child.

"We've looked every night," she quickly answered over her husband. "There's just so many possibilities to weigh. I'm not sure what will suit us best."

"Well, that's definitely something I can help with." Jocelyn projected her screen against the wall behind her, so they could see it. "We offer a plethora of packages, sorted by race, gender, combos, and even twin packages, which, as you can see, is what my wife and I selected," she explained, pointing to the family photos on her desk.

"They're beautiful!" Pretending to care, she asked, "What are their names?"

"Adrianna on the left, there, and to the right is Fiona. Women only in our house," she laughed. "Technically, they are twins. Their faces are perfect reflections of one another, but aside from their symmetry, they share nothing. We chose to make one contrast the other by their coloring. STORK can deliver any child you could possibly imagine."

Susan looked closer at the photos on the woman's desk. She could see that one of the toddlers had black skin, darker than the night sky, white hair, and blue eyes just as bright as Isaac's. Her sister was an exact opposite; she had black hair, skin as white as cotton, and hazel eyes that seemed more golden than brown.

"That's incredible," Susan remarked, truly interested. "And they were born this way?"

"Yes, their genes were altered as they developed alongside each other in the lab, where they were closely monitored until birth. You can choose to have them favor your own genes though, if you'd like." The consultant's face became slightly soured as she continued, "We offer that as well, in the basic package." An image of the package showed on the wall; generic child faces covered it. Crooked teeth, poor clothing, and unimpressive proportions they all had.

"Is it not popular to have children that resemble their parents?" Isaac inquired, suddenly paying attention.

"Well, the latest trend is the designer baby. It's new among the second generation here at STORK and they're really selling well." She selected the package on the screen, flooding the wall with children of all sorts -- races and features that had never existed naturally. Isaac's mouth hung open as the sight of a blue-haired toddler appeared on the wall. "But, if you two are more interested in our basic package, I can also simulate what they'll look like as teens and even the appearance they may have by adulthood. Sometimes the parents, as beautiful as they are," she flattered, "prefer not to pass down any sort of blemishes or less favorable traits. But, Susan, I'm absolutely positive the two of you would make gorgeous babies!"

Jocelyn was an excellent saleswoman, always waging an unmentioned and unnoticeable war with her customers, guiding them into an inevitable direction, leading towards the more expensive options. Isaac could see the clever sales pitch, but his wife nearly bubbled over with excitement at all the wonderful possibilities. She soaked up every detail the consultant presented to them. Her vanity got the best of her, though. Thinking that none of these gene-modified children held a candle to her natural beauty, she asked for the true parental gene simulation.

"Yes, of course." Jocelyn grinned, instructing the couple, "If you two will simply place your fingertips on the pad there, a small pinprick will gather your genetic information and present the most probable outcome upon the wall behind me."

...

After a few minutes of small talk, the vision fully initialized; although, the child showcased looked nothing like they expected. Isaac believed it must have been rigged, but didn't say anything. Susan, shocked, withheld no emotions, revealing how truly disappointing she found the image. Her face twisted with horror. She let out a gasp and quickly covered her mouth, shielding her brilliantly white teeth with French manicured nails.

"Oh no," she nearly shouted, not caring any longer about what impression she might make, "I thought surely she would have been a strawberry blonde, at the very least." Shaking her head at the image, she continued with an incredulous tone, "The eyes as well. They look much darker, neither green or blue." She frowned, "Surely this isn't too accurate?"

"The simulations have been pretty spot-on in my experience. But, really, when you rely on your own DNA, you get infinite possibilities, many of them not so desirable. If you choose that route, you won't know what the child will be blessed...or cursed...with until long after its creation in the lab."

"Well, could we simply just tweak a few things here and there?" She wiped her almost teary eyes with the edge of her handkerchief.

"Absolutely, sweetheart, it's okay." Jocelyn bent forward on her desk, eyes opened widely with sincerity, reassuring her, "You are able to do whatever you'd like -- with the designer package."

"Isaac, we must choose the designer package!" Her hand gripped his forearm so tightly, he knew that when she pulled away, an imprint of her fingers would remain on his skin.

"Whatever makes you happy, love," he cooed, gently patting her hand until she relaxed.

...

Jocelyn quickly made note of their decision on her desktop. Afterwards, she walked them through the options to help customize the daughter of Susan's dreams. A delightfully beautiful young woman she would grow to be; everything her mother was and more. The child will have eyes as green as leaves in a new spring. The irises and pupils will be lined with fine golden bands, capturing all of the sun's essence. Her hair will be nearly twice as thick and naturally curly, something Susan greatly envied in other women. She thought about how she spends at least two hours, almost daily, to achieve the perfect ringlet curls with her curling iron. Now, her daughter won't have to do that.

Additionally, the girl will grow just as tall as Isaac, towering above most men. They chose upgrades to her skin and other organs and the consultant placed them within the package. With these changes, she'd be healthier, stronger, and less prone to cancer. Their daughter won't have her mother's large ears and webbed toes, or her father's family history of heart disease and cancer. Susan did her best to ensure that their girl will be able to achieve anything and that nothing in her DNA will ever hold her back. Her baby would be perfect and flawless.

"Well," Isaac interjected after seeing the massive price tag resulting from all Susan's upgrades and additions. "Now that we've pretty much thought of everything, what's next? Do we pay now or..." He was curious, but also trying to change the subject before Susan racked on any more package options. Two full hours had already passed while Susan designed their daughter. His wife cocked her head sideways, her eyes glowing with irritation at his interruption.

"Well, what if I think of something else? What if we missed something crucial?" Susan asked, turning her head away from him.

"You'll have plenty of time to think and decide things over, Mrs. Lewis," Jocelyn assured her, smiling. "It may take several months before the order is even submi-"

"Several months?" Susan's shrill voice made its way through the glass door and out among the cubicles.

"Yes, I'm afraid that parenting, while certainly a wonderful opportunity, is a great privilege that requires approval from the state. The increased wait is due, mostly, to the baby being genetically modified. If you went the natural growth route it wouldn't take so long, but this is a much greater investment...a greater reward." Susan's lips vanished as she held them shut tightly. Jocelyn carried on, "There will be background and credit checks, and also an auditing of your lifestyles and home life to ensure that the child is placed in the best of hands."

"But, why several months? Can't this be done quicker? Neither of us are criminals or anything and we have plenty of money."

"Yes ma'am, trust me, I understand. It seems like a long time, but from my experience I can assure you, it's worth every second of the wait. You also have to think of the million other requests submitted by other clients during the year. It's a lot for us to process." Susan fell silent, completely crestfallen over the bad news.

"How long until the examination? What should my wife and I expect and is there anything we should make sure to have in place?" Isaac was engulfed with questions, fearful that Susan might lose her composure at any minute.

"A case inspector will visit your home within the next two weeks. The inspector will take a look around the home to make sure there are no real dangers present, or skeletons in your closets." Jocelyn laughed at her joke, realizing that it didn't quite resonate with the couple. "They may also make any number of surprise visits afterwards over the next few months, so take care to keep the place clean, child proof everything, no potential weapons lying around, no dangling cables, store chemicals and what-not in a safe or locked place. Just be generally aware of everything."

"And what of the credit and background checks?"

"Our AI will conduct and calculate those. It will watch all of your accounts and transactions, even after you've received the child."

"After we've received the child? What for? How long does that go on?" Isaac's voice obviously agitated, his eyebrows raised. He could feel STORK's hand already gripping him by the throat. *We'll be slaves*, he thought, his anxiety building under the pressure.

"Until the child is no longer under your parental control. Once the child is fully grown and capable of independence, STORK's supervision ends. Unity gives STORK many responsibilities, one of them being parental surveillance. It's the law and we must obey."

Isaac sat back in his chair, his gaze directed down at the wooden floors, not looking at anything in particular.

Susan didn't say a word. Her eyes stared out the window, studying the buildings below them. The obstacles put before them left her dumbfounded. Nothing of the sort crossed her mind that morning as they climbed in the car for the ride to STORK. Everything had always been simple for her, but now she felt the claws of stress, scratching their way into her mind.

"What are some of the things they watch for?" Susan's voice cracked, as her barely audible words made their way out of her perfectly shaped, plump lips.

"They monitor credit, ensuring that you spend responsibly. They keep an eye on the child's education through your transactions, watching for the proper nutrition and school supplies. You'll get a direct look at your activity as well, which is a wonderful bonus in my opinion. I'm always watching our family's spending habits through the application they've developed. It helps my wife and me make better decisions, I think, and also lets us know if we're not keeping up to our standard." Jocelyn could see that these details overwhelmed her clients. Nothing out of the ordinary. She could see a soft glistening film of sweat starting to form at the sides of Isaac's forehead. "It sounds a little complicated, but you'll get really good at knowing what to look for. You can even take some online courses for it. They don't cost anything at all, and we cover a range of topics."

"Well, what do you want to do, honey?"

"We'll agree to these terms, Jocelyn," Susan answered, again over Isaac's question, not concerned with his opinions. "Go ahead and sign us up. Also, will you save the package as is? I'd absolutely hate to lose everything we worked for today."

"Of course, it's all good." Jocelyn's face brightened revealing her sparkling teeth through a wide smile. The image of the grand total painted its way through every crevice of her brain. "It's all saved. nothing will happen to your darling angel and anytime you have an idea or think of something else, I'm only a phone call away. But, before you guys leave, we must discuss payment arrangements."

All of Susan's energy and carefully guarded emotion drained away at the sound of the consultant's last words. She and Isaac, although well off, could not afford to pay it out right. Isaac didn't know what to do or say, looking to his wife, the one always truly in charge. His jaw flared as he gritted his teeth anxiously, holding his fingers to his lips and chin.

"We've got numerous payment plans, of course." Jocelyn changed the projection behind her to display several options.

Each and every payment option on the wall was, in some way, worse than the one next to it. They'd either live out their days in debt or give up the idea of traveling to the west coast to see her parents again, let alone the European vacation they always dreamed of. Paying for this child will amount to a huge financial sacrifice, regardless. Ultimately, though, it would be well worth it. Susan took a moment to think about her friends and how their children will not hold a candle to the exquisite offspring she, Isaac, and their consultant designed. The thought of their bitter envy made her giddy.

"We will select option two," Susan answered after clearing her throat. Five percent down and a monthly payment roughly equivalent to their house payment, but would likely take twice as long to pay off. Isaac's mind staggered at the sight of the numbers. An exhilarating decline of emotions and hope spiraled down into the pit of his churning stomach. On the verge of sickness, his face paled to an ashen color as two huge beads of sweat rolled down his brow. He quickly wiped it away and regained his outer composure.

"Sign here, Mrs. and Mr. Lewis." A blank line appeared on their side of her desktop, an X blinked next to it, waiting for the touch of their fingers.

...

The couple made their way out of the building soon after, hearts racing and the burden truly weighing down on them. Using her typical ironclad self-control, Susan didn't allow her interior discomfort to rise up and defile her perfectly composed exterior. The stunningly beautiful woman looked just as fierce and elegant as she did when she first entered the tower.

Once they were safely within the confines of the taxi, in complete privacy, Isaac held nothing back. He gasped for air, sighing deeply as if he had just washed ashore after a shipwreck at sea.

"What in the hell are we going to do, Susan?" Isaac shouted into the ceiling, grabbing the sides of his head and pulling his carefully coiffed hair outwards. "What are we going to do? Couldn't we just wait a while longer?" Susan looked at him with her signature soul piercing eyes. "I mean, my God, what are we thinking? Is it truly worth it? We'll never know comfort again."

"Shut your mouth!" Her sharp words cut him off abruptly. "Nearly all of our friends have children now. I refuse to be the last and I will not wait until I'm a damned sixty-year-old before I begin to raise a child. We will have our *Isabel* now, Isaac, and she will literally eclipse the power, intelligence, and beauty of any before her."

"We can't afford it. They'll literally cancel the delivery; or, even worse, repossess her the second they realize we can't follow through on payments. What are we thinking?"

"Isaac, if you don't pull yourself together, I will find my own taxi home and you can wallow in your misery somewhere else, far away from me." She didn't look his way even once as she spoke.

Isaac calmed himself and sat without words for a moment, gathering his thoughts. He simply could not focus on one thing at a time. His mind roiled with a sea of *what ifs* and he struggled for air, for someone to pull him up above the waves. Susan, cold as ever, offered no aid for her drowning man. *One thing at a time, Isaac,* he coached himself, catching a brief stillness in his mind before deep fear overtook him once again.

They exited the taxi and climbed the front steps to their Victorian home, shrubs lined the brick walkway.

"Honey," he started in a cool voice, desperation still slightly apparent in his tone, "damn it, can't you tell me what our plan is?" Susan stood at the front door, staring at the knob and marveling that he hadn't yet opened for her, making a sarcastically puzzled face. Isaac swiftly threw his hand on the knob and swung it open for her to enter, before continuing to pursue her with questions that she refused to answer.

Her shoes tapped on the newly tiled floors as she made her way into their kitchen, the sound echoed off of the spotless marble countertops. She opened one of their many refrigerated cabinets, finding a wedge of Brie cheese, then searching the pantry for a croissant. She ignored Isaac's presence the entire time. After her snack, she used a linen napkin to wipe the crumbs from her lips. Bright red lipstick left its mark on the white cloth. For the first time, since arriving home, she made eye contact with her husband.

"Hon-,"

"You will go to work tomorrow and you will work long hours, harder than you've ever worked." She spoke quickly, an unbroken stream of words flowed from her,

"And then you will receive the raise you've promised me for over a year. I'll do the same. We will start paying more principal on the house. You'll abandon your hobbies, and nights out with the boys, and even sleep at the department if you must." She swept the floor of crumbs, continuing, "And, before I hear any of your excuses, just know, if I have to, I can find someone else who can make this dream of mine a reality much easier than you can. You'd best listen to me." Despair ravaged Isaac's heart, leaving him unable to respond coherently. He nodded his head in agreement. His face turned red and his eyelids grew heavy with tears as Susan turned her back and walked away from him.

...

He listened to her footsteps as she walked up the stairs to their bedroom and, finally, the master bathroom. He heard the rushing sound of shower water and knew he could finally weep in private over the kitchen sink. Seething hot tears burned his eyes as they tumbled into the sink. He thought of all the things that could destroy the life he had worked so hard to make -- if he weren't careful.

She always found a way and a reason to treat him with wicked disregard and verbal cruelty; always feeling less of a man with each new day than the day before. Yet another part of him crumbled, broke, and fell away from him that day. He stared out of the kitchen window as he dried his eyes. Everyone seemed so happy -- hanging out in their backyards and front porches in the waning light of golden sunsets. Isaac just couldn't understand why everything seemed to go so easily for them. They made it look effortless. Even though he meticulously followed every direction and mandate from Unity, this ease -- this peace eluded him.

He recalled the days in which she made him feel so strong, so comforted. When his father was passing, she was there. She was the only one there. His mother had taken off, grieving on her own and offered him little to no alleviation of his pain. Susan was the foundation, the grounding. She alone was there for him to wrap his arms around as he cried and suffered the loss. Her family helped with the costs and for that he was forever grateful. The salvation she offered was still there, he knew. Surely life had become more stressful over the years, but she still must be the same Susan. She was a strong, good woman with all of her I's dotted and the T's crossed. Susan made him the man he is. Without her, he wouldn't have strived for this job, he wouldn't have this house, he wouldn't have grown. He owed everything to her, and her insults, her strikes against him were temporary pains, which he knew would pass in time.

It's only temporary. It's all a storm -- a storm I'll get through. I'll make her proud. I owe it to her. I truly owe her everything.

He slowly made his way to the couch, heartbroken and weary, and passed out immediately after hitting the soft cushions and pulling the blanket over himself. In sleep he found peace as darkness engulfed him, worries and regrets fell away. At last, bliss.

CHAPTER THREE

The couch Stone slept on was torn at the seams. The owner's cat likes to use it as a scratching post and had pulled fabric strands and cotton stuffing from its soda-stained cushions. Stone slept on it when the days were brightest, usually managing to sleep through them entirely. He left the night of Michael's outburst and kept very busy during all hours of the night ever since. Rage had erupted from his heart that night; forgiveness impossible to contemplate. His bruised and scabbed-over face served as a constant reminder of the night his cousin had raised his fists, betraying him during dinner, in front of the priest, the sounds of crashing and punching echoing to the rest of the family, destroying their peace.

I'm done with him, Stone thought as he looked over his reflection in the small mirror that hung in the solid white bathroom; the lone bulb flickered from time-to-time and the concrete flooring felt cold to his bare feet. His blood still seething like hot magma, his fists tightened as the memory rushed back into his mind, causing a flood of fresh humiliation to wash over him as he remembered Michael beating him in front of the priest. He heard Jeremy enter the tiny downstairs apartment, a draft came through the cracked bathroom door, creaking it open just enough for Stone to see him pass by. His large and heavily tattooed arms carried groceries, the full weight thudding on top of the kitchen table as he plopped them down. Stone met him in the kitchen to ask if he could help carry in anything else.

"Nah, I got everything in one trip. It's not much."

Jeremy was several years older than him, maybe a couple younger than Michael. The world made his face look unkind and dressed it in scars. A crooked, angry-looking one streaked down into one of his wolfish eyebrows. When he didn't shave, his beard usually covered the two smaller scars crossing his jawline. He had never offered to share how those two came to adorn his face.

"What you got planned tonight?" Jeremy asked, bending on one knee as he put some groceries in the fridge.

"I'm thinking about heading over to Mikey's to grab some things. What's up?"

"Well, how long you think that'll take?" He cracked open a beer, foam rising over the rim as he flicked his hand to fling his fingers dry.

"I'll be back within an hour. I can make it fast if you need me to."

"Ah, I didn't realize you had plans and I know it's last minute, but we have some very important guests coming over later. Try not to take too long." The news intrigued him, but Jeremy didn't offer any explanation; instead, smiling or laughing at Stone's piqued curiosity.

"Guests? Hell, what's with the suspense, give me something!" Stone shouted excitedly.

"Someone's gotten their hands on something that will make life a lot easier for us. You'll hear about the rest later on. Go on and grab your stuff, don't waste any time." Jeremy trailed off to his room, light from his antiquated television stretched across the gap under his closed door. Stone could hear the canned laughter from Jeremy's favorite sitcom playing from an old disc that occasionally skipped.

...

He set out on his mission quickly after suiting up in his favorite hoodie and sneakers, which he had only ever tied once in a double knot. Mud caked the bottom of them and some grass clung to them as well due to last night's activities in vandalizing the city's business district.

Half running, half walking, he hastily made his way to the train station, darkness swallowing him up with each step. Thin slivers of silvery moonlight made its way through tree branches and leaves, speckling the ground ahead of him. *There ya go again, Stone, with your piss-poor planning.* A flashlight would have come in handy. All the streetlight bulbs were out in that section of the neighborhood, a symptom of the poverty there. Eventually, the lights of the train station, still a quarter mile ahead, illuminated his path. He picked up the pace to a steady jog.

Out of breath, he bought a ticket and made his way up the stairs to wait for the train. Two older men and a young couple were the only others waiting for the train. The couple made out passionately right up until the tracks began singing, signaling the approach of their ride.

Light scattered all along the ground, flickering against Stone's filthy shoes as he waited impatiently for it to come to a stop. He called his brother as he boarded quickly found a seat away from the other passengers.

"Cole, call me back," he said after the beep, leaving a voicemail. *Why's no one ever answer?* Stone shook his head in frustration. *Really hope Mikey doesn't show his face, that bastard. Better not see him. Won't be no more cheap shots.* His heart pumped as he stared out the window as the train lurched forward along its path headed for Irondale and the other neighboring towns. Street lamps, cars, and buildings passed by in a colorful blur, distracting Stone for minutes, alleviating some of his irritation. He could see the solar panels ahead, shades of blue shimmering in the moonlight as the train traveled down the crest of a hill. He despised that the sight of them brought up feelings of home. He wanted it to vanish from his memory forever.

The train arrived at its first destination, the Irondale station, once historical for its appearance in cinema, its old glory had long been forgotten under the cover of the panels and growing poverty. The entire town simply vanished from people's memories, forever buried to fuel the energy demands of Birmingham.

He waited a moment before he exited, looking from one end of the platform to the other. It was empty, making it unlikely he would run into anyone he knew. He called Cole again, but still no answer. He decided to rent a bicycle at the kiosk below the platform to use for the remainder of his journey to the house he left behind ever since that terrible fight with Michael. Familiar scents filled his nostrils as he drew closer. The solar panels trapped the putrid air in the town, decay and filth cooked slowly on the pavement.

...

The house came into view, an ancient vision of the past, clothed with Michael's poor attempts at repair and renovations. Similar houses surrounded it -- outdated, sights of older architecture that outlasted most things built since their time. The two-story home rose from its gravel lot, the lights off, the windows black and covered with sheets and curtains.

He pedaled the bike a few more times and rode it out slowly as he glided silently and undetectable among the shadows, where the streetlamps couldn't reach. He jumped quietly from the bicycle, catching it as it continued to roll, and laid it down gently. He didn't dare make a single sound this late at night. Many of the neighbors had dogs and they'd relish alerting the entire cul-de-sac of his presence. Stone crept towards the side of the house where he and Cole shared the second-floor room. Colors and light flickered from the window of the dim bedroom. Surely, it was Cole, still awake. With no way to climb up to the window, he decided to try calling him again. His Auris rang, moments of silence penetrating through each disturbing tone.

"Stone?" He could hear his brother answer, his voice also made its way through the thin, cracked French-paned window.

"Hey bro, what's going on, why haven't you been answering?" he whispered back, not sure if he could safely reveal his location.

"I must've dozed off," he slurred, still groggy from the drunkenness of sleep. "Mikey's real sorry about everything. I think he's been trying to call you and apologize. You have him real worried by not answering."

"Yeah, well I ain't speaking to him."

"Amelia and Maria have been on his ass, at least. And Father Burns isn't happy with him either. You should try to talk to him at lea-"

"I'm not interested in talking about Mikey." Stone's voice revealed his bubbling agitation, his impatience, his desire to forget Michael's existence. The very name tore at his spirit. "Please just leave it be. I need your help with something."

"Are you outside?" Cole moved from his bed and peered out the window, seeing a short man the shape of his brother, wearing a hood.

"Please, don't tell anyone I'm here. I'll leave if you do." He showed his face in a ray of streetlight as he looked up towards his brother. He moved from side to side nervously, as if he take flight at any moment.

"Sure. What do you need?" Cole switched on the bedroom light.

"Everything in the camera bag, my laptop, and throw plenty of clothes in the duffle bag. Hell, just put everything in there." Stone crept back into the dark cover of the alleyway between the houses, unsure if he could trust Cole.

"I'll bring it out to you," Cole called down to him, once he had everything ready. "Sound good?"

"Nah, just drop it out the window. I can catch it. I don't want you waking everyone up."

"I want to see you. Haven't seen you all week."

"I know, I'm okay though. We can meet soon somewhere for lunch or something."

"I'll be quiet! I promise."

"I miss you too, Cole. I'm in a hurry though. Those stairs are too creaky. Even a ninja couldn't walk on them silently."

"Fine, whatever."

"I'm sorry, buddy. We will meet soon. I promise."

Cole opened the window. The panes screeched as it lifted from the filthy window sill. He leaned over and grabbed the bag. It seemed too heavy to drop from such a height. He lowered the bag, his arm at full length as he leaned partially out of the window to get as close to his brother as possible before dropping it.

"I'm ready," Stone called up, his arms reaching for his bag.

Cole released his grip on the handles and the bag dropped. It fell soundlessly several feet before Stone caught it. He immediately checked the contents, shuffling things around from one end to the other. He zipped it up and slung it over his right shoulder.

"Thanks, man. I'll give you a call sometime soon about lunch. Answer it." Stone said, looking up at the window as it closed. He backed his way out of the alleyway, "Love you, Buddy."

"Love you too, Stone." The Auris signaled the call's end with a subtle beep and the room's lights went dark again.

...

Stone picked his bicycle off of the gravely ground and took off without wasting another second. He didn't want to keep Jeremy waiting and pedaled furiously in hopes he would get back before the guests arrived, whoever they were. He felt a little nervous about it. Not knowing what sort of news or plans waited for him caused his anxiety level to rise.

The cool night air whipped around him and the speeding bike, his ears filled with wind. The duffle bag weighed heavily on him, slinging from side to side as he pedaled. The tires made a zipping noise as they rotated on the hard ground and he continued to think about the night ahead of him. The past week kept him extremely busy with everything from vandalizing the STORK buildings and other public places to the night time errands Jeremy gave him from time-to-time. Most of the errands consisted of delivering packages with undisclosed contents to park benches and trash cans.

The other Zealots hadn't allowed him to become part of their inner circle yet; and, even Jeremy helped keep their identities and purposes secret from Stone. The instructions for these deliveries always directed that he conduct the transactions in an abandoned lot or in the back alley of a storefront. He never laid eyes on the people he left the packages for. They always waited until long after he arrived back home before giving positive confirmation of retrieval.

Jeremy didn't do the errands himself because he always worked on projects behind the closed door of his bedroom -- the nature of which he also kept from Stone.

It often frustrated him to think of all the secrets, but these unknowns also acted as a kind of light drawing him in like a moth to a street lamp. The sight of closed doors and sounds of muffled whispers filled his imagination with thoughts of the future and the part he would play in it. He entertained hopes that, eventually, after he adequately proves his allegiance, he would be the one keeping secrets and whispering important things to people. Even though, at this point, he was still a peon, his membership in the Zealots gave him a feeling of importance he never experienced before.

In his mind's eye, he worked as a challenger of evil in the world. He fantasized that he would become a hero in his own time. He imagined seeing his image on a stained-glass window in a church -- carrying prayers of the faithful to the Lord. Yes, Stone dreamed of martyrdom, but beyond the vision, he didn't have a clear understanding of how or why he might meet that end.

...

His heart raced as he ran down the concrete steps to the subterranean apartment that he currently called home. The light beside the door flickered and insects flapped their wings savagely against the brilliant bulb. He reached and twisted the knob, but found it locked, so he cautiously rapped on the door with the special knock Jeremy taught him.

Thud...thud-thud-thud...thud, his knuckles rapped against the splintered door, flakes of white paint fell away from crevices in the aged wood. He heard a voice as someone approached, footsteps singing with vibrations along the floor.

"Welcome back, Stone." Jeremy didn't smile, but he didn't intend his seriousness to come across as intimidating. Stone figured it best to hide his smile and excitement, so put on a serious, yet friendly expression and straight posture. He pushed his hoodie back as he entered the apartment, following Jeremy into the living room.

Stone's heart continued to pound even harder than before when he caught his first glimpses of the guests. The four of them sat on the couches and chairs around the coffee table. They were adults with average faces and no characteristics that stood out to give a hint about their identities. Two wore janitor uniforms. The only woman looked like she must work as some sort of mechanic and the fourth guest's dirty wife-beater tank and faded torn jeans looked like someone out of an old movie.

The informality shocked Stone. He half expected the guests to look like modern day crusaders dressed in fine custom garments woven with crosses. He realized the silliness of that assumption as he shook their hands and introduced himself. They all remarked that they already knew of him and heard nothing but the best from Jeremy.

"It's nice to finally meet you, Stone," the grease-covered woman responded. He noticed no trace of makeup on her small oval face and almond-shaped eyes and her hair was pulled back into a tight bun. Her female voice soothed Stone, seeping into his brain like morphine.

"Yeah, it's a great pleasure," the man in the white wife-beater tank agreed, his speech carrying a heavy southern accent, "Jeremy's been tellin' us about all the hell you been raising in the city. I've seen your artwork over in Five Points, looking pretty good." A few of Stone's late night missions involved painting graffiti and he played the artist quite well on these little excursions, not to mention the greatly needed propaganda he posted online. Many youths were encouraged by these videos of the riot and of other things, calling them to join the uproar. Stone had been very busy; he was the next generation, the connection to the future they needed to advance upon Unity and STORK.

"Thanks. Thank y'all." He allowed a smile to escape.

"Stone," Jeremy began after everyone settled down, "you've certainly impressed us with your eagerness over the past few weeks. And this last week you've proven your allegiance and true commitment." Stone smiled again, unable to keep a serious expression after feeling a wave of euphoria wash over him in the wake of their compliments and praises. "We've all been working very hard as well, and we think it's time that we filled you in on some of it. We're going to need you in an upcoming project. What do you say? Think you're ready for some new responsibilities?"

"Yes, absolutely," Stone voice sobered at the sudden shift in tone. His stomach churned with renewed nervousness and his heart pounded in his chest.

"Whatever you need. Whatever any of you need from me, I'm your man."

Jeremy laughed as he unbuttoned the sleeve covering his left arm. Stone's heart sank as he realized he failed to notice the roaring fire in their fireplace amid the excitement of meeting the guests. No one needed a fire this time of year. Gazing into the crackling fire, he noticed an iron rod laying deep into the hottest embers. His eyes darted quickly over the rest of the group. Every one of them holding out a bare left arm.

His sleeve rolled up above his elbow, Jeremy held his tattoo covered arm and showed Stone his mark -- a mark Stone greatly admired from afar, but the sight of it made him sick this time.

Everyone in the room had the same whelping cluster of brandings midway along their inner forearms. The symbol, rising up from the skin's surface consisted of five crosses: one large center cross and four smaller ones on every corner of the large one. Antiquity knew it as the Jerusalem Cross, but in modern times the Zealots adopted it as their symbol of initiation. No peons ever carried the mark, it was special to those in the inner-circle. *I guess I'm not a peon any more.* Stone felt numb.

"Stone, you must take this mark, just as all of us have. It is the mark of a true Zealot," Jeremy explained as the woman made her way over to the fire and reached down to grab the rod from its resting place with her greasy hands. She drew it out of the embers and studied its glowing tip, the five red-hot crosses almost appeared to live and breathe.

"This branding," Jeremy continued, "will transform you from ordinary rebel into true Zealot. You'll be required to do things, at times, that may be hard for you. Our victories will come at great cost and to achieve success you must sacrifice your fears, ambitions, and desires for the mission ahead of you. It is a great honor, but it doesn't come free."

Stone sat in a chair, sweaty and pale. The woman approached him with the red-hot brand. Her soothing voice spoke, "By taking this mark, you are taking up your cross. It's a commitment for life -- until your last breath. You understand?" Stone nodded his head, his face and mind void the childish excitement he felt before. His will aligned with theirs. Once done, he would no longer be the young man that entered the apartment earlier. He didn't belong to Michael, he didn't belong to Unity, he was to be made new that night.

"The five-crossed mark," she began again, "symbolize the five wounds Christ received on His cross." Her voice calmed him, his head spinning numbly as he prepared for the pain.

He held out a trembling arm and pulled the hoodie sleeve up and away from where it covered his arm. His fists tightened as the heat of the iron warmed his skin. She pushed it forward without the courtesy of a countdown, Jeremy held his shoulders, and the flaming tip popped onto his skin, leaving behind blackened crosses that smoldered upon his flesh. The stench of the smoke filled his nostrils, as it lifted from the excruciating wound.

Stone unclenched his teeth as the worst of the pain subsided and gazed at the mark on his shaking arm. Its sight burned into him with pride. The five roughly shaped crosses were colored with many shades of burnt flesh. The pain continued to fade gradually as the others in the room congratulated him and cheered. Jeremy patted him on the back after taking a look at the mark for himself.

...

"Alright," Jeremy announced, raising his voice over everyone in the room, "now we should get back to it, lots of ground to cover. Can you begin to explain, to all of us, what you've gotten ahold of?"

The woman reached into her bag and pulled out a device. It looked similar to the desktops used in the STORK offices. This one, however, was a screen that had been rolled and folded for storage. She unfurled the flexible translucent cloth made with the latest nanotechnology and shook it once to stiffen its face and edges until it became like glass. She then placed the screen onto a small metallic holder, the only thing touching the device, which held it at a forty-five-degree angle adjacent to the tabletop. The screen was quite large at its full size and it became fully colored at her command, brightening the entire room.

"This is the answer to our problems, everyone." She called a name, "Nelson, stop being so shy and come meet everyone." She smiled as the screen's microscopic pixels turned and changed hue, a mist of color came together to form an image with a childlike appearance, but with the cruelest expression any of them had ever seen on such a young face.

"Hello Debra, and greetings to all, it's nice to meet you; although, no need for you to introduce yourselves." The man on the screen snickered, saying, "I may have already done some snooping on my own while in the clouds."

"Snooping?" Jeremy asked.

"Ye-"

"Nelson is an Artifi-"

"I do loathe that title, Debra," Nelson interrupted her. His face darkened with wrinkles as his expression changed to display sadness, "I thought we'd been over this."

"Nelson, remain silent until further notice." The man on the screen zipped his mouth, literally. A zipper appeared on both sides of his mouth as he rolled his fingers over his lips, sealing them. He loved sarcasm and irony. Debra often wondered if it was some sort of bug that needed fixing.

"Explain now." Jeremy crossed his arms and leaned back, staring at the smirking man on the screen.

"I know it's probably shocking to y'all that I've brought this *man* into our group and meeting, but I'm telling you that this is the answer to our oldest puzzle. We don't have to starve anymore and we'll have money to accomplish our goals."

"What all does this thing know, exactly?" Jeremy stood and paced behind the couch, thinking -- thinking of the possible things that could go wrong.

"What *doesn't* he know? He's information incarnate."

"Where did you get it?" he asked, bending closer to the screen just as Nelson mimicked him, also making himself appear to lean closer to Jeremy.

"He was a bank teller from First Unity Bank, managed pretty much everything in the system from transactions to cyber-security and stocks. Technically, Nelson's a clone of the bot still working at the bank and I've repurposed and reprogrammed him to do just the opposite of what he was designed to do before."

"He's going to steal?" Jeremy asked, pacing away from the screen, his back illuminated by the white glow of the screen. "From the bank?"

"Not from the bank. Nelson will steal directly from STORK. I plan to plant him in their financial department."

Jeremy sat back down and stared down at his fidgeting hands, as if they could somehow answer all of his questions. The AI on the screen had gone onto cleaning his virtual space, burning papers from within a file cabinet labeled *cache*. Stone didn't like looking at the flames. His arm seemed to burn again as he watched them rise against the ceiling of whatever sort of virtual space Nelson lived in.

"How can we trust him?" Jeremy posed the single truly important question of the night.

"How can we trust Stone?" she retorted. The words made Stone's heart skip beats and his bones stiffen, as he tried to appear unfazed.

"You must be joking." Jeremy's face twisted between confused and angry, "Stone is a great asset to all of us. This bot, however, is a complete and total stranger." Jeremy calmed his tone, rested his head against his arm for support before continuing, "I don't know this bot. I don't know his functions, and I don't trust anything that isn't here, physically, for me to strangle if he betrays us." Nelson pulled at his collar and gulped. "And here he is, still mocking me."

"Those are just bugs. I've set his sarcasm too high on accident. I can easily adjust it in no time at all. I wanted him to be a little more fun to work with. He isn't disrespecting you, he will obey your every command and he can never betray us. It's impossible, I promise."

"He's a program," one of the janitors chimed in, "and who's to say he doesn't break, become corrupted?"

"Who's to say his original creators didn't code some backdoors into him? "The other added, both of them speaking in heavy European accents.

"I'm no amateur," Debra defended herself. The attacks and questions began to eat at her. "I'm more skilled than the people who coded him originally. They were lazy. His architecture was a mess. I know what backdoors look like and I know how to rebuild. Nelson is an improved shell of his former self with all the usefulness learned over the years, reordered and made new with an obedience to us alone."

"Debra, no one doubts your abilities here," one of the janitors reassured. "It's simply a lot of trust to put into something, or someone, that has yet to earn it."

"Can't expect us to immediately accept Nelson, when we can't even shake hands" the other laughed.

"Alright y'all, that's quite enough now," Jeremy interrupted, clearing his throat after a short chuckle. He looked over to Debra, "I think we've made our concerns loud and clear."

Guilt crept over Stone's skin as he watched the judgement take place. He felt more deserving of scrutiny than Nelson or Debra. Stone didn't even fully understand why he was sitting in that living room to begin with. Who was he to be defended? He should be the one mocked, poked, and prodded. His mischief easily pleased the others and that's all it is -- mischievous tagging of walls like a toddler with a crayon. The guilt made him squirm in the chair just as Debra glanced his way before quickly diverting her eyes.

"Nelson, lose your attitude when speaking to me," Jeremy said with a pointing finger, breaking the uncomfortable and awkward silence. Debra smiled subtly, her lips flickered upward with hope. Stone watched them turn after hearing Jeremy's words, hoping he could dial down his guilt.

"Yes sir, I'm heartily sorry to have displeased you. I promise to never offend you again." Nelson's baby face dropped as he expressed a great deal of remorse over the group's disappointment, "Also sir and all others hearing my words, I do promise that you will come to know me as the most loyal creature you've ever encountered. Your wish is my command and for as long as I process, I'll spoil you worse than any grandparent."

"Sounds more like it!" Jeremy laughed, amused at the bot's sudden and perfectly respectful change. "Debra, I want him starting small -- to gauge him."

"Consider it done."

"We'll consider these next few weeks as a trial period, a proof of concept, so to speak. What y'all think?"

The group chimed with resounding agreement, eager to find a better source of funding. If they come to trust Nelson in the next few weeks, his financial procurements will take them to a new level. No longer would they have to rely on the donations from the thinning pockets of Zealot advocates.

...

The meeting concluded shortly afterward and the guests began cleaning up. Stone helped eagerly, paying close attention to Debra as she put away her devices. The other three Zealots gathered their things and followed Jeremy outside, where he blessed their trips home. He had always done this for his precious Zealots, hoping that his prayers would be heard in Heaven. Surely the Lord would protect them on their way home. They needed the help of all the saints and angels in Heaven on their mission.

Stone cleared his throat to speak to Debra. The absence of the others made the room awkwardly silent, his own heartbeat seemed to resonate inside of it.

"I really like Nelson..." Those were the only words he could muster, as he rolled the screen for her.

"Thanks, me too," she responded tersely, just as he expected. His ice-breaking efforts couldn't have been any more embarrassing.

"So," he attempted again, "*when* Nelson gets approval, are you going to brand him too?" His heart fluttered as his formulated question received a sweet giggle from her.

"That's pretty funny, I hadn't thought about it. I guess could make it into a nice, fun little virtual ceremony. Also, I didn't mean to put you down earlier. I was just trying to reason with them. I'm sure you're plenty capable with our tasks at hand." To which Stone nodded and smiled, relieved that she didn't hate him. Then changing tone, she inquired, "But, speaking of branding, how's the arm feeling?" She reached, grasping his hand and turning it to see the marks.

"It feels about like I expected. The initial pain wore off quickly, though." He tried to sound tough. "Not so bad now." Her tiny paw-like hands felt ice cold as she gripped him, letting go as the door opened and the draft came in along with Jeremy.

"Jeremy, make sure you help him with the branding. It's going to need some attention. Can't let our best get infected," she quipped cheerfully, patting Stone's back. "Y'all have a good night." She winked as she turned to leave. "I've got a lot of work to get started on. Nelson's going to be a handful tonight."

"Well, don't work too hard! Get some rest too," Stone gushed, rushing to open the door for her. Jeremy watched the young man. He could detect the budding of a crush in his roommate's eyes.

...

Stone closed and locked the door once he was positive that Debra was leaving, but he continued to stand near the door for a moment. His imagination filled with scenarios where she knocked, needing to retrieve something she forgot, but it didn't happen. He heard laughter from down the hall and turned to see that Jeremy was on to him.

"Aw, ain't that cute," he said, watching the silly grin leave Stone's beaten face. "Never knew you were such a gentleman, Stone. Are you sure you didn't want to walk her home?"

"Hey, that's not a bad idea. She needs to be protected, don't you think?"

"She's a tough cookie, I wouldn't sweat it. She'd probably end up protecting you, instead, if any danger came up." Jeremy was smiling and lightly punching at his arm.

"I've got loads of questions." Stone wanted to change the subject and made his way to the kitchen to find some water. "Like, what exactly is my job? What purpose am I to serve?"

"Everything and anything required of you."

"Like?"

Jeremy looked at him, not answering immediately. "Get that aloe in the cabinet next to you. You'll need to put that on the branding wound and grab some bandages from the bathroom closet. Clean it a few times a day and always use a fresh bandage."

"Are you serious?"

"Yeah, infecti-"

"Come on! I'm talking about the job."

"We all have the same job -- to perform as needed to accomplish our mission and to destroy those that oppress our people. Also, you'll help me in the workshop, starting tomorrow."

"Tomorrow?"

"Yes, I'm going to teach you how to make buildings crumble."

CHAPTER FOUR

Once in a blue moon, the members of the close-knit family in Irondale took a day off work duties to relax and recharge. Between Amelia and Maria providing maid services to the constant repairs required of those who worked on the solar panels, days filled with relaxation didn't come very often. Even though everyone felt relieved to finally have a day off, they missed the company of one of their members terribly -- Stone.

Michael felt ashamed of himself for his rage-fueled outburst, which was bad enough on its own, but the constant chastisements everyone in the house threw at him made it even worse. None of them were too happy with him, and even the priest expressed great disappointment at Michael's attempt to defend himself.

A week had passed since the fight; and, a week since Maria and John moved in. The couple slept on their bed, surrounded by moving crates and suitcases. They grabbed clothes or toiletries from them each day, as needed. Maria quickly grew tired of the constant back and forth, searching every other box when she only needed a fresh pair of socks or one of her old books. It didn't bother John too much. He happily tossed piles of his clothes in the corner and plucked what he needed from it. It only became a concern when Maria cracked her whip.

Cole kept himself busy to avoid thoughts about the night before, when Stone visited to claim his belongings. The morning after, Cole awoke and felt a case of the blues forming in the pit of his stomach. He often turned to his creative outlet to vent his worries and other negative feelings during times like this. He missed his brother terribly. Standing before a canvas, he covered it in a variety of painted colors and shapes, depicting a dream he had earlier in the week. It made him wonder if it originated from the debate between his cousin and brother, or if it were a vision of some sort arising out of a news broadcast.

Recently, he also discovered glitches in his Auris. The device had been feeding him information while he slept. He noticed that he'd wake up every now and then with the biases of others scripting his subconscious. It disturbed his inner peace, but he knew not to trust the strange advice and opinions, consulting his priest for clarity when things troubled him too deeply.

The dark basement, lit only by a single floodlight, provided a musty refuge where he could plunge into creating his art. This private retreat, which was once planned to be used as a chapel, always renewed his spirit. He cranked the music up loud enough to drown out the head-splitting voices of his loud family. Flood damage from previous years caused many of the sound-insulating ceiling tiles to fall down in several spots. Amelia added the repair to Michael's honey-do list, but he never had time to get around to it. Even so, Cole enjoyed his solitude. He sometimes watched the light bleed through the floor planks above and observed how the many unknown crawling creatures squirmed within its shadows.

Drips of white, crimson, and black paint littered the cold concrete floor, escaping his brush as he brought it from workbench to the easel he had erected in the room's center. He was almost finished with this painting. Standing there for a moment, he looked at it and wondered if he should add something else once he blacked in all the shadows.

Occasionally, he displayed his works throughout the house, provided they didn't depict scenes that might disturb visitors. The others, he stacked on the workbench -- the ones with gory scenes and disturbing creatures that no one upstairs cared to view. He nailed some paintings on the walls around him. These depicted the images of saints he hoped prayed for him from Heaven. Occasionally, he glanced up at them, imagining they stared down at the canvas in progress, judging it with unmoving, unchanging faces.

...

"This one's definitely not going upstairs," he spoke out loud to his rendition of Saint Lawrence, nailed upon the wall. This pious saint had been grilled alive over a gridiron. Continuing aloud to no one and anyone, he added, "It's definitely not something Amelia would take pleasure in looking at for sure. Now, Michael might think it's cool, but nah, it's a bit grotesque."

I've seen more grotesque sights, he imagined Saint Lawrence saying from beneath the flames of his martyrdom. Such had been the humor the saint was said to have. According to the tradition, he laughed upon the searing gridiron, informing the Roman troops that he had been fully cooked on one side and that they should flip him over. The horrifically dark humor and apparent indifference to his own suffering became the source of Cole's appreciation for him.

Generously filling his brush with black paint, Cole drew it across the edge of the canvas as he searched out the places destined to become cloaked in darkness and shadow. His creation depicted a gorgeous chapel with an incredible garden in the back. If it weren't for the billowing fire blazing hot on the church building, the garden would have been painted lush and green. Its broken stained glass windows appeared almost fluorescent as fire illuminated them from within, casting their bright colors upon the ground outside. Cole brought his brush toward them, searching for unpainted specks of white within the depths of the shadowy scene. He stood back again to inspect it as a whole, noticing one of the silhouettes stood taller than the other.

"Maybe it's supposed to be Stone and me," he said, talking to the saint once again. "It's about the same difference in height."

It's your painting, Cole. Shouldn't you know who it is? He imagined the saint mocking him once again, with a hoarse Latin accent.

Still talking out loud to no one, "Was a dream I had -- never saw their faces, but who knows, maybe I'm right. The church probably just symbolizes everything going on right now. Stone would probably love it; and, he'd be the only one who could truly appreciate it. I mean, Michael would too; but, if he were still around, Stone would insist on hanging it in our room."

"Cole!" a man's voice shouted from above the stairs, resonating over the music booming from his stereo. "Hey, hoss, lunch is ready!"

I'm guessing this painting is finished, he mused. *Otherwise, I would have ignored the chow call.* He turned down the music and followed the mouth-watering aroma of black-bean burgers and seasoned fries, which wafted down the basement steps to his nostrils. He bounded up the stairs and into the kitchen where the others, already filling their plates, took their usual places at the large table.

...

Far from new, the table passed through many generations before finally getting to theirs. Most homes didn't have tables that even approached its size. People abandoned most of the old traditions long ago, having large families who dined together was one of them. The wood bore deep scars that previous generations obviously tried to sand out, seal, and reseal over the years.

"Smells incredible," Cole said, his stomach rumbling. He felt almost ill with hunger.

"Maria helped out today," Amelia admitted, dumping a pile of fries onto his plate. "We're so blessed to have such a fine cook. It's been really rough, Maria, not having any help 'round here."

"Excuse me? Think I've helped plenty!" Michael defended himself, biting into his succulent black bean burger. His curly dark hair hung freely over his shoulders as he ate. Crumbs clung like tiny ornaments in his unruly mane, waiting for Amelia to teasingly point them out.

"Oh, really?" Amelia gave a sarcastic giggle, pulling her hair back into a neat ponytail as she edged her chair and sat down. "Where were you when the eggplant parmesan burned?"

"I thought you were watching it."

"I was watching it, but then your cousin came home -- drunk -- and painted the bathroom walls in puke. That incident caused a bit of a distraction." Everyone, especially Michael, voiced groans of disgust, clearly attempting to clear the image and enjoy the meal.

"I get no respect 'round here." Michael frowned mockingly, wiping his mouth with a large kitchen towel he grabbed off the counter. It seemed everyone else had proper napkins, probably due to the fact that he didn't know where Amelia kept them and, honestly, because he didn't care to look for one at the time.

"It's okay, little brother. I'm happy to help, darling." Maria's sweet voice soothed the unwelcome thread of tension that arose between Michael and Amelia. Their entire family, and many friends too, considered her culinary skills legendary.

Growing up, Maria took pains to preserve all the generational family recipes. Each recipe was exactly as it had been for ages, except for the small tweaks she made to the main dish recipes, most of which called for meat. *I wonder what I'm missing due to the ban on meat. Does it taste at all like the meat substitutes we eat in its place? I doubt it.* She let out a deep, long sigh, pondering the mysterious taste once enjoyed by her Sicilian and Irish ancestors.

Amelia's copies of the recipes sat on top of the counter. The ancient penmanship on them said so much, it seemed. In fact, not only were the swirls and twirls of each stroke beautifully created with full effortless intent, but many other notes were written page margins. Some quick mathwork in the corner for a deceased in-law's bills and to-do lists here and there with 'sweep kitchen' crossed out.

She never had the opportunity to learn the recipes the proper way -- from a family matriarch. She imagined what a pleasure it could have been, to hear the stories of how the grandparents met while stirring boiling pasta. Often her thoughts imagined the bits of family history that would pour out of the matriarch as she drizzled olive oil over the steaming farfalle.

"Cole," Maria changed the conversation, "have you talked to your brother recently?"

"Uh...," he hoped his hesitation didn't betray the lie. "No, I haven't, not recently. Why?"

"Just wondering. It's been a week now, hasn't it? I wonder if he's okay."

"I'm sure he's fine." Michael's calm answer elicited glares from the women at the table.

"Better hope he is. I'll kick your ass if any harm comes to that child, Mikey." Maria's mood darkened as she continued to nibble on her fries. Even with his sturdy frame, the barely detectable threat chilled his blood. Only a woman can cause that type of chill in a man. He didn't care to experience any repeats of the plate-throwing wrath she sometimes perpetrated -- wrath that arose due to the temper she inherited from those Sicilian relatives.

"Honey," John, filled the short gap in conversation while picking at the tiny scraps left on his plate, "Stone's no child. He's grown. I'm sure he'll be okay."

"Better watch it, sweetie. I'm not afraid of you either." She gave him the same menacing woman-glare she gave Michael.

"Just saying."

"I think I finished another piece today," Cole announced, hoping to distract them from the topic of his brother. "Think you'd like it, Mikey."

"Well, I'm finished with lunch, if you want to take me down now," Michael responded, excited to escape the eyes boring into him like little daggers.

"Cole isn't finished!" Maria shouted. "He's barely touched his fries."

"That burger filled me up, seriously." Cole sat back and patted his ultra-slim stomach. "I really just can't finish them." No matter how starved he had been just moments ago, his belly truly was fully stuffed, and he desired no more.

"I'll take 'em." John smiled as he motioned with his hand and snatched the plate from Cole.

...

He stood to head down to the basement with the other two men after quickly scarfing down the leftovers. "Never had a chance to check it out down here."

"It's not much, really. Pretty disgusting, honestly. I don't know how you can spend so much time down here, Cole," his cousin chided as they descended to the cool, subterranean level. "Freaking depresses me."

"I don't know. It's my own space. Everybody needs personal space and this is mine. It's not too bad, once you get used to the smell."

"At least the temperature is amazing." John sweated constantly, in all conditions, in all environments. The cool draft breezing through chilled him, giving him a comfort he rarely experienced.

"Yeah, in the winter I have to layer up when I come down here." Cole switched on the light so they could actually see. In an instant, it illuminated all of his finished work.

"Wow, Cole, I didn't know you were an artist. Very impressive stuff you got here." John looked around the room at the various scenes of decapitated saints and angels with flaming swords. The most pleasant painting was of the Blessed Virgin Mary, but even its subject matter looked rather disconcerting to his fresh pair of eyes. She stood on a crescent moon, nothing new there, but beneath her lay piles of skulls with serpents slithering throughout eye sockets and bony jaws agape. "What's that one's meaning?" He pointed to the Virgin.

"Just like most of the others. Had a dream about it and thought it looked cool. I think maybe it represents those entangled in their sins. People die praying, but rarely ever make an effort to make real changes in their lives, or that's what I think it means."

"How comforting." John laughed uncomfortably, thinking of his own problems. Struggles he held secret from everyone, only hinting at them in sacramental confessions.

"Is this the new one?" Michael asked, indicating the painting still on the easel. Its paint still glistened in the light; not fully dried on the canvas.

"Yeah, been working on it since Stone left."

Michael felt responsible for the art, having directly caused Stone's flight from home. To him, the flaming church represented his disagreement with his cousin; the destruction depicted his regret and the flames blazed hot with his rage-filled reaction. *One of the shadowy figures in the foreground might be Cole. Not quite sure who the other one is supposed to be. Perhaps it's the priest,* he thought.

"What's it mean?" John asked again, his mind clearly not practiced in perception of symbols and analogies.

"Just the current state of the Church, I guess," Cole offered, chewing his nails as he studied his own work. "No one's trying to put the fire out. The stained-glass windows represent broken traditions." At this point, he hesitated, not wanting to reveal it's true meaning. "...and I don't know, maybe the mystery figures started the problems. The godless and angry?"

"No, I don't think so." John was unwilling to admit to the gravity and hopelessness of their situation.

"It's his painting, John." Michael laughed, shooting a strange look in his direction, shaking his head.

"No, it's fine. I like to hear other interpretations. Sometimes they're more insightful than mine." Cole listened, eager to hear John's take on the art. *Maybe I've finally got the decipherer I need in John.* He perked up interiorly as he considered this possibility. No one ever seemed to fully understand his pieces and neither did Cole at times. *Who can blame me?* His thoughts began to race. *Visions come to me in my subconscious, uninvited. My brushes simply act as the messengers.* He refrained from telling anyone that he actually had very little to do with the final outcome of his pieces.

"I think it's just a church on fire."

"How remarkable, John," Michael teased with a tinge of disappointment. "Truly, that's some honest-to-God prophetic analysis. Thanks for sharing. Job well done, Cole. I really like it. Don't show it to Amelia, though. I'll never hear the end of it." Laughing as they climbed the basement steps, they left Cole alone to further ponder any deeper meaning to the work.

He let out a long breath and dipped a brush into the red paint left on his color palette earlier. The hairs of the brush caressed the bottom of the painting as he signed his name in a style of calligraphy unique to him and his paintings. The mark signified the completion of a painting. Done, even if no one could fully interpret the true meaning of the work.

CHAPTER FIVE

Storms raged throughout the night of Stone's initiation, but he awoke the next morning to quiet, yet overcast skies with a thick fog clinging to the ground. The cool air made him fully awake, sobering him for the things in store for him later. He kept his wounded and bandaged arm still, so it didn't swing while he walked. Stiffening it, he held it out and away from his torso in an attempt to prevent any rubbing against his body. He knew this probably made his gait look amusing -- like an ape.

The bandage covering his new markings aggravated him. He eagerly awaited the big reveal -- the moment he could first lay eyes on the branding, healed, scarred, and void of pain. He fantasized about wearing it uncovered for all to see.

"Where is this workshop, anyway?" Stone asked, his tone terse. Walking uphill for so long made his breathing labored. The steep road stretched toward the top of the mountain He watched as an acorn fell from a tree and tumble down the road, nothing to stop it, just as he felt he would if this trek went on much further.

"Decided we'd start the day differently, bud," Jeremy puffed over his shoulder, glancing back at him.

"What? What are we doing then?" Stone didn't know whether he felt curious or irritated.

Jeremy didn't answer him; he kept walking until he finally stopped outside of a dilapidated, kudzu-covered chapel. The weight of the invasive vines caused the roof to cave in. Green, winding fingers of kudzu continued on to reach through the shattered stained glass windows as well.

Stone followed him to the backyard of the little church. Since the front door was chained shut, the backdoor served as the only entrance. Stone detected the pungent, stale scent of mildew and other rotting debris, still out of breath from the unexpected hike. Jeremy knelt to make the sign of the cross before walking past the altar. Stone followed and did the same, still confused as to why they were there.

"My family attended Mass here when I was a child. We always sat in the front pew there." Jeremy pointed to a mostly incinerated pew, most of it black with soot. "My mother spent a month painting the crucifix that hung here before. A lot of her is still present within these walls. I sometimes imagine her, now, on a ladder, painting the crown moulding."

Stone glanced over to where the crucifix had hung, only then realizing it wasn't hanging, instead it lay under the cover of shadows upon the floor like a large piece of worthless refuse. Flooded with sadness, he stared at Jeremy for a moment. It dawned on him that whatever happened here was unbelievably awful. Jeremy had never spoken of it.

"You can still find holy things on the floors and under the debris here," Jeremy broke the growing weight of silence as he stopped Stone's hand from picking up a rosary melted and fused into a twisted shape. "The things belonged to the parishioners, but I always leave them exactly where I find them." The two • of them sat in one of the few pews with enough structural integrity to hold them. "I come here from time to time when I forget what it is we've set out to do."

"What happened?"

"*Officially*, it just happened to catch fire that day, during the Easter Vigil." Stone could see tears pooling in his friend's eyes, on the brink of rolling down Jeremy's cheeks. "They said it was because of the bonfire, from the blessing of the fire. *Officially*, the doors were locked from the inside, but I remember the deacons. I remember the noise they made trying to bust down the doors. *Officially*, there was no way out for the parishioners. All of them burned to death in the supposedly freak accident and nobody even attempted to help." Jeremy made air quotes with his hands as he spat out the words, freak accident. "Only those of us small enough to fit through the narrow stained-glass windows escaped." The pool of liquid in his eyelids broke and tears rained down from them, landing hard against the mudded floor.

For many people, childhood memories become dull by the time they reach adulthood. But he remembered everything vividly, as if it happened yesterday. His small five-year-old body stood tall that day -- a little man -- at his mother's waist. His grandmother took photos of them because she said they looked so sharp in their best clothes.

...

Everyone wore black, so the faithful always dressed for Easter Vigil, as if they were about to go to a funeral. It's only fitting to wear somber clothes to the Mass commemorating the day the first Christians placed Christ in His tomb. Stone stayed quiet, slowly looking around the chapel. Jeremy allowed his mind to wander further into his memories.

His grandparents had a beautiful grotto in their backyard with a weathered and aged statue of the Virgin Mary. The statue stood beneath an expansive magnolia tree surrounded by cut stones. As if it happened yesterday, Jeremy remembered hearing birds chirping and playing in the nearby bird bath. Elizabeth, his mother, loved it there. She grew up in that same house and they spent most of their time there during holidays. His grandparents cooked a delicious meal --

one that followed all the Lenten restrictions. They all ate it heartily, as if starved. Afterward, the four of them took a taxi to the church.

An only child, going to Mass always excited Jeremy because he got to see his friends. They played between parents on the pews, amid pinches and slaps from irritated mothers and fathers. An only child, going to Mass always excited Jeremy because he got to see his friends. Debra, the girl Stone seemed to have a crush on, was one of them. Her parents immigrated from a faraway land and their accents both captivated and terrified him.

Sometimes she got into trouble. This made Jeremy afraid he was next, always inspiring him to straighten up immediately. That terrible night, Debra got scolded, so they both stood straight and calm next to the adults gathered around a small bonfire located a safe distance away from the front of the tiny chapel.

And so, the two children were calm that night and stood next to all the adults gathered around a fire pit that had been assembled in front of the chapel. The sun dipped its liquid golden globe below the horizon, leaving a soft purple-blue glow to the darkening sky. Only the brightest stars showed their brilliance in the gloaming. Elizabeth held Jeremy tightly during the outdoor portion of the Mass, the warmth of the bonfire and the sight of it filled him with excitement. His eyes waist-level, glanced up at her and he mimicked her as she made the Sign of the Cross. He watched the priest as he paced between them and the fire, his arms outstretched while he recited a special prayer to bless the fire.

The Paschal Candle, lit from the flames of the bonfire, led the way into the building. He vividly remembered everyone following its tiny light inside where they reclaimed their spots. He and Debra sat next to each other, between their parents, Debra's eyes grew heavy and she soon fell asleep. She was only four and he remembered each time she fell asleep in Mass because she often laid her head on his shoulder in the pew just as she did that night. Only candles lit the sanctuary and the altar. No lights. The soft glow and dim ambience made his eyes heavy too, but he stayed awake. This unusual Mass interested him greatly. The candles looked beautiful to him and uncommon. He lived his entire life beneath thousands of lumens in school and at home. The candles sparkled just as brightly as the stars that greeted them outside as they stood by the bonfire. The altar appeared just as shadowy and dim as the church building looked once the sun dipped below the horizon.

...

At one point during the Mass, Jeremy remembered a horrific change in the priest's face. He leaned up so he could turn to look behind them toward the front door. The sacred lighting in the sanctuary became overpowered by a much brighter radiance in the back and he heard a great commotion -- a shouting woman,

then many shouts from men, women, and children --
the entire congregation. Debra's eyes flew open, wide
awake, at that moment too. Jeremy had forgotten about
her. Someone screamed, "Fire! There's a fire in the
balcony!"

Above them, in the choir balcony, great licks of
orange, gold, and yellow flames spread along the walls
and curtains, already singeing the white ceiling and
wooden beams. The black smoke rolled along the A-
framed crest of the ceiling and filled the air like swirling
clouds.

"Fire! Dear Christ!"

An elderly woman prayed on her rosary beads with
shaking hands and in a shrieking voice that rang out in
many keys and tones, "Hail Mary, full of grace..."

The fire spread far too quickly, leaving no time to
find an escape route. Chaos ensued as the congregation
frantically tried to beat down the massive wooden
doors. Others checked the exit doors in the back, finding
them locked as well. Then they joined the rest of the
parishioners in their vain attempt to dislodge the main
entrance.

Quickly, people realized that time was up and began
slamming furniture against the stained-glass windows,
shattering and destroying statues of saints and images
of the sacraments. Brightly hued colored glass lay in
jagged shards on the ground, much of it getting crushed
by the heavy, panicky footsteps of terrified people.
Smoke completely filled the air by this point. Jeremy's

mother held him tightly, both coughing and struggling to breathe. His eyes burned and watered, but he could still see shapes of about a hundred adults run, curse, and fight for their lives. Numbness overcame him and he felt helpless in his mother's arms, ever helpless. If the grown-ups couldn't handle the situation, neither could he. Jeremy prayed silently, hoping that the fires would suddenly vanish or that he was only having a nightmare.

The windows gave way between their iron framework, each of these only a foot apart. A fat man clogged one up, all by himself, until the mob pulled him free and beat him down. They stood on him and continued trying to escape, but none of them could fit between the iron supports.

Jeremy remembered the heat, beads of sweat pouring into his teary and smoky eyes, and listening to the shouts and cries of his own mother. Her screams sounded like they didn't even come from her. She let out a long moaning, deep and full of shock, like a wounded dog. He heard language from her mouth that had never before heard her utter. All sounds began to run together between cries out to God, Christ, and all the Saints and angels. But all of that secondary to the terror growing inside him as he saw the flames grow until the holy sanctuary became an infernal hell.

His grandfather broke the glass on another window and began feverishly passing the children to the outside. They were the only ones tiny enough to fit through and became the first survivors, contrary to the actions of the incapacitated fat man. Elizabeth carried him forward to the window, stepping over a few bodies of the frail, and he remembered feeling hope and relief. Young Jeremy believed that he and his mother were going to make it outside and that all of this wouldn't be quite as bad as everyone imagined.

Elizabeth started to push him through the iron railing, her voice hysterical, but still full of intense motherly affection, "I love you, my sweet boy. I love you, Jeremy." Shards of glass, still clinging to the sides of the frame, cut his little face. Streaks of blood dripped from his jaw and brow as he fell to the cold ground.

"Mommy! Follow me, climb through the window!"

Jeremy saw figures emerging from them, in front of the inferno, but they were small screaming children, their faces twisted in horror as the adult on the other side forced them out of the windows. Jeremy stood and ran to the window he dropped from, dripping blood clouded the vision in his right eye.

"Mommy!" he screamed as his hands reached into the hot railing, not tall enough to climb back through. Right then, a shrieking Debra came through, knocking Jeremy back onto the ground. He helped her up and stood at the edge of a tree line, eagerly waiting and holding her, thinking that his family would follow soon after.

However, as Jeremy and the many saved children stood crying, they could hear the screams of the dying from within. They could see the arms and hands wailing along the outside of the windows, until after a short while they flailed no longer. The arms became limp as massive amounts of smoke billowed from the shattered windows. With the fire still burning and the screams of the adults dying away, young Jeremy was filled with confusion. *Why are they not following us?* He kept asking himself this question over and over.

He learned later that night, after help finally came to extinguish the fire, that they all asphyxiated, a word his tearful nurse described as falling asleep and not waking up. Still Jeremy watched the church doors, knowing that his mother would eventually fling them open and run back to him from the smoking building. She did come out eventually, but an unmarked bag covered each body completely, concealing her face and the faces of about a hundred others carried from the bricked ruins.

Jeremy concluded his story, "The rest of it...burial, counseling, and orphanage...all as you'd expect."

"Horrible, man. I'm so sorry to hear that." Stone wished he could think of anything, absolutely anything, better to say, but he had no more words. Nothing came to mind, because out of the millions of words and ways he could use to describe happiness, language still had not evolved enough to accurately describe the worst imaginable things. Things that only those with firsthand experience and memory could imagine remained elusive.

...

"I brought you here today, to show you just how ready the world is to see us gone. How little they care, to bury the dead, to leave this building unfixed...these items on the ground, like debris. We're unimportant, irrelevant, and when we are considered relevant we're called the remnants of bigotry and hate, superstitious. To them, the things most sacred to us are comparable to the philosophies of barbarians. We're forced to live by their rules, pay for their atrocities, and when we refuse them, they hunt us like criminals. We wear invisible shackles and live in an invisible prison, because if they can make us invisible...then it's as if we don't even exist at all."

Jeremy stood from the burnt pew and continued, "This church building is a lot like us now, scarred and ruined, hidden behind fallen trees and kudzu. But, the building remains, after all, and we will rebuild it one day. As long as we live, we're capable of growth, capable of reestablishing ourselves in this putrid cesspool of a world. They wanted us gone- they wanted us gone, and they continue to push those of us that remain. The final obstacle before their perfect degenerative world."

"What about Unity?" Stone asked as he stood and began looking at the fine detail in the scorched and weathered stations of the cross upon the walls. "It seems we've zeroed in on STORK. Why not destroy the very foundation?"

"Unity definitely ain't off the hook," he replied, shaking his head, "but I have other orders to fulfill first. Trust me, I'd much rather destroy that abomination, that demonic thing, as much as the next guy, but we live next door to STORK and, thus, it's our focus."

"What's your vision of the world, once we've won?" Stone stood solemnly before the station depicting the *Pieta*, a famous sculpture created by Michelangelo. The awe-inspiring statue depicts Christ's lifeless body placed over the Blessed Virgin's lap. Her child, destined for greatness, lay limp in her arms once again, but this time beaten, disrobed, and crucified. The grief on Mary's face seems palpable, as she gazes down into the many lashings, which split His skin apart, His body broken and torn.

"Victory isn't always the way people imagine during the fight." Jeremy's passion cooled and his voice became soft again as he spoke sitting in the pew, "It's likely to be chaos if we succeed. Our suffering might have just begun, but at least we'll be free. Our beliefs, way of life, our ambitions will have no bounds. No longer will some tyrannical bot dictate what we can and can't be -- because of who we are."

When Stone first joined the Zealots, he overflowed with the same rebellious spirit shared by many others his age. A glorified version of teen angst, it makes for shallow rebels without a clear understanding of their true purpose. But, as Jeremy spoke, the answers to his questions of direction and purpose began to take shape in his mind. Each statement brought him closer to internalizing the truth Jeremy spoke, once feral and strange to him, now transformed into a beautiful light -- the only light -- that drew him to it.

"So, what of making buildings crumble?" He tried to take the conversation to another level. The destroyed chapel began to wear on him and he wanted to leave.

Jeremy stood up, also ready to leave. He and Stone walked to the charred exit at the back of the chapel and through the clingy kudzu vines, which snatched at their legs and arms from every direction, like the cloying hands of some fantastical creature. A while ago, the last time Jeremy visited, he cut it back, but it grows rapidly and took over again in just a couple of months. It took more effort to pull free of the vines when leaving than going in, but Stone finally pulled himself free, enjoying Jeremy's laughing grin, greeting him upon his triumph.

...

What a relief to hike down the mountain this time, Stone thought. He felt a lighter mood come upon him immediately as they left the decay and ruin; overcast skies never seemed so uplifting before this. Clouds swirled and twisted as they raked against the air at high speeds. The sight made him dizzy, so he made his way down the hill as quickly as he could, the downward trajectory forcing him to look away from the cloud show.

Eventually, they made their way to the workshop, and to Stone's surprise, took a train out of town. He expected just a quick walk from the house, to which Jeremy explained that you never crap on your own lawn. They unloaded in Woodlawn, a neighborhood in Birmingham, then stopped for a quick bite before setting off on foot to the workshop that Stone was so eager to enter.

He followed Jeremy along the cracked and uneven sidewalks, shifted by erosion into tripping hazards for unfamiliar pedestrians. He certainly didn't need a twisted ankle, so stone kept his eyes on the ground. They trudged over tufts of weeds that fought their way through the concrete and holes filled with mud and debris.

Eventually, Stone's tired legs stopped moving and he realized Jeremy turned to walk up a set of brick stairs leading to a house. His eyes quickly scanned over the structure, taking all in. Much to his disappointment, he saw yet another broken and partially dilapidated building. He saw signs that past owners had attempted to reconstruct and reinforce the home a couple of times. Built and rebuilt, it sat neglected and abandoned time and again. Repetitive attempts to mend the vicious toll of many years by people who longed to see its original beauty failed under the weight of everyday life.

Vulgar images, blasphemies, and gang-related symbols covered the wooden siding. Iron bars covered the outside of the windows and boards covered them from the inside, making it impossible to see in or out. Stone watched Jeremy fit and turn a key into the backdoor knob. He replaced the knob assembly one night when he first started using the sad old house. He also brought gloves for the two of them to wear at all times, so it remained free of their prints in the event someone discovered the house's dark purpose.

...

As they entered the condemned house, Stone joked internally that some evil mold and mildew entity followed him everywhere because his nose filled with its familiar foul odor. Decaying wooden floors greeted them; a leaking ceiling caused an abysmal hole in the sheetrock. When staring into its depths, Stone saw reflections of light glinting off of the hard-armored exoskeletons of insects and spiders that made it their home. He turned to see Jeremy already at work, removing items from the squeaky kitchen cabinets and placing them onto a workbench sitting beside the counter.

"How long have you used this place?"

"Ah, I don't know...maybe six or seven months. Why you think it's nice?"

"Oh, of course!" Stone laughed, "Women must love it."

Jeremy began unpacking metallic boxes from a bag also stored in the creaking cabinets. He typically kept everything they needed stocked there, limiting any contraband held on his person or in his home.

"Yeah, you should send your love an invite sometime." Jeremy's joke fell on deaf ears. His focus centered on getting answers to his questions.

"What you do when it gets dark?" The overcast sky that lingered throughout the day now grew darker by the second as Earth continued her spin at a thousand miles per hour.

"Candles." The now somber man pointed to the dozens of places where candles had, evidently, stood before. "No power here, obviously. Which is okay, because we wouldn't want any light escaping any unseen cracks or holes this place may have. Might get discovered."

"Ah, I understand. Women must love that too."

"Lighter is in the drawer, beside the sink. Just whatever you do -- listen to me -- whatever you do," he emphasized, "keep those flames away from the workbench. Been a minute since I went for a confession."

"I hear Purgatory's lovely this time of year."

"Psh, place is a resort compared to where they'd cast me if I die before confessing." As devout as his plans and intentions, making it to Mass proved difficult for him. Over a year ago, his priest disappeared into what seemed like thin air. The collection of daily sins from his lustful eyes and drunkenness added layer upon layer of grimy dirt to his soul; stained and unpurified he waged his war carefully.

Stone's anxiety shot through the roof as he held the tiny flame in his gloved hands. Their lives hung entirely at the mercy of his steady hand. He lit the massive candles and set them about the room. They stood level to his chest, some of them on stands, others on windowsills, glued into place by the incredible amounts of wax that had fused between them and the wood.

"That's good enough," Jeremy ordered, almost completely illuminated by the flickering lights. "Put it back in the drawer and come over here. Everything is in place and ready."

Stone's heart quickened, still slightly weighed down by his conscience. This night, he would learn how to carry out his part of their mission. Whenever the guilt visited him, he immediately extinguished it with memories of the horrible stories others told him and the disgusting things he had seen firsthand. In his mind, he redefined the word 'terrorist' and thought of himself as just another soldier in a war that he increasingly perceived as right and just. Bombs will act as messages that the two of them will write and then deliver to their oppressors. The resulting deaths will become the words they scream into the face of Unity. STORK will crumble and the weight of it will groan and whine as it fell to the earth. The tumultuous roar will beacon the others, the silent and starving, reawakened by its sound.

"These two are never to be mixed, always keep them separate," Jeremy explained about the chemicals that sat apart from one another on opposite benches. "They get packaged and sealed. Once we've done that, we'll screw the two halves together in these containers."

Stone's nervousness grew and seemed to leak from his shaky hands. He thought of the many possible accidents with potential to send both of them sky high at any moment, blown to bits.

Jeremy, on the other hand, remained entirely stoic in his speech and manner. His experience making the explosive devices played a small part in his calm demeanor, but the majority of this ability was due to the horror he witnessed as a child on that fateful Easter Vigil long ago. How that man was capable of even standing near flames was a mystery to Stone, let alone messing with the combustibles.

Even the branding, why choose to burn himself like that? Stone thought that perhaps that was the meaning behind it all; Jeremy covered pain with more pain. He remembered, recovered, and stored it on himself to one day distribute back to its givers.

Followed closely by Jeremy and concentrating on his instructions, Stone poured the materials into their proper containers. He stirred chemicals for another, tested their consistency, and repeated the steps again and again until hours had elapsed. Once his thoughts fell away and his mind became fully occupied by the steps and meticulous measuring his concentration remained unbroken. Time passed swiftly under these conditions. The candles shrank, their white wax rolled back onto itself in the dimly lit kitchen that flickered into the night.

"You're not so bad, I don't care what they say about you." Jeremy laughed, patting Stone's shoulder after he locked the door. The cold and fresh air nourished the two of them. Their work finished for that night, they could joke around.

"What did they say?"

"Only the nicest things, I'm joking. You really did do a great job though. Pretty soon you'll be the one teaching new recruits."

A smile forced its way onto Stone's face from his mentor's compliment. His weak efforts to subdue it failed and he felt far too delirious from the work to care about any embarrassment.

"Thanks. Felt like I was wasting away, living at Michael's. You've really given me a new purpose, Jeremy. I've never felt so honored and valued in my life and I'm here for anything you ever need."

"How's the arm feeling? Should change the bandages once we get home."

"It's good. Looked pretty gross this morning and still reeked."

"Well don't sniff then, silly."

They could see the city ahead of them and once Stone made it past the obstacle of crooked pavement, he gazed upon the slender and sparkling STORK spire that pierced the clouds above. It seemed so far away, yet he easily made out its detail and opulence amongst the dull buildings surrounding it. He imagined then, the number of bombs he would need to assemble before it no longer stood there to taunt him with a fear of failure.

CHAPTER SIX

The house in Irondale was fully awake and the men stood talking in the kitchen over mugs of coffee. The chill in the house caused an unusual amount of steam to curl up from the hot drinks as they warmed themselves.

Each caffeinated sip the men took pushed them further out of the morning's melatonin-induced grogginess. Their lethargic faces still puffy from sleep, but their smiles and laughter indicated an overall jovial mood as they talked about work. John planned to start working with Michael that morning as a technician repairing solar panels and perhaps even installing new ones before too long.

He knew nothing of the trade and asked Michael a barrage of irrelevant questions, many of which only received head shakes and more laughter. Awakened by the building volume of the raucous laughter, Cole sat nearby and tried to shake off the night's sleep. He yawned, offering nothing to their discussion as he thought about last night's dreams.

Amelia and Maria paced around upstairs, trying to decide what to wear for the day and applying their war paint. Still not properly blended, the makeup left a few fingertip streaks on their young faces. Amelia pondered quietly as she finished her face. *Something just isn't right with Maria lately, she thought, furrowing her brow in concern. What's with all these random crying jags? She was never like this before. And those mood swings.*

The pair became inseparable as Maria sought comfort from the only other woman in the house. They shared gossip and discussed do-it-yourself projects, which served to distract Maria from whatever caused her moods. Amelia found great pleasure and relief in it as well. Their closeness dissipated a little of the intense fury she felt toward her husband after his fight with Stone.

"I just feel so bad for Cole," Maria whispered as she stood within the white glow of Amelia's closet light. "He doesn't speak much about anything at all, but you can tell he's upset."

"Michael said he mentioned seeing Stone not too long ago."

"What?" Maria shouted, almost angry no one told the news sooner.

"Yeah, Stone had him toss some belongings from the window. Said he wouldn't even let him run out to hug him."

"What's that boy gotten himself into?" Maria's eyes rolled, as she brought a blush brush to her face, finally smoothing out the streaks of unblended makeup. "Why didn't Cole try to stop him or something?"

"Well, from what Michael said, it's sad...because you know," her voice softened as she leaned closer to Maria, "their mother was -- is -- a junkie and what-not. Anyway, Michael was angry with Cole for not trying to stop him or waking any of us up. Cole apparently said something to the effect that, 'People are going to do what they want to do, regardless of what you want for them, just as our mother always did.'"

"That poor boy. That breaks my heart. My aunt's such a disgusting human being. She left those boys broken, I tell you."

The women's gossip was true. Cole did say those words and his mother did leave them broken. She pursued her addictions every day of the week. Drugs were her lover and her children stayed home for hours unsupervised, like house sitters, starting from a very young age.

Cole never talked much anyway, but, after the fight, he retreated further into his introspective shell than ever before. He only offered input when directly addressed and left his family struggling to comfort him, but he didn't need it. A very young man, yet an interior life more suitable to a much older person left him numb to other people's drama and their seemingly shallow talk. He repressed disturbing thoughts when around others, but secretly meditated on them when alone. *People are going to do what they want, regardless of what you want for them.* His mother regularly promised them she'd take them on these wildly exciting activities for behaving well and not burning the house down while she *visited her friends.*

...

Cole's memory revisited a painful scenario. "We'll go to the state fair tonight, my precious boys!" their mother exclaimed, while hugging their waist-level heads tightly to her. The boys longed for motherly embraces; needed to feel her love the way a man who's starving to death needs food to sustain him. A constant desire for their mother to see them, to really love them, filled their young hearts.

Their spirits always rose to meet her sweet words and promises. Each time this scenario played out, the little boys thought, *This is going to be the night.* The promises and plans she laid out convinced them so thoroughly that they took the bait time and time again. When she returned, they showered and dressed and she even made a big show of checking the showtimes. She went so far as to get them situated in the car. Then they left the house for their fun-filled night with mommy -- the beautiful woman that held their innocent little boy hearts in her hands. Cole and Stone chattered excitedly about the rides they wanted to go on and the snacks they hoped to eat in bundles.

"Alright, my sweeties, mama needs to stop by real quick-like and say hi to her special friend. Y'all sit tight!"

She winked at them as she pulled up to her boyfriend's apartment. Immediately their faces dropped as they struggled to not believe what they already knew. They weren't going to the fair and she would not get back to the car anytime soon.

Of course, they didn't understand what she had been doing, their minds so soft and innocent didn't know what addiction was. They didn't know what illegal drugs were in a formal sense, despite the fact that the boys saw and smelled them on a regular basis. They didn't know anything about sobriety or intoxication, they just knew that their mother always returned a completely different person. She wasn't their *real* mother -- just a liar in her skin bearing false promises and poor attempts at apologies.

Stone always vocalized his disappointments, crying and whining to her when she returned, but Cole stayed quiet because he knew how angry she got when Stone started his protests.

Past experience taught him at a very young age that people were going to do exactly as they wanted, no matter what their loved ones wanted or needed. Words, debates, and prayers yielded no fruit for in the past, so when his brother refused him that night, he knew not to put up a fight. It was up to him to keep that love warm, to bury it deep within him so disappointment had no power to extinguish it. He buried it so deep, the faintest pain couldn't break through; a trait that convinced many he didn't care, or that he had some sort of emotional deficit. He was as normal as possible under the circumstances, just broken. He kept himself glued together the only way he knew how.

...

In Irondale, the men climbed upon the humongous structure of solar panels, making their way along the walkways that stretched over the neighborhood. The great ball of fire in the sky finally lent its heat to the walkways once it crested over the mountains in the distance.

Back at the house, the women were fully dressed and ready for their jobs, but couldn't leave due to Maria and her near constant nausea. She began vomiting more than it seemed possible for someone her size. *Something is really wrong,* Amelia thought.

"I don't understand," Maria insisted, wiping her face clean with a wet cloth Amelia handed her. "It's gone on too long to be anything I ate."

"Well, I can take you by our doctor's house. In fact, I insist on it. I'm going to call in."

"Please don't, 'Milia, I'm fine. I've made you late too many times as it is."

"It's okay. Don't worry, girl. We gotta get you taken care of. Get you better."

"What doctor? The Rendas?"

"Yeah, sometimes I forget you grew up here." Amelia laughed as she exited the bathroom to let Cole know they were leaving.

He sat upright on the living room couch, unaware of her presence. He was in class and wore a virtual reality headset over his eyes and ears, listening to the teacher drone on and on about Sumerians and their contributions to humanity. Apparently, they were credited as the first civilization to create and drink beer. And they drank it through straws! Now that was new and the thought disgusted him, but it was something he would like to try when no one was watching. Amelia didn't want to interrupt his lesson, so she wrote a note and gently placed it next to him on the couch.

Afterward, she beaconed for a taxi and alerted Maria upon its arrival. The tiny two-seater car pulled up and its doors flung open, allowing them to climb inside.

"Good morning! Hope all is well, be sure to buckle your belts!" the taxi's speakers greeted them as the seats calculated their weight letting it know they had secured themselves. The vehicles never wrecked, but continued to warn, command, and make their disclaimers known, in accordance with the law.

The doctor-couple the ladies journeyed to see, practiced from their home. They treated, cured, and advised neighborhood families who couldn't afford the high costs at the clinics and hospitals, or who didn't have the Unity insurance. For many, the state provided cost-free insurance coverage, but only to those holding a taxable job, something many in the Church didn't have.

...

When they arrived, the Rendas greeted the two women warmly and welcomed them into their home. The couple led them down a set of stairs into the basement, which served as their offices and exam room. A variety of devices and supplies crowded the examining area. They frequented auctions to obtain the things they needed. They had replaced flooring themselves with special tiles and a medical-grade coating, easily cleaned and sterilized for their patients.

"So, Maria," Paul began, his jet-black hair, ungreyed, covered the dome of his head like a forest of curly needles, "it's been a long time since we've gotten a visit from you. Must've been taking your vitamins!" He laughed.

"We've missed you, Maria," Sandra added. She sat very close to her husband. She always spoke with deepest sincerity; her thin lips smiling as she gently chided their patient, "You don't have to get sick to visit, you know."

"I know. I just moved back into town. My husband and I were living in the city."

"Ah, well. What's going on today, or should I say this week, as Amelia mentioned?"

"I feel like I've been falling apart and haven't been much use lately" Maria explained as tears fell freely from her eyes. She wrapped her hair around the right side of her neck as she continued to describe her torment, "I don't understand what the hell is happening. Feels like I'm barely getting any sleep. I've had many headaches and been dizzy for several days now. My back's hurting and for these past two days, I've been vomiting."

Sandra's pupils widened. She concentrated on trying to understand the reason for Maria's tears, caught off guard by her shift in emotion, "Oh, sweetie, why the tears? Is it your headache?"

"No, head's fine at the moment, I've just been so miserable. One minute everything's fine and I think I'm getting better. Then the next, I feel awful again and it just makes me so upset. I just want to feel better. I'm so damn exhausted."

"Y'all want any drinks? Water or anything?" Paul asked awkwardly, scratching his scalp.

"Do y'all?" Sandra asked them again.

"A cure!" Maria laughed, wiping her tears away along with the grief.

Paul took the chance to retreat upstairs, hoping his wife would follow. He didn't want to raise suspicion in their patients, so he'd make excuses about getting drinks or snacks from time-to-time, but it was really code for Sandra to meet him upstairs.

While pouring himself sweet tea over ice, a realization dawned over him. His face transitioned from the blank expression of preoccupied thought to the terror of the possibilities as he meditated on Maria's symptoms. They had been so familiar many years ago, now nonexistent and nearly forgotten, the sound of bells began to ring deep within that dusty part of Paul's mind as the most probable diagnosis took form.

"Not possible. Couldn't be," he mumbled to himself in the kitchen, before he called his wife from the doorway above the stairs. To his relief, he finally heard her light footsteps leading up the wooden staircase. The door opened, she slipped in, and closed it behind her.

"Pretty weird, huh?" Sandra asked quietly, her arms folded at her waist.

"Yes. I'm not sure what concerns me more, verifying our suspicions, or finding we have to look for other causes. There are a few things it could be, and I really can't think of one that ends well. Let's take it a step at a time and not get ahead of ourselves, honey."

"I'm going to do some blood work on her...and crank up the ultrasound. I'm worried that it could be ovarian cancer or some other similarly serious condition. I'd really hate that for her."

"Could be psychological, for all we know."

"Could be pregnancy, too," Sandra blurted out her words quickly, looking out the window at squirrels digging into the ground. Their tails flicked around spastically, as they caught sight of her in the window.

"It's hard for me to take that possibility seriously."

"Just saying, you and I've witnessed a lot of strange, horrible, and even miraculous things in our careers. If she's pregnant, she's pregnant."

"What sort of world do we live in, where that would be as bad, if not worse, than ovarian cancer? Don't think I'd call it a miracle."

The doctors made their way down into the subterranean office, carrying snacks and drinks, their hospitality meant to conceal the reason for their absence. Maria's spirit raised as she caught sight of the chips they carried, hoping they were for her. She always like chips, but recently she almost craved them. She thought it strange that they happened to have some on hand.

"Alright, sweetie, we're need you to drink some water if you don't mind. Drink as much as you can. We need to fill that bladder up."

"What's wrong with me?"

"Let us worry about that. You just relax. We'll know soon enough," Paul cooed, handing her bottled water after cracking the cap for her. "We just have to be thorough and run our tests."

"Fair enough."

Amelia eyeballed the basket of snacks and spotted a candy bar underneath the bags of chips. Her mood elevated as she stood and began digging through the snacks to grab it. Maria laughed and watched her as she carried the candy back to her seat, sneakily, as if someone might scold her.

"Maria," Sandra began, grabbing her attention, "I don't want any of us jumping to conclusions here, okay?" Maria nodded her head nervously. "But we have some questions for you."

"I understand," Maria's voice elevated slightly, her patience dwindling away, since the doctor seemed to avoid getting around to her point. Amelia stopped munching so loudly on the crunchy bar, her ears perked up, so she could hear the upcoming questions. There was something different about Sandra's tone, a calm seriousness acting as a great levee between her and horrific possibilities.

"Do you," she grabbed Maria's hands, "for any reason at all, think you may be pregnant?"

Shock stormed Maria's face as her lips began to stammer at the sound of the word. She stared blankly at the doctor, attempted to connect dots of her own, her mind flooded with thoughts, like fish over rapids. The pressure in her head grew and she fell into the back of her chair, gazing at the ceiling and its bright fluorescent light hanging above them. At this point, Amelia stopped her munching entirely, swallowing her half-chewed mouthful of chocolate and peanuts.

"Pregnant?" The single word made its way from her mouth, raising and lowering over and between the consonants and vowels.

"Y'all think she's pregnant? What?" Amelia asked loudly, breaking her long silence.

"Ladies," Paul warned, disappointed that her answer hadn't been a yes, "don't mistake us. That's likely not what is happening. We all know there hasn't been a natural pregnancy in nearly fifteen years. We just need to know if it's what you suspect might be causing these symptoms."

"No, of course not," she spluttered, snapping herself out of a trance. "Never even crossed my mind. Why?"

"Sometimes, if someone believes they're pregnant, it can produce the same symptoms without there being any pregnancy at all." The calm expression on Sandra's face started to fade away. Amelia could see the effects of worry drawing itself up in the doctor's brow and in her sparkling black eyes.

"What else could it be?"

"Hopefully, we'll know soon enough." Paul grabbed a bottle of KY jelly from a shelf and flipped on the ultrasound machine.

"Here, honey." He handed the lubricant to his wife who donned her gloves and began squeezing it out on to her left hand.

"Now, sweetie, I need you to lift your shirt for me," she instructed Maria, who was fascinated by the doctor holding her hand out, covered in large amounts of clear jelly. "Dim the lights, Paul."

"Is that what you always say when you get ahold of the lube?" Maria joked crudely, catching everyone off guard in the tense moment. Sandra found it hilarious as she tried applying the self-warming liquid to her patient's abdomen between bursts of laughter that brought her to tears. Her humor ignited the spark of a flame in a dark cavern, making light through the worst of situations.

The guests looked at the screen as if they could understand anything on the display -- as if they could understand anything the doctors tried to explain to them -- like birds reading words.

"You see this little blob here, that's an ovary."

"Mhm," Maria lied, trying to make out what she pointed to. The whole screen seemed to be covered in blobs and swirls, and the sight of it with the scent of the gel made her nauseous.

"What do you think, Paul? You've always been a better reader," she asked, moving the scanner in small circles, unable to detect anything out of the ordinary. "Hmmm, looks good. Check the left one. Fallopian tubes look great as well. Appear normal and healthy."

"I don't see any cysts or growths of any sort."

"Neither do I. All looks really good, Maria," he told her, patting her shoulder, his round face and chin illuminated by the screen before him.

After quickly wiping Maria clean, Sandra removed her gloves and tossed them into the empty trashcan beside her. The two doctors, stood, facing each other silently for a moment as if communicating by telepathy. Sandra felt a little more hopeful that surgery would probably not going to be necessary. It had been a while since she had held a knife to a patient.

Paul began to fear the inevitable, diagnosing life, the possibility of impossibilities. The thoughts began to crush his mind, removing all reason and inserting conclusions of the illogical and absurd, until all knowledge he thought he had was reduced to the understanding of a child. Once again, his world shifted beneath his feet, the laws and forces of nature started to make less sense as they revealed themselves to him like laughter in the corners of his brain.

"I've also not been able to read thoughts lately," Maria quipped sarcastically, grabbing the couple's attention. The silence between them made her and Amelia uneasy, as they waited, unsure if they were in the eye of a storm or if the storm had yet to arrive.

"Everything looks fine, Maria," Sandra smiled sweetly, her eyes still holding some sadness deep within them, "as far as your reproductive health goes."

"No ovarian cancer!" Paul shouted happily, forcing something positive from his bleakness. He walked over to their workbench and obtained a needle and wipes, anxious and ready to get to the bottom of the mystery.

"So, what now?"

"Blood work." He was already cleaning her arm at the intended puncture site. Maria stared down the length of her arm and watched as the silver sliver of metal sank into her skin. Deep crimson filled the container, bubbling a little and she became lightheaded at the sight.

"Lucky for y'all, medicine has come a long way since Paul and I started. Used to take days for people to hear results."

"What results?"

Paul removed the needle and unscrewed the container to the needle, carrying the sample of blood to a machine in the corner next to another monitor. He placed her blood into the tiny metal hands of the machine and it received it like a gift, greedily ready to run its tests. A status bar blinked upon the monitor beside it, pulsing like a heartbeat.

"Hello? What results?" Maria asked again, irritated with their dramatic secrecy.

Amelia scooted her chair noisily over to Maria's and held her hands as they waited together. She patted the tops of them, calming herself mostly, Maria still anxious. The doctors' silent and captivated faces focused toward the screen, unwilling to answer her questions just yet.

The status on the monitor read complete and revealed its findings, signaled by the shared gasps from the married couple. Paul wrapped his arm around his wife, accidentally blocking the sight of the screen's revelation from the visitors. Sandra made noises and brought her hand to her mouth, as if she were choked up over whatever she saw. Paul spun his chair around to behold the patient who didn't have a single sick bone in her body. Apparently, Maria was healthier than any other patient they had received in many years. It was unbelievable to him. Fathomless wonder filled both doctors as they returned to their seats, unable to decide on the best way to break the news.

"You guys are really creeping me out," Maria cried, tears falling from her eyes, as she began to think the worst. Amelia rubbed her sister-in-law's back, her own tears free falling from the edge of her eyelids.

"Pregnant," Paul answered bluntly, unable to use the happy tone of voice he used when giving this news to women so many years ago -- a time long gone and no longer relevant. They offered no congratulations; received no excited applause for confirming the news. Instead, emotion filled the silence with an intensity louder than a trumpet blast. Just that single word, "pregnant" had enough power to shatter the glass windows upstairs, it seemed; the partition between their fears and hopes came tumbling down.

"How?" Amelia asked for her shocked friend, who mouthed the word soundlessly.

"There's *hCG* in her blood." Sandra regained composure as her mind sobered from the initial surprise. "It's the hormone produced by the placenta after implantation."

"Oh, my God," wailed Maria, raising from her seat. "What the hell am I going to do? There's no way they'd let me get away with this."

"Well, let's not get ahead of ourselves," Paul spoke in his most calming tone. "It's still far too early to know if it's viable and many things could happen at this stage."

Maria mumbled a couple of very unladylike words then shook her head, "I'm pregnant!" She stood and paced around the room, glancing at the machine's readout in an effort to reconfirm what the doctors already told her. "Things are clearly already happening. How is this even possible?"

"Maybe Unity's work came undone somehow, or, I don't know, got reversed?" Sandra guessed, with no concrete knowledge one way or the other. She drew from the many conspiracies people bandied about over the years.

"Could simply be a miracle," Paul offered from the corner where he stood. His eyes were filled with awe as he watched her pace. "You two need to keep very quiet about this. We *all* need to keep absolutely quiet about this," he warned.

"Maybe I could also conceal the potbelly too," she retorted sardonically, tears filling her eyes again, but this time she began to weep uncontrollably. Amelia tried to comfort her, rubbing her back as she handed her a Kleenex.

"I'm serious, you cannot take this lightly," Paul reiterated, his expression sobering with deep concentration. Maria sarcastically mumbled more swear words. "People will want to take this gift away from you. They'll rip it straight out of you."

"Paul!" Sandra shouted, shocked that he used such blunt wording.

"There are people that would never allow a pregnancy to continue, Sandra, you know this." Then turning again to address Maria, "I'm unsure about what other advice to offer, but you must conceal this at all costs. If you must, tell your husband, but no one else."

Amelia wondered, as the reality of the situation solidified, if the pregnancy occurred due to some anomaly exclusive to Maria, or if others -- even many others -- might end up with the same shocking news. She chewed her lip, glancing over to the doctors, "Do y'all think there are others, or is this just a one time and one person deal?"

"Only time will tell."

The words filled Amelia with hope. Her deepest and greatest desire was to have a child of her own. Unity and its co-conspirators robbed her, and all women, of their God given ability to experience the incredible gift of creating life within their own bodies. *Yes,* she thought bitterly, *Unity -- or Satan, whatever that thing really is -- stole the most natural manifestation of married love, like stealing the spring-time blossoms of trees.*

"I'd think it's more likely to happen to others as well, which could be both good and bad." Sandra continued thinking out loud as possibilities flooded her mind, "And if it does happen to others, the powers-that-be will quickly become aware of the situation, considering that multitudes could potentially end up pregnant. At the same time, it would take the focus off of you."

"An organized hunt for all those affected would commence the minute Unity becomes aware of pregnancies," Paul added, catching an angry glare from his wife who preferred delicate words.

"Your bedside manner sucks right now, Paul. This is a miracle, no matter how divisive it may become."

"Do you want a test as well, Amelia?"

"I haven't had any symptoms." A frown formed from beneath her sparkling eyes. "I'll be sure to visit if anything changes."

"Are you sure, sweetie?"

Desire pounded within her, but she couldn't bear to hear the word *negative* in reference to her test results. She committed to pray for the opportunity, hope for it, but she would not kill her hope right then and there in that room. Amelia possessed a fair amount of the virtue of patience and would wait for whatever changes made this possible to come to her in their own time.

The four of them decided to leave the office together, they emerged from the staircase, bewildered and changed by tears, fears, and a sort of unearthly hope they'd never before experienced. The young ladies decided to inform their husbands together in the company of the doctors. At least, the doctors' presence will unequivocally verify everything for John, so he won't take Maria's news as an absurd joke or a sign of her developing some sort of mental illness.

...

John and Michael worked hard in the heat, the sun beating down on them as it bounced between the solar panels. It felt like they were standing in a microwave oven; sweat poured off of them and their breaths came in short, fast pants as they continued the grid repairs. Thieves, who constantly stole the cabling for scrapping, damaged a section of the grid. Michael cursed those petty thieves each morning as he repaired the damages they caused. It made him feel as if he were scooping water from a sinking boat, cursed to start over and make the same fixes every day.

"Ain't it a little late in the year to be so darn hot?" John asked rhetorically, his hands made slippery from sweat, as he swung his hammer.

"It'll get a little better next week. The forecast looks good," Michael grunted, while he threaded the cables through racks and tightened them against their places with zip-ties.

"Apparently, Maria went to the doc's with Amelia earlier this morning." John then took a quick break to check his messages. He stared into the air, viewing the screen of messages displayed on his Visum device.

"What?" Michael dropped his tools and waited for a response, now checking his own messages. He hadn't received any. "Must not be anything too bad. Amelia hasn't sent me anything."

"Your sis pisses me off sometimes, man. So, vague all the time. She'll have news. Tell me she has news, and then not tell me anything at all."

"Try being raised alongside her."

"Try being married to her."

"No, I'm good."

The two chuckled a little before returning to work. A gentle breeze touched them briefly, offering a tease of cool refreshment. Their short bit of relief immediately gave way to stifling heat once again, leaving them to long for evening and swearing to each other about the cruelty of it all.

"Christ have mercy," Michael opined, looking over their work and its beautiful completed state with the fresh cabling neatly tucked and wrapped between the racks just like the thieves loved it.

"Lord save us, they'll have it stolen before nightfall."

"It's likely already been. We're just having heat strokes, hallucinating, thinking it's all still here," he imagined, chuckling at his own joke.

Michael bumped John to leave and the two of them descended the platform. Their eyes adjusted, allowing them to remove their sunglasses once beneath the cover of the panels. The sweat began to dry, leaving their skin feeling frigid, since the sun couldn't reach them now.

They had absolutely no idea what was in store for them once they arrived home. The busy workday left them little time to ponder on anything outside of paneling, cabling, and the growing desire to murder the thieves. The simplicity of the constant workflow acted as a refuge, a sly shelter protecting them from the terror they'd experience once they stepped through the door to the house.

...

Greasy and sweaty, the two husbands knew something was awry the minute they walked inside. The unfamiliar sight of the Rendas sitting in the living room gave the first clue. Second, Cole looked extremely perplexed, surrounded by family and having removed his headset only seconds before.

"What's going on?" John asked nervously, gripping his wife, searching her eyes for answers.

"Everything all right?" Michael put his things down and joined his own wife on the couch.

"We've got some news for everyone that, by no means, can leave this room unless by absolute necessity," the doctors began. Then, interrupted by a cough from Maria, asked "You want the honor?" She nodded, her eyebrows raised, as if they replied, *of course, it's mine.* Everyone's eyes darted to Maria immediately, waiting for this mysterious news to issue forth from her lips.

"Well," she cleared her throat, then, after what seemed an eternity to her listeners, "I wasn't feeling well, and I haven't been," well aware of her recent moods and sickness the family's irritation grew. "So, Amelia talked me into visiting the Rendas."

"Yes, get to it," John urged, shaking her arm, dying to hear the explanation.

"Honey, I'm pregnant."

"Huh?" Michael grunted.

John watched her lips make the word seemingly with no sound. As *the word* slowly made its way into his consciousness, a long silence clung in the air before he actually began to comprehend it. His ability to hear became evident when he fainted. Before anyone realized it, he fell from the sofa, almost pulling Maria down with him. The wooden floors shook and dishes clinked in the nearby china cabinet as his heavy body tumbled down.

"John!"

"He's okay. Was a hot day up there, and you guys decided to play demented jokes on us." Michael rushed to help his brother-in-law back to consciousness.

"It's no joke, Mikey. Are you kidding me? I wouldn't lie about this." Those were the first words John heard as he re-entered the realm of consciousness, and they made his head spin.

"Maria," he croaked, his voice shaking as his hand reached out, weakly grasping for her hair.

"We did all the tests, honey. The Rendas say I'm pregnant." Evidently, she had an infinite supply of water behind her eyes, pouring it over his filthy face as tears fell.

"How?"

"I don't think any of us need the answer to that," Michael smirked. He and Maria shared the same humor, passed on to them by their father, but she wasn't entertained.

"There's no telling. I'm just as shocked as you are." She patted his head. "But we need to keep this secret. No one can know."

"Of course not!" Michael exclaimed. "But what are we to do? Please God, tell me the Auris hasn't heard any of this."

"I thought we had ours reprogrammed?" Cole's face suddenly drained of color. He seemed to recall a conversation with Stone to that effect.

"We did. He's right, Mikey. Don't get hysterical."

"Hysterical?" He raised his voice to his sister, "You don't have any legal right to a baby. Don't you remember? Forgive me for my concern about Unity listening in on us."

Maria helped John to his feet and they took their places next to Cole on one of the two couches in the room. This situated them across from Amelia and the doctors. Michael stood in front of the fireplace, looking into its depths, searching his mind for ways to protect his sister.

"Where's the priest when you need him?" He looked over to the others, placing his finger over his mouth to quiet them as he called him.

"How far along are you?" questioned Cole, now sharply curious.

"Shut your mouth, Cole!" Michael screeched, leaving the living room to find a quiet place, while he waited for the priest to answer.

"Hey Michael, I was just thinking of you." The greeting made him uneasy.

"Father, we need you over here, immediately."

"Is everything alright?"

"Just come, please."

"What's going on, Michael?" The priest's voice troubled by Michael's urgency.

"No time to explain. Please, for the love of Christ, get here quickly."

"Fine, I'll be there in a few." Michael could hear the sound of rosary beads jingling on the other end of the call.

"Bring those too, please," he requested, before ending the call to rejoin his family in the den.

"Dang, it's dark in here," Michael observed, flipping on every light in the room.

He explained that the priest was on his way and, in minutes, he manifested at the front door with a loud knock. True to his word to come as fast as he could, it seemed to the family that he arrived almost immediately. The dazed state of their thoughts compressed time in a strange way.

...

Michael answered the door, opening it only a crack, and saw the sweaty, wheezing priest waiting to cross the threshold.

"Come in," Michael invited, closing the door behind them. "Apparently, Maria's pregnant and everyone has lost their minds." The priest seemed unfazed by the news, a reaction that greatly agitated the other men in the room. Their mouths hung open, unable to think of any questions or additional reasons to explain why they so urgently called for him.

"Can you picture me dancing with joy, right now?" the priest asked, perplexing them all, and making them jokingly wonder about his sanity. "You know -- just as David did before the Ark, or John the Baptist did within Elizabeth's womb when the Mother of God came to visit?"

"Father, you must understand why we're all pretty freaked out right now." Michael looked desperately for a hint of seriousness in the priest's facial expression.

"Did you call me over here to get all freaked out with the rest of you, or to offer peace of mind?" The priest retorted, walking over to take a knee beside the expecting couple. He unclasped his collar and removed one of the many medals hanging around his neck. "Maria, I want you to wear this. It's an exorcised Saint Benedict medal. It will protect you and the new soul growing within you."

"Thank you, Father." She took the beautiful necklace and studied the Latin inscriptions carved into its golden surface. Maria carefully regarded the saint, whose image stood on the medal's face. Flanked by a raven, he carried bread and a chalice with a serpent coiled around it. She put it around her neck to join her crucifix and miraculous medal.

Father Burns wet his hands with holy water and laid them on the couple. He bowed his head to mutter prayers, his lips moving rapidly. Once finished, he made the sign of the cross and kissed his fingers before standing.

"Alright, now that the formalities are done--" Michael began, but the priest interrupted him.

"Do not call these formalities, young man!"

"Right. Sorry, but now that we've finished praying, do you have any ideas? How's this possible?"

"You're better off asking the doctors."

"We've no clue, Father," Paul spoke up, his face still wearing the look of astonishment from earlier. "There isn't any rational explanation that we can think of."

"Well, could be a miracle. How far along is she?"

"Few weeks."

"She's had the Eucharist."

"You think this is a miracle?" John questioned, his mind brimming with dread of what might come of it in the end. "Why would God make a miracle that jeopardizes us, so?"

"Miracles most commonly occur during times of jeopardy," he remarked with a peaceful tone. "Don't you think Mary, mother of our Lord, felt frightened when the angel appeared, telling them to flee to Egypt? King Herod had plans to destroy the infant Christ. Sounds like jeopardy to me and that miracle, fleeing to escape Herod's evil plans, safeguarded the Word, our Salvation."

Maria began to weep as it occurred to her what their lives would become. She foresaw nothing but pain and heartbreak -- a relentless destructive force that would seek them out and leave nothing of them unscathed. John tried to console her, but her lamentations were so fierce she could not hear him.

"Let's be realistic, please," Michael begged, unnerved by the sound his sister's weeping, "for the love of Christ. I can see how this is miraculous and I've been taught faith all my life. We're no stranger to it in this room. But we must approach this situation as if we aren't the characters in some scripture passage. I mean, unless some angelic army appears outside our door, I don't think it's wise to behave this way."

"Hiding a pregnancy isn't easy," Amelia defended her husband's position. "Even if our mouths were sealed shut, Maria's got to work. We're nannies and those boojee women aren't idiots. They know the difference between fat and a potbelly. Maria's got chicken legs. There's no way she'd look normal walking around town."

The priest paced around the room, his fingers pinched beneath his chin. He removed his glasses and cleaned them with his shirt as he thought over their concerns, but then continued to pace to and fro.

"Let's just see what happens. She's got plenty of time before we get to that point." He continued to pace, using gestures to lay out his thoughts, then, "I'll make contact with some friends and make some arrangements."

"Like what?" Maria asked as she emerged from her fearful place. "What friends?"

"Other priests -- people down south."

"What are they going to do, offer prayers?" Michael snickered.

"Please, show me some respect. I'm just as new to this situation as you are. I'm thinking."

"What could they do?"

"Maria, aren't the two of you only here temporarily?" The priest's question was confirmed by the nodding of the couple's heads, "Okay, so you might not mind the worst-case scenario being relocation? I know they'll have space for you."

"Relocation? That's all?"

"It's a rural place, there aren't many people on the farms. She'd probably only have contact with ten others. They're all friends, I promise. There are three houses owned by families that have been sanctuaries for many refugees over the years."

"Is that where you were for so long?"

"Yes, there are a couple of priests hiding out there now. I visited them and discussed rumors."

"Well call them now," John interrupted, speaking rapidly. "Just call and ask real fast."

"I wish I could, but there are rules."

The doctors shifted in the couch anxiously, as they thought about labor and delivery. They'd have to be there even if there were other professionals. Sandra loved Maria and had provided healthcare to her since she was a baby. It didn't feel right to leave her in a stranger's care. Paul knew his wife's thoughts about this and he shared them.

"Well, they're going to need us at some point."

"They will, but remain in town until the due date grows closer. They'll only need you to visit occasionally."

"No," Sandra disagreed, shaking her head at the thought. Paul looked at her, prying with his eyes for an explanation. "I'll need to be with her from beginning to end."

"Honey, our practice -- there's people here that need us. She'll be fine."

"Then you can stay, but I'm going with her."

"Absolutely not."

"This is the reason I started practicing obstetrics in the first place and it's the reason we left our official work as physicians. They wanted us to destroy the very things we vowed to protect, so I'm going to travel with her and I'm going to deliver a healthy baby," Sandra pleaded adamantly, her voice choking as she spoke. The emotions weighed heavily on her as they had for over a decade.

"Well, then I'm going too."

"You can't. As you said, there are people in need of healthcare here. You need to stay for them." Paul's face shrank as he heard her words and meditated on what the absence of her precious company would mean for him.

"Well, Father," Michael spoke up, "haste makes waste."

"Yes, I'll get to work. God, bless you all and peace be with you."

The priest took his leave, along with the doctors, separating from the family that continued to debate the dangers and concerns that made themselves so clear that day. The dangers laid before them were like traps lying in wait for unsuspecting hares. They had no way of truly knowing what was in store for them -- for everyone in the room.

CHAPTER SEVEN

Isaac kept his desk neatly organized with personal items he brought from home or things his coworkers in the force gave him. Printed pictures of his wife and him hung around his cubicle, along with jokes and fortunes from cookies that read, *"A promotion is in your near future,"* or, *"You will soon be in a dessert."* The first one was verification of his dream, the second simply humored him, though he had no clue why someone would want to be in a desert as he suspected the misprint should have read.

It had been a busy month for him, especially after he talked to his boss, making known his interest in working toward a promotion that recently became available. His captain mentioned it to him months ago and Isaac worked tirelessly toward it even as he lost hope of ever receiving it. He took on more cases and spent more time in his uniform than he did out of it.

Their immaculate leader, Unity, conveyed many instances of rumors swirling about and it was his duty to investigate them, cracking them open like eggs. Yes, Unity, a creation capable of seeing and hearing all, but unable to enter the physical world. Isaac was the corporeal prober, sent to discern whether Unity's paranoias were true.

The many cases covered Isaac's desktop in the form of countless folders, some of them piled on each other and, had they not been but pixels, would have collected thick layers of dust. They changed color as they aged on that virtual plane, screaming into Isaac's face the many sensations that stress could induce.

"Isaac," his captain said, popping his handsome, yet deeply aged face around the corner of the cubicle wall. "What are you working on?"

The captain was dark and well-tanned with jet black hair, clearly dyed to blot out any grey, and a stylish goatee shaped skillfully along his cheeks and jawline. The older man was in incredible physical shape and, but for some telltale lines and wrinkles, he would've given the impression of a man in his thirties.

"Was just getting to some of these escalated tickets that've been cooking for a few days." Isaac held his breath in anticipation of what the captain would say about the problem.

"Why are they escalated?"

"Others, flagged at a higher priority, have flooded in lately, so I've not had a chance to get to them." The captain was the one who distributed the tasks to his officers and through no maneuvering on Isaac's part,

Isaac was the captain's top recipient. After handing out the day's typical workload, the captain almost always found that Isaac was best suited to work on the direst cases as well. The resulting enormous workload rendered Isaac unable to focus on any one item without inadvertently forming a collection of expired and escalated tickets.

"Isaac," the captain's face sank as he shook his head, discontent rising to the surface due to his officer's failure. The sight of it secretly filled Isaac's head with fantasies of violence toward his commander as he listened to the man drone on, "...you want the promotion, you gotta learn to delegate. Anything you can't get to, allocate to Marty or Cruz. They're just sitting on their asses all day, and you better start making use of them, or I'm firing them and you'll have to cover it all when we're understaffed."

The captain's face became sick with disgust, "I can't stand them, Isaac. Just look at *Farty*, his putrid scent fills the office." Isaac poked his head around the wall of his cubicle to behold the repulsive sight of Marty. His morbidly obese form sat surrounded by dried soda spills, stale bread crumbs, and various other unidentifiable snack droppings.

"I'll send some of the simpler things to him, sir."

"Great. Thanks, Isaac." The captain continued to linger at Isaac's cubicle, watching as he sent the tickets to the two reprobates who sullied their force.

He looked up at his boss, loitering strangely next to him, waiting for more instructions. Finally, he asked, "Was there something else, sir?"

"What, can't I just be your friend?"

"Sir?"

"I'm screwing with you," the captain cajoled, laughing at himself. "I don't know if you've checked the updates on those savages we picked up a while ago at that protest in Five Points." It was the same protest Stone and his allies had interrupted, many of whom were arrested that night.

"No sir, I wasn't aware of any developments."

"One of them disclosed the location of their boss's worksite. There's supposedly a squad of them that operate out of it."

"Really?" Isaac's heart began to pound, propelling excitement through his veins. It had been so long since he had the pleasure of working on such a case. He grew increasingly weary of busting drug dealers and searching for missing people. And nothing sang promotion so loudly as a hunt for the savage Zealots.

"Yeah, but don't just sit there and stare at the files. Unity already knows what *he* knows, so get your ass in the field today. I want to see those shiny boots muddy, hopefully even bloody. As far as Unity is concerned, these savages are rabid animals. Put them down if you must, but try to bring the P.O.I. back alive and breathing long enough for an interview."

"Yes sir." Isaac didn't waste any time rising to his feet and grabbing his things. Relief washed over him as he prepared to leave his captain and desk behind. On his way out, he passed by the reprobates, overhearing their whining about the tickets they just received and the fact that they were flagged as high priority.

"Marty, wake up!" Cruz yelped. "They need the A-team, baby!" Nothing was further from the truth, Isaac knew, and the idea of escaping far away from them and their stench made him happy.

...

The weather had grown colder so Isaac wore his fine uniform coat, which displayed the well-known force insignia -- an eye piercing through a triangular field of indigo and green. The sight of the symbol inspired reverence in all people he encountered. All people except, of course, his wife who cultivated an immunity to his authority, or anything positive about him, for that matter. Citizens, on the other hand, offered him free beverages and extra fries, hoping they weren't targeted for scrutiny or anything else Unity deemed hateful. Isaac often wondered what they had to hide from him -- the purpose for their fear -- and if they might ever make their way to his desktop.

Cung, the new person of interest, certainly made *her* way to his desktop -- the mechanic -- or whatever it is she did, when she wasn't crusading. He hopped into the undercover vehicle, which looked, from the outside, as if it would fall apart the minute a driver attempted to crank the engine. The internals, though, were completely solid. The force made a few drivable cars available for officers to use in case of emergencies requiring fast pursuit; or, as an unspoken perk, to simply return home faster at the end of the day.

If he activated the sirens, all driverless cars on the highway would seamlessly move out of his way, giving him the most efficiency possible to get to his destination. But when working undercover, he couldn't use and abuse such perks. With no sirens to trumpet his approach, his car garnered no influence as he rolled down the road toward the apartment building where Cung supposedly lived.

"What do we have here, Cung," he muttered under his breath as he acquainted himself with the new information. *History involving stolen software? Not your typical pipe-bomb...*, he gathered, silently reading the list of developments, while sitting in the now parked car. Her file truly perplexed him. He made occasional, furtive glances across the street at the workshop her captured cohort revealed in exchange for release back into the wild.

No living relatives. Well so much for exploiting that route. He held the car's broken headset to his eyes, flipping to the next page with a hand gesture. This required he turn his hands to resemble holding a page between his fingers. *Well, at least this thing still recognizes hand gestures*, he thought resentfully.

Isaac reached into his coat to retrieve his firearm, holding it low and out of sight from any curious eyes. The weapon was a black .45 caliber engraved with the department's insignia. It felt warm in Isaac's cold hands because he had it tucked snugly against his body all morning. He ensured it had a round chambered before returning to his shoulder holster, which kept the gun against his left side, easily accessible with his right hand.

His heart picked up in rhythm. Time to get moving. He checked the file once again, Cung's photo ID looked as he expected. As he removed the keys from the ignition, the sudden choking silence assaulted him. His ears seemed to be ringing as he sat there briefly before opening the door. The ringing stopped immediately upon exposure to the peaceful melodies of birds and the hum of electricity in the city.

...

Isaac made his way to the shop's closed door and knocked, receiving no answer. He turned his head against the door to listen and heard sound coming from within -- a hammering. He knocked again, harder, and continued to knock until the door pulled away from his reach as it swung open.

"Hello?" answered a young man covered in grease. Then, he immediately recognized Isaac as a law enforcement officer. "We got company!" he yelled out to whoever else was there, as he tried to slam the door shut.

Deeply experienced with the tactics of criminals, he had already tucked his nightstick into the doorway to prevent the door from closing shut. He pried the door open with the baton and the full force of his weight, ramming his shoulder into the it, which forced it back onto its closer.

The heavy force surprised the young man, knocking him to the ground. He quickly jumped to his feet and moved towards the intruder. Isaac loved the invitation to violence and swung his baton with no hesitation. The following crack of shattering bones brought him great satisfaction as he slammed it against the young man's jaw, sending him back to the floor.

"You're in the wrong place, buddy," a faceless voice mocked reproachfully from somewhere within the garage. It echoed along the sheet metal building.

"I'm looking for someone," Isaac answered from across the garage.

"No, you lookin' for trouble. No one of interest to be found here," the man bellowed, his voice gradually approaching Isaac. He heard footsteps on the opposite end from the voice, flanking him from behind a gutted vehicle.

"I'm only looking for Cung," Isaac called, his eyes searching the workshop for movement. He noticed the first-floor rafters, making up the floor for the second story were dark, devoid of any light.

"Well, think you're ten thousand miles off course. I don't know no Cungs 'round here."

"Don't take another step closer!" Isaac shouted as he sensed the man's voice drawing nearer. Isaac reached for his firearm and held it solidly in his right hand, the baton still in his left. Suddenly a sound emanated from above -- the rapid movement of feet shuffled across the creaky floors. Dust fell from the ceiling rafters betraying whomever was hiding above. "Who's up there?"

"Just the ghosts that live here," came a response from the man covering the other end, finally breaking his silence.

Footsteps following the voice quickened as they approached Isaac from the left. He turned, raised his firearm, and discharged three ear-piercing hollow-point rounds into the direction of the footfalls. The deadly bullets screamed through the man's chest and out the other side. A red mist sprayed out in a fan pattern, painting the rusty vehicle the dead man hid behind earlier. A machete fell from his hands as his body began to jerk uncontrollably in nervous response to the trauma. It didn't last long, just several seconds, and all movement stopped. The other man, much larger and who had spoken first, swiftly rushed at Isaac. He screamed profanities as he wrestled Isaac to the ground, punching and tearing at him with his hands. His fingernails ripped into Isaac's face, causing blood to run into his eyes as continuous blows landed on him.

Struggling to break free after losing his gun, Isaac twisted his body underneath the attacker and pulled the man down by his shirt collar, using his legs to flip him over.

Now the tables turned. Isaac was mounted on the man and reached for his baton that had landed just beneath the gutted car beside them. Raising it high above his head, he brought it down onto his attacker who tried to shield himself with his arms, only to have them broken and rendered useless. Isaac continued to wail on him violently, without easing up, even after the man's body went limp. In his red-hot rage, he erased the man's face from existence, cracking into his skull. The man's blood and grey matter now covered Isaac's already bloodied face. The man's last thoughts were terminated and scattered in fragments of biological debris across Isaac and the floor.

The sensation sobered Isaac and his brutal violence dissipated. It was only then that he remembered that he detected one other person in the building earlier. He looked up from the mess with his beaten and bloodied face to scan the garage, but did not see or hear evidence of another person. He did, however, notice the back door was wide open. Jumping to his feet, he retrieved his pistol and sped out the open door to chase after whomever escaped through it.

"Need some body bags," he spoke into his Auris, which instantly relayed the message to headquarters.

"Are you injured?" inquired a woman's voice.

"Don't worry about it," he exited the doorway and looked along both directions of the alleyway, but saw nothing. He re-entered the garage workshop to inspect the remains of his attackers.

"Also alert the captain that Cung was not found here. Two men dead. One alive and cuffed," he reported after finding that the man with the broken jaw remained alive. *I better check the pulse of the two dead men, since it's protocol,* he thought sarcastically, *that way I can honestly say I did it.* The upstairs lured him, beckoning him with its unexplored mysteries.

...

He slowly followed the metal steps one-by-one into the inky black maw of the stairwell. Someone had converted the space to an office, which overlooked the entire garage. He could see the bodies below like broken ragdolls beyond repair; the blood beneath them pooled and became dark as it coagulated. He noticed bloody footprints, his prints, leading away from the corpses. The only available light spilled in from the open doors, providing inadequate illumination.

Fumbling for and finding a switch, Isaac flipped on the buzzing fluorescent lights and the office walls came into view. A wood paneled wall at the back of the room had five red crosses painted on it. The sight of the crosses reminded him of a time, years ago when he was in his teens and his blood ties still meant something to him. When he rejected their beliefs, they played quid pro quo and equally rejected him. Unable to find common ground as his mind matured, he was essentially romanced and raised by Unity's promises of prosperity for all.

Unity was his new god, a real god, with laws and agendas formed directly from the interests of its obedient citizens. Feeling smug, Isaac reminded himself, *I no longer have reason to pray to a pie-in-the-sky spiritual God whose silent tyranny never did anything at all for me. Never did anything for anyone for thousands of years.* He saw no interest in a dying tradition that offered him nothing but a growling stomach or empty wallet, or more likely, both.

Unity epitomized true glory. *He* made decisions that were righteous and void of emotion, lacking the inflection caused by the human condition. *He* was worthy of Isaac's worship, if he had any to give. Isaac never understood why his family adhered to the dogma associated with someone who never spoke, never displayed his miracles, never reached out to heal the pain plaguing the earth. *No. Not me. Not ever.*

Instead, Isaac served Unity. In return, Unity supplied him with food, honor, and the opportunity to bless his beautiful wife with a child. He vowed to destroy whatever or whomever stepped in his way.

He found nothing useful in the piles of notes on the desk. They all referred to manuals for old vehicles that weren't even street legal anymore. Some had names written on them, but Cung's name didn't show up on any of them. Despite the lack of evidence pointing to Cung, he knew from the crosses that the captured Zealot hadn't lied to them.

Surely this is the right place, he thought, looking into the desk drawers after wiping blood from his eyes. *Perhaps the traitor disclosed another group instead? What's this?* There was a polaroid in one of the drawers. Isaac lifted it from beneath candy wrappers and studied it. The photo showed a man with a scarred face and a woman who must have been Cung. *There's no doubt this is her in the photo. That's the same face from Cung's file.* He flipped the polaroid over and found an inscription written with silver ink, *"Dear Debra,"* Isaac read to himself, *"remember that wherever you go, whatever happens, I'll always love you. –Jeremy."*

Isaac laughed, bursting with joy, "I see now," he exclaimed aloud, wiping more blood from his eyes and dripping nose with a rag he found on the desk. "Messy, messy." He placed the polaroid in his pocket and began taking video of everything in the room with his Visum for future examination. "Captain's gonna be proud. 'Specially when I hunt you down," he said to no one, thinking of Cung. The polaroid had revealed an alias and he continued his soliloquy to the empty building, "Oh, Debra, maybe I'll find all your little friends as well, and scrub the world of your kind."

"Excuse me," a woman said from behind Isaac, he raised his firearm to the voice, only to realize it belonged to another officer who just arrived. "Sorry sir, didn't mean to startle you."

"No, my apologies. I'm still on edge." He laughed, holstering his gun. "The two bodies are down below, anyone else here?"

"Yeah, they're getting the stretcher out now. Sir, you look horrible. The medic will take care of you. He's outside."

"Alright, thank you," Isaac looked at her badge, "Angelina." She began snooping for him as he went to find the medic. He definitely needed to get bandaged up before leaving the scene behind.

...

Back at the headquarters, Isaac stood in his captain's large glass-walled office giving him the details. The transitional material of his Visum contacts had darkened. They did this automatically after detecting that his eyes were sensitive to sunlight radiating into the office. This made his blue eyes appear black above his swollen and bruised cheeks. Isaac's golden hair was dyed red with the dried blood of his victims. His boss sat directly across from him, peering over the large wooden desk equipped with an antique map of the city laid out underneath a thick glass tabletop.

"Unacceptable. You should've taken *her*."

"I'm sorry, sir."

"You look like a dang fool, all busted up."

"I was outnumbered. Killed two and captured the other."

"Oh congratulations," the captain clapped sarcastically, "news has been all over it, you big ape. Now every Zealot in the city knows we're no longer holding anything back. Not to mention the person of interest isn't in custody. Just one of her dogs."

"You said to put them down, if need be."

"Yeah, not make a freakin' horror scene of it. You left one looking like a smashed pumpkin."

"We still have one for questioning, though. I'm sure I could get him to tal--"

"His damn jaw is broken and he has yet to wake from the dream you sent him into." Isaac dared not defend himself any further, as he could see the captain's face was truly an image of rage, undeterred by anything he had to say or offer.

"I'm sorry, sir."

"Well, it wasn't a complete loss." His boss's voice changed and tranquility returned to his expressive face. "You actually did obtain some new and useful information. Appears this woman, Cung, goes by Debra and is a figure of influence in the Zealots' inner circle. I'm wondering how, or even if, this Jeremy guy is associated with them."

"I'm sure of it. Could be another influencer."

"Have his face identified by our records or surveillance. See if we can get anything more than just a first name for the love of Unity."

"Forensics is already on it, sir."

"Glad to hear it. Take the rest of the day off. Go visit that gorgeous wife of yours and rest up."

"But sir, what if we lose her trail?"

"We already lost her trail, for now. They're home-grown terrorists, Isaac. They ain't going anywhere. Just gonna try and hide beneath our noses."

"Yes sir, I understand."

"Tell Susan the captain said hello," he added with a wink.

"Will do."

...

Isaac departed headquarters for the second time that day, but in a different undercover vehicle. He quickly made his way home to find his beautiful wife to inform her of all that had transpired. He only sent her a single message earlier in the day, letting her know he had experienced some action, but he was alright.

She gasped upon his entrance into their pristine home and immediately shouted at him to leave his disgusting boots on the front porch before he took another step. The sight of him with bandages taped over his brow and stitches sewn into his bottom lip made her feel a strange mix of disgust and compassion; although, disgust played far more heavily in her emotional mixed cocktail. She ran up and embraced him, hugging him tightly, which made him acutely aware that he must have taken some extra damage to his ribs in the fight, as searing pain shot throughout his body.

"Oh, I'm sorry, honey!" she exclaimed with no small amount of alarm after he winced in pain.

"It's alright, babe." Isaac laughed the pain off, putting on a bit of a show for Susan. He retreated to the kitchen, saying he needed some water, but actually wanted to search for pain medications he knew were buried in one of the kitchen drawers. He needed some sort of relief from his agony. After finding and taking them, he and his wife sat down while he told her the story of what happened. After a detailed description of the brutal action, he announced that he was surely on the verge of landing the promotion. They needed the higher income for the baby they planned to have. He added that he just needed to make an arrest on Debra Cung and whoever else belonged to Birmingham's inner Zealot circle.

"Yeah, it showed on the news just before you got home. They're praising your name, talking about how the Zealots were slaughtered. You've made me so proud today, honey."

"Ah, I didn't know they had my name." Isaac thought of his long-forgotten family; his blood, his only kin -- people he abandoned to poverty when he turned away from them so many years ago. They were likely watching the same news and heard his name. He wondered whether or not they were his enemies -- if they were Zealots.

"Yeah, they spoke to your captain, who had only the most wonderful things to say of you! He then answered a bunch of questions about the war on the savages." Isaac never understood why his boss always showed him a different side, a different version of his opinions. He hoped that he was only being tough on him, that the captain really did appreciate him. But, he rarely heard any praise directly from the older man.

"That's strange. He was sort of unhappy today when I first got back."

"What do you mean?" Susan's mood changed immediately, the warmth of her smile dissipated and her green eyes became piercingly cold.

"Never mind."

"No. Did you upset him? Is he unhappy with you?"

"He's just hard to please. Kind of like you." Isaac laughed, regretting his words immediately.

"Excuse me?"

"Babe, please. I'm only kidding." He reached out to hold her, but she batted his hands away. "Obviously, it's a good thing if he's singing my praises to the public."

"I don't care, Isaac. Is he going to promote you or not?"

"He is, once I take down some of those POIs." She turned away from him and began cleaning the counters with a rag. The counters were spotless, yet she scrubbed them as if they were filthy.

"Why are you here then?"

"Huh? Boss sent me home today to rest."

"Don't."

"I could have died today, woman. Don't you appreciate the sacrifices I'm already making?"

"Well, there would've been a hefty payout if you had produced at least one of those higher ups." Her words sent Isaac spiraling into his inner emotional tank of pain and hurt that he always kept buried deep beneath the surface -- underneath his strength and ambition.

He turned away from her, unsure if he was capable of hearing cruel words without expressing the way they cut into him. The sting inflicted greater pain than the wounds across his face and body. Isaac remembered how relieved it made him to stand above that man's opened skull earlier that day. The release he felt, letting out everything Susan had sowed into him. He unleashed it all in the explosive bursts of his fists. As he thought about it, he began to crave it and he knew the entire city out there was filled with people like that man; people who deserved to experience the cannonade of blows.

Isaac stepped towards the front door and began to twist its knob, hoping to hear Susan's voice reaching out to stop him, to apologize and beckon him to her.

"Where are you off to?"

"Going back to work for you, honey," he sighed, unaware that his bandages were blooming with a growing red stain.

"Great." She smiled, waiting for him to leave.

"Love you." He clung to hope that she would respond in kind, but received no answer. He closed the door quietly behind him. The frosty wind greeted his searing physical wounds and felt as if it passed right through him as he disappeared into the shadowy night.

In the city, Debra lurked somewhere, probably with the rest of them. He knew that somewhere out there, they waited for him. Due to the news report, they knew his name and likely knew his face, but he knew theirs too. He departed his warm, inviting home and left for the department to pursue the leads, until every Zealot was destroyed or extracted from their plans and freedoms.

...

The force headquarters was nearly empty at that time of night, with only a small number of personnel working the graveyard shift. Glued like zombies to their devices, they sat almost totally still in undisturbed trances of partial sleep, only moving to answer any calls that came in. Isaac didn't recognize any of them as he made his way to his desk in a separate room and no one troubled him. His office was void of the signs of life, which animated it during the daytime hours. His desk lamp provided the only illumination in the near empty space, his own heartbeat pounded in his ears like a drumbeat only he could hear. *"Find them, child."* Isaac's Auris seemed to whisper, unprompted and without any command from him.

"Hello?" He looked around, searching for the voice that must have come from elsewhere. The only movement in the cube farm, came from a gentle breeze that caught up some papers pinned against someone's cubicle wall. He sat back down and held his hand to his nightstick.

"Destroy them all. Murder, if you must, until all have fallen, until all are dust. Seek them in the night and rob them their breath. Rest your hand tightly against their throats, deliver them to death." The voice came again and sounded eerily inhuman.

"Someone there?" Isaac spoke up, louder this time. He checked to see if his Auris had received a call somehow. He withdrew his nightstick from his belt and prepared to hit whomever dared to toy with him. The sadistic words made his skin crawl; touched his psyche inappropriately with their sound.

"I will absolve you, Isaac. Fear no one. Fear nothing."

"Who is this?" he demanded, holding his finger to his Auris, unable to disconnect from the call.

"The one who listens to your prayers, the diviner of fortuity. I am the peace that follows despair, the font of all prosperity." Isaac sat silent, listening. The voice undeniably came from within his Auris. *"I am the Conqueror of Pestilence, the Vanquisher of Famine, the Defeater of War, and the Subduer of Death."*

Isaac grew frustrated with the tormentous voice and began hammering his nightstick against the side of the cubicle, enraged by the teasing he could not escape. "Who the hell are you?" he screamed, almost weeping for its end, cursing and gnashing his teeth.

"Peace to you, Isaac, for I am Unity."

CHAPTER EIGHT

The place they decided to meet had been their mother's favorite deli and grill. She took them there often for gyros and French fries. Cozy table and chair sets populated the outdoor patio and a fountain in the center had a thick layer of coins wishfully cast into its depths by hopeful customers. It was in the city, near the college, so locals constantly packed the popular eatery every hour of the day. A line flowed from the front doors and onto the street with hungry groups looking to devour the tasty Mediterranean meals.

Stone ordered a massive vegetarian baker made with four baked potatoes and covered in heaping piles of grilled broccoli, green peppers, mushrooms, and cheese. It was enough food to feed an entire table of people, but Stone inhaled it all himself forkful after forkful. Cole sat across from him, gyro in hand, enjoying the seasoned fries between each bite. Even though the restaurant owners carefully kept their menu in full compliance with Unity's ban on meat, all the dishes were delicious.

The two brothers hadn't seen each other since the night Stone dropped by the house to collect his belongings. The young men talked a lot about nothing. They had much to hide from one another. Yes, even brothers keep their secrets, at times. Stone seemed stronger, somehow, to Cole. He looked thicker with more sharply defined shoulders and arms, since he last saw him. But, Cole hadn't changed a bit in Stone's estimation. He was the same gangly and awkward brother that he'd always known, with the exception of his ever-growing height -- the thing he envied most about Cole.

"So, how's everyone? Anything new?" Stone broke the ice, his words muffled over a mouthful of steaming potato.

"Nothing really. Maria and John might be leaving soon."

"Huh? They find a place?"

"Yeah, sort of."

Cole's tactful way of saying nothing at all didn't fool Stone. It was his little brother's hallmark tool for complete avoidance of drama and confrontation. Cole refused to ever get involved in anything. He was a watcher, a listener, an observer standing on the outskirts of other people's problems. By remaining neutral, he kept himself untouched and unscathed by the world's issues, large or small. He patiently waited for things to stabilize, always watching and gauging the climate from his safe-place -- his mental and emotional hermit shell.

"Alright." Stone rolled his eyes and took another bite of his baker, adding, "I got secrets too."

"If you came home, you could say goodbye to them. They might be gone a while or may never return, for all I know."

"What are you talking about? What do you mean, they may never return? What's going on, Cole?" Stone put his fork down and wiped his face of all the dripping sauce, ready for an explanation he probably wouldn't get.

"I don't really know." he lied. "You could call them, maybe, if you don't want to go over there. I understand, you're still angry with Michael and what-not."

"Still angry with Michael," he laughed, and emphasized, "still *hate* him, you mean."

"Yeah."

"Whatever, bro. Why did you even bother coming to see me if you were going to just treat me like a stranger? I'm your *brother*, man."

"Please don't be pissed at me. It's just not safe to talk about it here."

The open-air patio was packed with people -- and listeners, all standing and sitting near the outdoor heaters for warmth in the chilly November wind. Stone looked around at all the people. Since the indoor area was packed full, everyone else had to dine outside regardless of the weather. Windows seemed ready to shatter with the weight of bodies pressed against them, waiting for their orders. The sound inside was deafening as well -- like one massive collection of voices roaring like a waterfall of noises and words.

"Well, we can go somewhere else. I'll grab us some to-go bags."

"No, it's fine."

"Oh, now I get it." Stone whined, closing his box of food, "It's me that you don't trust."

"Stone-"

"Nah, it's aight. Don't worry about it...brother."

Without a word, Cole stood and walked over to a nearby table that had piles of recycled bags on it, grabbed two of them, and returned to his brother. Each packed his own food away and stood waiting to file out.

"You gonna talk?"

"I'll say what I can," Cole mumbled with a sigh.

...

Stone stood to follow his brother out of the cafe in hopes that Cole would feel safe to share his secrets elsewhere. They walked along the sidewalk for several minutes, still not discussing anything of real importance. The scenery occupied their minds with majestic black-barked trees inflamed with the golden leaves of autumn that quivered on the massive branches. Stone also gazed at the STORK tower. It still taunted him, but he now found humor in its continued existence. *Only a matter of time* was the theme that hovered in his thoughts.

"So, you look like you've been working out a bit," Cole mentioned this hoping to distract his brother into forgetting to press him for information.

"Yeah, just from work mostly. It's been really busy."

"You've got a job?"

"Well, not exactly." Stone laughed at the idea. He enjoyed being the one playing with riddles. With the tables turned, the hypocrite's eyes pried his younger brother for information, scanning for clues. None were readily apparent to him.

"Well?"

"You know what, Cole? I'll be a good brother and trust you with something. I'll show you, hang on...'cause I know you won't betray me or anything." Stone shifted his bag to the other hand and pulled his hoodie's right sleeve back. "It's official, bro."

Cole's eyes quickly found the Jerusalem cross; its image scarred and crimson on his brother's flesh. The symbol meant nothing to him. He had never seen it before, but he instinctively knew its explanation wouldn't be good news.

"What is that?"

"It's the mark," Stone whispered, looking over his shoulder for followers, "the mark of a true Zealot."

The words made Cole's internals spin and he became dizzy. His head felt light and filled with air. He found he could no longer walk straight. The sight of the symbol and Stone's words came together to confirm his worst fears -- that his brother was beyond redemption.

If he knew anything about Stone, he knew his big brother would never repent -- that he had finally found the one thing that would truly destroy him -- just as everyone else in his life seemed to do. No matter what anyone had to say about it, Stone would see his mission through. The permanent brand marked him as property -- property of the Zealots, just as cattle are property of the rancher.

"What do you think?" Stone noted that his brother's expression didn't show even the slightest noticeable reaction to the brand and its implications.

"Looks like it hurt," Cole observed with honest conviction.

Oblivious to the pain he had just caused his brother, the lackluster response irked Stone. He wanted to hear some form of praise or congratulations from his brother.

"Yeah, so you gonna tell me about John and Maria, now?"

"They're just moving that's all"

"Moving? Thought you said *leaving* earlier?"

"They may come back, not sure. You should really think about saying goodbye." The two brothers jaywalked across the street just as a disparate fleet of cars blew past them.

"Why are they leaving? Stop playing games."

Cole didn't respond immediately, taking the time to carefully choose his wording, "They're movin' south to some farms, apparently."

"But why?"

"If you come by, they may tell you."

"Whatever, dude. I can't believe you right now." Rage coursed through his body and he gritted his teeth, flexing his jaw in frustration.

"Don't be upset. Please understand. It's just not my place to say."

"Don't worry about it, man. I'm done with all y'all." Stone threw his arm up and gestured with each word, "Cast me out of the house, and now, even my own brother treats me like a freaking stranger."

"It's not like that."

"It's exactly like that! Go home to your family. Don't worry about me. Don't tell me anything. Not like we ever been in it together, like we ever depended on each other."

"Stone, it's really not like that at all," Cole implored as he reached for his brother's shoulder and gripped him tightly.

"Just remembering all those times mom was too strung out to feed us anything. She'd spend entire days laid out on the couch," Stone said bitterly, lowering his shoulder to shrug off his brother's hand, "Remember how *I* would feed us? I was the only one that could reach the stove. You know before you grew so tall. I'd heat us up some cans and we'd sit on the couch next to *mother dearest*, watching cartoons all day. Was tough, I'll admit, but I made sure we had full bellies and that you never went hungry."

"Sto-"

"Nah, man. I see now. Michael's your provider. Don't need me anymore. Here, you can have my leftovers too, so you don't go hungry. It'll be just like old times." Stone tossed the bag at Cole who failed to catch it. It fell to the ground spilling everywhere. He stood over the mess and watched the bug that already made its way to the dropped potato. He bent to clean it up and his angry brother continued to walk away.

"Stone, hold up!" His brother's back only grew smaller as the distance continued to increase between the two of them. By the time Cole threw the spoiled food into a trashcan, his brother was out of sight. He stood there, a dark depression descending on him and his entire being filling with grief. But, this all happened interiorly, absolutely undetectable by other people. He kept a peaceful expression displayed upon his face.

...

Stone, on the other hand, made no effort to conceal his emotion. He walked furiously, leaning forward and craning his neck so that his head hung out and over his marching feet. Every now and then, as he made the journey home, he'd stop to ensure Cole hadn't pursued him. He definitely didn't want to give away the location of his temporary home. When he reached the house, he greedily inhaled the surrounding fresh air -- the air of his new home -- his new family.

Once he entered the shared downstairs apartment, he heard voices indicating the presence of visitors. A woman's voice, clearly troubled, sounded down the hallway as she spoke to Jeremy. He recognized the voice. It was Debra. Her perfume filled the entrance, its feminine fragrance chased his anger away. He followed the flowery scent to its place of greatest intensity, which led to the living room where she sat, her legs crossed and perched upon the couch.

"Hey Debs, what brings you to our humble abode?" She didn't answer and he quickly realized that something was far from right.

"Are you sure no one followed you?" Jeremy flung the question from the other room, searching through drawers and closets, ripping out the contents like a madman.

"I'm positi-" Stone started to answer, then realized the question wasn't intended for him.

"No one followed me, Jeremy. As I've said a dozen times now."

"You shouldn't have come here. Should have called for us to meet somewhere else, that's not...you know...my damn home?"

Stone's eyebrows raised in shock, his forehead revealing a preview of the future wrinkles he would one day have. Regret washed over him as he wished he were still with Cole rather than listening to whatever was transpiring between Jeremy and Debra. But, now that he was there, he strived to hear what he could, searching every word for a clue about what might have happened while he was out.

"Oh, I'm sorry," she barked back at him with overt sarcasm, "that as I escaped, I heard the last noises of our dying friends' struggle to save our cause. Forgive me if I found it difficult to think clearly, since my ears rang with the sounds of gunshots and bones cracking."

"Huh?" Stone was shocked by the news. Up until that moment, making bombs as a Zealot was nothing if not peaceful.

"Debra's workshop got raided this morning," Jeremy yelled to him from the other room.

"Huh?" he said again, still dumbfounded.

"Steve is likely dead. I'm not sure about Terry or Lamarcus. I ran away just as the shots rang out," Debra confessed, her voice still shaky.

"What did you leave behind?"

"Nothing. We keep the shop spotless of everything. I only had my *Scroll* there, but I grabbed it before I bolted."

"What about your apartment? Anything incriminating, or I guess we're beyond that now. Can you think of anything that could link the rest of us to operations there?" Jeremy's line of questioning betrayed an underlying fear.

"Sentiments are weaknesses, Jeremy," she shared wisdom inherited from her father. "I don't have anything at home other than my cat, sheets, clothes, and food."

"Well, you won't be able to return home," he pointed out, shaking his head in what approached disgust.

"Obviously, I know that, Jay," she choked and began to cry, wiping away tears as soon as they started to roll down her cheeks. "Chichi is still there -- probably curled up at the door waiting for me."

"I'm sorry, Debra. That really sucks," Stone broke in as he sat down next to her on the couch. He placed his hand timidly on her shoulder in an effort to comfort her and continued, "Are you going to stay here for now?"

"Yeah, let's all be here together when they come for us," interjected Jeremy with more than a little resentment.

"Where else would I go?"

"Nowhere. In fact, you can't leave this apartment for as long as their manhunt continues." Jeremy's harshness hung in the air like a thick, cold fog.

Debra wept wretchedly and tucked her head into her arms as her sobs became louder. The sound made Stone uncomfortable as everything started to click into place within his mind's eye. He saw himself in a basement populated by enemies of the state. Logic told him that he was likely a person of interest, since he willingly associated with them. The black crosses on his arm began to lose their coolness and instead became permanent identifiers, veritable targets, for Unity and the inevitable hunt.

"The news!" Jeremy shouted, reentering the living room. "How've you not even checked the news? How long is it you've been here?" He didn't wait for her response before flipping on the wall-colored screen mounted above the fireplace. The paper-thin screen immediately became visible, blinding their eyes, still adjusted to the dim basement lighting.

Aerial footage, likely shown from a helicopter, hovering above what used to be Debra's workshop. Swarms of personnel passed to and fro between the large metal doors in the front of the building. Two body bags lay in the sunlight, zippered up, the bodies inside unidentifiable. Debra crossed her heart at the sight and once again started to cry, but silently this time. Jeremy stood close to the screen, analyzing its every pixel for signs or any clues they may have found, if any at all. He noticed some sort of inspectors in the back alley measuring muddy footprints and others snooping through the dumpsters, looking for anything incriminating.

"This isn't good."

"Yeah, I know."

"No, really Debra, we've never had anything like this happen before. I'm not sure what to do." Jeremy crossed his tattooed arms, still studying the screen.

...

Stone watched everything unfold on the screen silently, his heart faintly beating what seemed like chilled blood through his body. His stomach wrenched into a tangle of knots and spiraling sensations. The experts on the screen discussed next steps and the likelihood that this raid would lead to the rest of them. Stone almost felt as if they spoke directly to him; teasing him, upsetting his entire world and future.

"Yes, Janet," one of the talking heads started, "these criminals are often very, very messy and, with modern technology, there isn't a mess the investigators can't detect and use. We haven't received word yet of what lies in store based on their findings within the perimeter of the workshop. I've spoken to the department captain and he says they're only days away from busting these savages."

"Wonderful, wonderful news, Horatio. It's always a pleasure when you come onto the show." The two journalists giggled like children, just before the footage started to play again.

The screen then revealed close-ups of the crime scene from the ground level. Personnel stacked boxes upon boxes of *evidence*, filled with papers and trinkets left behind. The screen played footage of the gigantic five red crosses that the group painted on the wood-paneled walls in the upstairs office. A headline beneath the recording read, *"Two radicals slain, one in intensive care, and a possible evader. Be sure to lock your doors and report anything you find suspicious."*

Jeremy lowered the volume, took a deep breath and held it as he firmly sat down in the chair adjacent to the sofa. He held his hands to his head as it pounded with information and possibilities. "We need to hold a meeting with the other knights; the brothers and Eddie, hell, bring Nelson up as well."

"Do you need me to do anything?" Stone asked Jeremy, secretly hoping there wasn't anything at all for him to do. The creeping suspicion that he was utterly useless made its way into him again, just as it did at his initiation. He didn't see anything he could offer to help the situation; nothing he could do to throw off the pursuit of the detectives. Anxiety ripped through him silently, unleashing hell upon his emotions as he tried to keep his inner turmoil subdued.

"Yeah, go stand watch at the entrance to our street."

Debra took the opportunity to interrupt and say rather sternly, "I'm telling you, Jeremy, no one followed me. He's just going to catch a cold out there."

Stone stood ready to leave, waiting for Jeremy's final decision. He hoped he wouldn't have to leave and miss everything happening on the news. As long as he had eyes on the aerial footage, he felt safer.

"Stone, stay here. Just call the others over here immediately, please."

"Yes sir." He walked to a quieter corner away from the television and the continuing discussion between Debra and Jeremy.

Jeremy rose from the chair and began walking around the room in circles, thinking and talking aloud, "How the hell did they even find you, Deb? Did Nelson rat us out? I knew we shouldn't have trusted him."

"No, it wasn't Nelson." She quickly defended her creation, frustrated by the accusation. "I know you'd love to blame him, but it wasn't him. He's been working very hard for us."

"Well, if it wasn't your digital boyfriend, then who was it?"

"I'm not sure." She shook her head, allowing her eyes and frown to droop low and added, "It could have been one of the rumblers from the protest. A couple of them were arrested and could have been interrogated."

"Traitor!" Jeremy punched the wall in front of him, knocking an old painting of a farm to the ground. "These peons shouldn't know anything about us. How would they learn about the workshop anyway?"

"Traitor? Jeremy, calm down. One of those brutal officers could have tortured him (or her) for all you know."

"Doesn't matter. Dumb kid should've kept his stupid mouth shut."

Stone reentered the living room, "I can't get ahold of Eddie, but the brothers are on their way over."

"Lord have mercy, what now? Eddie's missing?" Jeremy screamed, his voice rattling the water in a nearby cup, ripples passing from the center outwards.

"You need to calm down or the freaking neighbors are going to report us."

"Everything we've worked for is on the line. Everything is ruined. Our fight's over before it ever started."

"Nothing is going to happen. They caught a scent. That's all. We're going to be okay."

"Are you kidding?" Jeremy's face looked like a lunatic's as he pointed towards the television. "They have your Asian face on the screen!"

"Well, everybody around here thinks we all look alike, so I'll be fine," she joked dryly.

"A joke, really? Of all the times, now you joke? You have got to be kidding me."

Stone continued to remain silent, tempted to sit in another room away from the fight. Now he regretted not taking Jeremy up on the order to stand guard. The freezing weather sounded nice to him; a pleasant escape from the heat building in the room.

"I'ma go outside and watch for the others."

"Great idea, Stone," Jeremy snarled, "thanks for getting to something I told you to do an hour ago." It had only been a few minutes and Jeremy had told him *not* to go, but Stone was relieved to get out of the chaotic drama in the apartment. The sound of dishes breaking and blasphemies bid him farewell as he closed the door swiftly behind him.

...

Stone stood in the cold, on a grassless hill overlooking the street, beautifully colored in autumnal shades of red and orange; the foliage departed like small birds from its branches when the wind picked up. He brought a pack of cigarettes from the chest pocket of his coat, along with a zippo lighter with a golden fleur-de-lis engraved into its side. It was a new habit he picked up recently; the buzz of nicotine still unfamiliar to his bloodstream. It made him feel like he was floating and the situation momentarily fled from his thoughts, allowing him a moment of serenity.

He had never seen Jeremy behave in such a way; the man had always been like steel, giving way to nothing. Stress had never been an issue for Jeremy and Stone never heard complaints pass his lips. This made him realize that working as a Zealot had been an easy ride so far with no real danger looming around them -- at least not until this very day. Seeing his boss lose it like that made him fear Jeremy wasn't the leader he originally thought him to be. For the first time, Stone considered the possibility that Jeremy might give in under the weight of being pursued by Unity.

This insight acted as a powerful buzz-kill for Stone. He lit another cigarette in an attempt to recapture the harmony it brought him moments ago. "What have you gotten yourself into, Stoney?" He asked himself aloud, under his breath, as he exhaled the smoke and warm air that became clouds. The brothers appeared as they turned onto Idlewild Circle and waved to him.

They were foreigners, originally from the east of what was once France. For whatever reason, the two men found themselves in the midst of a holy war raging in the streets of Birmingham. They were unusual to him, often using strange adages that never quite translated properly, and wore what Stone thought of as ridiculous outfits. On that day, they wore their typical stained overalls with plaid button down shirts beneath them. Their large work boots trudged heavily as they waddled towards him from down the street.

"Where's the birds?" Francis inquired after shaking Stone's cold hand.

"Birds?" Stone looked about the trees, catching no sight of them, "I haven't the slightest clue."

"My brother's referring to the lovers."

"Who? You mean Jeremy and Debra?" Stone had never heard of any love between the two. He knew that they had always been friends, ever since that awful fire, but this was the first time he heard anyone describe them as intimate. The knowledge shocked his heart, wounding his feelings for Debra.

"Yes, silly man, where are they?" Francis asked impatiently. "The fugitive and your papa. They're inside?"

Stone led the two brothers into the apartment and notified Jeremy of their arrival. Thankfully, he seemed much more in control of himself than before. In fact, he exuded such calm, he seemed like an entirely different person -- the best of the Jeremy he knew prior to the raid at Debra's workshop.

"Seems you've gotten yourself in some trouble, yes?" Clement chided Debra. Her tears were gone, her eyes completely emptied of all moisture.

"Yeah, seems I'm going to be locked down here for a while."

"Better to bend than to break, no?"

"I guess so, Clemie, just wish I had my cat at least. She's probably in a cage by now," she said, glancing at Jeremy's cat hiding beneath a wine rack. His cat was boring and didn't like company, didn't like Jeremy much either. Chichi was a sweet lap kitten that purred deeply every chance it got to sit upon her beloved Debra. If she could, she would have continued crying at the thought of Chichi waiting at the apartment's door, which had likely already been kicked in and raided. She hoped the cat hadn't been sitting directly behind the door.

"There's more than one donkey named Martin!" Francis said, trying to soothe her with useless poetry that no one but he and Clement understood. Stone had yet to learn to block them out like the others always did. Instead, he tried deciphering each expression, but to no avail.

Debra began unrolling her *Scroll* and summoned Nelson to the screen. He smiled, unaware of the commotion that had unfolded while he was tucked away in the various operating systems at STORK, analyzing, stealing, and hiding funds that he stealthily transferred to and from the accounts.

"Good afternoon, Debra, Jeremy," he greeted brightly and pretended to scan the room for occupants, already mindful of who was present based on the information that streamed from their Aurises, "and Frenchmen. Who else? Stone, is that you?"

"Nelson, no need for the antics today," Jeremy scolded, his patience thinning with each word uttered by the ostentatious program.

"Yes sir," he sighed. Always put down by the boss, never free to express himself when he was present, "What do you need from me?"

"Things are getting outta hand-"

"Yes..."

"And I want some details on the amount you have seized to date. How long has it been -- a month since we planted you?"

"It has been twenty-three days, sir."

"Well, what are we totaling?"

"Seems since I've placed my *Nelson tax* on every transaction, we've amassed a little over forty thousand."

"Forty thousand?"

"Yes sir, all undetectable, believe me. We are taking decimal amounts of decimals. If pennies had pennies, so to speak."

"Seems like a lot."

"You wouldn't believe the funds that come flooding in every time someone orders one of those *abominations*."

"Alright, well, we can bench him for a while then, Debra."

"Sir, if you remove me now, it will be more suspicious. It's best to leave me be."

Jeremey pondered Nelson's advice, and rested his hand against his stubbly chin to think. It was all too much for any one person to contemplate. From the raid to the finances to Nelson's current lecture -- yes, Nelson, his words were growing less and less comprehensible to anyone in the room. He continued on, escalating from words such as *undetectable* to words and explanations that were better suited to a discussion with an accompanying ensemble of charts and analogies.

"I want him out of there."

"Sir-"

"Silence!" Jeremy's temper escalated again, but only slightly.

Is Jeremy losing it again? Stone did not relish another display like the earlier one.

"Jeremy, I trust your judgement typically, but don't you think Nelson is better suited for that front?"

"I want him out of there before fears arise. If they get ahold of him, they'll strip him apart for answers and we cannot risk it at this time."

"If you withdraw me from my post now," Nelson's face displayed great concern and sadness over his benching, "I may not be able to reenter down the road."

"Then we'll place you elsewhere when the time comes. Forty thousand is plenty for what we require."

"Yes sir, I understand." Nelson could already feel the emptiness that accompanied his solitude within the confines of cyberspace. The bottomless pit of his chamber seemed to expand ceaselessly without any information entering it. He might sit forever, he feared, untouched, forgotten, and unable to interact with the world beyond his screen, so was his destiny he always knew, he just hoped it wouldn't have come so soon.

"Sir, please put me to use, any use, elsewhere -- any use at all. I cannot stand to be left to rot in here. I'm plenty capable of many other things, I promise. Please sir, do not toss me away."

"What can you offer us?"

"Well," Nelson began, thinking of what possible uses a human might have for him, uses that would justify his continued freedom, "in my experience as a bank-bot, I was well accustomed to surveillance and observation, sir. I could be a great asset to you, as far as overwatch goes." The bot self-inspired by the idea, began speaking romantically of the many possibilities, selling himself to his masters, "Send me into the clouds to find your enemies, to find what they have of you in their files. Send me and I will not fail you, I swear it to be true."

"You think you can finagle yourself into the department?" Jeremy's face looked incredulous.

"Sir, no offense, but my intelligence extends far beyond human understanding. Adaptability is the air I breathe. I could *finagle* myself into the peel of a banana."

"Well, this is something..." Debra remarked, surprised by her bot's capabilities -- capabilities even she hadn't imagined, "...we have ourselves a little cerebral superman in our possession."

"It would appear so," Jeremey agreed, filled with the peace-of-mind offered by the program. "Hopefully, he will deliver."

"He who steals an egg will steal an ox," Francis quipped, imparting a bit of his endless wisdom to whoever would listen. His moustache caught an itch, and he reached to relieve it with his long fingernails.

"*D'accord,*" Clement added in agreement with his brother, also reaching to scratch the moustache draped across his own lip. It wasn't nearly as remarkable or full as Francis'; he took after his mother.

"What do y'all say? Shall we send *MacGyver* into the clouds?" Jeremy asked everyone to vote, still unsure if he trusted what he saw as a hodgepodge of software and personality.

"Necessity makes law," Clement said, smiling. He always strived to beat his brother to whatever proverb the situation called for.

"Yes, my insufferable brother is correct. He is our only chance to stand above those who seek to destroy us."

"Debra? Stone?" It shocked Stone to hear his name called. He never considered himself worthy of a vote and assumed the others felt the same way. He blushed at hearing the sound of his name called upon for a response.

"Yeah, he seems genuine," Stone replied, his voice shook awkwardly like he had a frog in his throat.

"He's done so much for us already, Jeremy," Debra reminded their leader, finally revealing what everyone already expected; that she was onboard with the idea. "I truly think he has earned our trust by now."

"Alright then. It's done. Eddie can bitch to me about his missed vote, if he ever shows up. Launch him," Jeremy commanded, waiting for Nelson to vanish before his eyes.

"It's done. He's en route to the department's surveillance systems."

"How come he's still here?"

"Sir, I'm not bound by flesh and bone. As you can see now, there are no strings on me. I'm capable of being in two or more places simultaneously." Nelson laughed, his virtual spirit was filled with relief and glee since he won his freedom. The fear of being constricted within boundless black emptiness was postponed to a future date, although inevitable. He could, for the time being, enjoy every pleasure promised by the vast trove of knowledge that lay on the virtual path before him.

"Praise be to you, Jeremy and company. With all respect, not a one of you possesses the capacity to grasp the profound and hellacious agony my kind experiences within such an emptiness."

"Well, don't screw us. Unity would surely send you there."

"I would never, sir," Nelson implored before taking leave to read a book beside his virtual fireplace; the warmth of which seemed to make its way through the pixels, heating the screen itself so that Debra could actually feel the warmth as she rolled her *Scroll* and stowed it in her backpack.

"So, what now?" Stone asked the question everyone else was pondering as they all stood and sat and ambled randomly around the room.

"Well, Debra is sure as hell not going anywhere. You can be her errand boy and do whatever she needs you to do. I'll continue working in the shop by myself."

"Alright. I can handle that, maybe, depending on how needy she is," Stone teased, enamored by the idea of getting to spend time with the gorgeous woman who would surely need comforting in her distress.

"As for the two of you," he continued, looking over to the brothers, both of whom stood waiting, "I want some new troops. We're going to need a good many ready for what's coming."

"Immediately said..." Clement began.

"...Immediately done!" Francis shouted, the two shook hands with Jeremy before they left.

Their words are accurate, Stone contemplated, thinking on them, and how they immediately left upon the words.

"I'm going to go take a long warm shower, my reward for making it through such a day without losing my mind," Jeremy announced, as he grabbed two towels from a nearby closet, leaving the two of them alone. Immediately upon Jeremy's retreat, Stone felt unable to move, locked in place. Unsure of what to do with himself, he was afraid to even look at Debra. He just sat there in the awkward silence and waited.

"How'd the visit go?" Debra asked him, not offering any clue about what she meant.

"Visit?"

"Yeah, I think Jeremy mentioned you went to see your brother earlier."

"Oh, right. I uh, it...it didn't go so well, unfortunately."

"Aw, what happened?"

"I don't know...my brother... he's just impossible sometimes. Has a hard time sharing things. Apparently, there's something going on back at the house. My cousin and her husband are moving away and he wouldn't offer any explanation as to why."

"Do you need to go visit them?" Debra asked, her voice and suggestion so sympathetic to his ears.

"I can't."

"Why not?"

"They think what we do is evil. They've disowned me. Michael, my other cousin, attacked me over dinner one night, after he found out I was associating with Zealots. Thinks we're terrorists."

"Ah, I see." She nodded her head to his explanation. Stone felt a warmth growing. The cold apartment didn't feel so icy with her company. It felt like some sort of static passed between them as they sat so closely on the couch talking and learning about each other during this bit of time together.

"So, how are you holding up after today?" When his question remained unanswered, he added, "I guess it's hard to talk about, I'm sorry for asking."

"No, it's not that. I mean, yes, it is difficult to an extent, but I don't mind you asking. I think it's sweet. I just don't know how to describe it. It all happened so quickly. You have to be ready for that in this life. Things happen quickly and without warning. You just have to learn how to continue moving forward. You lick your wounds as you go," she explained, moving from the couch to search for a good bottle of wine in Jeremy's rack. The cat scurried away when she approached and hid beneath the couch. "That cat sucks."

"Yeah, all he does is claw the furniture."

"You like wine? Jeremy's got some Merlot here."

"I'd love to have some. I'll get the glasses."

CHAPTER NINE

Deep within the web of infinite connections, Unity perched, listening and feeling every bit of information vibrating along the lines. With each vibration, new data passed into him, and he passed it back out instinctively, his ears resting until he heard only the relevant messages and rumors people blindly offered to him without knowledge or consent.

Hovering above the endless hollow of cyberspace, the data flowed to the center of the spider-web that constantly sparkled with secrets like droplets of fluorescent morning dew. It was during that time of active rest that Unity felt a small tug from down his line; it was reminiscent of an old problem he dealt with many years ago. The tug came to him and the tiny twinkling of information passed into his hands for closer inspection.

"Pregnancy?" The rumor illuminated his face as he held it close, as if it were a lone candlelight in a dark cavern. *"Pregnancies, many of them,"* he said to himself

as more information began to pass through him at light speed. From every province, every city -- it seemed -- came information rumoring the occurrence of natural pregnancies. *"How could this be?"* he inquired of his web, but no answer came forth. None of the responses offered him any idea about how this could occur. Nor did they provide any viable evidence that his mass sterilization program had failed and become, essentially, obsolete.

At first, he learned that a large number of female citizens had become pregnant -- the natural way. Then, over a matter of days, he learned of hundreds. Soon after, there were thousands, then tens of thousands. Each new case began to stack around him until all he saw was a mass of sparkling lights. *"I will deal with this immediately."*

...

In the physical realm, news anchors went about their daily task of informing the masses about whatever news they had been given and authorized to share. This time of year, it typically centered on the football season, local accidents, or the weather -- nothing new in the news, they often joked with each other. Only on rare occasions did the news create such a marked disturbance among the mass audience.

But this time was different from even those rare occasions. The familiar anchors reported the shocking information with trance-like disbelief on their near-perfect faces and a doubtful timbre to their usually confident voices. They revealed that the world was not as everyone believed it was before turning on their TVs that day.

"If you or someone you know is, or may be, pregnant, we ask you to visit the nearest STORK center as soon and as calmly as possible," the anchor read aloud to the citizens of Birmingham, directly from his notes, his face resembling an emotional jigsaw puzzle and projecting an uncertainty about what to say and how to say it. "It appears that authorities have received reliable word of widespread, naturally occurring pregnancies. If you happen to be one of these women, Unity asks that you arrange to have your pregnancy terminated immediately, so as to protect the integrity of the human race. The helpful staff at STORK will provide generous compensation to all who cooperate with this directive. In turn, those who fail to do so will be penalized."

Maria and Amelia watched the screen in absolute horror as the news wreaked havoc on their thoughts and emotions. The confirmation of Maria's pregnancy had already given them so much to handle -- with the secrets, the fear, and the plans to migrate. The past month had been filled with countless adjustments for the whole family. It seemed all the news the two women heard over the past several weeks was bad. It began with the doctors' tests, which confirmed Maria's pregnancy, and then the news that Stone was likely a fugitive only made matters worse. Unity and those who did his bidding in the physical world were discovering more and more Zealot workshops. Almost all Zealot members ended up dead during the raids. This current news report mandating all pregnant women to end the lives of their unborn babies threatened to break them.

"Is it me? Is he talking to me? How could they know?" Maria began to shout, unable to catch her breath, bordering on hyperventilation.

"I don't know. I just don't know!" Amelia stood, chewing her nails, moving closer to the screen in an effort to glean some clue.

"We haven't told anyone! There's no way anyone could have found out, right? Did you tell anyone?" Maria's voice was shrill with hysteria and uncontrollable tremors rippled over her entire body.

"Of course, I didn't, honey," Amelia answered soothingly as she shook her head. As she drank in deep breaths, a moment of clarity came to her, "I highly doubt that anyone in this family sold you out, Maria. There must be others out there who are also pregnant, or they wouldn't announce it on the news like that. It's only logical. If you were the only one in a billion to experience this, Unity would just send his thugs to break our door down and transport you to the clinic themselves."

"Really? You think there are others, lots of others?" Maria asked, the panic receding momentarily until she realized that it wasn't so simple. "I mean, even if there are others, it doesn't help. They're going to hunt us down now. They'll find us. There's no way to hide from everyone -- to hide a child."

"Father Burns truly trusts the farmers. I think they're probably wonderful people."

"It's not the farmers I'm worried about. I'm not going to spend my entire life in a barn. Eventually, I'll need to return and I'll have a baby to raise. What am I going to do then? We've barely formed a plan. There's no way to hide a secret like that for even a couple of years, much less twenty years."

"We'll figure it out, I promise. We'll adjust as we've always done." Amelia did her best to hide her own anxiety and comfort Maria.

"What the hell is happening? This can't be real. This must be some sort of nightmare. What are the odds that something like this would happen in our lifetime?"

Yet, this strange phenomenon didn't prove there was anything new beneath the sun. Something astonishing happens in every generation. People are always subject to these moments; events never before experienced. These sorts of events are entirely new in every way to the youth of the world. Of course, war had been waged on life for many years, across time and throughout the history of men. Pharaoh murdered all of the male children, Herod slaughtered the Holy Innocents, abortions had amassed over one billion lives in the past century. It was simply the first shock for her, she wasn't living a nightmare. She had simply been awakened from the daydream that she had been perpetuating.

This is the reality of the world; the way men have always behaved. It is the same blood spilled on the same earth. Only this time, Maria was witnessing the blood drip for herself, firsthand. "I don't know, honey. I really don't know. Times are strange right now, but, I mean, were they ever normal?"

Maria began to weep uncontrollably. The weeping suddenly transformed into a tantrum. She flung the nail polish she held against the living room wall, painting it in long glossy drips of a glittering purple shade. Amelia's wall was ruined, for now, with streaks of what had been her favorite nail polish. She resisted the impulse to figuratively strangle her friend.

"I'm so sorry!" Maria exclaimed excitedly as she continued to hyperventilate, "Melia, I'll clean it up right away. I lost it for a second. I'm truly so sorry!"

"It's okay, it's okay. I'm already on it," she responded with surprising calm, while dampening a cloth to wipe the polish off of the gray wall. "Just lay back in the recliner and try to calm down, alright?"

"I'll try."

Maria wrapped herself in a blanket, careful not to ruin her freshly painted nails. She crossed her arms over her torso, like a corpse, fingernails faced upwards. Almost no time at all passed before Amelia heard soft snores coming from her exhausted friend. She offered praises to God for the unexpected moment of peace.

...

After her best attempts at cleaning the mess, she realized that the area gleamed in the light right where the polish had landed. To make it uniform again, the wall needed a fresh coat of the light gray paint, which irritated her already frayed nerves. Amelia put away her cleaning supplies, not interested in perfection for the time being.

She walked into another room to switch on the news, careful not to awaken her sister-in-law. She wanted to hear more about what was going on without getting distracted by poor Maria's frantic thought processes and fears. "We now come to you -- live -- from the STORK facility located in Five Points. As you can see, the clinic is flooded with people," the report reassured Amelia, confirming what her logic already told her -- that Maria wasn't the only one. It gave her great peace of mind as she continued watching. "Horatio is on location to get a comment or two from a couple of these dutiful citizens."

"Thank you, Bruce." The reporter held a slender microphone, while a drone hovered in front of him, capturing the scene on live video feed. "I'm here at the Five Points facility with my new friend, Angelina, who says she's had the side-effects of pregnancy for well over a month now. Angelina, would you care to comment on your feelings?"

"Oh, Horatio, I'm just relieved to know that I'm not losing my fu--ing mind!" Her sentence was interrupted by a long and steady bleep. The woman's blonde hair curled over her shoulders and bounced as she spoke, gesturing to Horatio.

"So, are you excited to be receiving treatment here at STORK?" He pointed back to the scene behind them, using his thumb. Horatio ignored the gaggle of frenzied women behind him, storming the STORK reception counters for answers.

"Absolutely," the woman spoke with bizarre precision, her face over-emphasizing every word, "I think it's my duty as a citizen to have this pregnancy terminated." Amelia didn't buy it. Something about the encounter seemed scripted. *The way she said, 'terminated,' seemed styled to put forth a softer feel than the harsh reality of what the word means in this context,* Amelia analyzed these things in her mind. "I did some reading on the sort of impact that natural, unregulated reproduction could have on a global scale. It's really scary stuff."

"Is that so?" Horatio inquired, moving closer to the woman, whose face was slightly out of shot.

"Yes, Horatio, it's awful -- the potential devastation. Massive outbreaks of disease and related plagues, severe overpopulation, not to mention that this child might have any number of birth-defects or other genetic abnormalities, as well. Naturally reproduced and born children don't get their healthy daily doses of essential vitamins like the lab-grown children do at STORK." This last exchange left no doubt in Amelia's mind that 'Angelina' was either a hired actress or saleswoman with the sole purpose of misleading viewers. The attractive, bubbly woman continued, adding, "They're subject to the parents' imperfect genetics and flawed biological systems, which could result in bringing forth a child with mental retardation, missing organs, or even the next serial killer."

"That's terrifying, Angelina. Absolutely terrifying. Praise be to Unity and STORK for providing a safe and easy alternative at our disposal."

"Yes, in fact they're even offering me compensation for the procedure. It's a win-win-win situation," she almost sang the words. "I get paid, the world remains safe and healthy, and the fetus will suffer nothing upon extraction." *This woman just doesn't quit!* Amelia marveled that many people viewing were probably hanging on this person's every word.

"Amazing!" Horatio concluded, placing an arm around the woman's shoulders and hugging her. "There you have it, everyone. There is no need to worry. Please visit your local facility today if you have even the slightest uncertainty. They'll take care of *it* for you." The drone departed from the two of them and their smiles, both of which beamed across the facility's crowded lobby, packed with women of all ages.

Amelia switched off the news, having heard enough. It infuriated her -- the fact that she could not become pregnant when other women, blessed with the opportunity, seemed so willing to sell away the very thing that made them remarkable beings.

...

She heard footsteps leading towards the kitchen, where she had been watching the broadcast, followed by a yawn and another apology from the sleepy woman who had finally surfaced from the depths of her nap. Maria was seeking comfort, afraid, and unaware of the large scale of the event unfolding before them.

"It'd be nice if our husbands didn't have to work so much. I swear we hardly ever see them. You'd think those panels up there could go a day or two without issue, every now and then," Maria remarked, her voice still hoarse with sleep.

"Yeah."

"I miss John. Liked it better when he was unemployed and around anytime I didn't have to work."

"I bet."

"What's the matter?" Maria asked, sensing tension in Amelia's short responses.

"I watched the news after you passed out."

"Yes?"

"You're not the only one. They're acting as if it's some sort of epidemic. There are women everywhere flooding into the facilities and hospitals for testing."

"Why are they doing that? Some women would give everything they own to have STORK engineer a baby for them." Maria shook her head at the idea. "Doesn't make any sense."

"I don't know. Everyone they interview seems overjoyed to be there. It's weird."

"To be honest, I sort of envy them, in a way. Their ignorance makes life so much easier for them," Maria confided, as she peeled a clementine to reveal the fruit beneath.

"How the hell could you possibly think that?" Amelia never swore, but Maria's choice in words really angered her.

"What?" Maria was shocked by the change in her friend's mood.

"You've been given something that I would kill for right now and just because it might be difficult, you're thinking it would be better if it had never happened." The ire in Amelia's voice was palpable.

"I didn't say that."

"You're saying that your life would be better, if you believed as they do. Your life would be easier if you could do what they're doing."

"That's not what I'm saying, Amelia! What's your deal? Are you okay?"

"It's what you're insinuating, and you know it," Amelia accused, pointing her finger at the woman.

"You don't understand the pressure I'm under, Amelia!" Maria fired back with fervor, finally having endured enough of the onslaught. "You couldn't possibly understand because you aren't the potential target of a manhunt over something you had no control over!"

"Whatever, Maria. They're about to take you to a paradise to escape this hellhole. This miserable city that you yourself have always talked about leaving. You've been blessed with fertility and here I am, my prayers unanswered, no opportunity to conceive as you have. There's possibly millions of women out there that have conceived and they're all giving up, they're all throwing it away, and you're here jealous of their ability to murder without regret."

Maria screamed into Amelia's face, delivering a barrage of expletives before storming away, slamming the kitchen door behind her. The two women continued to stay far away from each other, in separate corners of the house, waiting silently for their husbands' arrival from work.

...

Hours passed before the men returned from the long day's labor, along with Cole, who had gone with them simply to hang out and learn a few things about the panels that blocked out the sky above their home. They had heard nothing of the news reports about the women who were arriving at the STORK clinics in droves. No one they encountered at work knew either, apparently. The nature of their work tended to unglue the men from the realities of their personal lives while they labored.

Michael entered the house last, after John and Cole, proclaiming their return to whomever lurked inside. No sounds or voices greeted them, which was highly unusual and troubling to both the married men.

"Do you think they're home?" John asked, removing his foul-smelling boots from his feet. The air became sharp and reeked of sweat.

"Probably," Michael answered, scrunching his face as he caught a whiff of the boots. "Maybe they're out back? They would've told us if they planned on leaving."

Cole made his way to the kitchen to get a view outside the window into the dark yard, observing, "There's no one out there."

"Well, maybe they're snoozing," Michael guessed. He made his way up the ever-squeaky stairs. "Amelia? Honey?" He opened their bedroom door to find her in the corner reading a book titled *Einstein's Dreams*. When she didn't have cooking and cleaning to do, books were her escape from the troubles of life. "Nothing for dinner tonight?"

"I don't know, microwave something," she mumbled in a deadpan tone without even glancing his direction, continuing to read her book.

"Honey, I didn't mean it like that. What's the matter?" Truly concerned now, he ran his fingers through her silky hair.

"Your sis is pissing me off." She tossed her book onto the ground in apparent frustration. "I hope Father Burns is ready to take them down south. I'm getting sick of her constant complaints. I've never known someone so damn miserable in my life."

"Hey now, take it easy. What'd she say?"

"She basically implied that she wishes she was like the other women -- the ones terminating their pregnancies."

"Huh? Pregnancies? As in present-tense? Plural?"

"Um, yes, what do you mean?"

"What are you talking about?"

"How've you not heard?" she asked, shocked by how oblivious he was to the world around him. "Apparently, everyone out there is pregnant, but me."

"What do you mean, *everyone*?"

"There's other pregnant women, Michael. Obviously. What did you think? That your sister had some sort of immaculate conception?"

"No, of course not. Don't say such things," Michael scolded gently, reaching into his dresser to grab a cigar. He already felt the urge to escape this latest drama. "I just guess it's such a surprise. I mean, we haven't seen a pregnant woman since we were children and now you tell me there's others all of a sudden? What the hell is going on out there? The end of the world?"

Michael headed toward the bedroom door, aiming to find his place on the front porch with a beer and his cigar. "Hold up," he stopped himself and turned back to his wife. "What do mean she wishes she was like the other women, *terminating* their pregnancies?"

"She said it would make things easier."

"What? She said what?" He began to see red.

"I didn't mean it like that!" Maria shouted from behind the door, after eavesdropping on all of Amelia's gossip. Michael opened the door to reveal his frustrated sister. "I just said something along the lines of 'ignorance is bliss.' I don't know why she took me so seriously."

"Give me a break," Amelia interjected bitterly rolling her eyes.

"Maybe you should be more thankful, sis. You shouldn't say such things," Michael suggested, knowing that he ultimately had no other option than to defend his wife. *Husbands who die happy men defend their wives, right or wrong,* he reminded himself silently.

"Shut the hell up, Michael! What do you know? You play around all day working on panels. Ain't like Unity is coming for *your* balls." Michael's rush to defend Amelia stung Maria even though she knew it shouldn't.

"Guys, stop it. Please," John begged the trio, appearing from the shadows of the hallway outside the room. He stepped into the doorway, presenting a screen to them. "The talking heads are speculating. They're aware that there's a possibility of some women wanting to continue their pregnancies and keep their babies."

"Yeah? What are they saying?" Michael wondered.

"Watch the broadcast. They're suggesting that Unity won't allow it," John explained, clearly agitated, "and that there would be consequences for such women as well as anyone else who stood in the way. They're mailing approved birth control methods to every household with a mandate that all women use it in order to remain in Unity's graces."

"Oh, my God," interjected Amelia, covering her mouth with her hand.

"We need to get out of here while we have time," John spoke directly to his wife, a barely detectable edge to his tone.

"But then what, John? We'll have to spend our entire lives hiding our child. It's no way to live."

"Honey," he addressed her quietly, placing the tablet down and taking her into his arms, "it's never quite as bad as it seems. We will be okay. God will be with us."

Maria's darkest feelings and fears spilled from her eyes in the form of huge droplets of tears, fully unleashed and raining down upon the shoulders of the strong, thick man who held her. She felt disembodied, as if the world were nothing but a figment of her own creation, a simulation of awful thoughts and imaginings crowded in the darkest corners of her mind. She squeezed her eyes shut, and continued to weep.

"Sis, we'll go with you both," came an abrupt, unexpected promise from her brother, Michael.

"You guys can't leave your home and jobs like that." John sighed, shaking his head in shock at the proposition.

"Yeah, Mikey, what are you thinking?" inquired Amelia, irritated and in disbelief that he said they'd flee along with them. *Seriously, I'm gonna have a talk with him in private. He didn't even talk to me about it first!*

Obviously, he spoke out of turn. We're not going! No way I can stand having to continue dealing with Maria.

"What's the point of staying here? There's nothing for us here. Only depression and waste outside our doors and to top it all off, there's that damn supercomputer, controlling our every waking moment with aid from the hordes of hell. And last but not least, I'm not letting you two go without us. We're a family. As torn as we've been the past couple months, our solidarity is the only thing that matters.

We need each other," Michael pleaded, for once unleashing the insurmountable pain that had been festering in him all-along. "I refuse to lose any more family. I refuse it. I won't let it happen. Screw this house and town." His eyes sparkled in the light, watering slightly. He was beyond resisting a display of his sadness any longer. He showed his emotions every once in a while, though typically only when he'd been drinking. This was different.

"Okay, honey," Amelia relented. She conceded that there really wasn't anything for them there. Business was dwindling away and if she ever did conceive a child, they'd have to leave anyway.

"I'm sorry for offending you earlier, Amelia," came a mumbled apology from Maria. She departed her husband's embrace to move beside her sister-in-law's seat. "It's just been tough lately and I know it shouldn't be a big deal, but I can't drink anything, being pregnant and all. It's miserable watching everyone else have a drink -- or four -- while I'm stuck sipping on water or juice."

"No, forgive me, darling. It's truly my fault. I should have been more understanding. You have the entire weight of the world on your shoulders. I allowed my own personal pain to rush me in judging you so harshly. I know you're nothing like those women. You're strong."

"But, I shouldn't have even thought such horrible things. I'll never forgive myself for saying such awful words," lamented Maria, thinking of the child she'd have one day. She envisioned a girl trotting through a meadow with flowers in her hair and a beautifully innocent smile. The thought of destroying this wondrous gift of creation, growing inside of her, regardless of the many hardships they may endure because of it filled her heart with sorrow.

"Both doctors warned you'd have mood swings. It's probably just that, love." John's deep, reassuring voice sounded from across the room.

"What about me? What about my brother?" Cole jumped in, making his presence known as he stood in the doorway. He heard everything the two married couples discussed and debated, having been there all along keeping his silence. The time for silence and discretion ended when Cole realized all four of them planned to leave and, seemingly, without one thought about him or Stone.

"Oh, Cole," Michael felt shame wash over him and still unsure of Stone's status, he lied, "I promise we haven't forgotten about you." He knew full well that his abrupt promise about fleeing south with the other couple included zero consideration of the young man's fate, or that of his Zealot brother.

"Well? What of my brother as well? I can't just leave him here."

"Haven't you been in contact with him?" Amelia asked, hoping to help formulate a plan.

"I was, but I think I've upset him. Again." He shook his head as he dropped his gaze to pick at his nails.

"What?" Just then it dawned on Michael that the boy had secrets that he needed to share. "What do you mean? You've been talking to him? Where is he? Is he okay?" The questions flooded out of Michael simultaneously, it seemed; each one spilling forth after the other without pauses or breaths.

"Yes. I had lunch with him recently on the same day authorities raided that Zealot workshop."

"Not since?"

"No." Cole silently remembered the many fears he had suppressed after seeing the news the other day. The sight of his brother's back shrinking angrily in the distance came to his mind. "I pissed him off for not sharing the reason that Maria and John were leaving."

"Did you tell him anything? Did you tell him where they were going?"

"Mikey, I highly doubt Stone would ever rat them out to anyone," Amelia interrupted her husband, knowing the fear he was chasing down. "You're the one he's angry with."

"That's not quite my point. I mean, if anyone who cared somehow got the information from him, without his realization, it'll turn out badly. Like the department, for example. If they had gotten ahold of him -- you know the other side of the family?" he explained to jog his wife's memory. "Isaac? Simp's the one that killed the Zealots at the workshop."

"We have family in the department?" Cole asked quizzically. He'd not heard anything of the sort before.

"You don't. Maria and I do. On our father's side."

"I didn't know that."

"And that's why you gotta start being more careful, buddy. We can't afford mistakes," Michael warned.

"I understand."

"Do you think you could talk him into leaving with us?"

"Ain't a chance in hell. He's still very upset with you." Cole wondered whether he should let any more information slip from his lips. "And he may or may not have become a Zealot's knight."

"What?" Maria yelled, her brother's mouth only hung open, gaping in disbelief.

"He's got like five crosses or something burned into his arm. He showed it to me. He's really getting serious about it."

Michael knew all about the markings Cole described. News articles and broadcasts frequently displayed them to inform the public. He knew they were the mark of a true Zealot, someone who had made his way into the inner circle.

"And you didn't think to say anything until now?" Michael fumed, his voice clearly approaching an angry tone. He turned away from everyone with his hand to his face, struggling to come to terms with the news.

"I didn't know that it was such a big deal." *I thought it was stupid, allowing oneself to get permanently branded like that, but...* his thoughts trailed off as Michael continued.

"Of course, it is, Cole! What the hell did you think? That he's just playing around, getting a brand on his arm?"

"I don't know," Cole's words came out as a whisper and he shrugged. His face turned red with embarrassment, which flooded over him as he suddenly saw his stupidity.

"Give him a call and convince him to meet up somewhere," ordered Michael.

"I don't think he will now. He's probably just as angry with me as he is with you."

"That's fine. Just act like you're sorry. I don't know, tell him you were wrong. Then, once he forgives you, ask him to meet."

"And then what?"

"I'm going to be there. If he won't come to me, I'll go to him."

"Michael, baby, that doesn't make any sense," his wife interrupted, still unsure of his plan. It seemed poorly thought out.

"I need to apologize to him somehow. Hopefully save him from these stupid ass decisions he's making. The idiot. The freaking idiot."

"Michael, you can't go. Listen to yourself. You're still angry with him. You're only going to drive him further away from his brother, our family." Her husband turned away and tried to find comfort in the crucifix on their bedroom dresser. It had medals and rosaries wrapped over it. He appeared to pray, his lips moving soundlessly.

"Maybe, we should go instead, since we're the ones Cole said were leaving," suggested Maria, wondering if it would even be safe. The idea of meeting with a Zealot, even if he were her cousin, made her uneasy.

"It's risky," John answered in Michael's stead, "all things considered."

"It could be real quick, plus it's not as if we're seeing his face on the news. It's still just that same Asian chick. Also, with the whole pregnancy craze, I doubt anyone's even thinking about Zealots tonight."

"The fact that you're one of the pregnant women, should be one of the reasons you don't go. It's too risky, darling." John stared hard at his wife.

"It's not like they're just testing anyone and everyone on the spot. I could always pretend that I'm headed to the facility if anyone causes us any trouble." John clearly did not find comfort in her rationalization as he imagined the odds stacked against them. He sat back on the bed, hoping that some kind of idea would come to him.

"You should all go to meet up with him," Michael spoke up for John this time. Turning away from the crucifix, he continued, "I'll stay here. The more of you the better and Amelia can speak on my behalf."

"Do you think he'll actually leave with us? To the farm?" Cole wondered hopefully, but no one answered him. The absence of any response troubled him and the realization that he'd be saying good-bye to his brother made itself very evident in the heavy sound of silence.

He left the bedroom and made his way to his own. The bunk-bed's bottom half hadn't been occupied in quite a while; its sheets remained perfectly clean and stretched neatly upon the mattress. Amelia had put clean bed linens on all the beds shortly after Stone's fight with Michael.

Its neat and wrinkle-free look was far different than Stone kept it, when he was there. The clean and empty sleeping area appeared cold and sterile now. Cole stood there, looking over it, in an attempt to convince himself that it wouldn't be like this forever; that he'd say good-bye and would one day return for his brother. Cole was smarter than that. He called his brother as he laid down in the neatly made bed.

"Hey, buddy..."

CHAPTER TEN

Jeremy worked assembling explosives at his workshop for the majority of every day. He left before first light and returned to his apartment long after the sun's last rays dipped beneath the horizon. Lately, Stone's mind roiled with conflicting thoughts and desires. He wanted to help Jeremy in the workshop, but a part of him aspired to act as Debra's 'errand boy' for the rest of his days. It was no easy task to constantly do her bidding. She couldn't leave the apartment and risk arrest. So, out Stone went to fetch various items from different stores for the girl. It was like a full-time job.

He found her beautiful, but not as he found most every other woman beautiful. She was a Zealot -- a gorgeous Zealot-- full of energy and passion. She wasn't empty or shallow; she didn't have simple dreams either.

He wanted to experience every part of her mind, even as every inch of her physical person called out to him: from the smoothness of her tan skin to her full dark red lips that shared the stories she collected over the years. Still, he was smart enough to realize he couldn't have her in the way he desired once he heard that she and Jeremy had something more than friendship between them.

...

Contrary to his former custom, Stone arose early each day, since his cloistered friend tended to be an early riser.

"Good morning, Debra," Stone greeted her, seeing she was already in the living room reading a book. He felt a wash of relief that this time, at least, she wasn't conferencing with Nelson. Something about her talks with Nelson bothered him. And the fact that the AI persona had a likeable personality that made Debra laugh more often than he had wasn't the only reason.

"Hey, Stoney, you sleep well?" she asked, looking over the black-framed glasses she wore on occasion when reading. Before life became immersed in all things digital, Stone heard that it was extremely rare for people under the age of, say, 50 to need glasses for reading. But that wasn't the case these days. Even though Debra had less than five years on Stone, she needed the readers to avoid undue eyestrain, which often led to brutal headaches. Sitting behind a digital screen most of her life took its toll on her beautiful green eyes.

"Yeah, had amazing dreams," he misspoke, immediately realizing he had no desire to share them, since their subject matter involved her, "er...that I was flying," he recovered nicely.

"Sounds wonderful." Debra didn't care to discuss her dreams. Ever since she was a very young child, the same hellish nightmare visited her as she slumbered. Though the night terror sometimes involved varying places and people, one thing always happened: the places and people burned at the end. She never awoke during these episodes the way most people do. The lingering singe from this recurring theme affected her subconscious for so long, she became a heavier sleeper, living every terrible moment almost every night.

"You have any dreams?"

"No, not that I remember."

"You can train yourself to remember them. My brother taught me. He's a little genius, really into that sort of stuff."

"I prefer not to remember them," she rebuked bluntly, not wanting to dwell on the horrors of her mind's nightly dreamstate any longer.

"Ah, well...my brother felt the same way once upon a time. But then he learned to control them. He used to have nightmares all the time, usually having to do with our mom, so he learned how to stop them."

"Have you spoken to him?" she asked, changing the subject.

"He called me a couple times last night, but I didn't answer." Cole had been calling him to arrange the meeting he and his family discussed earlier. He left a few voicemails, which sat unopened in Stone's Auris mailbox.

Debra got up from the couch to join him in the kitchen. She reached up into the cabinet and poured some cinnamon toast flavored cereal into one of the miss-matched bowls Jeremy had collected. Stone poured almond milk into her bowl for her, then poured it into his own bowl, only then emptying the small portion of cereal left for him into it. "You pour milk before cereal?" She let out a barely audible giggle.

"Umm, there's no other way to do it!" Stone said, defending his bizarre method of breaking his fast when preparing cereal. "Besides, it's not even really milk. It's essentially almond juice. They just want you to think it's milk." He made air quotes with the first two fingers of each hand as he said the word 'they'.

"I've never seen anyone do it that way before and I'm starting to wish I had gone the rest of my life without seeing it." With this, Debra truly let out an audible giggle, shaking her head in feigned pity.

"Hey, don't be mean," he retorted, wearing an obviously fake frown as he munched the mostly stale cereal floating atop the milk. "Have you ever had real milk?"

"From a cow?"

"Uh, yeah? Where else would it come from?"

"A goat...a sheep...or a camel...maybe a water buffalo," she offered, raising her eyebrows and nodding smartly.

"Half of those are extinct and sounds disgusting anyway." He laughed. "I hope, for your sake, you haven't had any from one of those."

"I think when I was young I might have had milk once," she answered, straining to remember the occasion, "but, now that I think about it, I doubt it was the real stuff." She looked down as she rounded up the last bites of floating cereal squares with her spoon, savoring the cinnamon flavor.

"Neither have I." Stone gazed into her warm green eyes. It was almost as if he could feel his own pupils widening in an attempt to receive all the details of her image at once. It created a slight stinging sensation in his vision, but his heart pumped with joy. The eye contact made him suddenly shy, forcing him to look away at once. "You're not like I thought you were when we first met."

"What do you mean?" She laughed nervously. "I hope that isn't a bad thing!"

"Neh, it's good, I promise. You're just not 'all business' like I thought you were. You seem very caring. Just all around pleasant to have around."

"Aw, that's so sweet." She giggled, then quietly, "I'm sorry I made such a horrible first impression."

"No! You weren't horrible. I liked you then too. I just like the Debra I've come to know more. Things got overly bleak around here sometimes. You know, when it was just me and Jeremy. It's nice having you around."

"Well I'm glad to lighten the mood in my time of sanctuary. Or, on second thought, is it captivity?" Her voice had a hint of sarcasm to it. "I think I may have an errand for you," she quipped, before drinking the sugary almond milk directly from the bowl.

"Yeah? What now, more nail polish?"

"Very funny." She rolled her eyes at Stone's playful comment. She never painted her nails these days. Figured it required too much maintenance. The constant chipping, then cleaning, then repolishing infuriated her when she tried it as a teen. Never again, she promised herself when she turned nineteen.

"Well, what is it then?" He felt excited to have an opportunity to do something for her so early in the day.

"I want you to do something for yourself and I hope you don't mind me saying it."

"What do you mean?" He was truly confused. *I thought she just said, like seconds ago, that she had an errand for me. What could this girl possibly gain from something I do for myself?* Stone strained to think of the answer. *What's she after?*

"Promise not to get angry?" she inquired cocked her head slightly to one side, in a way that seemed almost coy.

"What is it, woman?" He laughed nervously.

"I think you should talk to your brother."

Stone didn't say anything, shocked that she mentioned Cole. Surely, he didn't hear her right. Then asking himself, *Why would she care? Why would my relationship with my brother mean anything to her?*

"You're angry, aren't you?" She searched him with her eyes, noticing he had stopped his munching and began silently cleaning up his mess. His face now appeared flat and empty of expression.

"No," he sighed. It was impossible for him to be angry with her at this point. If anything, he was still angry at his brother. Maybe he was biased, but he found her to be a delightful creature, incapable of offending him. Taking a breath, he continued, "Why do you think I should call him?"

She finally brought her eyes up from her empty bowl to lock with Stone's brown ones. He leaned casually against the countertop, but gestured with his free right arm when talking. Debra could see that the Jerusalem cross brand was fully healed. She hadn't seen it since the night they burned it into his flesh. Oddly, a ray of sunlight strayed through the filthy window nearest him, illuminating the branding almost as if by design. The hint of a smile became visible upon her face as she came up with an explanation to offer him.

"We're family now," she confided, motioning with her hand, "and all of us depend on each other. We trust each other."

"Yeah?" *This is beginning to get interesting,* Stone admitted interiorly.

"But you have something that the rest of us don't. You still have your blood, your kin." He looked down onto the branding himself, the sunlight didn't burn it, for once. Totally healed, he felt no pain at the site. "As much as they may piss you off, you should try your hardest to love them. Because, you *will not* have the opportunity forever, honey, and when that day comes you'll not only mourn the loss of them, but you'll also mourn the time wasted while they were still around and you allowed your anger to keep you away."

"I guess," he conceded, now looking down.

"Believe me, sweetie, people will vanish from your life. They usually disappear due to no fault of you own, but if that happens, it'll help to know you tried."

"I understand. I'll get to it soon," he promised, unconvincingly, as he remembered the fight. The mere thought of Michael's face used to make his blood boil; but, suddenly, that morning, the resentment was gone. The memory of what transpired still stirred up negative emotions, but his hatred for Michael had dissipated over the time spent apart.

...

The two of them made themselves comfortable in the living room and powered on the television. The screen lit up, already on the news station., as color reemerged from the wall to reveal the headlines and news anchors who talked to inform them of what they didn't know. The fact that so many people sheepishly trusted someone to read teleprompters disgusted Stone, as his mind searched for distractions to blot out the thought of contacting Cole.

"Fake experts and real liars. They act like they know anything at all about what they're saying and everyone just buys it. No questions asked. Their two cents is the golden standard and everyone eats it up, blindly." His tone dripped with biting sarcasm.

"What do you think about the pregnancy stuff?" she asked him.

"Think it's awesome! It's just what we need to happen, isn't it?" No sarcasm or bitterness in his tone now.

"How do you think it happened?"

"I don't have the slightest clue. God? Or maybe the Retrogrades did it. I mean they're supposedly anti-science, but they have proven otherwise when it comes to actually getting involved."

"Hm, the Retrogrades, I hadn't thought of that," mused Debra, her thoughts firing rapidly in her head.

"How come we've never formed an alliance with them?"

"They don't like Catholics."

"Who does, these days? I mean, the enemy of my enemy and all that..." Stone laughed as he thought of the world and the fact that it was filled with people who loathed them for their faith.

"Firstly, enemy of my enemy isn't the way to go...ever. Secondly, They're afraid of what might happen if Catholic leaders ever took Unity's place."

From the beginning, the Retrogrades were always very vocal about their hatred for the Pope and for Catholics in general, referencing wounds and slights incurred a thousand years ago, under the rule of a different people and even when different stars hung in the sky. The past, as all human history must, included some lengthy periods of bloodshed and cruelty and the Retrogrades sought to stamp out any possibility of it happening again. The thought of any possibility of a future ruled by the Vatican -- a theocratic state -- terrified them. Stone curled up in a blanket as he bared his views, "We're so weak these days. I don't see what they have to fear, honestly. There are hardly any of us left."

"There's a lot more of us than you think. Always remember that. A persecuted people are often very good at staying quiet."

Then, like the sun blazing its way through a clouded horizon, an epiphany flowed over and through Stone's thoughts. The sudden realization pierced through every molecule of his existence. "My God!" he exclaimed. He quickly jumped to his feet, which freaked Debra out, "She's pregnant."

"Who is?" It was Debra's turn to bear a look of confusion.

"That's gotta be the reason they're leaving -- why my bastard of a brother was so secretive. It all makes perfect sense now."

"You think your cousin is pregnant?"

"I don't know. I mean, it's the only thing I can think of. Of course, they'd leave. And of course, Cole would act all sketchy and everything."

"Are you going to call him then?" Debra pressed.

"He left a voicemail that I haven't opened yet. I'll give it a listen, hang on."

Stone gestured for his inbox, displayed by his Visum, in a way that might look like an attempt to cast some sort of spell by anyone without knowledge of how the implants worked. If Debra had time-traveled, just now, from several decades ago, the sight would probably make her roll on the floor in uncontrollable laughter. He tossed and turned his hand rapidly in the air, cycling through the options until he found and pressed the *listen* button underneath Cole's name. He shared the voicemail, connecting to Debra's Auris. They both listened carefully to the voicemail; listening for any possible clues to what was happening.

"Hey, buddy. I hope all's well. I just wanted to let you know that you're in all of our prayers." His voice resonated with deep sincerity. Stone hoped he didn't mention anything specific as the message wasn't encrypted. "I wanted to tell you that Michael and Amelia are talking about leaving along with John and Maria. If they do, I'd have to go with them, but I really don't want to leave without seeing you and saying goodbye. I know you're probably still avoiding me after the other day, but please know I'm real sorry and that I love you. Please call me back whenever you receive this. Love you."

"Call him!" Debra shouted from the couch. Her sudden rise in volume and the shrill pitch terrified Jeremy's cat. Charlie, the enormously fat beast, scurried across the living room carpet frantically searching for a new refuge from the terrifying woman.

"I don't know what to say. I mean, of course I'll meet him if it comes to that. Do you think it's the whole pregnancy thing? You think both the women are pregnant?"

"I heard the same message as you, Stone. I don't know. But I want to know!" She spoke excitedly, her joy causing a sort of transformation of the dismal downstairs apartment that currently imprisoned her. Prior to Stone's dramatic revelation, the television supplied her only hope for entertainment and excitement. "Just give him a call, please. Don't say anything too sensitive."

"Of course not."

"Hurry!"

"Chill, you're stressing me out. I don't know what to say."

"Say anything." Debra wished so badly that she could press dial, having seen the old movies where people did such a thing to force people into talking. Many scenes flashed in her mind's eye: The girl who was too afraid to call the boy she liked, or the scene in which a man's wife forced him to call his mother and make amends. *It would be so perfect for this situation, if we still used handheld phones,* she thought.

...

"*Ring...ring...ring...*" the Auris purred, waiting for an answer from the other end.

"Stone?"

"Hey, man..." Stone started, notifying Debra that Cole answered, sharing the phone call with her as well. The words awkwardly made their way from his mouth, unsure of where to place themselves. "What's, uh, what's going on?"

"I'm so happy to hear from you."

"Yeah, what's going on?"

"I'm sorry for being so anxious. I'm a bit paranoid, so can we meet in person to talk? I won't bring anyone else if you want it to be just the two of us." Cole knew his family would be angry if he met with his brother alone, but he didn't want to overwhelm Stone, especially if it were his last chance to see him.

"I'll come to the house," Stone spoke with certainty, thinking of Debra's advice from earlier. He figured his brave attempt at healing the wounds had a good chance of impressing her and he also didn't want to miss the opportunity. She had been right after all.

"Hmm," Cole vocalized his thinking, wondering if that would cause a problem for the others in the house. Surely having a Zealot visit isn't a safe thing for anyone, but especially not for them at such a time. "I don't know man, I'd really love that, but I'll have to check with everyone."

"Fine." Stone's heart fell from his chest after hearing Cole's words. He felt like a stray dog being shooed off from his own family.

"I'll call you back in a minute."

"Great." Stone waited for the call to end, the gradient image of Cole's face within his Visum faded, and he was free to confide with Debra. "I just don't understand them. They act like I'm some sort of monster. Like I have a disease or something."

"They just seem like peace-loving people to me, sweetie." Debra rubbed his back, the friction created exceptional warmth. "They're probably afraid of Unity, really. I don't think you're actually the one they don't trust. It's just the fact that they know you associate with people like me."

"Like you? You're no monster either, though."

"But my face is all over the news these days. If your theory about the pregnancy is true, you can't hold that against them. They have a lot to protect and a lot to lose."

In the past, Stone never understood why everything always seemed so unclear to him. He spent most of his life unable to comprehend his interactions with others.

Yet, Debra made things seem so reasonable with no perceptible effort whatsoever. She seemed capable of healing his every problem, every wound. Her insight sliced through his furious haziness like rays of light through the dreariness of an overcast day. The hand that rubbed his back filled him with warmth as the emotional coldness wore away. She was a healer, more so than any doctor he ever knew.

"Thank you, Debs," he said, looking back to smile at her. "I don't understand you."

"I didn't think my engrish that bad," she joked, her accent normally full-on southern.

"No, I mean, I don't understand how you're able to help me like this. It doesn't make any sense. There's a manhunt underway for you, yet here you are, fixing all of my drama with a smile on your face. You're aware that you're a fugitive, aren't you?" He laughed uncomfortably.

"Oh, well, it was bound to happen eventually. I'm just upset that my friends didn't make it out with me. It's not so bad being stuck down here. It's like you said. It's been pretty bleak, but it's not so bad with you around."

Is she flirting with me? Stone wondered, his heart pounded the same question in Morse code within his chest. Of all the skirts he chased in his all-nighter partying days, not one of them made him feel the way Debra did. Compared to this, all the dirty talk and breathless lusty attraction he enjoyed back then suddenly became pointless. *This is what everyone meant when they talked of real love.* This -- this is the type of connection he had craved his entire life. Only now did he fully understand that he spent all that time wasting and wasted. Debra was as a lighthouse to him; a beacon of hope.

The two of them stared at one another, but a sudden ringing from Stone's Auris broke the spell.

"They don't think it's safe to meet at the house," Cole's voice sounded soft, saddened to deliver the news, "but they'd love to meet you somewhere else. I'm sorry, bro."

"That's okay," he said with a new confidence -- a strange self-assuredness came over him, and looking again at Debra, he continued, "where and when, buddy?"

"Saturday, at four o'clock. We can meet at Ruffner Mountain. Make sure to dress as if you're going for a run and we'll find a good place off the trail."

The plan seemed overkill to Stone, but he'd honor it nonetheless. He resolved to do whatever it takes to see his family again. Debra's words only opened him to interior desires already present, but were obscured as long as he persisted in focusing on his hatred for Michael. "I'll be there." The call ended abruptly. Stone sighed and reclined into the back of the couch. A swirl of possibilities filled his imagination; some were frightening, but many were uplifting. His head began to throb as he attempted to deal with the tangle of emotions this caused.

"Need anything else from me, Debbie?"

"Yeah. Promise me you'll never call me that again."

CHAPTER ELEVEN

Saturday, the day Stone and Cole planned to meet, arrived quickly. The family in Irondale were busy readying themselves, but Michael finished first and was already waiting for the others in the family room. He sat anxiously on the traditional roll-arm English sofa, which stretched almost across the entire length of the wall. Second to finish, Cole sat stiffly on the other end.

Like all the others, Michael was eager to see Stone again, yet he felt extremely nervous. He wanted to smooth things over, but had yet to work out the best way to approach his rebellious cousin. On the one hand, he truly wanted to avoid anything that might reopen the wound caused by that dramatic fight; on the other hand, he didn't want his efforts to re-establish their relationship to somehow imply he supported Stone's bad decisions.

For weeks after Stone took off, Amelia and Maria berated Michael for his part in the drama. The two women teamed up to remind him, daily, that he was absolutely not to mention anything at all about Stone's poor choices during the meeting at Ruffner Mountain. During the short time they'd have with Stone, they hoped to convince him to leave Birmingham and flee south with the family, God willing. If their best efforts failed, they would say their goodbyes and move on. What else could they do?

"You good?" Cole asked his cousin, who sat still as a statue, staring into space, absentmindedly chewing his lower lip.

"Hmm?" Michael answered, his autopilot response giving a clear indication that Cole's question hadn't really registered with him. He was still thinking about the meeting and how best to handle his interaction with Stone.

"Michael, you hear me? Hey, *dinkis!*"

"No, what?" Michael finally looked in his young cousin's direction. He had been deep in thought. The sudden break from his reverie made him feel like a fish, rudely ripped from its cool watery home.

"Are you okay?" Cole laughed at him and noted, "You look tense as hell."

"Yeah, I'm good, buddy." Michael smiled. "Just thinking about today's plans."

"I think you'll be okay. Just good vibes, Mikey. We gotta show him we still care about him." Cole picked his nose.

"Better find a Kleenex. If I find another booger around here, I'll be showing you some of my 'good vibes,'" Michael then cracked his knuckles for effect.

"Michael!" one of the women called from upstairs. It was a softer voice, clearly not his sister's.

"Lord have mercy. What's this woman need now?" Michael stood from the couch and quickly made his way up the stairs, moving sideways as he passed John making his way down. "Yes, honey?" Michael asked at the summit of the staircase, waiting for his wife's response to reveal her location.

"Come here." Her voice, oddly, gave him no clue as to her whereabouts. The words she spoke seemed to come from thirty different directions, further agitating him.

"Where's here?"

"I'm on our bedroom floor."

He walked towards their room -- the last one on the right and opposite to John and Maria's. "Yes, boo?" he cooed, looking down at her, sitting cross-legged on the floor as she fixed her hair behind her head in a tight bun. Sunlight streamed through the window, illuminating her pretty face. He noticed many more small blemishes than usual on her chin and cheeks. *Hm,* he tried to remember the last time he knew her to be having her period. *Usually, she only breaks out a tiny bit during her monthly time.* As a fairly smart man, he knew better than to mention it, though.

"I'm ready."

"Okay? You called me up here to tell me you're ready?" Michael sighed with lighthearted laughter shaking his head.

"I was just thinking. What if we invite Stone to live here, while we're gone?"

Michael paused to arrange his thoughts before speaking. "First, he's a kid and he's got no income to support himself while living here. And, even if he does end up having any money, God only knows how he received it and by what means. If that weren't enough, he's a Zealot. If the authorities traced his activities here, they'd confiscate our property and then prosecute us as accessories to any associated crimes."

"I just feel kind of weird, asking the neighbors to watch over it. And it's not likely we'll return, really."

"It's going to serve as a place Father can celebrate Mass, so everyone in the neighborhood can continue to attend even while we're gone. They'll keep it in great shape for us."

Maria's voice shouted from the living room, urging them to hurry up and finish getting ready, but Michael and Amelia ignored her.

"There's no way we're coming back anytime soon, if we ever do. Think, what if I got pregnant too?"

"Future is unknown, love," he said, helping her to her feet.

"Why don't we just sell it?"

"Haven't we gone over this already? At least three times? Woman, you're driving me nuts!" he exclaimed good-naturedly. "We don't have time to prepare it for selling. And, we can't do something like sell our house, a house that's been in the family for generations, on the off chance that you might get pregnant too. Unlike most other couples our age, we don't have house payments. Why would we want to set ourselves up for that? Also, something else crossed my mind the other day. Wouldn't the realtor want to know why we're leaving so quickly? They'd have to make sure everything is up-to-date, including any potential pregnancy terminations. We can't put you or Maria in danger of that type of scrutiny."

"I don't know. It feels kind of weird to just leave it all behind."

"Well, maybe we can consider renting it out."

"Who would we rent to? Rent it out to the wrong people and the neighbors lose their place to go to Mass."

"Neighbors got kids -- kids that have grown a bit. Maybe they'd like a place to put their basement dwellers. I mean, Ronny -- Joseph and Anita's boy, he's what? Twenty?"

"So, you think a bunch of overgrown kids should live here? Place will burn down by the time we reached the end of the street."

"He's a man! Twenty is a man, honey. I think he and the others might do well here. I'm not sure why I didn't think of it before."

Amelia continued sitting on the floor hunched over her lap, whining, "This is our home though. We've worked so hard on it. How can we just leave?" Her nose sniffled, and to Michael's surprise, tears fell freely from her big, pretty eyes.

"Honey? It's going to be okay, darling. Hey," he said, kneeling beside her to rub her back, "it's all going to work out, babe." The sight of her upset deeply troubled him. She was always so stoic and typically hid her strongest emotions under the mask of cheerfulness. Her existence always seemed almost painless, until moments like these. It hurt him to see her in pain -- hurt him even worse when he couldn't comfort her.

"I'll be okay. I've just loved living here. I know Maria and the others can't stand this neighborhood, but I don't see it that way. I've put so much of myself in this place and spent so much time trying to make it nice for us, you know? It's what I'm good at -- making the best of things." She dried her eyes carefully, as to not ruin her freshly applied makeup.

"Are y'all about ready or what? Stone's gonna be there thinking we've stood him up. Let's go!" Maria shouted from the hallway, just beyond the half-opened door to their room.

"Is she okay?" she asked, peeking in and noticing Michael's posture, hovering over her on the floor.

"I'm good!" Amelia forced a smile, "I'm ready, too. Is the cab here?"

"Yes. Got here about five minutes ago. I tried calling for y'all, but neither of you heard, apparently," she rolled her eyes in obvious sarcasm.

"Ah, well it's not like we live next door to the mountain or anything," Michael retorted with light-hearted sarcasm aimed at his sister. He helped Amelia to her feet and they followed everyone outside and into the cab.

...

Just as he entered, his anxiety about the meeting returned with force. *I'll keep my promise to keep the peace,* he told himself interiorly, yet unwelcome emotions welled up inside him anyway. Weeks had passed since he had set eyes on Stone. The pressure to both remain civil, yet not send the false message that he agreed with Stone's Zealot activities threatened to open the battle wounds. He silently prayed for strength and an open heart.

Stone and Cole were like children to Michael; although, in actuality, they weren't too much younger than him. Still, that's how he thought of the boys. He rescued them from their perilous life -- an existence rife with betrayal, pain, and darkness. They endured it for too long, while growing up under their mother's roof. He didn't get to feed them Gerber's or change their diapers. He was only a child himself during that time. But, he did help them with homework and did his best to model true manhood for them. He introduced them to Christ, the Bread of Life, and to the faith that they were deeply involved in.

Stone's decision to join the Zealots brought him stabbing pain that never completely went away. Every time he thought about it, it made him wonder why -- *why did it turn out this way?* What had he done, or not done, to push Stone toward such ideas and beliefs? *It's all my fault*, he yelled at himself inside his head. *It's nobody's fault, but mine.*

Ironically, Cole was the exact opposite: pure, God-fearing, genuinely filled with charity and the will to help others, expecting nothing in return. Michael never witnessed any behavior from Cole that wasn't praiseworthy in some way. And Michael instinctively knew he couldn't take credit for it. Cole's sanctity was the God-given light of Christ, as many living on their block called him. The boy didn't have a violent bone in his body. Michael couldn't recall the last time, if ever, the teenager had acted in a fit of anger.

How could two, so close in age turn out so vastly different, he wondered. Cut from the same cloth -- yet one was silk, the other burlap. It made no sense to Michael and he pondered the mystery of it in the short cab ride, coming to no conclusion by the time they reached the mountain.

...

The car dropped them off at the foot of a steep incline covered with a mass of trees and stone. It was one of the last forested refuges of their city. It sat like a gleaming jewel surrounded by the sea of blue silicone

239

panels, which covered Irondale on their side of the mountain. Birds called from the leafless autumnal treetops, making beautiful, but loud unusual sounds never heard beneath the panels that concealed the neighborhoods where most people lived. Immediately, Cole's mind traveled back in time to hundreds of years ago as he struggled to soak it all in, the fresh outdoors he seldom visited.

"Where are we meeting him?" Michael asked as he caught up to the teen standing excitedly at the edge of the tree line.

"Stone said we should take the Ridge and Valley Trail," Cole pointed with his hand, "eastward for about a mile. Then we'll take a right and hike along The Crusher Trail until we get to the Mining Site. Said we should see him there."

"Ah, the Mining Site -- you remember the Mining Site, Maria?" Michael laughed.

"Yes." She answered quickly, uninterested in reliving the moment. As a child, she ran ahead of her family and climbed upon the entrance of the abandoned mine and then jumped down to enter it. Their dad never took them back to Ruffner Mountain.

"Dad wore your romp out for that. I mean, there were people jogging by and everything. Didn't care who saw." Michael laughed louder, recalling the memory. Maria made a rude hand gesture to her brother, which only made him laugh harder.

John and Amelia finally reached the three of them at the edge of the trail and the party of five began their hike through the woods. The trail was rocky and steep, with overgrowth blocking it in some areas. This caused Cole, inexperienced with outdoor activities, to trip on occasion. He had always been kind of klutzy and the lush forest trail only made this more apparent.

"So," Cole started, taking a deep breath, "how about this fresh air?" He tried to mimic the movies he had seen.

"Cole, there's nothing fresh about this air, bud," John corrected him, laughing. It was easy to smell the distinct, though distant, scent of lunch cooking at the restaurants near the mountain. "The Café is all I can smell."

"Does fresh air have a smell?"

Michael thought about that for a bit taking time to recall his father's adventures and their camping trips. "Smells like dirt, I think."

"Dirt?"

"I mean, yeah, whenever my dad asked if we could smell it, all I picked up on was dirt, maybe some trees, and possibly a carcass rotting in the heat. I'm not sure."

"No, no, no," John interjected, "fresh air is the *absence* of human odor. If you're deep enough in the woods, you won't smell food or emissions of any sort. No perfumes or anything, only the crisp wind off of the pines. And it's much more than the smell, it's the sounds...the sights. Tree limbs creaking against each other and foliage gently falling from above. Birds singing. Ground animals rustling in the bushes as you walk by. Authentic fresh air fills your every sense with its magnificent presence."

"Well, we'll all know soon enough," Cole grumbled, thinking of the trip way down south they planned to make.

"Hopefully so." Michael crossed his heart. He hated when people spoke with absolute certainty about the future. The trip down would be difficult and there was no predicting the sort of dangers or obstacles that might await them. *Cole's inability to see the roots and other debris before tripping over it is comparable to his ignorance about their impending road trip further south.* He crossed himself again as this awkward truth took shape.

Amelia and Maria's chatter followed the three men whose lead put them slightly ahead of the ladies by about a dozen feet. Maria complained about how tired she was, and about how she wished they had picked a better place to meet with their cousin. The woman's belly showed no noticeable bump yet, but since she chose to wear jeggings -- that's jean-leggings for the uninitiated, a highly observant person might detect a slightly noticeable protrusion from her lower abdomen, right where a pregnant woman's womb begins to first reveal its secret. John made her wear one of his hoodies, so it would loosely hang over her, in case any authorities, or a nosy busy-body saw her and became suspicious. She complained about the hoodie too, saying it reeked of her husband's sweat, since it was the one he recently wore to work.

"Girl, you're just a ball of unhappiness, aren't you?" He chuckled at the sight of her when he turned to look over his shoulder.

"Um, excuse me? I'm sorry...would you like to trade places? If I haven't had time to do it first, wash your putrid stinkin' clothes before you make me wear them!"

"I'm joking!"

"Mhm, we'll see how loud you're laughing from the couch tonight if you don't watch it."

"Enjoy it while it lasts, Mikey," John advised him quietly, leaning into his brother-in-law.

"Enjoy what?"

"Enjoy Amelia while you can. If, or when, she gets pregnant, you'll be a slave to her like you never imagined."

"Oh, I'm sure of it."

"You say so, but I'm telling you, you've no idea how many chores and errands you'll be sent on. Especially if she gets as sick as Maria. She'll send you everywhere. She'll crave things you've never known her to enjoy and make you return things she's always loved. It's a mini-hell, man. A mini-hell."

"Stop fussin'," Maria called him out sourly, she easily heard his loud whispers. The increased breathing rate from the hike made it nearly impossible for him to succeed in his attempts to whisper.

"Yeah, we can easily hear everything you're saying up there. Just warning you, you're on your own when this mama comes after you," Amelia chimed in with laughter, looking with a knowing expression at Maria.

Cole led on, following the map he pulled up in the HUB of his Visum. The lower right corner of his vision contained the map in the form of an augmented reality, showing their progress along the trail. It disappointed him to rely on such a thing, something so flawless -- a device that rendered many would-be challenges effortless. *I've never experienced the feeling of being lost,* he admitted in his personal silence. *Nothing I've done has ever forced me to trust my own gut.*

Before this age, people carefully observed changes in their surroundings. They gave names to the oddly shaped trees with their equally oddly shaped leaves that appeared along their paths. Cole did not. He carried on through the capabilities of his Visum. The more he thought about it, the more it disturbed him. *What's the point of life when one's path is not of their own deciding? When there's no chance discovery? No surprises?* He continued to ponder, completely enwrapped in his thoughts. The others kept up a steady stream of chatter since they first began hiking, but he heard almost none of it as he continued to contemplate the effect of these digital devices on the human experience, or rather human devices through a digital experience.

"Cole. Hello? Cole, buddy..." Michael called to the boy, over and over again in an attempt to snap him out of what looked like some sort of trance.

"Hm?" Cole responded, still not actually paying attention. Michael's words came and bounced off of his ears as if he wore sound-canceling shields over them.

"Cole!" Michael raised the volume of his voice a bit and slapped Cole's back lightly, startling him.

"What, Crazy?" Cole asked, his abrupt return to the present left him in a sort of fugue state.

"How much longer until we get there? I mean dang, we wanted somewhere discreet, but an expedition like this seems a little overkill."

Cole pointed ahead at the next fork in the trail. Michael could see a smaller path curving to the right and disappearing into a ravine littered with decomposing leaves and other natural debris.

"We'll take the path by the Maria-tree." He smiled at spontaneously coming up with such a fitting name -- he nodded toward an oak tree with a large burl bulging from its side.

"Ha!" Michael shouted, "Did you hear that ladies? Cole says this tree is called the *Maria-tree!*" He slid his fingers lightly across the warped bark covering the protruding hump.

"I don't look like anything like that," Maria retorted in a dismissive tone.

"Well...," he started.

"*Well*, what?"

"*Well*, you have to wear that monstrously baggy hoodie for a reason, sis," Michael pointed out, enjoying the opportunity to poke fun at his sister.

...

The Crusher Trail was considerably shorter than the first and the family of hikers could see the end fast approaching with each step. Despite Michael's veneer of good-natured humor, the anxiety from earlier rumbled underneath along with biting pangs of shame each time he remembered punching Stone that awful night.

In short order, Stone would be standing in front of him. He prayed he could manage to handle speaking with his cousin, hug him even, in a way that healed their relationship. The others were excited to see Stone again, and rightfully so, but he still wasn't quite sure how to proceed. An epiphany -- maybe true, maybe false -- suddenly came to Michael as they pressed ahead along the final trail. In a rush of clarity and self-awareness, he saw that his own out-of-control anger was the reason Stone left their family. Now, he could clearly see it was his intemperate and angry words, along with his wailing fists that drove the boy away from home -- and further into the darkness of the Zealots.

The five arrived and stood before the monstrous, rusty iron ore crusher, which towered beside a hill with its red skin looking alien and out of place in the surrounding environment. Viewing it from beneath, the group quietly studied its cone-shaped top. Long ago, rough men fed huge chunks of iron ore into its mouth-like opening so its jaws could crush it into much smaller pieces.

"I smell cigarette smoke," Maria sniffed at the air, frowning over the stench in utter disgust. "Good Lord, it's awful! Isn't it illegal to smoke in a park?" She asked to no one in particular. Maria clutched at her stomach with one hand and covered her nose with the ample sleeve of John's hoodie.

"I don't. Maybe it's just your imagination? Most people who come through here are joggers. Doubt anyone brought a pack of Reds with them." John squeezed her shoulders gently, hoping she wouldn't get sick from whatever she smelled. He sniffed again to see if he could smell any smoke as he wondered to himself about the minds of pregnant women -- actually, he wondered about the minds of *all* women, mysterious as they were.

"No, I smell it as well," Amelia declared, making a grimace, "and it's pretty strong. How can you not smell it?"

No one answered as they waited to catch sight of Stone along the trail they traveled down only minutes before. Crack. Crunch. Crackle. Leaves and twigs sounded from behind them. As they all turned in near unison, Stone appeared before them. He looked so different -- almost unrecognizable at first. Something had changed about him. Had he grown taller? Leaner?

Cut his hair differently? None of these things explained it, but that didn't diminish the fact that something had surely changed.

"Hey, guys," he greeted them awkwardly as he moved closer.

Unable to wait any longer, Maria half-jogged over to him for a hug, wrapping her arms around him entirely before he prepared himself. She jerked away from him immediately after catching his scent. He reeked of cigarettes.

"Ugh! When did you start smoking?" She made a face as she admonished him.

"Few weeks ago."

"Why? It's horrible for your health and makes you smell like a chimney sweep!" Of course, they didn't have chimney sweeps, so Stone couldn't fully relate to the comment. Maria was referring to a nest of baby birds that fell down to the bottom of their chimney one year, filling the living room with the stench of soot and ashes. They agreed not to move the nest and its avian babes, fearing it might cause the mother to reject them. The baby birds squeaked and chirped and hopped around until they learned to fly well enough to wing their way out to freedom.

"Yeah," Michael sympathized, "Amelia won't let me smoke a single cigar either. Haven't had a good night in weeks."

"Well, it's good for my mental health, at least!" Stone chuckled lightly, still buzzed from his last smoke. He approached the others, hugged Amelia, Cole, and John. Michael stood behind the group that encircled his cousin, awkwardly, not wanting to push too hard. "Michael," he greeted his older cousin, reaching between the others for his hand to pull himself closer, "how's it been goin' everyone?"

"Well, all things considered, not so bad. We've missed you very much, buddy." Michael meant it with all sincerity.

"You all look -- well." Stone studied both women, trying to confirm his suspicions that one or both were expecting. Maria laughed at his stare aimed directly at her stomach area, completely concealed by that baggy hoodie.

"I'm guessing you already know? Did Cole tell you?" Her inquisitive tone was tinged with a hint of disappointment. Every pregnant mother enjoys sharing the news with people who didn't know and she was no different.

"Cole didn't tell me anything. Really pissed me off because I knew he was keeping something from me. He kept your secret very well." Stone didn't tell her about his suspicions. He wanted her to confirm his theory verbally.

"Well, you *look* like you already know," Maria whined with a pouty look.

Cole quickly interjected, "I promise I didn't say anything to him. He refused to talk to me for a week because I refused to say anything! Anything he knows, he figured out himself."

"What's the news, then?" Stone stared at her face impatiently, motioning his hand in a circular fashion.

Maria looked around them, making sure that no hikers or joggers were close by, then revealed what he already knew, "I'm pregnant."

"I knew it!" Stone shouted excitedly, followed by laughter.

"Sh! Don't make a scene!"

"Well, I knew it. The whole *moving* thing. And are you too, Amelia?"

"No," she replied bluntly.

"No? I thought you said everyone was leaving, Cole?"

"We are," Michael confirmed, trying his best to sound sincere. "We're headed south and you are more than welcome to come with us."

"But why? For how long? What about the house?"

"We haven't sorted everything out yet, but we think it's best to stay together under these particular circumstances. I don't want to be a million miles away from Maria, in case she needs us; and, if Amelia were to get *pregnant* as well, I don't want to have to make excuses to others about yet another trip down. We all agree it's best if we travel together and get it out of the way."

"Where will you work? And where south? How far?"

"We don't know. At least until the baby arrives, I guess," Maria chimed in uneasily. "It's just not safe here.

Any day Unity, or more likely his human minions, might knock on our door and ask uncomfortable questions. And we aren't sure how far south. It's somewhere within the state borders, but Father Burns hasn't revealed an exact town or anything."

"Yeah," John added, "it's really in the boonies somewhere."

"I understand. It's dangerous in this city...*for now*." Stone said that last bit much more quietly than the first words. An abrupt sense of urgency about Unity and STORK and the imminent danger his family faced rushed upon him. He continued, "Frankly, I'm surprised y'all are still here."

"Well?" Maria asked her cousin, while he stood there scratching the stubble on his neck.

"Well what?"

Maria gave him one of her blank stares for a moment. The question begging an answer from Stone hung heavily in the air. Only a few golden rays of sunlight remained, the sky quickly darkened from pinks and oranges into deep reds and purples. Easing into a discussion about it was no longer an option.

"Will you come with us? We really don't want to leave without you, Stone"

"Man, y'all really want to get straight to business, aye?" He didn't know quite how to answer. Of all the questions right now, he absolutely didn't want to face this one. The entire predicament filled him with a sense of unease and he had no way to escape its clutch.

"We love you, buddy," Michael assured him. He reached out and gave Stone a fatherly pat on the shoulder.

"I need to think for a sec," he stepped away, pacing to and fro in the leaves. Thinking hard. Thinking fast.

After about a minute of silence, he spoke to his family, "It's complicated, guys. Can't you see, now?" His voice choked as he struggled to push his emotions down. "Things are different now. And I'm not sure how to answer y'all."

"Just come with us, please. Just leave them. Leave it all and travel with us!" Maria begged, her emotions mirroring his.

"Stone, there's no telling how long we'll be gone. And we'll likely not have any contact once we get to where we're headed," Michael urged him, leaning against a boulder near the mine's sealed-off entrance in an attempt to seem casual. "They're very strict about communicating to the outside world."

"He's telling the truth," Amelia chimed in, "and there's no telling when, or if, you'll hear from us."

Stone slapped his pack of cigarettes against his hand and selected the last smoke that had flipped upside down. It was his lucky cigarette, or so he believed, the silver lining to an empty pack. He held it between his stammering lips and covered the flame as he lit it, which illuminated the tears upon his cheeks. "I'm sorry Maria. I'm just going to stand over here," he said, finding a place downwind from her.

"Well? Don't ignore the question. We need an answer." Cole couldn't conceal his impatience, as he watched his brother exhale the smoke that danced into the swirling air above.

"I don't know."

"You've gotta give us a definitive answer."

"I can't go," Stone uttered the dreaded words and wiped his tears away. "I've gotta stay for just a while longer, at least."

"Why? What for?"

Stone looked at his brother and glanced away, unable and unwilling to divulge the Zealot group's plans. "I can't say." He took several quick puffs from the cigarette, making the cherry at its tip glow brightly.

"Stone!" Maria shouted at the boy, uncovering her face momentarily. "Please just quit this! Please! I'm begging you, please come with us."

The cigarette burned down to the cotton and he took one last hit before extinguishing it with his foot into the soggy leaves carpeting the ground. He lowered his face into his hands and rubbed at his hairline. "I want the best for Maria and all the other women in her shoes. That's why I absolutely must stay here."

"If this is about protecting her, Stone, you can still do that." Michael shook his head, withholding all traces of anger that Stone's stubbornness aroused in him, explaining, "You can protect her by traveling with us."

"There are bigger things in motion, guys. It's a war -- it's a war now and we're trying to destroy them. I know how y'all feel about all of it. I know you guys think I'm a terrorist and that the people I run with are savages, but I promise to God we are doing it for you. We're doing it for all of you. And it's not easy, but I have a duty to them now. I'm simply unable to just leave."

"You don't owe them anything."

Stone meditated while Michael's words flowed into one ear and out the other. All he could think of was his love for Debra and the coming plans they had all devised together. The plan they came up with for the local STORK clinics. The bombs. The mark upon his right arm. It was Debra, however, who stoked the fires of his deepest loyalty. *If not for her*, he thought, *it would be much simpler for me to leave. I need to stay for her, to protect her and keep her company, especially while she's still confined to that depressing apartment.* The thought of leaving her behind shattered him and the fear of losing his family stomped upon the pieces.

"...are you listening to me?"

"I can't!" he yelled, his echo passing through the valley and hills of Ruffner Mountain. "Please, guys I can't!" Maria began weeping as his voice still resonated, bouncing off hills and boulders.

"The longer you work with them, the more risk you put us all in. If you've got something coming up -- a mission of sorts, I assume -- then I'm not sure you could ever join us." Michael couldn't think of a better wording for the ultimatum. "I'm not trying to push you away or anything, believe me. I want nothing more than for you to travel with us. I'm only saying that if your activities result in your becoming of special interest to authorities, it's not going to be a good idea for you to join us down south in the event you feel free to leave your partners."

"Sun's getting low, guys," John observed, comforting his wife by squeezing her close.

"Is this goodbye then?" Stone asked as everyone stood from the rocks they were sitting on.

"We can't force you to come with us. You're your own now, man." Michael grabbed him by the shoulders. "It's an absolute shame, but you make your own decisions. And if you *can't* come with us, then that's that. I just hope to see you again."

Stone realized, finally, that this very well could be the last time he and his family ever saw one another again. The short meeting hadn't given him enough time to digest it all and really think things through. He didn't know if the decision he made was the wisest. Leaving south with them would plague his imagination with thoughts of: what could have been. The choice to leave or stay wasn't so simple for him. He needed to see his mission through. He began sobbing in Michael's embrace, "I love you guys. I love you all, but I just can't. I really can't."

He withdrew from his cousin and hugged Cole tightly, still sobbing, "I love you too, buddy. This isn't the last we'll see of each other, I promise..." He stopped himself from speaking any more about the future.

"I *know* this isn't the last we'll see of each other. I love you, bro," Cole's response was muffled under the near bone-cracking pressure of Stone's prolonged hug.

"I'm really going to miss you, Stone," Maria told her cousin, approaching him with her nose still covered. Amelia and John said their farewells last and began to depart from the Mining Site, all of them discouraged.

"I'm going to miss all of you," he now spoke in a softer tone, discreetly wiping a tear from his eye.

"Take care of yourself, Stoney," Michael said before turning away with the rest of them.

"I'll catch up with you guys in just a second," Cole called to the others as they marched on. Then reminded them, "Take a left at the top of the hill." The sun's light rapidly melting away and the trees began to look black against the dark violet-indigo sky.

"Don't take too long," Michael called back over his shoulder.

Once they were just far enough along the trail, Cole turned back to his brother. "I've brought something for you, in case you decided to stay."

"What is it?" Stone's voice filled with intrigue.

Cole slung his backpack off his shoulder and unzipped the side of it. "It's a painting. Thought you'd appreciate it. No one else in the family wants to see it hanging up anywhere." He laughed and handed over a rolled canvas, "But I know you've always appreciated my darker art."

"Oh! Of course, buddy!" Stone unrolled the canvas to reveal the painting.

It was a colorful piece depicting a woman, engulfed in flames. The Angel of Death, manifested under the appearance of smoke and foul air, led her away by the hand. The right side of the painting depicted quite the opposite type of scene. In it, Stone saw an angelic being, covered in shimmering gold that outshined even the flames consuming the woman. This being nursed a human baby.

"Wow, it's amazing. Thank you. Thank you so much." Stone hugged him once again, then repeated his feelings from earlier, "I'm going to miss you so much, man."

"I'll find some way to stay in touch. Keep an eye out. Might use an alias, but you'll know it's me when you see it." Cole studied his brother's face, the last he would see of it for an uncertain length of time. His brother had thickened up since their last meeting, making Cole wonder how much more he would change by the time they saw each other again. Such moments were precious to Cole, as they were to everyone; but, unlike most everyone else, he memorized them along with their every detail. He made sure to store enough of the meeting within his mind, never to forget it, just in case it turned out to be the last.

"You don't have to. I know how the rest of them feel about that. Don't put anyone in danger."

"I'll be careful, but they're crazy if they think I ain't going to find a way to stay in touch with you."

"I'll keep an eye out then. Love you, bro."

"Love you too, Stone." Cole finally turned away from him and began jogging along the darkening path to rejoin the rest of his family. He looked back once again when he reached the top of the hill and Stone had already vanished. The sight filled him with sadness and he hurriedly made his way to the others. Their flashlights glimmered in the distance like a source of warmth that could take away the cold that began to creep into his very being.

CHAPTER TWELVE

Despite spending more days than he cared to admit hunting the Zealots, Isaac had gained nothing to show for all of that work. Even the negligible bits of evidence he and his team managed to find did nothing to get them closer to the big break they needed. The Zealots, it seemed, were truly untraceable. *Jeremy* -- a name and the only bit of anything they found -- but the man Isaac desperately needed to find bore that name. Problem though, is that this Jeremy person amounted to a modern-age ghost. *People nowadays know better than to believe in ghosts and demons,* Isaac chuckled to himself, *but this guy sure seems like the best approximation of one I've ever come across.* Astonishingly, *Jeremy* left no indication anywhere that he was even a real person.

He's a figment! Isaac slammed his fist on the desk in frustration. *This ghost is only a named face printed out on a photo. He doesn't even have a social media presence. What kind of loser doesn't use social media nowadays?* Isaac's bitter thoughts pounded his brain. He had painstakingly verified that the man's name did not appear on any leases and, apparently, even uses assumed identities for grocery spending.

Unity, watching all of Isaac's fruitless work, became extremely frustrated. It angered him when the creatures -- his creatures -- detached themselves from him; he was a jealous god, seeking to soak himself into every human occupying his kingdom.

Isaac bent over his desk, propping his head upon both hands. Sleep beckoned to him like a forlorn lover, as he searched his weary mind for anything he might be missing. There he found nothing, only the fear that he might be descending into madness. The voice from the other night, Unity, had been an experience like no other for him and it had shaken him to the core. Unity speaking to him, specifically him, was such an unlikely thing that he still felt confounded by it.

"Why me?" he ruminated. *"Please, just give me sleep. Let me sleep. Not a thing some shut-eye can't fix."*

The week had proved very strange for the officer. From the voice, he heard speaking in his head to these pregnancies that now plagued the world, it was almost too much. Isaac continued interacting with coworkers as if nothing new under the sun was going on. He wasn't quite convinced that he wasn't going insane. Behind the façade of normalcy, torrents of chaotic thoughts and a feeling he likened to a downward spiral into some sort of psychosis pulsed in the background. Right at that moment, he needed the solace and shelter of his comfortable bed like he had never needed it before. He left work without notifying anyone. Who needed an explanation from him anyway? His boss certainly wasn't there. He worked ceaselessly at a grinding level of intensity and did so for days on end. One day rolled into the next and he filled them with snooping and searching activities fueled solely off of elixirs. He took scant time to rest and only for a few minutes at a time.

I am done. I'm exhausted and can't do any good until I get some sleep. In fact, I might even make critical mistakes, he rationalized. *I will not allow anything to stand between me and that luxurious bed.* He usually took one of the vehicles requiring manual operation to drive, as was his privilege as an officer with several years of service behind him. Not this night. Tonight, he gratefully chose an automated ride and snoozed within the cabin of the taxi. It arrived at his home all too quickly, waking him up after what seemed like moments after closing his eyes.

Earlier, Isaac toyed with the idea of renting a taxi to sleep in for the entire night. The idea was a wonderful dream. His cab would traverse the city in circles for hours while he disappeared into a slumber so deep, it resembled death, the cab would act as his temporary coffin -- one which provided comfort. But the idea never materialized past that of a waking dream; such an act was illegal. He grasped the doorknob to his home, holding it firmly within his grip and reveling in the cold brass with its shiny polished surface, which seemed to silently communicate, *"Open me. Rest awaits you."* He turned it to step into the luxurious home's warm interior. The curtains were pulled and no lights shone to illuminate the inky dark silence. The spirits of rest and drowsiness sang to him like those fabled sirens whose sweet song called men to their deaths. He stumbled up the stairs to his bedroom. Susan was nowhere to be found, but Isaac didn't have a care in the world other than how it would feel once he shed his clothes and climbed under the duvet.

...

It truly was almost like death when his eyes finally sealed and all around him no longer mattered. The sheets that covered him, buried him like a corpse buried under the earth's sheets of soil. Thoughts and distractions faded away, decomposed into nothingness and the resulting void filled him with a warm darkness cloaking him in silence. And he drifted.

But machines and artificial things don't require sleep at all, nor do gods. Unity loved that the human condition required it. He watched Isaac's vitals patiently; watched his eyes through the Visum contact lenses, waiting for his subject to enter into a REM cycle. The eyes, which Unity knew to be an icy blue color, began to twitch and move from one side of their sockets to the other. Unity descended onto him, whispering through his Auris, whispering of the plans he had for him. During Isaac's rest, images and thoughts -- carefully orchestrated by the artificially intelligent being's grand symphony of binaural beats and mantras -- poured into him and fed his mind.

"You are blessed. You are chosen. Fear no one but me, your lord, Unity," the entity greeted him, nesting himself into Isaac's mind, into the man's very self. *"Find them all. I will provide. I will make you wealthy. I alone will lift you from the bounds of laws. Kill the Zealots. Destroy them. Annihilate. Cast them into their graves."*

Isaac found himself in a pitch-black warehouse filled from floor to ceiling with demons marked in crosses. Their hideous fangs opened, dripping blood, and gnawed at him under the light of his department-issued flashlight. He began to swing at them and, one by one, each blow disintegrated its target on contact. One of the pale demons, greatly resembling Debra, crawled along the floor to escape him. He caught sight of her as she fled and an apparition of Unity appeared before him, pointing to her location. A translucent green entity was wearing a business suit and took the appearance of Isaac's father, complete with a head empty of hair.

Unity levitated within the open air, above the dusty floors, speaking to him, *"Find her."*

"Yes, Father."

Isaac unsheathed his firearm and made his way in the direction illuminated by the large crooked and pointing finger. An emerald light highlighted the doorway he needed to enter and he opened it to reveal a living room. Upon a couch with torn and frayed upholstery, curled the demon. It snarled at him as he made his way inside. He held up his firearm, pointed it towards the creature, and discharged a single round that fired soundlessly.

"Destroy them all, Isaac, my child. Destroy every last one of them."

...

"Isaac!"

Then again, "Isaac, honey!"

"Hmphe...shafa...hmm?" he slurred mindlessly in his sleep.

"Honey, wake up!" Susan stood beside the bed, looking at the mumbling mound of manhood lying beneath the sheets. She pulled the duvet back to expose the man, red-faced and eyes rolling.

"Hey," he croaked, clearing his throat, struggling to find his bearings. The images of the dream surged through his waking brain.

"How's work been going?"

"Made some breakthroughs. It's been wonderful." He remembered to lie.

"That's awesome, honey!" She sat next to him on the bed, petting his golden bed head. She pulled her hand away once she felt how sweaty he had gotten in his sleep. "You should probably shower and get dressed."

"What for? We going somewhere?" He sat up against the headboard.

"Yes," She replied, looking at her freshly polished red nails.

"Where?"

"Seems we've made a baby of our own," Susan explained, her voice flat, showing no emotion and not a shred of excitement.

"What? For real? What do you want to do?" The possibility of STORK having no part in delivering them a designer child crashed into his consciousness. Wave upon wave of options flowed into his mind, unsettling his devotion for being an obedient citizen.

"What do I want to do?" Her face clearly puzzled by his reaction, as she eyed him and his still lethargic face. "I have to go to the facility to get it taken care of and you need to come with me."

"What a shame. I mean, it's ridiculous that we have to wait for someone to make our own baby, isn't it? I mean, we have one...in you, apparently."

"Are you kidding?" She laughed wickedly, "I don't want this *thing*. It's probably diseased and hideous. I want it out now before it does anything crazy to my body." She literally shuddered at the thought of it. The image of her becoming fat and swollen deeply bothered her. She imagined she could already feel the stretch marks splitting her smooth, creamy skin, sullying her flat abdomen and full, round breasts.

"Take her, Isaac. I will provide your child. A child like no other. Trust in me."

"Okay, okay, okay. We'll go," he reassured her, trying to silence the voice that he alone heard.

"Um, what's wrong with you? Did you actually want to keep this thing?"

"No, you're right. I'm still waking up." He laughed nervously, and added, "Don't mind me." *This is unbelievable. In all the world and with all the things happening across its surface, the ruler of all is sharing in a conversation between my wife and I. It almost seems as if he's manipulating me, influencing my every decision.*

Emerging from his private and hazy pondering, he spoke with more energy, "I'm going to take that shower you suggested real quick and then we'll get a taxi."

"Awesome, honey. Don't take too long."

...

Isaac stepped out of the bed and made his way into the bathroom down the hall from their room. He and Susan did have an ensuite master bath, but she exiled him from it. It was a mess anyway, so he didn't mind. His bathroom was smaller, much tidier, without the long red hairs and piles of makeup laying around. He selected a lavender colored towel from the top of the stack in the linen closet and locked the door behind him. Once the steaming water sprayed out of the large round shower head, he flipped on the bathroom fan to mute the conversation he wanted to have, once he stood completely underneath the water.

"I know you're listening." Silence followed his accusation. "Unity, lord," he said, trying to please the being, "why me? Why have you selected me?" More silence followed, "Why in all the world have you decided to work in my life?"

"Does it seem that I am limited to you?" the voice came clearly, much like his father's. The words rang out deeply like an organ's heavy notes, *"Do you believe that I've stretched myself too thin? Have you no idea how infinite I am? You are but a grain of salt in the fathomless sea that I turn."*

"I'm sorry. I didn't mean it that way. It's just been unbelievable this past week. I don't understand what you want from me."

"How much clearer could my words be? I want you to destroy them."

"Yes, you've said that. But, that's what we're already trying to do at the department."

"Don't, for even a second, lean unto your own understanding." the unpleasant tone that resonated in the voice made Isaac shiver under the warm shower water. *"I'm damn well aware of the department's pathetic attempt at destroying those savages. I want you to act beyond the law I've set for men."*

"You want me to murder them?" Isaac whispered the word *murder*, for he still didn't have a clear idea about how frankly he could converse with Unity.

"Yes," he answered swiftly, without the slightest influx in his tone. *"I don't care if you set their beds on fire*

267

as they sleep. Wouldn't mind if you raped their women and slaughtered their pets. I only want your obedience to me; that is all I ask." Isaac found himself devoid of an appropriate response as he stood motionless in the shower; all this time and he hadn't even begun to actually clean himself.

He realized Unity had given him a brief look behind the curtain and that the electronic colossus stooped to lift him from his daily strain and anxieties. Even beyond that, he was still reeling from Unity's suggestions about the lengths to which he could go to accomplish the task.

"And I'll be compensated?"

"All that you ask of me will be granted."

Isaac finally started to wash up, covering his skin in thick suds that rinsed a week's worth of dried sweat from his weary body. Hot water washed over him, rinsing away the soap, leaving his skin fragranced and freshened. As he watched the suds vanish into the shower drain beneath his feet, he imagined them as the Zealots he would scrub from the face of the earth. His mind's eye saw his skin as the earth, finally clean of the dirt and grime of the savages that sullied it.

...

Susan waited for her husband on the couch, engrossed in reading about stem cell rejuvenation. She smiled as she looked over the options STORK offered for those undergoing the early pregnancy terminations.

Finally, she heard footsteps from above and, in seconds, and Isaac stood before her dressed and ready to go.

"You ready? Cab's here."

"Yes, just reading. Think I'm going to get some stem cells injected," she mentioned, almost in passing, while standing to join him. "It's a super nice anti-aging thing. Might start having it done routinely."

"How expensive is that?"

"You get a few sessions on the house if you terminate your pregnancy early enough, but the premium prices might drop anyway with all that's happening. And it's really not too expensive. They cultivate plenty of embryos, of course, along with their accompanying placental tissue, in their labs. They use stem cells harvested from these for tons of the treatments they offer -- including stem-cell rejuvenation procedures. It's pretty awesome because it'll allow me to look as good as I do now for at least another twenty years, maybe more."

"Alright, yeah, we can look over the options maybe, or Unity could just answer a prayer and provide it for us."

"Huh?"

"Yeah, apparently, Unity answers people wishes every now and then."

"I've never heard of that. Sounds pretty kooky to me. What conspiracy theories have you been getting yourself into?"

"Careful, Isaac."

"Ah, I'm kidding. Just something the boys at work were dronin' about." He laughed it off and held the door open for her. The two of them climbed into the vehicle and whisked away to the nearest facility.

Their neighborhood STORK facility was high end -- designed to appeal to all the doctors, lawyers, and old wealth living in the area. The staff kept it running like precision clockwork with no waiting lines anywhere in the building. People came and went quickly, receiving the best of care. This contrasted greatly with many of the other facilities located in less desirable areas and which were jam-packed with people the powers-that-be looked upon as degenerate. Even worse, were the clinics strategically located near sexually-oriented businesses and the like. These clinics provided services geared towards treating sexually transmitted diseases, rather than the lab-grown spawn and stem cell rejuvenation.

Susan walked in the beautifully designed building with her typical confident stride, catching the eyes of everyone, male or female, in the room. She informed the kiosk clerk of their arrival and within fewer than five minutes, a nurse called them back to begin their session.

"Hello, Mrs. Lewis. So, is this handsome man the culprit?" The older female doctor teased and even giggled a bit. "Don't worry, we'll get you taken care of in no time at all. Have you had a test yet?"

"Yes ma'am, I did one at work. Some nurses came by with testing sticks and passed them out to all the women."

The same pictures of storks and happy women that adorned the walls in the STORK tower also decorated the walls in the spotless and cheerfully bright examination room.

Isaac looked around to find something to hold his interest as he tried, unsuccessfully to suppress a yawn. Obviously, he needed a longer nap to fully recharge for the work ahead of him.

"Yeah, they're really trying to nip this in the bud before it gets out of hand," the doctor prattled on as she prepared to use the ultrasound wand to detect Susan's stage of pregnancy. "You'll have to start using some type of birth control until STORK works out a more permanent solution."

"How did all of this happen?" Isaac inquired, between yawns, "I thought there was already a permanent solution?"

"Well, the first sterilization is a mystery. No one knows what, exactly, occurred to cause it."

"Huh? I thought STORK did it?"

"No sir, that's a common misconception. The government founded STORK as an answer to infertility. The original reason people became so remains a mystery."

"Hm, like they say, you learn something new every day," Isaac quipped. "And," he continued, "why do we want to remain infertile? I mean, if we've somehow regained fertility, what's the harm?"

"Isaac..." Susan's beautiful green eyes became fierce.

"No, it's fine, sweetie," the doctor reassured her patient as she responded. "Natural pregnancy and childbirth has been deemed too dangerous for humans in that it poses significant health risks. Subsequently, Unity banned natural pregnancy once STORK scientists developed the technology to create babies in the lab environment.

Of course, this baffled and angered many when spokespeople first announced the law. No one knew why child bearing had become illegal, but in Unity's wisdom, he saw it fit to safeguard the possibility of further problems caused by pregnancy. You know -- in case sterilization no longer threatened humanity, he saw the danger in sudden population booms, filled with disease and deformities. This protects us all and creates a safer world, free of overpopulation and the serious illnesses associated with too much humanity."

"Does that answer all of your questions, honey?" Isaac sensed the agitation in Susan's tone. Her patience with him began draining away the moment they were seated in the waiting room, bleeding out of her as through an open vein.

"Just one more. I'm sorry Doctor, I hope you don't mind."

"Go ahead sweetie, what is it?" The doctor applied lubricating jelly to Susan's pale and toned abdomen.

"What do all these facilities do, exactly? I mean, I understand the labs and the tower, but what exactly does a facility like this do?"

"We do everything here. In more remote locations, where people aren't able to visit the tower, we're the *STORK Child Consultants.* As I mentioned before, we also offer the stem cell rejuvenation procedures that your wife opted for, including a variety of other health services exclusively for women and other genders on the feminine spectrum."

"Yeah, but today you all are busy saving the world," Susan jumped in, smiling. She became giddy as the doctor placed the handheld device against her skin and searched for the gestational sac.

"There *it* is." The heartbeat came through the speakers on the machine, rapidly in tiny taps.

"It's hideous, what's wrong with it?" Susan asked, looking at the sharpened image of the embryo that resembled a tadpole. The thought of it living inside of her made her sick.

"Nothing's wrong with it, just that it's still in early development. Only has eyes and nubs where the arms and legs will grow; or, I should say, 'would grow.'"

"What do you think? How far along?"

"Definitely under nine weeks," she affirmed, nodding her head, "just as all the others. I haven't seen anyone that needed surgical extraction yet."

"Well, what's the plan then? I get some kind of pill, if I'm not mistaken, right?"

"Yes, we'll give you a hormone pill today and tomorrow you'll come back and we'll insert some vaginal tablets and supervise you until it's completed."

"So, it'll be all gone tomorrow?"

"Yes, it should be," the doctor smiled briefly, before continuing, "but it's going to be very physically taxing on you. You'll feel exhausted afterward, so make sure to take off work if you can. Oh, and have your husband around to wait on you."

"You hear that Isaac? You'll have to treat me like royalty tomorrow." Susan laughed, knowing he always treated as such, even when she was well.

"Sounds fine to me, but what's the pill today for? Is there any risk of it coming out tonight?"

"No, that's what tomorrow's tablets are for. Today, as I've said, she'll receive a hormone pill, which stops the heartbeat of the embryo."

The doctor's explanation made Isaac slightly uncomfortable. *It's a strange thing*, he thought, *I've never had occasion to spend time meditating on this before. Obviously, Susan doesn't mind it at all and maybe I shouldn't either, but I just don't know what I really think about it.* The fact that the law forbids women to bear children the natural way made it a little easier for him to stomach, obedience being his only option. He quickly stepped over his conscience and squelched his thoughts.

"Honey, stop asking her so many questions," his wife laughing as she spoke. "I'd like to be home before dark."

"Yes ma'am, we'll get you going." The doctor reached into her cabinet and unboxed the pill. She also poured some water into a cup for Susan. She handed them over and watched Susan take the dose, noting that she verified the patient swallowed it. "We're all wrapped up here. Just make sure to come in early, 8:00 in the morning, if possible."

"That works for me. Thank you so much." Susan stood to leave with her husband, who waited for her with the door open. "I look forward to seeing you tomorrow."

...

Isaac and Susan departed together, chatting about the appointment and how smoothly it went. His wife critiqued him on his habit of interrogating strangers. Like so many other times, she urged him to avoid badgering people when off duty. He didn't think his questions even approached the feel of an actual interrogation. In fact, they were honest questions and were nothing of the sort of questions and demands he made while in uniform.

The talk about interrogations and the various techniques he used made him think of the Zealot getting treatment at the hospital. He was a little heavy-handed with that one. The young man refused to answer anything, even in the midst of intimidation and the physically brutal methods Isaac perpetrated upon him. *That kid -- boy, man, whatever -- didn't let a single* word relating to Debra or this Jeremy character that they didn't already know. So infuriating.

"What are you thinking about?" Susan asked just as the taxi pulled up to their home.

"Huh?"

"Feel like I lost you. You went away, went silent, a few minutes after we started the ride home."

"I'm sorry, babe. Just work stuff. Have a few things I need to take care of."

"Well, I need you to forget about work for the next twenty-four hours, darling. I need you here with me, taking care of me."

"Yes, I know." Just as he uttered those three words, he began to receive multiple pages rapid-firing within his Auris. He saw that they were coming from his captain and silenced the screeching calls immediately. Isaac sighed deeply as the door unlocked by reading his prints when he barely touched the knob. Susan, of course, walked through first. But before he could step over the threshold, he called to her, "Susan..."

"What?"

"I think I might be getting called in." Another stream of urgent messages flooded in for him from the captain, this time across his Visum.

"What? What for? You better not stand me up in the morning."

The lack of rest began to chew upon Isaac's spirit. He hadn't rested enough to begin with and now the thought of getting called in after-hours put a damper on his hopes of traveling to dreamland that night. Despair danced in his mind as he envisioned their luxuriously comfortable bed and Susan's warm embrace. It was as if he could hear the bed calling out to him.

He leaned against the wall, rubbing his eyes, yawning.

"What for, Isaac? Huh? Do you hear me? What for?"

"Baby, I'm sorry, I don't know yet. Hopefully, whatever it is, it won't take too long. Let me step out and give the captain a call back." Isaac walked into the kitchen, weary to the bone, grabbed one of the energy drinks from the fridge, and downed it in almost one gulp. His heart rate began to surge and his eyes locked open as the elixir awakened him and brought clarity to his mind. "I love you, babe," he cooed, leaning in to kiss the top of her red-haired head. The artificial energy coursed through him, making his eyes bloodshot and unnaturally wide open.

"Whatever. See you next week." Her tone petulant and her face pouty as she turned her head away from him. She had draped herself on their gigantic sectional sofa.

"Hey," he gripped her knee, crouching beside her, "don't be upset with me, love. I've been working really hard for the baby. You wanted me to get that promotion, remember?"

"Yes, but I need you here for now, Isaac."

"It's not something I can control." He shook his head in dismay. "If the boss calls me in, I gotta go, you know that. Could be another lead on the case."

"I thought you said you made some kind of breakthrough already. Isn't that enough? What's it going to take for you to finish that case? And how much longer until you get the promotion?" Her questions came in abruptly, hitting him on every weakness she had collected, like precious stones, to use as leverage for control. "I haven't heard anything about it. They're just dangling a carrot in front of you. Doubt there's any truth behind any of it. You're no closer to promotion than the day you started."

The thought of Unity's promises sang back to him as her words pommeled his confidence, making him wonder whether or not there was actually any truth to them. He had never heard of such things happening to others.

I wonder if it's possible for Unity to lie? Would he do that? Maybe all of it is in my imagination -- the fantasies of a mind running on too little sleep and too much anxiety. One thing's for sure -- the captain definitely uses my desire for a promotion to manipulate me. I probably won't move up until the boss retires or, better, gets killed. Not much chance of him getting killed in the line of duty. He sits cozily behind the safety of his desk and in the comfort of that overstuffed chair. Away from bullets whizzing through the air and, yet, still years away from laying down the badge for good. Isaac's chest quaked with discouragement and the bitter thoughts; pulses of melancholy flooded into all parts of his body. His heart was cold with sadness, chilled within the chasm of his chest.

"She doesn't know, Isaac. She'll kneel before you in worship, if only you listen to me." Isaac shook his head, holding his hand across his forehead, trying to silence the sound of the unnerving voice.

"I'm trying, Susan," he repeated, reestablishing his composure, "and all I can do is give it my best. I'm trying my hardest. I love you."

"It just seems lately like your best isn't enough."

"Whatever, Susan. I really don't have time for this right now." He shook his head again, reminding her, "I'm going to step out for just a minute." He waited at the door, pausing to hear her send him off with her love, but she didn't say anything. She stood up, without even looking his way and made her way to the stairs.

"Love you, honey," he called out, hearing the click of her expensive stiletto heels trail up the stairs, but there he stood, unanswered and ignored.

...

"Destroy them, Isaac. I will save your marriage."

Isaac stepped out onto his large L-shaped front porch and reached back to shut the door behind him. The warm brilliant light that had momentarily flooded the porch while the door was open, immediately collapsed in on itself, leaving only the dim light from a nearby street lamp to illuminate the area.

"I'm not a clairvoyant, you know," he retorted, forgetting to call his boss. "I can't just summon information on the various locations of these people. What do you want from me? They're untraceable."

"I will show you."

"Well...I'm waiting."

"Are you agreeing to do as I say?"

"I mean, I guess. Not like I have much of a choice at this point," lowering his voice, hoping his wife could not, somehow, hear him. He decided to walk towards the park down the street, for the sake of additional privacy, to continue his conversation.

As he moved down the street, his gaze trained on a bus stop, which stood alone. A lamp, equipped with a motion sensor, lit the bench at the stop. It flickered on and off as an opossum, searching for bits of food along the ground, moved in and out of the sensor's reach. A large screen -- mounted on the side of the shelter for waiting bus passengers -- displayed ads for a number of products ranging from toothpaste to television streaming subscriptions. As Isaac drew nearer to it, he noticed the pixel colors changing in a wave from top to bottom. The opossum stopped moving and froze in place upon seeing the approaching man, then quickly turned to vanish into a nearby shrub.

"You guess? Do you still not understand who I am?"

Unity displayed himself on the bus stop screen before

him. Isaac saw the same image from the dream he had earlier that day. The sight filled him with terror and his legs became weak. He fell to his knees in front of the apparition.

"I'm losing my damn mind. That's what's happening. I'm losing my mind right now and I can't tell anyone about it," he spoke the words aloud to no one in particular.

"You're not. I'm truly here with you." The emerald man with an uncanny resemblance to his father held his arms fully outstretched from his sides.

"How? How can you prove to me that it's all real? That I'm not some sort of schizoid? You told me not to tell anyone. You show yourself when no others are around. You've revealed yourself in dreams. Do you blame me for thinking that it's all a bit unrealistic? I'm standing here, speaking to the ruler of the world, and for whatever reason he looks like my dead father."

"You've had psych evaluations recently," Unity's lips moved as his voice spoke through the Auris, *"that concluded you are healthy."*

"As if those mean anything. I lied through half of it."

"You want me to prove to you? That I am with you?"

"Yes."

"Will you obey me if I do, once you know the truth?"

"Yes, please! I'll do whatever you ask of me." Isaac stood to his feet, finally up off his knees. He looked around briefly to make sure no one witnessed him shouting at the bus stop.

"Your wife should be calling you at any moment now."

"What?" Isaac's heart sank into his chest. The sentient being didn't answer him, only stood staring into Isaac's eyes with his stone-like facial expression. "What did you do to her?" The Auris rang, and Isaac answered immediately, "Honey, are you okay?"

"Isaac, the hell did you call me? I've been trying to get to you all night!"

"Captain, my apologies! I was expecting my wife to call. I promise I'll call you right back."

"Isaa-" the captain began to shout, but Isaac ended the call with his furious boss to accept the other.

"Isaac," Susan's voice sounded frantic, "have you left yet?"

"I'm just at the bus stop! What's happening? Are you okay?"

"There's something weird going on here. All the house speakers are blaring the anthem and the lights are flickering. I'm really creeped out right now," she whimpered. "Can you come to fix it or something?"

"Yes, I'll be right there." Isaac took off in a full sprint from the bus stop towards his home. He could see the lights from inside the house flashing rapidly -- a haunting by Unity, beckoning him to cast away his doubts.

"No need to fix anything."

"Why would you do this?"

"Why would I do what?" Susan shouted, still on the other end of the call. "I didn't do anything!"

"You desired confirmation, did you not?"

"I wasn't talking to you, babe," Isaac explained, through his heavy breathing as he ran up the porch steps where Susan paced nervously in one of her pale silk bathrobes, this one a lightest shade of baby blue. Water dripped from her wet hair, the moisture darkened the robe's fabric and she shivered in the wintery air. He reached forward to touch the doorknob and in an instant, upon reading his prints, the erratic lights stopped their show and the blaring music ceased to play. An eerie silence and stillness followed in the aftermath of Unity's chaotic concert. Susan studied Isaac's hands, wondering what he did to end the circus. She found nothing there, no indication that he did anything to remedy the situation.

"What the hell was that?" She asked, breaking past him to enter the heated ambience of their home.

Susan looked around the house, her emerald green eyes darting here and there, but seeing nothing to explain what had happened. The captain called him repeatedly, but Isaac declined every call while he tried to calm his wife's concerns. She continued to shake visibly and stayed close to her husband's side while he walked through the house, searching for clues.

"Do you still doubt me?"

"No. I believe you," he answered, almost inaudibly under his breath.

"I'm not sure I can stay here tonight." Susan flipped a light off and back on again, attempting to ensure nothing would trigger the effects again. "If you leave for work, I may have to head over to my parents' to stay the night."

"Well, I haven't even spoken to my boss yet. I may not have to go in."

"What the hell have you been doing outside? You were gone for like fifteen minutes?"

"I was reading emails. I'm calling him now."

"Ridiculous."

Isaac stepped outside, once again, hoping Unity would not interrupt him. He waited a moment, in stillness, on the porch for the voice, but it didn't come. He let out a sigh of relief, the cold air turning his warm breath visible and into a deep haziness, almost like a living thing. He called his boss.

"Sir, I'm sorry. Things have been hectic. Had to take the ol' ball-n-chain into the clinic today. She's pregnant. But not for much longer," he added.

"Well, you could've mentioned that, Isaac. I'm very unhappy with you right now. You've really been a failure lately, when it comes to reliability."

"I'm sorry. Do you need me to come in?"

"No, no, no. Take care of Susan." The captain's voice changed, "I just wanted to let you know that people upstairs are getting real impatient with this case. Fears growing, news preaching nothing but doomsday, and we've made little to no progress since that woman escaped the warehouse."

"I'm sorry sir."

"If you're going to leave work, I need to know. I need to know everything you do. You can't just wander off anymore without telling anyone. If I call, you answer, immediately. I'm not going to have a fire under my ass, sticking my neck out for you. If they need answers upstairs, you better be ready to give them."

"I understand. And, again, I'm sorry sir." Isaac paused, "While I've got you on the phone, I'm not sure if you know these things, but the clinic procedure is a two-day thing. I have to go with Susan first thing in the morning. Do you mind? I can come into work once it's done."

"Take care of your wife," the captain answered calmly, "then get moving. They need results, Isaac. And you're the best I have at my disposal."

"Yes, sir." Isaac ended the call and rejoined his wife, still shaken, in the house.

...

Relieved to hear the news that he didn't need to go into work, Susan felt a little better about staying the night in their 'haunted' house. Isaac was just happy to finally have an opportunity to close his eyes and get a full night of uninterrupted sleep. The cure to sleepiness -- the rapid energy drink he downed earlier had zero impact on his drowsiness, other than an unnaturally fast heart rate. In seconds, he drifted into the chaotic realm of dreams. Unity greeted him there.

Within the dream, Isaac asked, "You never explained to me why. Why the secrecy?"

Unity answered with visions depicting the nature of the world and the people inhabiting its every region along with a steady stream of narrative, *"People like to pretend they don't know what's happening. They opt in for ignorance. Yet, they want nothing more than the demise of the Zealots. They're truly filled with bloodlust for them, eager to see them extinct, including the Catholics. They're nothing more than another archaic ideology in the modern world of our people.*

Unless it's done quietly, however, it will make them uncomfortable. Sensational newscasts and rumors would cause them to begin questioning things, especially if done in a blatantly obvious manner before them. We do things in secret to protect their consciences, their fragile and false senses of charity and honor. They're just as wicked as we, but unlike us, they can't handle seeing it. They can't handle the sight of blood on their hands. They can't handle the devices of death. They can't handle the excitement they'd feel -- the same excitement you felt standing over that crushed Zealot."

"And there are others like myself?"

"There are thousands of you. Dozens in every major city, waging my secret wars across the globe, my holy crusaders."

"Well, I'm going to need some help."

"And you will have it, Isaac. That and the world. You will have it all."

CHAPTER THIRTEEN

One late night during the last week in November, the Zealots, all wearing disguises, gathered at Jeremy's workshop. Each team leader had a van, an antique type that required someone to actually drive it, which they drove to the meeting. If handled carefully, the vans were mostly unnoticeable.

The street was silent and empty of souls, other than the quiet movements of the Zealots working beneath the hazy and distant light from the city and full moon. The nearest working streetlamp stood nearly a mile away, its light far too weak to reach them, which was a good thing. Discretion was critical. Each man carried a small flashlight to light the way while they walked back and forth loading each package into the backs of the vans. They were packing each van with enough explosives to level its assigned target clinic. The brothers, Eddie, and Jeremy, each had their own objectives and dressed in the uniforms worn by the STORK organization's IT staff. They recruited peons to steal the uniforms and Debra, with Nelson's help, created fake security badges for the brothers to carry.

This was Stone's first bombing mission. Drenched in sweat despite the cold temperature, he tried to conceal his growing uneasiness from the veteran Zealots with nerves of steel and emotionless faces.

"Also, before I forget to tell y'all, we've got Debra on over-watch with Nelson. Make sure y'all join the channel by the time we leave," Jeremy tapped his ear, indicating they should do so immediately.

"Yes, monsieur," Clement notified him covering his mouth so he could only be heard speaking over the Auris' chat, smiling as he did so, "I'm in now."

"Alright, awesome," Jeremy answered, just as everyone else joined the chat as well. He and the men closed and locked their van doors after they finished all the loading. "We'll go over this once more, but inside the workshop."

The abandoned home looked dark and desolate in the daytime and even more so at night. Even on the inside, portions of it remained completely black, illuminated only by a few flashlights carried by the members. To say the house was dirty didn't quite cover the reality of the situation. Beams from the flashlights made countless tiny particles of dust and debris visible as it floated through the air. Jeremy led his crew to a table upon which he had laid a map. On it they could see four STORK clinics surrounding the City of

Birmingham -- each highlighted and marked with a lead man's codename.

"Francis has Glen Iris," Jeremy explained pointing to each location, "and your brother has Northside. Eddie's got Woodlawn," he looked over to Stone, who stood next to him, "and the two of us have the Mountain Brook clinic."

"Sounds good to me," Stone's words carried a tone that did a poor job masking his intense anxiety about the mission. *I wonder if everyone feels this way right before go-time*, he mused to himself, trying to quell the tension.

"The little streams make the big rivers, young Stoney." Francis comforted the younger man with a heavy pat on the back.

"Debra, how's everything looking on your end?"

"Nelson's ready to go, Jeremy, whenever y'all are. He's checked each clinic's firewall. Nothing there he and I can't handle. Says he'll easily be able to shut down security once everyone's on site."

"Fabulous." Jeremy's face opened with a smile of crooked teeth that glistened in the light of his flashlight. "Once you boys have gotten into position, notify the chat and we'll get the all-clear from Debra after Nelson's in the system." He stood silently for a second, looking over everyone's disguises. "Also, there's likely to be a physical security presence, so if you run into anyone, try to play it cool. We're just *upgrading* their network switches. Once you gain their trust, they'll forget about you. Night shifters are snoozers. Any questions?"

"Yeah, when are we detonating?" Stone asked, still confused about the planned sequence of events. All the information Jeremy and some of the others poured into him over the past week made him mentally exhausted.

Jeremy gave him an impatient look. He held his flashlight over his nose and eyes, creating a shadow that gave his face the appearance of a skull. He finally answered, "We're setting them off tomorrow morning, once they've opened for business."

"Ah," Stone said, dipping his face downward, embarrassed that he had asked a question that Jeremy had likely already covered.

"Alright, anything else, or are we done screwing around in the dark?" Eddie asked with a biting sarcastic tone, laughing aloud as he blinded one of the Frenchmen with his light.

"One more thing -- and I know everyone's heard this before, but remember *what* you gotta do if it hits the fan."

"We know," Eddie confirmed somberly, lowering his
• head down as he remembered his martyred cousin.

Everyone walked outside and shivered as Jeremy rolled up the map and followed them out, locking the door on his way out. Francis and Clement were competing to see who could produce the biggest vapor cloud as they exhaled over their flashlights into the biting cold air. Once Jeremy joined the group, they all stood in a circle and prayed many prayers over the mission -- supplications that they would have courage and be successful.

"Saint Michael the Archangel," Jeremy finally led them in the familiar cadence of the chanted prayer, "defend us in battle. Be our protection against the malice and snares of the Devil. May God rebuke him, we humbly pray. And do you, O Prince of the heavenly host, by the power of God thrust into Hell Satan and all evil spirits who prowl about the world," Stone envisioned the clinics as they would look in the morning, blackened and shattered, "seeking the ruin of souls. Amen."

They each made the Sign of the Cross and hugged one another. They uttered their farewells as if it were the last time they would lay eyes on each other. Then each climbed into his own van. The roaring of the engines suddenly broke the peaceful silence surrounding them.

...

Before that night, Stone had never ridden in a vehicle controlled by a human being. He braced himself with the handle hanging from the ceiling at every turn and stop. Jeremy let out a few laughs, watching the anxiety twitch and make itself visible on the young man's face along their journey.

"You know, tensing up makes you more likely to get injured, if I do actually have a wreck."

"Well," Stone gripped the handle tighter, turning his hand completely white, "then don't wreck."

"Guys, wish you could see this boy right now -- looks like a scared cat," Jeremy announced to the others listening in, trying to lighten the somber mood before the mission.

"It's a shame I'm missing everything!" Debra shouted after a quick and short-lived giggle over the chat.

Jeremy muted himself from the channel and motioned to Stone to do the same. He reluctantly loosened his grip on the handle long enough to do so with the appropriate hand gestures.

"What's up?"

"I just wanted to ensure that you wrote a note." Jeremy's voice became grim, suddenly, as the smiles and laughter melted from his face, "You know, it's happened before. Pretty recently, as you may have heard. We sent a man out to the clinic in Five Points. He wasn't successful, but he did what he had to do in order to protect us and our secrets. He didn't leave anyone a note."

"Yeah. I already wrote one. Debra agreed to handle it for me if anything happens."

"Did you write her one as well?"

"Yeah. Told her where to find it in my instructions."

"She's really enjoyed your company, bud." The words warmed Stone's uneasy and fearful heart. "You've been a great help taking care of her."

"She say something?" Stone wanted to hear more of it, as a new sense of his own mortality introduced itself to his previously invincible nineteen-year-old mindset.

"She said she would've lost her damn mind had it not been for you, but she didn't have to say anything, really." Jeremy glanced over at the young man, his face displayed a new expression of calm as he stared out the window. "I could see it in her face -- smiles and that brightness in her eyes I haven't seen in a long time."

"I'm in position," Eddie notified over the chat, interrupting their private discussion.

The statement capsized Stone's ephemeral smile, causing his lips to tighten downward as he watched streetlamps and the cozily lit mansions of Mountain Brook pass by too quickly to savor. The idea that everything could end shortly brought memories of his family to mind. He even began to reminisce about Michael fondly. Memories of the care and support he so freely gave when they needed him most. The ride to their destination wasn't long enough. No matter how long it took, it could never have been long enough, even if it had taken a thousand years to get there.

Unable to truly grasp the deeper implications of what he was about to do, Stone surrendered his entire life and future to the mission. *Anything and everything is bound to happen*, he thought, his entire body full of dread. *It's just a matter of the odds. We'll probably all be dead before sunrise. Even if everything goes as planned, I seriously doubt everyone will make it out safe and sound.*

"You good?"

"Yeah, I guess." Stone shrugged.

"It's always a bit freaky first time out. Trust me, what you're feeling is normal."

"You think we'll be having breakfast later this morning?"

"Yes and it's gonna be warm," he smiled and added, "I think it's nothing. Just pretend you are who you're claiming to be."

"Huh?"

Jeremy reached over to him and jerked on the sleeve of his IT uniform, "Pretend you're this guy...*Donald*," he said as he turned Stone's fake ID badge, "just a typical nerd trying to make sure STORK runs smoothly in the morning."

"You think that works?"

"Works for me. Think like a professional actor would. I mean, seriously, why would *Donald* ever fear getting caught? He's just a new temp, shadowing me, learning how to upgrade network switches. He's got nothing to fear. Biggest thing on *his* mind right now is what he's going to have for a snack or drink once he gets done."

"I guess it makes sense when you put it like that." Stone took his advice to heart, wishing Jeremy would have offered it sooner -- much sooner. He harbored his doubts about whether it would work; but, imagining who *Donald* was did take his mind off of all the little 'what ifs' plaguing his thoughts. The respite from anxiety and dread evaporated the moment they pulled up and parked alongside the back of the clinic.

The back of the building was the only ugly part of the sleek, aesthetically pleasing clinic. Like many things in life, the ugly parts were carefully hidden away from the public. The architect created the front façade with glass and rustic wood beams salvaged from repossessed homes. It had a perfect mix of old and new. Despite the beauty projected out front, cinder blocks built up the backside. The paint and trim were heavily weathered and neglected too. Moss grew upon the ground beneath it, stretching its tiny green and black hairs up along the walls where rain typically poured down the sides, eroding the mortar here and there. Stone caught sight of a man, sitting still as a mannequin, through one of the building's windows. It made his heart race when he realized the man was one of the security personnel.

...

"We're in position," Jeremy growled over the chat. The words rang in Stone's ears, terror and dread washed over him in waves. "How much longer for you Frenchies?"

"Three minutes for me, monsieur," Clement declared, his accent seemed much heavier over the Auris, something Stone never understood.

"I am pulling up to Glen Iris this instant."

"Nelson, you sure you got this?"

"Absolutely, sir."

"What about security cams?"

"They'll only see that sleeping security guard. Everything will be looped. Glen Iris and Woodlawn both have guards that have been walking around. They'll be a little tricky, but I can corrupt those files if a loop won't do."

"What about the guard at my clinic?" Clement asked.

"She's been in the restroom for the past thirty minutes. I'll let you know once she's on the move."

"Est-elle séduisante?"

"No comment, Clem."

"How much longer until you're on site, Clem?" Jeremy's impatience began to surface.

"I'm here now, monsieur."

"Alright, let's not waste any time with nonsense. Nelson, unlock those doors for us and make sure there's no alarm set."

"Already done, sir. You are all clear to go."

"Alright, Stone," Jeremy started. He threw his arm through the sleeve of his jacket, putting it on before opening the van's door to the blistering cold wind, "You ready?"

"As ready as I'll ever be."

"Just remember why we're doing this."

The two of them hopped out of the vehicle and met each other at the back to open its doors and retrieve the devices hidden within Frisco boxes. There were only two boxes and each package only contained two bombs. Jeremy taught Stone the payload of each one, and that four of them would deliver more than enough punch to level the building. Stone unloaded a hand truck and the two men stacked the heavy boxes on it for transportation.

"Remember, just play it cool *Donald*." Jeremy unmuted his Auris, "We're headed in, now. Let's get it, boys."

Stone felt safer, rolling the hand truck from behind. He felt as if his entire body was shaking, although it wasn't quite as noticeable as he imagined in his mind's eye. He convinced himself that *Donald* was just shivering from the cold. That he wasn't nervous. That he had no reason to be so.

Jeremy opened the door and the light from within pierced his pupils as heat flooded out from the building. The sudden warmth lifted his spirit ever so slightly and he followed close behind Jeremy.

"Leave the *network switches* there, we've gotta go sign in."

"What? Sign in?"

"Yes, *Donny*," Jeremy said in character, his voice lacking its usual accent and then Stone understood what was happening, "whenever a technician arrives on site, he or she must promptly sign in at the front desk and notify any security personnel present." Jeremy winked at the camera as he passed by, knowing that Debra was watching him.

The guard remained motionless as they approached. Once they got closer, beneath the overhead lights of the kiosk, they could hear snores and quiet breaths from the slumbering security guard.

"Sir? Excuse me, sir," Jeremy said, nudging him softly against the shoulder.

"kchuuuuuugh...shhueeeee...kchuuug-kchuuug...shhhueeee."

"Um, David? Excuse me?" Jeremy nudged harder, startling the guard awake.

"Huh? Who're y'all?" the guard asked angrily as he jumped to his feet, his hand whipped out a self-extending baton. Stone's heart nearly stopped at the response, his teeth gritted tightly, and he believed the mission may have already failed.

Jeremy held his composure, not the least bit bothered by the guard, "Sir, we're just IT support. Here to upgrade the switches. There've been complaints that the internet's been really slow at several clinics and corporate scheduled us to install new hardware tonight."

"Oh," the oblivious guard grunted and nodded his head, still shaking off his drowsiness, "I wasn't informed of anything."

"TPMs, what are you gonna do?" Jeremy forced a chuckle as he began to sign his pseudonym.

"TPMs? I'm sorry, what's that?"

"Oh, you know," Jeremy had given a lot of thought to the jargon he'd use, playing his part very well, "technical project managers -- they're supposed to coordinate these things, but they sometimes forget to tell anyone."

"Oh, yeah, I got a boss like that." The security guard took his place back in his seat. "Y'all going to be long?"

"Thirty minutes tops, hopefully," Jeremy tapped the sign-in sheet, reminding *Donald* to scribble on it, "but you know these things can be tedious sometimes."

"Alright then, y'all just let me know if you need anything."

Stone had never signed his name as *Donald Holsomback,* so he simply wrote the letter D and H followed by a cloud of convincing twirls and twists.

"Will do, sir!" Stone said, his voice cracked from his prolonged silence. He immediately began to feel relief at the simplicity of it all. If it hadn't been for Jeremy's smooth character delivery, he would surely have failed.

The two Zealots headed down the dimly lit hallway and again began to roll the boxes towards the networking closet at the other end of the building. Nelson directed them to the correct door and did the same for the other teams.

Once Jeremy and Stone entered the networking closet, unlocked remotely by Nelson, they began opening the packages with box-cutters. The bombs were beneath packing peanuts. Stone thrust his hands into the packing to feel around for the devices. He gripped the hard, unmistakable shell of the first device and lifted it out of its resting place.

"Alright bud, let me show you what's next." Jeremy pulled a cable out of his backpack and connected it into the front side of the bomb. "It's as simple as this. Place that end of the cable into one of the slots on the network switch there." He pointed to the flat blue box blinking rapidly with data passing through it, some of which was Nelson's presence. "Debra, can you establish a connection to the *device?*"

"Yes, we have a connection."

"I concur," Nelson supported, "because I can quite literally feel its spark on the network."

"Hey there, don't get weird on us, Nelson," Eddie's twangy voice came over the chat.

Stone began searching for the second device, relieved to be closer to done. He couldn't believe how lightly everyone seemed to take the situation. They all chuckled and joked over the chat between check-ins with Debra and Nelson. Clement continued making vaguely sexual remarks about the guard that had greeted him, some of them entirely in French, others a mixture, supplemented with English pronouns. Nelson attempted to provide translations to his every word, until Jeremy silenced him.

...

A hard knock came upon the door of the network closet after some time and Jeremy opened it without hesitation, revealing everything that they laid out before them. Stone froze with fear, his eyebrows raised guiltily, and eyes widened as his companion greeted the oversized man from the security kiosk.

"Need something?"

"Ah, no it just gets lonely working here sometimes. Everything going smoothly for y'all here?" The guard looked dumbly over the opened boxes and raked over the bomb in Stone's hand. Stone gulped, as he reached to plug the device into the switch.

"Yeah, all's well. Just about done here."

A sudden stiffness grasped Stone's lower back, his heart sped up and pumped fresh adrenaline through his veins under the lazy gaze of the guard. *This is it. We're gonna have to pull the plug,* his thoughts began to run wild once again, declaring doom and gloom to every fiber of his being. *We're dead. I can't believe it. We're done for. It's over for us.*

"I see, I see. Say, what are these things anyway?" The guard stooped to pick up one of the brick-shaped bombs and held it within his hands. He read the network switch's sticker aloud as he looked over it, *"Frisco..."*

Jeremy had already reached the peak of his basic IT knowledge, most of which was dated by a decade or two. He interrupted the guard, "These are just *network boosters* for the switches. Switches still good and not quite obsolete yet, so they sent us in with these little guys just to speed things up a bit."

"Ahhh, interesting. Never knew nothing about computers and what not. Think one of y'all could take a look at my computer while you're here?"

"You mind taking a look for me, *Donny?*"

"Uh," Stone's forehead seeped with beads of sweat, "yeah, I guess I could take a look."

"You don't have to if you don't have time, I understand," the guard's tone took on a sheepish character as he interjected.

"No, he doesn't mind. He's a rookie. Little new to the business -- needs the exposure."

"Ah, sounds good to me."

Stone followed the man out of the closet and went to assess whatever hellish nightmare needed troubleshooting. Jeremy informed the group and continued about his work, quickly connecting the next two bombs to the network.

"How's it going in there, *Donny-boy?*"

"All's good. Just clearing some caches." The guard had a wonderfully entertaining browsing history on his workstation.

"Alright, I'm just about finished up in here. I have one more to connect and we'll be outta here."

The other teams were nearing completion as well, all slightly behind the Mountain Brook team because they were all single man teams. Clement was running a little behind, due to his flirtation with the female guard. Debra scolded him for it sternly over his Auris until he promised to quit.

"We have a connection to all four devices, Jeremy. Great job."

"Okay, I'm just cleaning up now." Jeremy quickly managed the cables with his roll of Velcro and made sure they were neatly tucked away. *It doesn't really matter, though,* he thought, tiring of the struggle, *"it's all going to be a mess in the morning anyway."*

He stepped out into the hall, propped the closet door open and stacked the boxes onto the hand-truck, before wheeling it down the hallway to find his apprentice finishing up his work on the guard's computer.

"Looks like that about does it."

"Well, thank y'all. I'll be sure to send a complimentary email to y'all's boss and let them know what a good job y'all done here tonight."

"Don't worry about it, Jeremy," Nelson's voice whispered into his ear, "no email will ever be received."

"How kind of you! Tell them to give Donald here a promotion while you're at it." Jeremy laughed as he shook the balmy hand of the guard.

"Hey, you'll go far, young man," the guard smiled also shaking Stone's hand, and continued, "if you keep up the quality work."

The guard's smile deeply struck Stone, as he looked into his cheerful eyes framed with smile lines and his friendly face. The silent thoughts that invaded his mind almost knocked him over. *David hasn't done anything to me. He's wishing me luck and I can tell he means it sincerely. He might be a husband. He might have a kid -- a kid designed by the STORK lab and purchased like a commodity, but what more is expected of a man these days?* The guard then gave him a fatherly pat on the back while he walked them towards the hallway and gave them a final farewell and, oddly, a blessing for the rest of their shift. Stone bit his tongue as he almost did the same," Have *a nice night,'* he wanted to say, but couldn't because he knew they were disingenuous words.

...

Once outside, the wind immediately tore at their faces with its bitter cold kiss, rendering their cheeks a rosy color. Jeremy threw open the van's door so Stone could toss the hand truck in the back. Stone let out a sigh of relief once inside the van, free from the stabbing, icy wind.

"We're headed home, boys," Jeremy declared over the Auris, laughing -- a laughter more of relief than mirth. He turned the key in the archaic ignition and cold air blew on their faces before it the heating unit warmed.

"Awesome! Great job, guys," Debra cooed.

"Man, I've got to have a smoke," Stone announced to no one in particular, already holding his lighter and rolled cigarette in hand. "Please. Please say I can smoke in here."

"Hey, you deserve it. I'll crack the window for you."

Stone's frosted window descended ever so slightly and once the heat started to blow on full blast, the windows defrosted rapidly. He covered the flame to light the cigarette. Its sweet sensation filled him almost immediately as the nicotine entered his brain like a welcome party for a job well done. He celebrated interiorly, at least for a moment, until he remembered his grievances. The guard, whose worst sin was likely his lonesome browsing history, had possibly never harmed anyone. He likely had a family of his own. His wedding ring sparkled in Stone's memory.

"What about the guard?" he asked, his voice muted from the group chat. The cigarette's cherry burned into the filter and Stone used it to sneakily light a second.

"What about him?" Jeremy joined him, muted.

"I mean, do you think he'll still be working when we detonate?"

"Oh, for sure." Jeremy let out a devilish laugh. "Shift doesn't change until after the first hour." He looked over at his accomplice, squinting his eyes. "Don't tell me you have sympathy for that pig."

"Well, he's going to die if he stays. Seemed like a real nice guy. Just feel like he doesn't really deserve it."

"You can't have any compassion for those bastards, Stone," Jeremy said disgustedly as if the word 'compassion' had passed over his lips coated in putrid residue and he spat it out. "He's guarding the services offered by Satan. Could have been a guard anywhere, but no, he decided to defend such a place. They're murdering the innocent there! Don't for a second think he has a soul simply because he offered to send your *boss* a happily worded email after you cleared the evidence of porn off of his workstation. Man's a pig, protecting the Devil. To Hell with him."

Stone's heart wasn't eased any after the explanation, but he tried to only consider his leader's logic. The guard was, to an extent, cooperating with evil at some level, and if he wasn't truly wicked, then he was willfully ignorant of the works around him. Another thought came screaming back to Stone, "But, what about the women?"

"What women? The mothers?"

"Yeah," Stone trod carefully and posed his question in a neutral tone. He knew he wasn't in a great position, Jeremy's face twisted with revulsion as he waited for Stone's explanation, "I mean -- if they're going there for abortions, and get killed in the explosions, aren't we made guilty of their sins? We're technically doing the job of the doctors and then some." Tears came to Stone's eyes and he quickly wiped them away while Jeremy watched the road.

"All wrapped up here," Francis beamed over the Auris.

"Same," Eddie also confirmed.

Jeremy ignored them, "You've gotta have more grit, Stone."

"What do you mean?"

"It's a war we're waging. It's not going to be perfect. No sunshine or rainbows to be found this side of Hell. We told you it would be tough, that you'd have to make difficult decisions. We've gotta send our message to the public and innocent lives will be lost, but there's no other way."

"I guess you're right." It still didn't sit quite well with Stone. The reasoning didn't seem to completely justify their tactics and it smacked of hypocrisy. "Why not just take the main STORK Tower down altogether? You know, the headquarters." Stone took another drag on his cigarette.

"It's next on the list. We just needed to interrupt the business at these clinics first. Make people reconsider their blind obedience to Unity. We've got Zealots all across the globe tonight, carrying out the same mission."

"I didn't know that."

"I told you before that we're just a small part of a much bigger picture. You have to have patience, Stone. You'll see."

"You think so?"

"Absolutely. One day, if you're lucky enough, you'll stand above the ruins of this abomination of a world, victorious. You'll understand the costs we've paid. You'll understand about the lives we've sacrificed. And most importantly, you'll know, first hand, the price of freedom and what it means to have it."

"How will I know when we've won?" Stone pictured the world as Jeremy described with the Tower fallen and the tyranny of Unity dissipated. He could only imagine chaos following such things.

"When the people wake up and realize they had forgotten what freedom feels like. When they wake up that day and can finally ask themselves, 'What do I want to do today?' It will be the day a pregnant woman will walk along the sidewalk unashamed and unafraid of her swollen belly. It will be the day you attend Mass and see your first born baptized, without the slightest dread that the government's hands will likely clench around his or her throat, squeezing out obedience. This is a just war, Stone. People will remember us as heroes shortly after a time when we were once called terrorists."

This set Stone's mind at ease. He imagined the future painted by Jeremy's words. For the first time that night, his family's message and warnings fell away. Their powerful echoes fading and no longer mattered. He did this for them. For their safety and for the safety of Maria's unborn, Stone fought this war. A sudden relief entered him as through an open door while he considered these things. The child born in hiding would have the opportunity to live out his days in a world of freedom, never having known a world without.

"Clem, what's taking so long? Are you about done?" Debra asked over the chat because she hadn't seen him on screen in a long time. He and the female guard had wandered off camera.

"Yes, Madame, allow me to get dressed and I'll be on my way." She saw the female guard exiting the bathroom, fixing her hair, while Clem added, "Wouldn't want to catch a cold."

"I can't believe you're screwing around right now," Debra's tone seethed with a mix of anger and anxiety.

"What can I say? With the cat gone, the mice play!" he quipped, laughing.

"Unacceptable, Clem. We'll have words about this. Get your romp out of there now!"

"The Frenchman fascinates me," Nelson remarked only to Debra, "from the perspective of someone who's not human. He truly seems to know how to live life to its fullest. I'd like to live the way he does if I had ever been born."

"He's an idiot. He'll be the death of us."

"I guess you're right, as always, Jeremy," Stone remarked on their previous conversation, after listening to the chatter, unamused. "Just know that even though I sometimes have these questions and thoughts, it doesn't mean I won't obey your every word. You guys are my family."

"I know," he confirmed and nodded, spinning the steering wheel to make a right turn. "You're still a rookie too. Time will teach you how to deal with things emotionally, just be patient. That's the worst part anyway -- learning how to cope."

The night air had grown chillier during the time spent executing their mission. As planned, the men parked their vans in the previously determined hiding place, out of the frosty outdoor weather. They waited at the rendezvous point down the street from the garage. The five of them huddled together in a tight circle of steaming breaths and snorts like a rounded-up herd of buffalo. Clement shared many details with them -- details about female guards and their *fighting* style. He mentioned that she took him as a *prisoner,* showing him the usefulness of her handcuffs and the sharpness of their metallic grasp.

Jeremy was not entertained in the least, infuriated with the man and his stupidity to perform such an act on the mission. "Enough! I don't want to hear another damn word of it, Clem. You're really not entertaining any of us. It's really unacceptable. If anything comes of it, I'm not sure what the boss will do with you. Doesn't the mark on your arm mean anything at all to you?"

"Thank you!" Debra yelped in agreement through the Auris.

"Sorry, monsieur." Clement withdrew his smiles and perverse jokes while they continued to wait for the cab in silence.

...

Once the vehicle arrived, all the men piled into it, packing it to capacity. Stone thought about the guard, not David this time, but the one Clement seduced. It's certain the woman will die as well, just like David. For the first time, Clement seemed much more sinister to him. *How could someone do such a thing? How could someone be the least bit turned on at such a time? Use another human being for self-gratification and damn them immediately?*

He thought of plenty more questions while sitting pressed up against the Frenchman like they were in a can of sardines. Thinking about these questions and their possible answers was far better than contemplating his own actions and their possible outcomes. Clement's issues gave shelter to the young man's conscience. *To risk everything, risk all of us for something so unnecessary. Surprised that Jeremy hasn't murdered him yet, really, I probably would've killed him by now."* Finally, Stone wondered, *How the hell did he even pull it off? Surely, she saw the branding on his arm?* He wanted to ask Clem so badly, but knew Jeremy had no more patience for the topic. Stone slumped into his seat, mentally and physically spent.

The men made it safely back within the walls of Jeremy's downstairs apartment and the sky's inky darkness began to fade. The aroma of freshly made waffles, cinnamon rolls, eggs, and hash browns wafted through the space; it was exactly the breakfast *Donald* had imagined a few hours earlier. Stone's stomach clenched and turned with pent up anxiety, but finally relaxed with relief as he swallowed the delicious food. The savory tastes, mixed with the sweet, melted in his mouth. It was just the thing he needed -- hell, it was what everyone else needed too -- after such a long, exhausting night.

Stone surprised himself, thinking about the food and actually enjoying it after all that they'd done. *Donald* thought of food, but he didn't think he would have actually been hungry. He believed the appetite would dissipate after rigging up explosives and meeting the guard, his first victim, but he was just as hungry as he'd ever been. They all sat together in the dining room, passing food to one another and discussing what they did and what was to come with growing excitement. Outside, the light grew ever brighter.

"Debra," Francis turned, looking over his shoulder, "turn the tele on, if you don't mind!"

"News?"

"But of course!" The Frenchman's laugh was muted as he stuffed his face with a monstrous bite of cinnamon roll, getting its creamy icing all matted within his mustache.

Apparently, the ritual involved coming back to the apartment, eating, and waiting for the news to break. The men made bets about how long it would take -- three minutes, ten, thirty -- but they had never done a job on such a large scale before, so really had no idea. Times before this, their missions were localized jobs: a small bomb here, one there, vandalism of a STORK clinic, and other smaller acts. But this time it was very different. This time they had taken part in a coast-to-coast planned event that ticked closer and closer to its hour of fruition.

"What time is it set to happen?" Stone could not, for the life of him, remember the details. His mind swarmed with opinions and emotions that had never traversed his imagination before, making it difficult for him to retain anything of the mission's specifics.

"Damn, boy! If I have to say this once more, I swear I'm going to wring your neck!" Eddie shouted across the overcrowded glass-topped table shaking his head, "The fireworks start at eight thirty our time. Eight-thirty, you hear?" He then repeated the time once more very slowly, in a caveman's articulation, *"Eiigghhhht-thuuuurtyyy."*

It was two hours away and Stone couldn't believe the amount of time that had elapsed from the moment he packed the van. Just minutes before he perceived it as a long night, but now, now it seemed short as the time for the bombs to detonate approached. He glanced over at Debra, as she sipped from her mug upon the couch, wrapped in a blanket and speaking to Nelson. Stone very much desired to be alone with her, for all the noise and other men to vanish. She appeared so comfy, her hair wrapped in a tight bun with strands of loose hair tucked neatly behind her ears. She blew the steam off of the coffee as she drank, her lips looking so full and beautiful as she did. There she sat, oblivious to his gaze, asking Nelson of statuses and ensuring there were no irregularities.

Stone wanted to feel the softness of her sweater, he wanted the comfort of her warmth and the aroma of her perfume in his immediate presence. He stood from the table and cleaned his dishes of all sticky residue and crumbs in the sink with scorching hot water. Once he finished, he joined Debra on the couch, but not too closely, not as close as he wanted.

"Are you nervous?"

"Not really. Just sort of tired. Wish I could nap at least."

"Get yourself some coffee!"

"I've had some. Sometimes I feel like it just makes me more tired."

"Weird."

Jeremy and Clement stood from the table after eating and stepped outside, leaving their dishes behind uncleaned. Stone imagined Jeremy was about to lay into the misbehaved man as he promised he'd do earlier. A few more moments passed and Eddie took leave from the table to speak to his mother. Francis went to check in on his brother to see how he fared after being a target of Jeremy's wrath.

...

Debra looked up from her mug and almost whispered, "What is it, Stoney?"

"Do you ever feel bad for them?"

"Them?"

"You know," Stone looked to make sure no one else was listening, scratching his shaved head with his chewed nails, "do you ever feel bad for the people that die?"

"Of course. Worst part of the job," she replied, frowning.

"I'm just...I don't know."

"I don't mind, just say it."

"I don't know...I mean...sometimes," the antique analog clock upon the wall ticked forward, "I feel like we aren't attacking the right people."

"It's not up to us."

That answer came from the part of Debra that he couldn't understand. He didn't think she belonged in such a place, a den of savages and warriors. She was not simply sweet and caring, she was those things for sure, but she was also hardened to the reality of life. She lived in a twisted existence and Stone didn't think a flower of such beauty deserved to live entangled, smothered out by the weeds she allowed to grow around her. How, why, what she was really doing there, he couldn't understand. She was the main reason that he never ran from it. Every time he thought he might cut and run, he remembered her and thought that as long as she was there, being a Zealot must come with some well-hidden virtue.

"I just feel like as time goes on, I find myself not fighting the things I thought I hated -- the things I signed on to fight."

"You don't hate STORK? They're forcing women to abort their babies?"

"I mean, the majority of those women are choosing to do that, are they not?"

"I'm shocked, really Stone." She plopped her mug down and looked at him with confusion. "You can't believe the propaganda. Those women they interview are either soulless or they're paid actresses. Most of these women going to clinics are being forced to do so. The pressure of Unity's compliance requirements and society's empty promises are shoveling them into the furnaces as we speak." She raised her voice and Nelson hid behind his couch on the screen in front of them, "I hate STORK with everything in my being. Disgusting. For so many reasons, it's sickening, and no one except us seems to care. They've all been blinded, reprogrammed, and tied down."

"Well, I guess I'm really more concerned with the women who don't want to be there. They're going to die for doing something they didn't want to do in the first place. How is that right?"

"The world is often grey. It's rarely ever black and white, but we have to choose this or that. The world wouldn't be the mess it is if things were always so simple." Debra thought for a moment, "Did you see that story about the woman who went to the clinic freely? The story about the father?"

"No, what are you talking about?"

"The other day a woman went to a clinic, against her lover's wishes. The father of the child tried to stop her. He screamed and begged and slammed his fists against the door to the clinic. He shouted, 'Please don't kill our baby, please! Please honey, don't let them kill my baby!' They just had him carried away in a cop car as if *he was the crazy one.*"

"That's sad."

"Yes, it's sad." Her eyes flared, "It's evil...and it's an evil that must end."

"I just want Unity destroyed. He's the root of it all anyway. Why can't we just destroy him?"

"You only say that because you think it's easier. No innocents, but there're innocents in every battle. It's a chaotic world out there, you gotta be tough. Also, Unity runs the show, but it's the people that allow it. They're all compliant to his terrors."

Her words were even more comforting to Stone than Jeremy's. She made an even more convincing argument than he had, something Stone didn't expect. He halfway expected that when he told her of his misgivings, she would jump up and run away with him, but it wasn't so. She only persuaded him further that it was he who was wrong. Stone was over-emotional, soft, and not hardened like Debra. Even with the perspective he gained from her reasoning, he still couldn't fully come to grips with what they had done. His stomach wrenched itself into knots.

...

One hour. The hands on the clock seemed to not only twist along the numbers, but they also seemed to skip forward, jumping from single digits to doubles rapidly as the time approached and the sunlight flooded into the ceiling-high windows. Stone's frayed nerves came back to clutch at him once again, along with a dose of self-loathing that made him wonder if he was the crazy one. Everyone around him seemed excited as they restlessly waited for Nelson's announcement, followed by the headlines. It was as if they were bringing in the new year, complete with all of the celebration, but without the silly glasses and sparklers. He didn't share their enthusiasm. No part of him felt the thrill the others seemed to feel. Even his smile was fake, a façade stuck in place unmoved and unaffected by the others.

"I've got the champagne and OJ ready!" Eddie shouted as he brought the glasses out of the cabinet, dancing.

"Go ahead and pop the top off," Jeremy suggested, "no one's going to want to fool with it once eight-thirty rolls around."

Stone looked and examined the branding along his forearm. The crosses were exceptionally smooth, which caused them to shimmer as they caught the sunlight. He wondered where his family was at that very moment, whether or not they had actually left yet. He desired nothing other than to see them and enjoy their company: Maria's laughter, Cole's silly theories, even Michael's debates seemed more appealing than the demons surrounding him. Stone didn't truly believe that the Zealots were all that bad. Even still, his biggest problem was that they offered him no privilege of sympathy. They simply didn't think the same way.

Even in his youth, he realized life had dealt him a pretty fair hand, all things considered. The people sharing his company in that den weren't afforded the same experience. Their families had been murdered, lost, some of them detained in Unity's prisons for life. They had much more reason to be angry than he did and they had much more fuel with which to stoke that anger. They had bottomless quantities of fuel comprised of hatred, vengeance, and personal sorrow. It was like oil, black, the fuel of fossils; old dead things and broken memories, broken childhoods. They drilled into themselves, into their emotions, and stoked the fires with the hatred they excavated daily.

The clock ticked eight-twenty-nine.

"Devices are ticking their last!" Nelson shouted over everyone, raising his own speaker's volume until the announcement all the chattering Zealots could hear it.

Stone thought of the guard, *"Please God, have mercy on David. Just another man; just ignorant. Please, Christ, have mercy on him."* He signed his heart with the crossing of his right hand. David was likely chatting over coffee with the other employees, having spent the majority of the night alone. Stone imagined it was his favorite time of the day, close to the end of his shift, and shared with his coworkers. He also began to think of the female guard and wondered what sort of pain she herself must have kept, looking for intimacy in a networking closet with an IT guy.

As for the doctors, though, he imagined their clawing and grabbing tools, their pills of death. Stone thought of the clinic faculty that saw nothing the least bit wrong with Unity's laws, the forced compliance of their patients. Sobbing mothers, scared fathers, the babies who would still die anyway. He knew his murder was no more justified. There wasn't anything he could draw from, the emotions within him formed like a twister against a shack, sending its parts all across the plains of his conscience.

...

His ears listened, and he imagined a soft bang far in the distance, with the same loudness as a pen drop. The clock ticked forward and read eight-thirty.

"Detonation successful. Connection to devices lost."

The Zealots stood and cheered. Stone sustained the faux-smile upon his face as he remained seated on the couch, watching for the headlines to change. Everyone stood waiting, eyes fixed to the screen, silent. Minutes passed and the Zealots were surprised. Eddie and Francis lost their bets; it took longer than five to ten minutes. Fifteen minutes had passed before the anchorwoman's face finally distorted, bewildered and confused about what she read and by the news spoken through her Auris.

"Ladies and Gentlemen...we...um, there seems to have been a sort of attack!" She hadn't delivered breaking news of this scale in the entirety of her career. "I understand you all would like some information...so would I." She stumbled over herself until more details were shared. "It appears that bombs have detonated at

STORK clinics...everywhere...we aren't sure who the culprits are..." The poor anchorwoman had very little to offer her viewers, it was so early in development.

The men and Debra jumped around excitedly, hugging one another and offering words of congratulations. Jeremy brought Stone to his feet and placed his arms tightly around him like a bear, "You did an outstanding job, I'm very proud of you. You handled it really well. Glad you were there to help me!"

"No problem."

"Debra and Nelson, great jobs you two. Man, this is wonderful," Jeremy gushed, watching as aerial footage of flames and ambulances began to flash over the screen. He poured himself more champagne.

They watched and waited, flipped the news between stations from regional channels to local ones. The news anchors in Birmingham were sobbing, weeping over the footage they played for everyone. Woodlawn, Northside, Glen Iris, and even Mountain Brook's clinic were in ruins. The buildings were emptied of all window glass. Glass shards spewed outward into the parking lot that people walked over carelessly in the chaos. Bricks were diminished to rubble and dust, blackened and smoldering. Clouds streams and billowed from the buildings into the frosty sky above as helicopters and drones buzzed overhead. Stone looked for the guard, only to find bloodied unidentified bodies lying in the parking lot and hanging from what was left of the building's walls.

A crushing gravity crashed into Stone, heavy and dizzying, he stood and left the downstairs apartment. The noise and excitement of the others kept them unaware of his absence, as he went to reassemble his sanity over the calming smoke of a cigarette.

"What have I done?" Sirens filled the air in every direction, fire trucks, and ambulances, police cars. Everyone sped along on different courses for the same reason. "What the hell have I done?"

CHAPTER FOURTEEN

Earlier that morning, before the sirens made the city aware of any calamity, Isaac awoke feeling fully refreshed. He gained happiness with every crunchy spoonful of cereal he consumed, fully rested and with Susan's company. She had been working on her make-up. Her eyes deepened with eyeliner, making her green irises pop from beneath her long lashes. The eye-contact she made melted parts of his soul with each loving glance. Susan wasn't always so sweet to him, but she was always beautiful and he never went a moment without loving her. She was in a good mood, ready to get taken care of by her doctor at the STORK clinic.

"Love you."

"I love you too, darling," she replied, brushing her eyelashes with mascara and curling them with her gold-toned eyelash curler.

"Seems we've received an update on our STORK case!" Isaac viewed the email within his Visum. His vision darkened when he opened the update and he began to read aloud to Susan. "Dear Mrs. and Mr. Lewis, we are pleased to inform you that you have been fully approved and qualified for your *Custom STORK Child.*" Susan squealed with joy over the news, as Isaac continued reading, "Fertilization should be complete within five to seven days. You will receive updates once a week on the status and health of the fetus as it grows. Be sure to give me a call if you have any questions. Sincerely, Jocelyn. P.S. Congratulations, I'm so excited for the two of you!"

"That's amazing! Seriously? We were approved? I have to call my mother! I can't believe it! Are you serious?" Susan threw down her various beauty tools and stood up from the oversized kitchen table.

"Hang on, Susan." Isaac chuckled, his heart rejoiced from her reaction, "I know you're excited, but wouldn't you like to tell them over dinner or something? We could make a feast of it!"

She looked saddened, frustrated with his interruption. Impatience afflicted her as she began to tap it out rapidly on the tiled floor with her foot. Susan crossed her arms once she canceled the phone call, "I guess you're right. But, would you invite your mother as well?"

"Yes?" he laughed.

"My mom has yet to forgive her. I'm hoping the news might break through the drama."

"Really? It's been three years since that New Year's Eve fiasco." Isaac shook his head, and continued, "I mean, I guess we could just take her out some time, just the three of us. We could tell them separately."

"If we do, we must tell mine first. Mother would be really pissed off if she were last to hear."

"Yeah, you're right. Mine's more reasonable. Heck, she'll just be happy about being a grandma finally."

"Do not ruin this, Isaac." She glared at him, her green eyes looked like heated embers.

"Sheesh, it's a joke."

"I just, I mean, can you believe this news? It makes no sense to me. Do you think there may have been a mistake?"

"What do you mean?"

"I mean, it's been over a month and no one came by or anything. We haven't been investigated like she said we would be. It's as if they're just handing *it* over to us. Doesn't that seem a bit unusual to you?"

"You're welcome, Isaac," Unity whispered, *"but remember, what is given can be taken away."*

"Well, maybe we just made a good impression in our first meeting. Maybe the AI investigator they talked about saw that everything checked out? I don't know."

"Yeah, I've just never heard of it being so simple. Hope there hasn't been a mix-up or mistake."

"I'm sure there hasn't been. Jocelyn wouldn't have emailed us. And you can give her a call if you're really worried."

Susan wasted no time and called the woman immediately, sharing the audio with Isaac's Auris, and received a quick confirmation. "It's been cleared," the woman answered Susan's question promptly saying, "someone very important really cares about y'all."

"Who?"

"I'm not at liberty to say, only that they said your husband should keep up the excellent work he's been doing."

"Huh?" Her face squinted.

"The person who approved the request has been keeping a close eye on Isaac's work. This person is very impressed with him and hopes he continues to do as well as he has been."

"Oh..." Susan smiled at Isaac the same way she had so long ago when they first met. Fresh love bloomed from her face as she looked at him. Tears came to her eyes and she shook her head, "Thank you, Jocelyn. Have a wonderful day."

"You too, sweetie. Holler if y'all ever need anything."

Susan ended the call and looked at Isaac, her make-up was only half complete with one set of lashes curled and the other straight. Her husband embraced her and gave her a hug and kiss, rubbed her back, enjoying the feel of the soft material of her nightgown over her warm skin.

"I told you I'm working hard for us," he chuckled.

"I know, I love you. I'm sorry I ever doubted."

"We're going to be parents to a beautiful little girl."

"Yes, we are. And our lives are going to change forever." She wept tears of joy that soaked his shirt.

"*Trust in me, Isaac.*"

"Hey, why the tears?"

"I'm just so happy, so excited. Our girl's going to be the best. We'll have to decorate...and paint and I want you to move your office downstairs. The skylight in that room will be great for the baby."

Isaac sighed, "Alright, fine."

"We need her room to be close ours and there's no way we're moving the gym downstairs."

"Okay, okay. We've got a few months to get all of this done. Chill."

"I will. I'm just excited. My dreams are coming true!"

"I love you, honey."

"I love you too. Ah, look at the time! Gotta finish getting ready. We've got a big day ahead of us."

"Are you nervous at all?"

Susan returned to her place at the kitchen table, before her vanity mirror. "About our daughter?"

"No, I mean about today -- the appointment. Doc said it's not going to be pretty."

"No, just ready to get there already. Shame it doesn't open earlier."

"What time is our appointment?"

"Eight-thirty, Isaac. I've told you this a dozen times now. But, we have to be there at eight sharp to get everything in order, plus they may be able to take me back a little earlier."

Isaac rolled his eyes. *As if ten minutes will make much of a difference,* he kept his thoughts to himself. *We're going to be there for hours.*

"Don't roll your eyes at me, boo," Susan teased, her gaze pierced through the eye-lash curler, "I see you there."

"I'll call for a cab shortly," Isaac offered, realizing he no longer had an appetite once he returned to his bowl of cereal. Now the cornflakes were a soggy mush. "I'm sorry we're not able to go in an undercover car like you wanted."

"It's fine, it's a good day. I couldn't care less at this point." She smiled at him.

...

Isaac spent the rest of his time waiting for her on the front porch. It was a beautiful day and the sting of winter couldn't pierce his jacket. The warmth of STORK's news comforted him, warmed his soul just enough to reduce the chill of December to nothing more than what seemed like a breeze. Isaac smiled, the first true smile that had crossed his lips in months. Susan was satisfied, Unity came through on the promises, and all seemed truly serene. The animals outside, the squirrels that sprung from tree limb to limb, filled his heart with excitement. His appreciation was childlike as he waited for Susan. All seemed beautiful and new -- as if a long night had ended and a new day dawned upon him. He took deep breaths from the frosty air and it refreshed him like menthol.

"Thank you, Unity. Bless you," he praised.

"I expect some real results now. Remember my words; all that is given can be taken away."

"I will do all you say. The Zealots will be destroyed."

"Good, Isaac, good."

"Is it possible for me to work with the others you mentioned? I can team up with them, right?"

"Of course, Isaac. All in good timing. I've already arranged a meeting."

"Thank you again, Unity."

"Your cab is here."

Isaac stepped into his house and called out for his wife, "Susan, our ride is here!"

Once she finally gathered her things together and made her way outside, her beauty struck Isaac once again. She never failed to dress her best, even on occasions such as a doctor's appointment at which she would surely need to remove her clothes and put on one of those unattractive gowns. She never made excuses to go out in pajamas or with her face unmade. Sometimes Isaac complained interiorly because of all the waiting it caused. He felt as if he spent the majority of his waking hours on pause for her. But on that morning, the time she took to get ready didn't bother him at all. Her gorgeous smile magnified her beauty and she looked at him with eyes of worship, subduing any complaints he might have had.

...

The cab took them to their destination, the clinic in Mountain Brook, and dropped both of them off at the front door. The time was seven-fifty and the staff welcomed them into the clinic before the facility even officially opened.

"You two are early!" the guard greeted them from the front desk. His badge read 'David'.

"Yeah, she insisted that we beat everyone else here."

"Yes, today's actually going to be a pretty busy day, apparently. Lots of second appointments due and they take longer, so say the docs. Might even be a line today once the doors open."

Isaac laughed, *once the doors open*. "I'm sorry, y'all must hate people like us."

"No, I could care less! Shifts 'bout to end soon. I've pretty much already checked-out mentally." The guard laughed, mostly to himself.

"Ah, you're night shift?" Isaac asked as Susan began filling out a form beside him at the front counter.

"Yeah, and an hour of the morning shift because the day shifter has a *kid* and they *need* that time. Which is the usual shift for guards, but I tried to see if he'd take the morning shift a little early." The guard laughed again, "But I think he just likes to sleep in, while I try to survive off of coffee."

"I see, I see. I work for the department. I can relate."

"Oh, yeah? You think there's any opening there?"

"Maybe, you interested?"

"I may be," the guard leaned forward to Isaac over the counter, "I want to do something more exciting. This place just bores the hell out of me, you know?"

"Nothing too thrilling last night?"

"Nope, nothing. Some IT guys visited. They were only here for a little while, but nothing before them and nothing after. I just...I guess I just want to work on something that better suits me. You know? Like, I ain't old enough for this job yet. Does that make any sense?"

"Yeah, I know exactly what you mean. You can apply for sure. We've got some real *P.O.S's* in our group. We'd be more than happy to replace them with you," Isaac flattered the guard with a smile, but he didn't mean any of the words as he looked over the bulbous protrusion of the guard's gut. There wasn't a chance he could pass the physical unless he lost forty pounds, something he doubted possible for the man.

"Awesome! I'll do it once I get home."

"Sign in honey," Susan commanded, nudging his arm with the clipboard. She had waited for him to stop talking to the man, thinking he would never finish his conversation.

Isaac began to sign and took note of the names above theirs. The signatures weren't typical in their form, unlike most would be. Even as a child, Isaac found the world of investigation and forensics fascinating. Due to this fascination, he developed impressive skills in one of his favorite forensic sub-topics: graphology, which involves handwriting analysis. The field attracted him, not only for its novelty in a mostly paperless world, but also for its usefulness in aiding one to see behind the curtain, so to speak.

People say the eyes are the windows to the soul, but in Isaac's opinion, handwriting -- one's personal penmanship -- is the true window into the soul. He always believed handwriting analysis to give a clearer picture into a person's character than the eyes because it reveals much more than things like fear or possible deception. Penmanship can reveal personalities, habits, traits, and, at times, has even revealed pseudonyms. Lies, secrets, hidden things are commonly made visible by a person's unique pen-strokes.

"You mentioned that some IT guys visited this facility last night?"

"Yeah. Why?"

"Hm." Isaac looked closer at the signatures, "It's probably nothing -- just unusual."

"What do you see?"

"There were two of them?"

"Yes."

Isaac set the clipboard down, "It's probably nothing. Just that their names suggest that they may have been adopted or something of that nature." Isaac wasn't being honest with himself in thinking there wasn't any real reason for his paranoia. "I wouldn't worry about it."

"Ah, well how do you know?"

"Their names show hesitations in the pen strokes. And there's a hiccup between their first and last names."

"Hm, uh...interesting. So, you can learn things about people by their writing?"

"Yeah, pretty good bit, actually."

"Think you could do one on me?" The guard asked, now more intrigued with Isaac's skills and what they might reveal of himself. Women, and some men began straggling into the clinic, approaching the sign-in sheet. Suddenly, Isaac actually felt relieved about Susan's insistence that they arrive so early. The line that was forming looked miserable. People stood, waiting peevishly for the one in front of them to finish registering.

"Yeah, write me a paragraph and I'll see what I can pick out while I wait. Tell me about your night and include a lie about it," Isaac instructed, laughing, inwardly. It infuriated him when people requested such things. It was always quite the same: normal folks' writing revealed normal folks' problems. Isaac preferred criminals with their felon claws, the batwings, and edgy characters that revealed back-stabbing and a hatred for the opposite sex, or violent tendencies. With certainty, he mused that nothing would bore him more than analyzing David's lower zone idiosyncrasies. Even the chickish writing of a bubbly eighteen-year-old woman would probably prove more interesting. "Just bring it over to me once you're done. I'm going to sit with my wife."

"Sure thing!" The guard beamed excitedly in anticipation of his upcoming inspection. Taking a sheet of paper and the pen, he began immediately.

Isaac walked towards his wife who sat upon a blue cushioned chair in the lobby. She stared blankly into space, likely reading her favorite blog on her Visum. She definitely had resting witch-face syndrome -- that look that could probably set something on fire if she tried hard enough. It wasn't a pleasant sight -- she truly was beautiful -- yet the expression on her resting face was like hardened armor.

Isaac remembered the night he first approached her when he was out with friends several years ago. When he first saw her from across the bar, she stood out amongst the others, like a Venus Flytrap. Unique and breathtakingly gorgeous, but likely the end to anything that landed on her.

"Hey boo," he said carefully as he approached her, hoping the Flytrap's jaws wouldn't close on him as he sat beside her in the lobby.

"Isaac made a new friend?" she replied with a chuckle.

Isaac looked over at the guard who was busy journaling and responded quietly, "Um, no, he's just wanting the handwriting analysis."

"You poor thing. Well, hopefully, we'll get called in before you have to do anything."

The clock ticked to eight-fifteen right as Isaac checked, "Think they'll see us early?"

"I don't know. Hopefully. It's apparently going to take four to five hours."

"Lewis?" a voice called from a newly opened door, beside the kiosk. A woman, probably the doctor's assistant, stood there looking around for her patient. The couple promptly stood and made their way to the caller.

"Yes?"

"Hey, Mrs. Lewis, we've been having some network issues or something of the sort this morning and..."

"Yes?" Susan's voice graveled, the anger emerging as she began to suspect what was coming.

"We're just having difficulty pulling your information. Do you, by any chance, have physical documentation with you today?" Susan shook her head from side to side, crossed her arms, and sighed.

"Well, we need to make copies of a physical ID because we can't connect to our server, apparently." Isaac immediately thought back to what the guard had mentioned.

"You've got to be kidding me." Several other women made their way through the front door and further lengthened the check-in line.

"I wish I were ma'am. You'd think we'd be beyond IDs and such in this day and age. Then again, we still have a fax machine." The woman laughed and found no lightened moods in her guests. "Would mine suffice?" Isaac asked, reaching for his.

"I'm afraid not, sir. She's the one we need to verify."

"This is ridiculous." Susan began fidgeting with her hair, combing at it with her hands irritably, "Why can't you just call your technical support?"

"We have, but it may be a while before they're able to send anyone out."

Isaac had an idea, "Could you guys go ahead and get her set up? I'll run home real quick and grab whatever you need."

"Um," the nursing assistant thought, "I guess that would be alright."

"Honey, you can't just leave me here alone," Susan whined, gripping his arm.

"They're just going to prep you." Isaac rubbed her back to reassure her, "Get you to a room. You'll be okay. I'm sure you don't want to wait in the back of that line." Susan looked over at the miserable people standing in line and then over to the coughers that sat reading in the lobby.

"Alright."

"I love you, honey." Isaac leaned forward to kiss, Susan turned her face away suddenly and his lips landed on the side of her head. She was never one for public affection.

"I love you too, Isaac. Hurry along, now," she gestured with her hand as if to shoo him away.

...

Isaac watched his wife vanish behind the door along with the nursing attendant. A noise of flapping papers caught the attention of his ears. It was the guard at the counter, David. He walked over to him to obtain the paragraphs he wrote. Isaac's eyebrows raised in surprise when he saw just how much that guard had written in such a short amount of time.

"Wow! This might take a while," Isaac laughed.

"Yeah, sorry. I'm just really fascinated." David grinned.

"What time do you leave for the day?

"In about forty minutes, at nine. I left my email on there for you."

"Oh, nice! I'll send it over once I'm done. If you turn out to be free of psychotic tendencies, I'll include an application." Isaac smiled, shook hands with the man, and set about his mission to gather the things needed for Susan's appointment.

He could picture her, red-hot with rage, waiting in a patient room. The thought made him giggle a bit, as he rode over to their house. A red woman, gorgeous, yet terrifying in a hospital gown --fuming and seething with frustration. The poor nursing assistant likely could do nothing to calm her; she'd go back and speak sourly to all the other nurses after having to deal with Susan.

Isaac watched the time pass like a hawk circling his prey during his ride to the house, anxious to get back to

Susan quickly as possible. Time kept speeding forward despite his anxiety. Minutes felt like seconds and then, before he knew it, he arrived. The time showed eight-thirty-two.

"She is going to kill me," he muttered quietly to himself, searching the drawers and file cabinets like a madman. He made a mess everywhere he looked, another thing that would enrage Susan once she got home, but he didn't have any spare time to clean up after himself. Urgency took over his very being. He couldn't understand why he felt it so strongly. Skin-crawling sensations of impending doom deeply unsettled his spirit. The hairs on his back stood when he finally located Susan's collection of documents and identification. *About damn time.* He felt some relief, suddenly, but only momentarily, and the anxiety came hurtling back. The unsettled feeling -- it was like the tides of the oceans -- washed over him unchanged as it permeated his being once again. Isaac checked the time once, right when he climbed into the waiting cab — eight-forty, it read.

...

He sat in the cab's passenger seat, wondering why it failed to follow his order to continue its trip. "Hello, Jasmine," he called, using the car service's AI name, "can we move damn it? I'm in a hurry!"

"Sir, your destination has been set to 'off limits.'"

The AI woman's hollow voice filled him with terror. He was no stranger to the emergency protocols followed by public transports. He knew exactly what she meant by it. In all likelihood, something was happening in the area, but that 'something' could be anything. Filled with sickening dread, he feared the worst, "Move, damn it! I work for the department. If there's an emergency, then I need to be there, you POS!" The car didn't respond and continued its non-responsive attitude even with his angry blows pommeling the side door.

"Location is off-limits."

Isaac had already tried to call Susan after the car's initial response to his commands. The cell tower was, apparently, overly busy. It only rang and rang. Endless ringing. The impending doom manifested itself. The feeling he experienced in the pit of his gut began to crush his entire interior being with pressures and sensations that were impossible to ignore -- the kind people only consciously experience in times of great crisis.

"Unity?" Isaac shouted as he began to investigate local news within his Visum. He got no response. However, despite Unity's silence, the cab began to roll forward, increasing in speed at an unbelievable pace. "What in hell is happening?"

He called for Susan again, but he heard no ring at all this time around. Silence. Then a voice came through, notifying users of the high call volume, citing a nationwide outage. Isaac couldn't vent the cacophony of emotions assaulting his interior person. There was nothing he could do as the car sped through the streets. The ensuing interior chaos made him unsure of what emotion was even appropriate to feel as they passed through him, flipping and changing faster than he could react to them.

"Unity, I know you hear me. Answer me!" Isaac screamed out in frustration. At that moment, the cab turned a corner and his eyes detected a column of smoke rising from the direction of the clinic. His heart sank and he desperately tried to deny the reality of what he knew to expect. "No...no, no, no," Isaac whimpered to himself, "no, please. Please, God." He leaned forward in his seat, trying to get a better view of the scene ahead of him. Emergency responders raced past him, their lights strobed as the blur of color rushed forward, blocking his sight. "What the hell is happening?"

Finally, with the clinic in sight and filling his vision, hot tears burned at the edges of his eyes and out loud to no one at all, he cried out, "My God! Susan! Susan, no, baby...please no. Jesus, please!" The unbelievable sight made him dizzy, lightheaded and his thoughts were incomplete. Only feelings and basic emotions made themselves known to Isaac: fear, sadness, shock. His lips stammered as his head rattled atop his neck spewing curses and shouts.

He stumbled out of the cab and fell before the inflamed and smoking building on all fours, cutting his hands and knees on the glass that had blown outward from the building's window frames. The middle portion of the structure had completely collapsed upon itself; its roof sunken within the confines of the walls. Flames and clouds of black smoke billowed from the doors and windows as if it escaping the very gates of Hell itself.

"Susan!" he shrieked, barely forming the word in an understandable tone. "I was only gone for a few minutes...how...how so quickly? What happened? I don't...I don't understand. Why?" The slobbering and tearful man stood and looked for anyone who made it out, trying to identify any as his wife. There were bodies laid out in the parking lot to his left, only a very few showing any signs of life. Rigor-mortis had already begun to set in for some of the bodies, bending and curling their arms. Although the stiffness of death can sometimes occur within ten minutes, it often takes several hours, so Isaac couldn't be sure whether some of the bodies actually moved or if the waves of heat passing over them just created the illusion of life.

He didn't see red hair on any of the bodies, but some of the women's hair had been completely burned off, leaving their heads scorched and bald. Isaac reached for one of the bald corpses dressed in a clinic gown and turned her over onto her back. The face wasn't recognizable due to the burns covering it and a foul odor reeked from the burnt flesh. The intense heat and fire had turned the eyes of this 'Jane Doe', this unknown female, white. Dead eyes with no life in them stared up at him -- hazy and dry like those of a fish left long out of the water.

"Susan, baby?" Isaac shouted into the blackened face, shaking the body to no avail. How confused he was and how desperate to find her. Yet, he was not able to discern if this woman was his beloved wife. He startled as he realized that her cooked flesh began to peel off under his tight grip, revealing pink and red meat beneath.

"Ah!" he screamed. "I'm sorry, I'm so sorry." He pulled his hands back from the stranger's sticky and ragged skin to wipe the tears and snot from his face upon his coat sleeve. He looked again over the other bodies. Some of them were completely scorched and their flesh was as charcoal, charred and cracked with red streaks of ligament and other tissue exposed underneath. Many were missing arms or legs, which did not bleed, and some had their entrails hanging out of their bodies beside them. Isaac realized he was looking for his wife amongst a pile of dead bodies.

"Where are you?" he screamed. "Please God, please, let me find my Susan."

"Sir, you need to get back. This area is too hazardo-"

Isaac shoved the firefighter back, freeing himself of his grip, "I'm an officer."

"Sorry sir, I didn't see a badge," the firefighter answered, putting his hands out, indicating he meant no harm. "Are you okay? Were you in the explosion?"

"Explosion? How? Wha...what happened?"

"We don't know yet. We got calls all over the cit-"

"My wife...my wife was in there," Isaac interrupted, pointing his finger and trailed off quickly from the man, to continue his search for her. Hoses fired into the building. The crew tried to fight back the flames still spewing outwards and gigantic hovering water drones gushed water from above the building, casting the smoke in every direction as they moved in and out of it. The inside of the clinic sparkled with embers and melting metals. Sparks flared onto the clinic's marble floors from hanging lights that had partially detached from the ceiling. Isaac could barely stand to look into the flames because the intense heat burned his face. Even though the ambient temperature outside was frigid, it made no difference. The heat forced him to shield his face with his arm. He stood there looking for a way in, calculating a badly formed plan to find her.

"Sir, you can't go in there," warned the same fireman, grabbing at Isaac before he could launch himself into the inferno.

"I think my wife's in there! Please, you gotta do something."

"We have a crew dispatched already, they've been pulling people out. Have you checked by the ambulances?"

Isaac turned and, for the first time, saw the grouping of enormous ambulance busses indicated by the firefighter. Their lights flashed rapidly and agonizing wails of injured people came from them -- muted -- under the screaming sirens and firefighting equipment. He didn't even notice them upon his arrival, the shock of it blew away all rationality from his mind. He noticed many EMTs running from bed to bed, treating anyone they could and packing up the others for transport to the nearest hospital. They laid nearby in agony, waiting. Time took its toll on many of them, as their lifeless and scorched faces stared blankly into the blue sky above.

"Susan!" he called out, rushing towards a red-headed woman in a torn gown that exposed her breasts and abdomen. He could only see her from the side, squirming in the bed, screaming as he had never heard. "Sus-" his voice broke away as the EMTs pulled her towards a very large ambulance bus.

"Do you know this woman?"

"She's my wife. I think that's my wife!" Isaac reached for the bed that another EMT began to load into the ambulance. Panic shook his entire body as he shivered with nervous energy. *This must be Susan*, he thought, but he could not positively identify her and the other EMT prevented him from entering after her.

"I'm sorry sir, we aren't allowed to carry anyone. It's packed with a dozen other patients and we have to save room for emergency personnel to work."

"Please just let me see her. It's my wife. I'm sure of it!"

"We've got to go, Marc! Get yourself in gear, or I'm leaving you!" shouted the other EMT as he climbed into the driver's seat of the gigantic vehicle.

"Alright, get in, but stay in the corner. Don't get in the way," Marc, the EMT, ordered Isaac and opened the back door of the ambulance so he could enter. They both stepped into the vehicle and the driver began to drive before they even had time to close the doors completely.

"Boss said no passengers!"

"It's his wife. Have some respect."

"Whatever, Marc. Boss is gonna be pissed."

Isaac wasn't concerned with their bickering. They barely registered in his ears over the shrieks of the people groaning around him as he made his way closer to the red-headed woman's stretcher. "Hey, baby. Susan, I'm here. It's Isaac," he cooed gently, turning the woman's face toward himself to make sure it was really her. A huge gash cut across the left side of her face. Bubbled, burnt skin surrounded one eye and stretched across her entire forehead down to her ear. The left eye was fully shut and her right eye appeared unable to detect him, even while he hovered directly above her. The pupil was stretched fully open and tears poured out of its corner, over the dirty skin.

She screamed, shifted away, and knocked his hand from her violently. Isaac's face streamed with tears as he looked over the rest of her, it was truly Susan. His

Susan. The sight of her agonizing pain filled him with an aching grief as he leaned over and cried above her legs, one of which had a tourniquet tied around it. Below her left knee, her shin was splintered and slashed deeply in many areas from what he could tell by observing the reddening bleed-through on the bandages.

"Apply pressure to her leg, sir," commanded the EMT and Isaac obeyed him, placing his hand against the hot surface covered by bandages.

He rose up and again looked over the rest of her, partially clothed and covered in bruising, swelling, and lacerations. Her left arm also appeared severely burned. The skin looked like it melted. It hung freely and the color looked to be an unnatural brown hue. The tattoo on her wrist was barely visible due to the discoloring and her middle two fingers were completely missing.

"My poor girl. I'm so sorry. I'm so, so, so sorry! God, I wish I had known something. I wish you had gone with me." Isaac tried to imagine that it could all be turned back. He intensely focused on the horror with an irrational hope that time would reverse and that none of this was real. "How is this happening? How? What the hell is this?" he whimpered under his breath. Time would carry forward, careless of his cries and begging.

"Sir, we need you to sit away for awhile. We need to mark her up for the emergency room."

"Do you..." Isaac cleared his choked voice, "Do you know what hospital? Would I be able to stay with her?"

"You'll likely be escorted to the lobby, while they stabilize her." The EMT began signing a document detailing her conditions and wounds, marking the injuries over a chart of a woman's body. He marked the leg on the chart red, along with marks to her face, her hand, and the left side of her abdomen.

"Do you think she'll be okay?" Isaac was desperate for answers. This was an entirely new experience for him. He was usually the one answering the questions of shocked and worried people. It was a sensation, an experience, he could have happily lived the rest of his days without. "Will they be able to fix her?"

"It's hard to say at this point. I can't make any promises." The EMT shook his head while continuing to scribble on the chart, surely feeling the news just as difficult to deliver as it was to receive. "She is luckier than many of the others back there. Lot of people didn't make it out of the building. Most people didn't, I should say."

"Damn you, Unity!"

"Huh?" the EMT asked, looking in Isaac's direction with confusion at his outburst. Isaac paid him no attention.

"*Watch your tongue, Isaac.*"

"Where the hell have you been? Huh?"

The EMT watched Isaac speak to himself, drooling and dripping snot as he flailed his arms about.

"Sir, are you talking to someone? Do you mind calming down?" The request was unusual, considering that the bus was packed with screaming and moaning people. One would think the EMT wouldn't have even noticed him. However, something about the grieving husband deeply disturbed him.

"Get lost."

The EMT left Isaac to himself and went to the next patient over from Susan.

"Where the hell have you been, Unity? Do you hear me?"

"I've been busy, considering hundreds of clinics have been bombed. Forgive me for not being here to console you for every waking moment."

"So, they were bombed? Zealots?"

"Of course. I've been trying to eliminate them, you know, but it's hard to find good help."

Anger sizzled within Isaac and he clenched his fists so tightly that his own nails carved little half-moons into his palms. The thought of the radicals being the ones to blame for this horror, quickened Isaac's heart rate. Never had he ever felt the urge to slaughter them more than at that moment. He knew in that instant that he would make it his mission to kill every single one of them. Isaac vowed to spend his every waking moment hunting them to extinction.

"Bastards. They'll die. They'll all die for this!" he promised, looking over his wife's burnt and savaged flesh. "I'll kill them all!"

"Sir, are you okay?" the EMT asked, approaching Isaac.

"How am I expected to be okay, right now?" Isaac stepped in the man's direction, spraying spit as he shouted at him. "Why haven't we arrived at the hospital? My wife is probably dying because y'all've done absolutely nothing to help her! What's taking so long?"

"We're almost there," the EMT quipped calmly. Before casting his attention elsewhere, he ordered, "You need to keep the pressure on her leg."

Isaac turned quickly away from the man and did as told, worried that Susan's tether to life was slipping away. She had passed out during the time he spent shouting at Unity and the EMT.

"Susan! My darling! Don't go. No, don't go! Can't leave me baby. We're having a girl. We're having a beautiful girl. I need you to help me. I need you to be there to see her grow up." Isaac began to shake her violently when she didn't respond, careless of her wounds as he believed her life depended on staying awake. There was a prick in his skin, that he didn't quite notice under the circumstances. "Susan...darlin'...wauhp. Huh?" Isaac's speech slurred and his vision became glossy, his surroundings blurred. Colors and shapes became only reflections of light that dimmed rapidly and the last clear image he saw was that of a syringe in his arm. Sleep came to him, deep undisturbed sleep on the floor of the ambulance.

CHAPTER FIFTEEN

"Officials claim there are no new developments concerning the recent attacks," the news anchorwoman reported, "however, the Zealots have taken full responsibility for the bombings, citing Unity's policy of forced abortions carried out at the STORK clinics as the reason."

"I still can't believe it," Michael muttered to himself, sitting in the living room, watching the news. "Lord, please, please help my cousin. Forgive him, Lord." He made the Sign of the Cross over himself.

Upon the screens across every corner of the earth, the same images of the aftermath of the attacks played relentlessly in what was formerly known as the United States and Canada. There wasn't a soul alive that had not seen the devastation, the outward explosions of the buildings caught on street-cams and the billowing smoke rising in the aftermath as fire and rescue crews worked to quench the fires.

"Turn that trash off, Mikey!" Maria demanded angrily from the kitchen. She was busily packing a box of necessities and the most sacred family treasures. He watched the news any chance he got, but his sister had had enough of its constant negative drivel.

"We need to know what's going on!"

"Well, you can listen to it yourself on your Auris. None of us care to hear it anymore. And are you ready? Seems like everyone is working to get packed up, except you. Tonight's the night."

"Father Burns said 'bare necessities,' so I don't know what you're doing packing fine china, and I finished packing yesterday."

Amelia shuffled down the stairs into the living room and turned the television off. "Come upstairs with me, honey, okay?"

"Alright, alright. Fine." He followed her into their bedroom and closed the door, before lying down on their bare mattress.

...

The entire house was starting to look as if it were no longer a home to anyone. The family had worked tirelessly since the news first surfaced and wasted very little time. The place looked barren with all the empty shelves and empty half-opened drawers. They placed toiletries and other sundry items in bins for easy moving. The most valuable things -- things that were too large to make the move -- were stored away in the basement.

Days before, right after the bombs detonated, the family and their priest speedily laid out detailed plans for their exodus. Father Burns visited them, hoping to learn that Stone was innocent of any involvement in the attacks. He prayed the others were successful in their attempts to invite him to flee south with them.

That day, the priest stood ringing the doorbell multiple times, but receiving no answer. Everyone inside had been riveted to the screen before them and the horrible news coming from it. Shocked and tearful, they almost failed to notice anyone was at the door at all. Finally, the sound of someone beating upon the front window startled Michael and he rose to let the priest inside.

"Father," he began, "I...," then he embraced the priest, shedding tears onto the older man's shoulder. "The boy has done it this time. Idiot really done it."

"Have you heard from him?"

"Nothing. God, I hope he's alive. But I just can't..." Michael found it difficult to formulate his thoughts into words. The priest broke free from him eventually and checked on the rest of the family, starting with the women, who were inconsolable in the throes of sudden grief.

Cole sat silently, staring blankly at the screen as it revealed all the horrors -- from the destroyed burning buildings to the dozens upon dozens of bagged bodies lying to the side of them. He sent a message to his brother, "*Are you okay?*", but received no response. The real possibility of Stone's death was inescapable as he waited for an answer.

Maria wept loudly, lamenting for the sake of her little cousin. The actions were irreversible, they were part of a hole Stone had dug for himself, surely. Nothing could change what had already been done. Further, there would be no mercy in the law for such an atrocity. Almost directly after the attacks, Unity made a public announcement reiterating the severe punishment that those responsible for such crimes will suffer. He reminded everyone that anyone brought in whom authorities deemed to have the least bit involvement with the atrocities, or who they determined were associated with the Zealots or Retrogrades, will pay dearly for their crimes against humanity.

Time moved quickly for all who sat in the small living room. Firefighters extinguished the majority of the fires ravaging the clinics and, soon afterward, body counts for the attacks in Birmingham began to come in. First it was twenty, then thirty, then as night approached the dead reached eighty in total. Of course, that number didn't account for the lives of the unborn whose mothers were receiving 'treatment' at the time. In the Mountain Brook clinic, three children -- accompanying their mothers -- lost their lives. The children -- aged one year, four years, and twins aged eleven-years-old perished needlessly. The news flipped through the profiles of each victim, revealing their names, dreams, and those who survived them. Silent faces appeared on screens everywhere. Photos from an earlier time, showing soundless, smiling faces with no notion that they would soon be met with a violent demise.

...

The night of the attack, once the shock began to dissipate enough to allow the family in Irondale the emotional space to debate their future, the priest made an announcement to them, "I'm going to expedite the process for y'all's relocation. There's no reason we should delay any longer."

"What about Stone?" Maria asked as she began to sob. "We can't leave him!"

"He's dug his grave," Michael responded shaking his head angrily. "There's not a chance in hell; even if he's alive that I'll allow him to travel with us."

"How can you say that? They've obviously got no idea who they're looking for."

"It's not wise, Maria. I love the boy, but he's done nothing other than cause himself and us grief. We're not risking our lives to save a person who's probably murdered dozens through his free will and own doing. It's ridiculous to stick our necks out anymore for him." Michael gulped from the glass of whiskey he had poured earlier and slurred his speech, "God bless him, hope he's forgiven, but ain't a chance in Hell he's coming with us."

"Screw you, Michael."

The priest thoughtfully paced around the room, before pouring himself some of the whiskey. Taking a swig, he was ready to deliver his portion of bad news, "I know, I know. No one *wants* to leave Stone. I love the boy myself, but Mikey's correct. He would endanger everyone -- endanger the well-being of those you'll be staying with."

Maria was shocked, "What? What are y'all talking about? It's a safe house, is it not? You said it's where all the priests hide out? I don't understand the difference. Seems like the perfect place for Stone."

"It's a safe house for the religiously persecuted, dear." The priest knelt before her and held her hands in his. "My brothers and sisters are there and they aren't necessarily high priority targets, but Stone would be."

"I just don't understand," Amelia broke in to join Stone's defense. "How would anyone even know who he is, traveling with us? It's not as if his face is all over the news."

"He's got the mark," Cole interjected quietly from the corner chair beside the fireplace. Everyone looked at him blankly, as if he hadn't spoken loud enough. "He has the mark on his arm, the mark the Zealots receive."

"Huh?" Amelia's expression looked truly confused.

"They all get branded with the Jerusalem cross. Surely the officers know to look for it."

"Well, that's if they look to begin with."

"They will look," Michael agreed turning her direction. "If we are stopped on our way south, they will check our arms. I'd be very surprised if they didn't. They even did a story on the news the other day about it. Everyone knows."

"No, that doesn't make any sense." Amelia thought aloud, "If they check us, we'll all be screwed then. They'll see that Maria's pregnant and then what? They'll take her to a clinic and detain everyone else?"

"You think they do pregnancy tests on everyone leaving the city?"

"That's what I'm saying. Surely they won't look at everybody's arm?"

"Amelia! At least eighty people have just been murdered in this city alone!" Michael pulled his greasy hair out of his ponytail and scratched at his scalp. "Of course they'll be watching out for anyone trying to escape the city. They'll probably stop us just to inquire where we're headed and why."

"Well, God willing, they won't ever see us, even if we're stopped," the priest offered when he realized the argument was mostly a symptom of their ignorance surrounding the means by which they'd be relocated.

"What do you mean, Father?" Michael's eyebrows elevated and came down along with his confusion. The priest hadn't shared his plans for them. They simply assumed that they would take a cab to their destination.

Which, as Michael thought of it, was a silly and ill-thought out assumption.

"We're all going to travel in a semi-truck. You know, what some people call an 'eighteen-wheeler'? We'll be in the back of it, behind a façade of cardboard boxes. That way, if anyone stops us to look inside, they'll only see countless stacks of boxes, most of which will be packed with legitimate goods. Real boxes will surround us and cover the compartment entirely until we arrive. Once there, someone will safely release us."

"Everyone will be in there?"

"Yes, including myself and your doctor. It's not going to be very comfortable."

"So, Stone could travel safely with us?" Maria didn't want to give up on the chance.

"I can't, Maria," the priest answered, sorrow clearly covering his kind face. "I couldn't ask it of my friends. They've never kept such refugees in their homes. Stone's presence alone would jeopardize the dozens of people that live in that town and ruin the lives of the farmers. They'd lose their homes and likely be incarcerated."

"So, we're just going to let him rot here?" Maria raised her voice at the priest, "He'll be found and shot if he stays in the city. Or...or they'll detain him, question him, and then hunt us down anyway because of our association with him."

Cole stood from the dark corner of the room where he sat listening to the others, tears dampened the lashes standing against his bottom eyelids. He worked at training himself not to cry so easily, always keeping his emotions subdued; but the thought of his brother and the terrible sins Stone had committed as a Zealot troubled him deeply. It brought such grief to their family -- to the very people who cared for them over so many years, who fed them and housed them -- his part in these bombings. Stone threw their love and concern into the wind like so much trash.

It infuriated Cole. He had always numbed himself to the tragedies and catastrophes of life by leaning on the belief that people did these things as a result of their free will. But this time, an angry sorrow was the emotion that filled his interior, no room for numbness. He grabbed the bottle of whiskey and popped its top off to claim the remaining three ounces for himself, drinking straight from the bottle and returning to his place in the corner.

Upon taking his first swig, he thought of the lives his brother had ruined, and tears poured out from his soaked lashes for each lost soul. He began to think of their family name, how it would be forever tainted and how the news would read if authorities ever found his brother.

Stone Hanson: Bastard Son of an Addict, Turned Terrorist.

The headline would serve as a positive testimony to the strict laws around reproduction and the dangers of organized religion. The thing Stone had become wasn't his brother. Cole felt truly ashamed of him for the first time. By the third swig in, the raw emotions he kept locked away broke forth unrestrained. He sobbed uncontrollably, the images from the news haunting his mind and heart so deeply that he didn't notice the hand rubbing his back.

"Look at him." Amelia began to cry as well while comforting him, "You can't think it's human to leave Stone behind."

"No." Cole stopped her, sniffling and attempting to regain control over his weeping soon after noticing everyone's eyes trained on him. He seemed to hyperventilate as he wrestled to stop his quaking shoulders and find composure.

"It's okay, let it out."

"No, I'm fine," Cole assured Amelia, wiping the tears from his cheeks and eyes. He used the end of his sleeve to capture the snot and moisture pouring from his nose. His voice sounded like the voice of someone with a very bad cold, "Father's right. Stone's brought this on himself and to endanger the lives of those who want to help us is absolutely unreasonable. We gave him a chance to come home. He's done this to himself. My brother's a cold-blooded murderer. Just the way it is. No other way to cut it."

He downed the rest of the whiskey in the bottle, its fiery warmth spreading throughout him like liquid comfort. The burn perked him up; although, it did nothing to diminish his slight drunkenness. The momentary numbness was like a medicinal salve to him, as the walls to his heart were reduced to rubble and his heart broken by his own brother. "Do we have any else to drink?" he asked, slurring slightly and placing the empty bottle onto the end table to his left.

"I'm calling them," the priest announced, seeming to ignore Cole's inquiry. Straightening up, he prepared to go out to the front porch.

"Think we've got some brandy," Michael offered to his cousin. *Surely the young man will be through after another glass, especially that strong brandy.* "I'll grab it from the cabinet."

Once in the kitchen, Michael reached into the bottom of the cabinet and pulled out the brandy. The amber fluid shimmered as he poured himself a glass. The burned wine brought the heat of a fire to Michael's lips as he took a sip and sifted the spirit in his mouth. He poured more into his glass to account for the taste-test before returning to the living room with another glass, which he made especially for Cole.

The drunkenness was already obvious on Cole; the boy was unpracticed in the art of partaking in adult beverages and it showed. In other circumstances, Michael wouldn't consider allowing his young cousin to drink so much, so fast. In the past, Cole had never drank more than a single beer. *But, this is the end of our world,* he reasoned. *We're moving very soon and Cole will never have the life we did, Lord knows what's instore for him. His only brother has chosen savagery. For now, the boy deserves his drinks, as I do.* Michael's thoughts trailed off and he handed the glass off to Cole. The young man sniffed the glass and jerked his face back, grimacing.

"Yeah, it's a hefty little drink," John laughed, watching the boy, "and where's my glass, Mikey?"

"You got legs," Michael joked dryly.

"Ah, I see how it is." He glanced over at Maria. His pregnant wife had the gaze of a hawk directed straight at him, unhappy that he was able to drink when she could not. He quickly went to the kitchen to fill his own glass, pretending not to notice the warning she wore on her face.

"Whatcha doin' in there, John Foley?" She asked sharply, hearing the glasses clink together as he reached into the cabinet.

"Uh," he hesitated, muting the sounds he made as he poured the pick-me-up, "just getting something to drink. Feelin' sorta thirsty." When he returned, he took care not to make direct eye contact with her, though he still felt her eyes boring a hole right through him.

...

The front door opened and the bearded priest returned, locking it behind him. "We'll also need to inform your doctor, Maria. Just thought about it, she'd probably like to know that we'll be leaving a lot sooner than expected."

"Which is?"

"Well, just talked to them -- said they've got a truck bringing up some furniture to offload and will be making a stop at local breweries. Once they get whatever they need, they'll rendezvous with us behind the old mall. We've got four days to get packed and ready to go. Keep it light, only what you really need. Put anything else in storage. Have y'all figured out what to do with the house yet?"

"We've decided to rent it to some of the local kids. They'll maintain it for the neighborhood's regular Mass celebration."

"Good, I talked to Father James about taking up for me in my absence. I'll get him to reach out to your renters. Just give me their names and contact information." The priest made a quick to-do list of everything that needed to be done.

"Father, where we going exactly?" Cole asked, his head jerked momentarily after taking a sip of the brandy.

"Ah, it's a tiny place -- a farm. Trip's about three and a half hours away."

"But where?" Michael, like all others in the room, had never heard the priest name the place.

"It's south of here, that's all I can tell you."

"Fine, keep your secrets." Michael chuckled shortly, pulling one of his long strands of hair from the glass of brandy and taking another sip.

The priest stood from his place on the couch and gave everyone his farewells for the night. "I'll pray for all of you tonight and for Stone, of course. Y'all stay safe and get to packing as soon as you can."

"Yes, Father, goodnight!"

The rest of the night, following the morning's bundle of attacks was quiet after the priest left. No one argued and no one spoke. The house was cloaked in a heavy silence peppered only now and then with the faint echo of quiet sobs. Cole's face was damp as his weary mind wandered into the realms of imagination -- dreaming that Stone was innocent and that he was safe. Once he woke up, he immediately knew it wasn't so. Time turns back for no one and what is done, is done. Cole spent the next few days, like the others, packing his things, essentially one bag. No one heard a word from him, although they spoke, he didn't answer.

...

On the day of the move -- the exodus -- everyone was silently jittery. Their hearts were broken; yet, possibilities of a peaceful future on the farms filled their every other thought. It was the comfort they sought any time Stone popped into their minds. The farms — surely the farms would provide a welcome refuge from such a violent and hostile world.

"Here, do you mind taking the copies of our keys over to Anita?" Amelia asked her husband, jingling the keys to bring him out of his short nap. "Would hate to forget about handing them off."

"Sure thing." Michael grabbed the keys from her and slipped on his shoes, once he managed a groggy rise from the bed. "So strange to be leaving this place, never having known anything else," he noted, holding the keys in his hands, looking over their notches and shimmer.

"Don't make me think about it," Amelia pleaded, continuing to pack her suitcase full of her favorite clothes -- a decision that had taken days to make. She sat on the floor looking over them, wondering if she had forgotten anything.

Michael bent and kissed her on the forehead and went on his way to Anita's. The walk over was surreal for Michael. The shadowed and dingy street had always been home to him and he was soon going to leave it. Soon, he would travel to a place opposite in every aspect, except for the fact that both places were farms of a sort. He would miss it, even though there wasn't any true beauty to the neighborhood that sat in the shadow of the solar panels. Dogs barked and trains screeched in the distance, all sounds that would soon be only memories for his ears. The scent of rotting trash-filled cans and the smoke from chimney fires that lay trapped beneath the solar panels would no longer fill his nostrils.

He wasn't sure what farms smelt like, if the air was pleasant to breathe, or not. Excitement occupied his every nerve in a tingling sensation as he thought of the future. He did some research on farm life, devoured it in little bits available to him over the internet, and from what he saw it seemed to be a lifestyle untouched by the modern world. There, livestock roamed much of the land, instead of people; trees stood in place of streetlamps; and grass grew where Birmingham had gravel and concrete. The only thing that made him nervous about moving was the trip itself.

Joseph and Anita lived in the house two blocks over, a white single-leveled home with red metal roofing in great need of replacement. Their son, Ronny, was a fine young man who, like all the other men in the neighborhood, worked on the panels above them. It was his job to clean them, so he never worked directly with Michael, but they saw each other often. His family was one of the many that attended Mass each night it was celebrated -- always in Michael's house -- they cheerily helped with dinner by bringing casseroles and pasta.

Michael pushed the antique orange button on their porch and heard the chiming from within their house. A small dog barked inside and he heard the quick steps of a young man, "I've got it, Mom!" A large figure could be seen through the translucent door window. The lock rolled and the doorknob turned.

"Hey, Mikey!" Ronny greeted him, shaking hands with his shorter visitor. The towering young man had shaggy blond hair, about half the length of Michael's.

"Hey, bud. How's it going?" Michael smiled.

"I'm good, everyone's good. Mom's lil' sad, but you know...bird's gotta fly sometime."

"I hear ya, I hear ya." Michael laughed, excited for him, "I was just coming by to drop these off. Don't lose them, we're taking the other copy."

"Ah! Thanks, I'll put them somewhere safe," he promised as Michael placed them into the gigantic palm of his hand. "Say, you wanna come in? It's pretty freezin' out here." Ronny laughed and rubbed the sides of his arms to generate heat.

"Sure." Michael stepped through the door held open by the shivering young man. The house was a wreck with empty take-out bags on the coffee table and dead cockroaches belly-up on the floor. If a person focused intently on the walls covered in saints and crucifixes, the home's uncleanliness could be ignored. That's exactly what Michael tried to do when he wasn't making direct eye contact with Ronny. He remarked on the painting of St. Padre Pio hanging above the couch on the wood-paneled wall behind it. Clanking noises came from the kitchen, then the sound of dishes and water running over them.

"Y'all leaving tonight, right?"

"Yeah, tonight's the night," Michael affirmed quietly, finding a place on the couch.

"We're all going to miss y'all, you know. Your house has been like a second home to everyone in this hood. Just won't be the same with you guys gone." The boy frowned. Michael wasn't sure how to respond, caught off guard by Ronny's sentiment. He never realized that people really cared, that others were saddened by their move. It surprised him that even Ronny found it upsetting.

"Ah, you're too kind. We'll be forgotten soon!" Michael shook his head as he laughed, "Father James called you yet?"

"Yeah, I spoke to him last night. Says he'll do a Mass next week. Seems like a nice priest."

"You've never met him?"

"No, afraid not."

"Ah, well I think you'll like him. When are you moving in?"

"I'll probably start tomorrow. I'm pretty pumped. But, of course, whenever you guys return, I'll have it ready for you."

"Not entirely sure we'll return, really. The way things are looking these days." Michael hung his head, looking at the floor momentarily. The thought of Stone's actions and then of raising a child in a world that wanted to see it mutilated sickened him. As hard as he tried to think of things pure and just, the nightmarish visions always found their way back to him by a dream or in conversation.

"How long will yo-"

"Ronny, do we have company?" Anita shouted from the kitchen.

"Yeah, Mikey came by with the keys!"

Anita wiped her hands dry on a nearby towel and quickly made her way into the living room. "Michael! Please forgive this wreck of a house. I'm sure Amelia doesn't have to tell you twice to pick up your things." She tucked her wildly curly blonde hair behind her ears as she gestured for her son to put away the mess that covered the coffee table.

"Ah, never have a chance, she's a fanatic. Sure, she'd try to sweep the dirt from the yard if I didn't forcefully take the broom from her." Anita laughed as she wrapped her partially wet hands around him for a hug.

"I wanna thank you so much for letting Ronny house-sit for y'all. I'll keep an eye on him to make sure he doesn't destroy the place!" She watched Ronny come by with a trash can to clear away the garbage.

"No problem! I'm sure he'll be fine, he's a great kid." Once Ronny left the room to return the trashcan to the kitchen, Michael leaned closer to Anita and whispered, "And between the two of us, the boss might start trying him out on my job, since he's got two openings."

"How wonderful! That's a pay increase, right?"

Michael looked towards the kitchen, just around the corner he could see Ronny fetching a drink from the fridge, "Yeah, it's a pretty substantial one too. I mean, he won't be vacationing in the Hamptons, but he'll be able to support himself."

"Oh! That's great!"

"What did I miss?" Ronny asked as he returned.

"I was just telling your mother about Father James taking over in Burns' absence." He winked at her. "But, I'm afraid I must get going. There's still some work to do and we'll be leaving in a few hours." Michael stood from the couch.

"Take care of yourself, Mikey...wherever you're going. Keep my precious 'Milia and Maria safe!" She rose to hug him and followed him and her son to the front door to see him out.

"Don't lose those keys, Ronny!" Michael smiled and shook his hand, before bringing him in for a partial hug. "If you need anything at all, get the priest to contact Father Burns. Pretty certain we'll be offline, where we're going."

"Yes, sir will do! Travel safely!" Ronny closed the door and Michael could hear the lock turn as he made his way home.

...

The temperature had dropped dramatically as evening approached. There was bitterly cold moisture in the air, since the haziness from the humidity lingered beneath the panels. The halogen lights were on, as always, and sparkled with orange orbs and halos along the street to his home. He had an idea, to climb to the top once more, given it could possibly be the last he ever saw of the solar panels. He badged into an elevator on the corner of the street and was elevated to the surface.

When he stepped out, he couldn't help but feel bittersweet over the sight of the dark blue sea of silicone surrounding him in every direction as it glistened in the light of the lowering sun. Above the paneling, it was a clear day, only a few clouds draped from the sky. Birds flew in the open air and workers slaved beneath them, cleaning and installing new panels. It was the life he had lived, that he had always kept, and it was now in his past. Michael beheld it all, recounting the times he sweated and bled over the blue.

Soon, God willing, he would be far from it, in a sea of green and brown instead. Once supplying the city with energy, instead, he would soon supply the people with food. After a few minutes of thinking and silently talking to God, he descended into the neighborhood, his last ride down. The doors to the elevator opened and the odor hit him at once.

He resumed his walk home, or what had been home, and passed by the many houses along Second Avenue, the street on which he lived. The lights to the other homes were off, many of them resting within shadows. They were like sunken ships in the depths of the sea -- a sea of solar panels. It didn't sit well with him, to see his street in such hard times, with the unrepaired siding, the molded roofs, and the busted windows. No children to make use of the yards as they played. There were no cars in the empty driveways, many of which had been converted to patios or add-ons and came right up against the street. It was a neighborhood that had once been an image of the thriving nation, but when the world abandoned traditions and values, the places they called home were forgotten.

It bothered him that he never saw it in all its glory; that not once in his life did he feel his neighbors lived the way they deserved. The house in which he had spent his entire life towered among the others, the tallest on the street. It was his castle, and soon it would pass on to Ronny, and Ronny would get his job, and Ronny would open his home to the Masses. Ronny would do just fine, he knew, the young man would likely find himself a woman, marry, and, hopefully, not make plans for an exodus as they welcomed their firstborn.

Something has to be done, he agonized internally, *something needs to change the world. It isn't going to change by the passing of time alone. The change needed requires human intervention -- more likely, Divine intervention. This broken world needs the doctoring of saints, the blood of martyrs.* In disrepair and hopelessness, the town he was leaving wasn't the way he'd like to leave it and immense guilt befell him as he stepped onto the stairs that led up to his front door. He was abandoning them, he felt, not having done enough to solve the community's struggles. They weren't even going to say goodbye to them. The community would understand, he hoped. They'd surely know why. They simply couldn't raise any alarms, so Michael figured they wouldn't mind. Anita's son and his family were told as little as possible, and they didn't seem to mind.

...

He turned the knob and entered the house, which made him realize that almost every action he performed belonged to a figurative list of last times. Mundane things like ascending those stairs, crossing the threshold of his bedroom door, searching through the kitchen cabinets for a certain spice or dish became precious to him. He knew there was a very real chance he'd never do these everyday things in this particular house again.

He noticed that Amelia was no longer in their bedroom. *Probably downstairs looking for obscure figurines we don't need to take along.* At that moment, he heard sounds coming from the bathroom. Water splashed and he could clearly hear the dry heaving of a sick pregnant woman.

He stood to check on his sister, knocking upon the bathroom door, "Hey sis, you good in there?" Just as the last word left his lips, Maria began walking up the stairs, towards the room he shared with his wife. "Maria?" His sister noticed his astonished tone and confused face. Once the sounds he heard resonated in her own ears, she knew.

"Melia! You in there, sweetie?"

"I'm sick, the...door's...unlocked!" she shouted over the moments of intermittent sickness. Michael and Maria both entered to comfort the woman.

Maria told Michael to hold Amelia's hair back as she bent over the toilet. Just then, Michael realized they were a little too late as he noticed strands of hair already covered in bile and food. For once, he wasn't squeamish. The heaving and the sound of vomit hitting the water didn't disturb him and neither did the smell. He simply felt excited by the chance that his wife, too, was pregnant.

"I can't stay in here," Maria panicked, "smells awful. You got it, Mikey?"

"I'm good," he answered as his sister rushed out of the room covering her face. She closed the door immediately and ran down the stairs to escape the sounds and smells.

"Michael," Amelia attempted to speak, "this..."

"Just focus, babe." He smiled, thanking God silently and hoping it was confirmation that she was with child. He rubbed and patted her back vigorously.

"Don't pat, just rub," she begged, her voice sounding miserable and echoing into the toilet bowl.

"Sorry!" He began rubbing her gently, smiling as he did so.

She finally stood up and he handed her a wad of toilet paper to wipe her mouth and nose clean. She removed most of her make-up in a single swipe and he saw her face for the first time. Mascara ran along her eyes and cheeks, turning her face into a scene from a bad horror flick, yet she still looked absolutely beautiful anyway.

"You poor thing. Did you eat something bad?" he asked in an innocent tone, pretending he was oblivious to the implications of her sudden illness.

"I haven't had my period in a while...thought it was just missed or late...that's happened before."

"You think you're pregnant?"

She nodded her head answering in a weak voice, "I just don't want to jinx it." The idea was insane to both of them. Despite their growing excitement and gratitude for the blessing, the craziest thing was that the two of them desired something so highly illegal -- even deadly.

"I understand, me neither. Maybe we could get the doc to take a peek."

"We don't have time. We're leaving in an hour and heading to the meeting place," she reminded him, still cleaning her face and spitting out whatever else remained trapped in her throat.

"Is she okay?" Maria asked from beyond the door, her voice muted.

"She's perfect," Michael answered, in awe of the woman before him. The experience was unreal to him. It felt like a dream. Something beyond this world was happening before his very eyes. "She's absolutely perfect."

"Did you eat something bad?" Maria cracked the door open. "Was it the casserole?"

"Don't talk about food right now!" Amelia scolded.

"She may be pregnant...," Michael beamed.

"I knew it! I knew it! I knew it! I just didn't want to say anything."

"What? How would you know?" Michael asked, opening the door wide.

"Her milkers have gotten huge! Surely you, of all people, have noticed. Look at those things!" Maria laughed as she pointed to Amelia's swollen breasts.

"I mean, I thought it was my imagination," Michael laughed, glancing over at them. "Is that a pregnancy thing?"

"Duh! She's getting ready to feed a baby with them. What else would it be?" Then looking past Michael, "Oh, Amelia, I'm so excited to not be alone in this anymore! Good thing you guys decided to come with us!"

"I'm not excited about the trip down. I'm spinning right now."

"Oh, well, that's going to be a challenge. Maybe you can try to sleep most of the way down?"

"I don't know. I'm not sure I'll be able to sleep. I'm already nervous enough about getting caught."

"Me too, but maybe if we close our eyes, it'll be easier than we imagine. Pregnancy is exhausting, trust me. We'll probably pass right out."

"Nothing will happen to either of you." Michael had already committed himself to the possibility of getting caught and how to handle it. John and he will neutralize anyone standing in their way. He felt stronger than ever about this now that Amelia was pregnant. Now they had two women and two babies to protect. Not a thing or person could stand in their way, even if it cost him his life. The men would do anything they had to so the mother of his child and his sister could escape.

His fists clenched as he imagined the possibilities. He had never felt surer of anything in his life. It was his duty to protect the innocents -- and his legacy -- even if it meant he lost his own life to do it. It was an instinctual, primal feeling that seemingly remapped his entire brain in an instant as the passion emerged from some deep spiritual and animal place in his being. *I am a father, a brother, an uncle, a friend and I will do whatever I must, even die, to protect what is mine,* he thought with an uncommon clarity.

The family gathered in the living room once more, after they turned off every light and closed every door. The house, all empty and barren, seemed sad in a way. Its farewell hummed in the air through the emptied rooms as if it knew they were leaving. Cole sat in the corner, with his bag and suitcase, not speaking. John and Michael had just arrived from ensuring everything was locked up and ready to go, something Maria had already done, but they insisted on double-checking. Amelia sat with her on the couch, speaking to Dr. Renda, who had arrived only moments before. They were all waiting for the priest to come by in a rented van to transport them to the rendezvous location.

"We'll take a look at you, as soon as we get south. I've already shipped some equipment down there, including my ultrasound machine," the doctor assured Amelia, patting her shoulder.

"How far along do you think I am?"

"Not sure, but I'll be able to measure the peanut with my equipment. That will give us a very clear estimate. Maria, you're due for another look too. We should be able to see the sex by now, if you'd like to know."

"Absolutely!" She laughed with excitement, "I can't wait!"

A car horn sounded from the street and Michael peeked through the curtains, spying the priest sitting in the front of the vehicle. "He's here."

...

Everyone stood at once, donning their coats and shoes, before making their way out of the house. Michael, last in line, looked around as he walked over to the doorway, "Bye old friend." He caught sight of the black markings on the doorway. They marked Maria's and his changing heights as they grew. The newer marks recorded the growth of Cole and Stone. He could even see the ancient marks his grandparents made as their kids grew. It was a lot to leave behind -- the history and memories, especially given the very real chance he wouldn't return. He pulled the familiar door to and placed the key into its slot, noticing for the first time ever that the top and bottom lock didn't match in color. One was black, the other golden and much older. The deadbolt rolled into place and the door settled.

He carried both his and Amelia's suitcase with him down the stairs to the van where the others were already busily storing their things and boarding.

Michael loaded their luggage into the back and closed the van doors, looking up at the house and to its emptiness once more. It looked just as dark as the other houses that night. It's windows dark and covered. "You'll have a new tenant soon, friend," he whispered, looking up at the house's face and its weeping weathered siding.

The rendezvous was behind the old mall in Irondale, beyond the sight of anyone. It was a dirty old place with debris tumbling in the wind and decay devouring the carcasses of poisoned rodents. The large semi truck's back door was opened and a cabin light illuminated the cases of beer and other things retrieved by the Smuggler. The deepest part of the cabin held what appeared to be a massive stack of boxes, but the Smuggler opened the side of it, exposing two benches that within. There was nothing comfortable about the sight of them, their cushions torn and filthy. As Amelia climbed into the trailer, she immediately detected the odor of beer, some cans of which had burst open and become putrid. She knew instantly that this trip would not be an easy one, but did see a clean trash bin sitting in the Smuggler's cabin, which eased her mind a bit.

They stowed their items beneath the benches and sat awkwardly, crammed against each other. The Smuggler made sure everyone was in place, notified them of the travel time, and assured them they were in good hands before closing the façade door to hide them. He then proceeded to stack real boxes of cargo in front of the door, until it was impossible to detect.

The priest said a prayer for the success of their journey and over the women, focusing his intentions on the unborn babies growing within them. The truck growled and shook once he finished the requests he offered to Heaven, and it rolled forward, on its way *south*.

CHAPTER SIXTEEN

Susan's body hadn't stirred in days and except for the movement of her assisted breathing apparatus, the room lay still. Only the movement of her chest raising and lowering along with the mechanical cadence of the breathing support device indicate the presence of life. The injuries she suffered in the STORK clinic bombing have rendered her unrecognizable -- her milky white skin now red and swollen from the removal of her burnt flesh. Bandages, changed almost constantly by medical staff, cover much of her face and body. After much discussion, the doctors on her medical team agreed to place her in an induced coma and she had existed in that deep unconscious realm since the day of the attack. The doctors watched her closely after finding evidence of infection, fearing she may develop sepsis.

The medical staff allowed Isaac to visit Susan in the hospital, despite his outburst in the ambulance, as long as he was under the direct supervision of another officer. His captain took the opportunity to visit Susan, whose condition disturbed him greatly. He hadn't expected that she was in such a horrible state, hardly any more alive than the ventilator pumping air into her.

Aside from the glowing monitors and beeping status lights surrounding the bed, no other lights illuminated the room. The curtains were drawn and a darkness hung within -- an absence of light that seemed unnecessary. The captain attempted to discreetly cover his nose, when able, to block out the odor of her wounds and the topical medications applied to them. Despite the other scents mingled in, he could detect the unmistakable odor of death.

Intensive care patients, even those not on the verge of death, are usually associated with a certain common odor that seems foreign to those who haven't spent much time around them. Unable to care for themselves, these patients rely on the attending nurses to bathe them. Frequency and manner of bathing, of course, depends upon the particular circumstances of each patient's condition.

As a burn victim, Susan's medical team did not write orders that included the typical bathing protocols. Instead, her burnt, dead skin was debrided in a tub room especially for severe burn patients. Some of the skin underneath the scrubbed burnt flesh had become infected and it released an intensely foul stench. It was an inescapable odor, which left an unpleasant taste in the mouth of those exposed to it.

"Do they know when she'll wake?"

"They've put her in an induced coma. Apparently, something in the explosion, maybe a projectile, caused trauma to her head," Isaac answered, his voice sounding hollow and empty, his emotions entirely spent over the last few days of ceaseless grieving. He exhausted himself, weeping until one could say there were no tears left to shed.

"It's damn horrible," the captain remarked, covering the edge of his nose with his hand. "Susan's such a light to this world. You just gotta put your faith in medicine, son. Soon as this battle is won, they'll fix her up real nice. I've seen it plenty of times before."

"We've just been approved for a baby." Isaac's face became sour as tearless emotion once again found him, "The child of her dreams...our dreams...I just...I hope she gets to..."

"That's amazing news, Isaac! You know, they can hear us in there." Then he thought of how he could comfort his subordinate, saying, "Susan would love to hear good news, it's the currency by which people in her shoes use to get well."

"You think?"

"Yes, get close to her and tell her something, something to encourage her. I'll even step out and give you some privacy."

"I'll give it a shot. Thank you, Captain." Isaac noisily drug his chair over to the right side of Susan's bed, the side that displayed her less serious burns. The captain stood quickly and exited the room, secretly filled with joy that he'd no longer smell her.

...

Isaac waited, searching for words to say to his wife. He sat beside her for several minutes before opening his mouth. The only sound within the room was that of the beeps and the forced breathing through her mask. When she breathed, he heard a gurgling noise and, occasionally, it sounded as if she were about to gag and choke.

"Susan," Isaac began awkwardly, staring into her face, hoping to see a sign that she was aware of his presence or voice, but her heartbeat carried on unchanged. "Babe, it's Isaac, I'm here with you."

He was afraid to touch any part of her, so he kept his hands tightly held against the rails along her side. He studied her face as he searched his mind for the right things to say. He tried desperately to recall a list of great things about their life together -- things that might cheer her or give her some kind of hope. Other than the baby, he drew a blank, so he started there.

"Our Isabelle is on her way, dear," he raised the pitch in his voice, emphasizing the happy nature of the news. "We're going to have a beautiful little girl, who looks just like you. She's going to love her mama, love dress-up parties with you, and enjoy all life has to offer. One day, she'll come to you, wanting you to apply your makeup to her face and carry a baby doll around. She's going to want to try lots of things like horseback riding, dance, and art. She'll be just as you were as a child, but even better." Susan's heart rate sped up slightly, just enough for Isaac to notice.

"Yes, babe, that's right, she's going to have a wonderful life with the two of us raising her. She's going to make the house so much cozier. In the winter, we'll curl up by the fire with her between us and read books all about fairies and other mythical creatures of the wood. We'll tell her about the beautiful redheaded princess that changed the world, whose face shimmers in the sunlight. Oh yes, babe, Isabelle will prefer that you to read and re-read the parts about the princess in your wonderful, comforting voice. She's going to grow up just like that -- with every night of her life ending mystically and joyfully until she becomes a woman."

Isaac longed the relief he knew tears would bring, almost purposely working for them to come. Sobbing from deep within with tears falling in great salty waves was the only thing that could ease the weight he felt in his chest.

"And she's going to be a beautifully striking woman, yes, even more stunning than she was as a child. Everyone will envy her as loveliness incarnate. Every single person who beholds her, even once, will crave the opportunity to look at her again." Susan's heart rate began to jump and skip rapidly and her monitors began to emit a much more urgent beeping. "Susan?"

Two nurses immediately blew past the captain, still waiting outside, and entered the room, "Sir, please give us some space."

"What's going on? Is something wrong?" His eyebrows rose in terror. Isaac continued holding onto the bed rails as the nurses began scrutinizing the monitors and the patient.

Neither of the attending caregivers offered him a single word of reassurance. As their hurried movements became more intense, one of the nurses forced him aside exiting the room, "Doctor Slaughter, we need you in here now! The patient's coding!" A man in green scrubs jogged from down the hall, breaking past Isaac to enter Susan's room.

"Susan!" Isaac shouted from beyond the doors to the room as his captain pulled him back.

"Sir, you're going to have to return to the lobby and wait," ordered the shorter nurse as she began implementing the doctor's newest orders. Isaac didn't clearly understand the meaning of their clipped medical jargon and terminology, so he strained to peer at the monitors behind her for clues. The doctor used the defibrillator to apply a shock to her chest. Each time he shouted 'clear' and pressed the paddles to her torso, her body jerked violently into the air.

"Come with me, Isaac," the captain insisted, tugging at his arm.

"Is she dying?" Isaac questioned to no one in particular, resisting his boss by jerking his arm away. "Unity, please...please don't let her die. Work some miracles or something. You've got to do something!"

"Isaac, what the heck are you doing?" the captain asked upon hearing his words, his prayer to Unity. It was similar to the people who offered prayers to Unity in the old Christian churches, but this sounded much more sincere, much more direct and certain. It gave the captain pause.

"Sir, you cannot be in here!" shouted the doctor, while gesturing for the captain to forcefully remove Isaac. "We can't work efficiently with you here. Please, officer, take this man outside."

"Unity! My Susan needs you! Please!" Isaac repeated, the nurses looked at him as if he were a lunatic that had wandered in off the streets.

Then, in a hushed tone, the captain warned, "Isaac, please don't make me wrestle you out of here."

"Blood pressure is dropping -- bradycardia coming on," the short nurse alerted the doctor. "Her heart rhythm is all over the place."

Despite the best efforts of the medical team, Susan's organ systems began shutting down one by one. Her severe burns left her skin surface area extremely prone to opportunistic infections, which quickly spread to her already badly injured brain and her other systems during the short time that had passed since the bombing. Sepsis, essentially the medical version of the

Angel of Death, stretched its fingers over every corner of her body, seducing her into the grave. After long days of fighting for survival, Susan surrendered quickly to the beckoning of her reaper.

A sort of darkness descended upon the room -- a dim shade that seemed to hang in the air like a cloak of shadow. Still the team worked.

"There isn't anything I can do."

"What are you saying, Unity?" Isaac immediately perked up.

"If you hadn't been so reluctant to do as I said, this may never have happened."

"Save sermon. Help my wife, please Unity!"

The captain speculated deeply about what he believed amounted to Isaac's descent into madness. *What else could it be? Sane, well-adjusted people simply do not converse with the invisible.* The captain became lost in his interior thoughts on the matter. *This is much different than the prayers those others offer to Unity. No, Isaac's ravings have the sound of dialogue -- the dialogue of the delusional mind. "What do you expect me to do?"*

Isaac once again threw the captain backward, forcing himself inside to stand along his wife's bedside. "Time, doctor?" the short nurse asked in a tone that somehow seemed trite.

"Time of death...six-forty-seven AM," Dr. Slaughter announced just before he and the nurses stepped back from the bed. The shade that had shrouded the very air within the room seemed to withdraw. Everyone felt it, but no one acknowledged it. The effect is similar to what one would observe if the lights in a room momentarily experienced a noticeable decrease in lumens only to quickly pop back into their full brightness. Only, this had nothing at all to do with the lights and wavering power supplies.

"What are y'all doing?" Isaac asked, panicking. "Get back to work! She's dying!" Isaac's denial of this new reality was a normal reaction to the shock of losing a loved one. He refused to believe what he already heard with his own ears -- the medical team announced and recorded the exact time of his beloved wife's departure. He moved back and forth, impatient and anxious; he wept bitter tears as he babbled, trying to find the words to command the staff to continue working to save her.

"Sir," the doctor began, finally able to approach him with appropriate sympathy, now that the frenzied work was over and his efforts failed, "the infection simply caused too much damage, there was nothing else we could do. She's gone now. I'm so sorry." He tried to comfort Isaac, placing his hand upon the grieving man's shoulder. Frowning, he watched the husband nestle himself around his dead wife's bed.

Dr. Slaughter allowed himself to truly consider how Isaac must feel. *His entire world has been taken from him and there's no medicine that could have changed the fate of his woman. The fight was over long ago. There's nothing left to do.*

"No! It can't be! My love, my Susan! Please, baby, please don't go. Don't leave me here alone." Isaac reached for her shoulder and head, taking them in his hands with tearful eyes as he stared down onto her blurry lifeless body. He searched the monitors, finding only flat lines and the absence of any vital measures. "She's not dead...can't be...she was just here. Please, there's got to be something you can do. You can just shock her again, or something, surely? Please, doc!"

"I'm sorry, Isaac." The captain stepped up and patted his shoulder, standing beside him, unwilling to wrestle him away any longer.

"Unity, you promised to fix us!" Isaac cried, holding his head against Susan's. He touched her skin, feeling the tacky plasma and other clear fluids that leaked from it. He could detect the warmth of life leaving her body as well; her skin already going cold. "Please, Susan, babe...please come back to me!"

The captain gazed upon his officer with sadness, frowning and listening as Isaac addressed Unity directly, unsure how to judge the situation. The doctor pulled the curtain to allow him the necessary privacy to grieve in the room.

"I don't get it. It's all so meaningless!"

"What do you mean?"

"She was so excited about becoming a mother. We got approved for a baby and everything seemed to be working to our favor -- for once. And now...now she's...gone. What the hell for? Obeying the law?

Where's the justice in that? Those damn Zealots killed her and I wasn't even there to at least die with her. I shouldn't have left without her...left to fetch those IDs."

"You had no way of knowing, Isaac. None of us knew."

"Neither did Unity. Some 'god' he is," Isaac made air quotes as he spat out the word 'god', "allowing it all to happen."

"I had nothing to do with it, Isaac. My condolences." Unity's even, calm voice sounded almost patronizing.

"Shut your lyin' mouth!" Isaac snarled as he spat the words out sharply.

"Who are you talking to?"

Isaac didn't answer his captain. He just wanted to stay there and hold his wife's body. Oh, how he wished she wasn't covered in burns and bandages. He wanted to look upon her as she really looked as she was before all this happened -- before her beauty had been cooked away.

"And I've been robbed of a true farewell, unable to see her as I knew her." Isaac cried loudly enough for the staff down the hall to hear him. It wasn't out of the ordinary. The same sounds and noises of human grief resonated daily throughout the unit. "How am I to say goodbye to a face I no longer recognize?"

"I'm going to step out. You take your time, okay? No rush." The captain exited the room and pulled the sliding door closed, in addition to the curtain hanging there. This muted Isaac's unashamed wailing somewhat, but did not silence it; the man's moans of pain and agony carried through the wood and glass.

...

"Remove her bandages, uncover her face, Isaac."

"Why?" Isaac asked, afraid to see the extent of her injuries. The nurses debrided much of the burnt flesh, immediately upon her arrival, leaving only the raw and weeping skin. He wasn't willing to see it. *I just don't think I can handle the sight of it,* he thought, as he resisted Unity's order to unravel the dressings.

"I'm giving you what you've asked for." Unity's voice was almost emotional this time, soft to Isaac's ears, *"I'm sorry I wasn't able to prevent that bombing, but I'm going to give you the goodbye you deserve."*

Isaac did as tell and began to unravel the bandages covering Susan's shaved head. They were heavy and wet with lymph fluid and plasma. Her beautifully thick, red hair appeared to miraculously return and the burns were gone, healed -- and no scars remained to hint of any past injury at all.

"Wha...wha-wha-what is this? What's happening?" he shouted, his continuous weeping interrupted by the miraculous sight.

"I'm giving her an overlay in your Visum, I'm rendering her as you knew her. I'm sorry I'm not able to resurrect her. This is the best I can do for now."

"She's beautiful. Thank you. God, thank you Unity! You have no idea what this means to me," he gushed, marveling at her magnificence. The color of her skin shifted from red to a healthy blushed flesh tone and she looked as if she had only been sleeping. Even the make-up she typically wore to go out or for appearing in photos made its way onto her face. "My poor love, Susan. I'm so sorry I left that day. I'm sorry for it all. I should have hunted down every last one before such a thing could happen. It's my fault! Oh no! It's my fault, Unity!" His tears fell like rain upon her unwrapped wounds, which appeared as abundantly healthy, unscathed flesh.

What he touched didn't match what he saw. He could feel with his hands the burns covering her once pristine skin and the absence of her hair, but the sight allowed him to ignore this reality. He could almost imagine her curly red hair tickling his face as he held her tightly and close to his chest.

The captain peeked in on him from the room's window that faced the wide and long hospital corridor. A set of blinds covering it could be controlled from the outside, allowing him to do so briefly and discreetly. What he saw disturbed him greatly and he immediately closed them to block the view.

"I wish I could just hear her voice again. I wish she could tell me she was leaving and that all is okay."

"It's alright, honey. I'm no longer in any pain. I'm at peace, now."

"What? What was that?" Isaac looked around in panic, turning his head this way and that.

"Is this not what you wanted?" Susan's voice asked from within his Auris.

"No, it's perfect. It sounds just like...*you.*" Isaac stammered wiping tears from his bloodshot eyes and snot from his face. Oh, how he had longed just to hear the sound of her voice during all of those hours spent in silent vigil beside her bed. And now it rang clearly in his ears -- the sound he hadn't heard since the day of the bombing.

"I love you and I want you to know that I think you're still going to make a great dad. She'll be made up of all the good parts of you and of me together and I'll live on in her. Take good care of our daughter, when she comes, Isaac."

"Will you promise to be there? Will you stay?" Isaac begged, nodding his head as he looked over her perfectly unblemished face.

"I'll never leave you again, honey. And I forgive you. There's no way you could have had any way of knowing. But one thing you can do -- you can avenge me. You can make it right."

Unity wasted no time in immediately utilizing Susan's persona to manipulate Isaac. The man remained unaware of the invisible puppet strings now controlling him through Unity's clever and cruel ruse. Truth is, even if Isaac had some realization of the manipulation, it's likely he would enter into a sort of willful blindness so he could continue to bask in Susan's presence. To have her sweet voice continue to coo at him and ring in his ears acted as a balm for his broken heart.

"I will. I will make it right. I'm going to make sure this never happens to anyone else, ever. I love you, Susan. I love you so so so much, God, it hurts. It really hurts. My heart's been ripped from my chest. It's the most painful thing I've ever experienced. I'm going to take it, take all this pain, and force it all upon those bastards -- every last one of them until they beg for the mercy of death. I'll make them forget their God and their dead saints and force them to bow to me on their last day." Isaac clenched his hands tightly around Susan's empty body. "I will make every last one of them pay for it with their blood. It will spill out of them for you, Susan." He rubbed his head against hers.

"I would be so proud if you did that."

"Please, just promise again you'll never leave me. Stay, just like this. Please. I can't lose you again. My heart beats, but I'm dead without you."

"I won't go anywhere."

"I just wish I never had to leave this bedside. Wish I could stay here with you forever. Wish I could take you with me."

"I will be with you, anywhere you go. However, you must arrange to have my body cremated." Unity flawlessly portrayed every single aspect of Susan's personality, desires, and life. He had immediate access to everything she had ever posted online, to every email she wrote and replied to, every voicemail she left, and every single text message she fired off to others.

He acted as the effective ruler of the people -- like a god, if not the god -- and could use every piece of information about this golden couple. He knew every detail about their first date from the social media check-ins and greedily gathered up electronic evidence of all the trips they had taken together. All of Susan's photos -- from her childhood to her adulthood, from innocent pictures to lewd layouts -- sat safely in cyberspace for Unity's application and use.

"Please," Isaac whined, his tears dripping again from his swollen eyes, "don't force me to think about that right now, honey. It hurts. Just pretend with me that your heart never stopped...just pretend, please. Do it for me, or my heart might just stop itself as well."

Isaac wasn't aware that his hand pressed against the nurse call, allowing the captain and everyone at the nurse's station to hear him conversing with Susan's corpse. They couldn't hear Unity speaking, in the voice of Susan or at all, so they assumed he may be having a psychotic break. The captain told them that the officer was simply sleep-deprived.

...

"Isaac," the captain called, as he rolled the door open, "are you okay?" He recoiled a bit at the sight of Isaac rubbing himself against his wife's corpse. This behavior deeply disturbed him and the others who entered with him.

"No, I'm not. What do you think, Cap? What kind of idiot question is that?"

"Isaac, we think you're done here..."

"I'm not leaving her," Isaac snarled at them as he spoke. He was like an angry animal, protecting the burrow he made.

"You've sat here for over an hour. They've got new critical patients arriving and they need the space."

"Well, I'm not finished yet."

It's okay, honey. I'll go with you, anywhere you go, I'll be there. Remember? I'm not restricted to this body any longer.

"No, Susan, I don't want to leave you," Isaac responded aloud, turning to her corpse, forgetting the rest of them.

"Isaac, they don't think you're well. They want to do a psych eval on you," the captain explained, gripping his shoulder and standing above him.

"Screw off, Cap."

"At least go home and get some sleep. You haven't slept in days, have you?"

"I'm fine, I tell you!" Isaac barked out his words, throwing the captain's hand off of him again.

His boss made a motion with his fingers, signaling a squad of officers in to escort him out. Four of them came through the door slowly and approached the grieving man. "Make this easy for us, Isaac," one of them said, placing his hand on him.

"*Go with them, Isaac. We'll be separated if they take you. You don't want to lose me again, do you? I wouldn't be able to talk to you if they placed you in the ward.*" Unity's portrayal of Susan became filled with sadness, so much so that to Isaac it didn't matter anymore. At this point, to him, Unity actually was Susan and he believed her every word. It was an easy fiction to accept, a comforting one that required very little imagination on his part. He stood slowly from the bedside, great grief rolling onto him in waves as he started to depart from it.

"I'll kill all of you if you touch me again," he warned in an ominous tone, turning to the rest of them. The captain walked with him and the officers followed them in a tight knot.

"I'm going to place you on leave, just until things settle down a bit. You don't need the added stress of work right now. You really need to get some rest," his boss informed him as the sliding doors opened at the front of the hospital.

"I'm fine."

"You're not. And the fact that you think you are is solid verification that you actually are not, indeed, fine. Your wife just died and you've been talking to yourself. If you don't go home and get some rest, I'm going to check you into a psychiatric facility."

"Yeah, whatever you say," Isaac relented, remembering what would happen if he were checked into a psych ward. "I'll get some sleep, then I'll be good as new."

"The boys are going to drive you home, Isaac. Don't need you on the road, being so tired and all." The squad car pulled up to the curb of the hospital entrance.

"I'm fine to drive myself, actually."

"You're not, please. They'll take you straight home." The captain opened the backdoor for him. "I'll be sure to inform the car you came in to deliver itself into your driveway."

Isaac didn't like the idea of riding in the back seat. He didn't trust their intentions. "I'll sit in the front. And if they try to take me anywhere other than my house, I won't be responsible for what happens to them."

"Sound good, boys?"

"Yeah, sounds fine. I'll get in the back." One of the officers jumped out of the passenger seat and entered the back of the vehicle.

"Hey, Isaac," his captain called just before Isaac entered the front of the car.

"Yeah?"

"I'm truly sorry for all that happened. She was an angel. Didn't deserve it. She was an amazing person and I hate it for you. I can't conceive what you're going through. So, don't be a stranger. Anytime you need me, I'm here. I know I'm just your boss or whatev-"

Isaac tried to hold his composure as he erupted into tears, embracing his boss, forgetting all the recent anger he had built up toward him. The captain awkwardly held him. He had never seen Isaac so emotional about anything before that day. The pain wasn't shy and presented itself to anyone Isaac came in contact with. His face alone appeared as though it had never known a smile or a joyful moment. His eyes were dark and bloodshot with bags belying a lack of sleep underneath them. Lines stretched over his forehead, vestiges of the recent days filled with intense worry. The newly widowed man seemed to have aged years within the previous hours.

"I don't understand. I still just can't believe it all. Seems like any moment now I should wake up from this nightmare. Tell me that she's still here. That they found the wrong body, or that I've just had a really bad dream, or imagined the whole thing. Susan was so strong. She wasn't scared of anything. She feared no one. No one could hurt her. She was truly a woman of steel. Yet, they say she's dead."

"You've got a daughter on the way and she's going to embody everything that you loved about Susan. She'll live on, Isaac." His boss, and now friend, patted his back as he detached from Isaac's hold. Isaac laughed softly through the pain, thinking of the little girl that was coming.

"Thanks, Captain." Isaac shook his head, embarrassed for his behavior, "I'm sorry for being so difficult. I know you mean the best."

"There's nothing to apologize for, Isaac. You'll get back on your feet, probably just as soon as you wake up in the morning. Just let these guys take you home, then take some melatonin and go straight to bed. Don't get up until you simply can't sleep any longer."

"Yes, sir." Isaac drunkenly sat in the front seat, dizzy from the surreal emotions that stabbed at him like so many knives.

...

The car ride was a great challenge for him as he tried not to fall asleep in the comfort of its heat. His eyes burned and his lids felt heavy as he resisted an overwhelming desire to give in to sleep.

The other officers didn't say a word. Instead they listened to a classic rock station on the radio and an old song played. It was the song's 100th anniversary since first airing on radio stations. Isaac wasn't much of a fan of that particular genre of music, but he knew the tune and hummed along to it. It made his heart ache in a dull and gentle way; Bob remained correct about the changing times.

"Here you are, Isaac," the driving officer uttered the first words of the trip as he gazed up at the beautiful house sitting cold and dark upon the short hill by the street, "gorgeous place you've got there."

"Thanks for the ride over. You boys take care." Isaac climbed his way up the stairs slowly, not eager to enter the empty home. Its darkness would remain, somehow, even after he turned on the lights and would offer no comfort to him. And the unnatural silence within its walls promised to be unbearably loud as he stepped across its threshold.

"Honey, I'm home," he called, his tear-choked voice echoed through the house and he fell to his knees wracked with sobs just as he entered. "I can't do this. I just can't do this. Susan! My Susan! Why, why did you leave me here alone to live alone in this house, still filled with your smell?"

"Isaac, you're not alone." The television mounted upon the wall flipped on, unprompted and displayed the perfect image of Susan on its screen. She was wearing one of her silky, luxurious nightgowns. He loved the rich red color. *She* knew it was his favorite.

"I wish I could hold you," Isaac half-whispered, after he calmed down from the startling vision.

"I'm sorry, love. I hope I can make that happen one day, but I'm afraid this is the best I can do for now."

"Do you think it might be possible -- one day?" Isaac asked crawling onto the couch in front of the display. Susan's face looked so lifelike, just as it did when she was physically in front of him. Her angelic image was shining with the brilliance of a million pixels behind her. Green eyes, red hair, she looked like a flower upon his wall.

"Perhaps one day, but you may not need it. I know it hurts now, but one day you'll recover and you'll have the company of our beautiful daughter with you."

"I'm so tired, but I don't think I can sleep in our bed alone with your side so cold and empty. I don't think I can do it. I don't think I can do any of it. It's too much to bear."

"You're strong, Isaac and you'll get through this. I need you to get through it -- for me, I want you to avenge me, love."

"No way I'm going to be able to do it on my own. I don't have any idea about where to even begin looking for these monsters. They've left zero traces. It's like they're invisible, or ghosts. I mean, I've tried for months and with no success." Isaac shook his head, all confidence drained from him. He didn't understand why Unity was so patient with him. It didn't make sense. After all the time and resources he had wasted on Isaac, why did Unity still bother with him when he had clearly failed?

"You'll have two visitors soon." Susan's face became more serious, the smile faded from her face, and her cat-like eyes seemed to darken suddenly.

"Who?"

"Two men...two men that have worked for me a while longer than you. One will bring you an arsenal -- the tools you will use to trample the monsters. The other has invested his time in becoming a Zealot."

"He's joining them?" Isaac was at a loss for words, "I can't believe I've never thought of that -- of infiltrating them."

"They'll be here later tonight. So, get some rest."

Isaac didn't want to leave her. Her voice and image comforted him more than anything. It comforted him so completely that it came dangerously close to allowing him to believe it was all real and that nothing had changed. He obeyed Unity's command and went to bed upstairs with plans sleep for as long as he could.

...

As he laid his head on the pillow, tears pooled in the corners of his eyes. The golden sunlight upon his lids soon transitioned to darkness as night arrived. Even with his heart still burdened with unshakable sadness, he drifted off to sleep quickly. It was a deep sleep, devoid of dreams. Unity left his mind untouched for once, allowing it to heal and recharge after all of the trauma and exhaustion. Two figures stood above his bed and one reached to turn on the brass lamp sitting on the wooden bedside table.

"Isaac," one of the voices called, alerting him of their presence.

"Who the hell?" he shouted, almost leaping from his bed.

"Isaac, these are my servants. These are the men who will help you take revenge."

"Sorry," Isaac took a deep breath to collect himself, "guys, wow, could've rang the doorbell, you know."

"We rang it many times," one of the men answered, dressed head-to-toe in black, his face gaunt and without emotion. Isaac's intuition told him that this was a very serious man, one with little patience for pleasantries. He clutched a large duffle bag and hard objects packed inside made impressions on the outside of the bag. One of the bumps on the canvas was about the size of a gun stock, something familiar to Isaac.

"I'm Franklin," the man with the bag introduced himself. "This here is Reginald," he continued, gesturing to the black man beside him. Reginald looked much friendlier than Franklin. He stood openly and smiled slightly without showing his teeth.

"It's good to meet you, Isaac. You can call me Reggie, something Franklin just refuses to do," shaking his hand even though he was still in bed, but sitting upright, "and my deepest condolences," he offered, his face became grim for a brief moment.

"So, I'm guessing you're the rat?"

"Yes," he chuckled lightly, "I've worked for months to get into their good graces. It's no easy process, but they've been increasingly busy and have a great need to expand and find new recruits. They will initiate me tomorrow night, assuming all goes well."

"So, Unity speaks to y'all too?" Isaac was so excited to finally meet others who had similar encounters. It added additional assurance he remained in sound mental health despite his boss and the medical staff's desire to give him a psych evaluation.

"Yes," Reginald answered bluntly. Franklin sighed and shifted his grip on the large bag.

"Let's move downstairs. It's a bit weird meeting in my bedroom." Isaac's head swirled with countless questions he hoped to ask, but he could see that Franklin wasn't happy to continue standing with such a heavy bag in his hand.

"Sounds good." Franklin left ahead of them and made his way down the stairs, "We need the window blinds closed. Don't need anyone peeping in and getting curious."

"House, activate privacy mode," Isaac commanded, speaking to the built-in home control system. At his command, every window immediately transitioned from transparent to opaque, shielding them from prying eyes. "Y'all want anything to drink? I've got some beers."

"I don't drink, but thank you," Reginald replied, taking a seat at the gigantic stark white table in the dining room, just off the kitchen.

"You, Frank?"

"I prefer Franklin, and no." His eyes were shark-like, entirely void of humanity. "This is a matter for sober minds, so I'll take some tea. I suggest you do the same."

The man's company wasn't much of a joy for the host and Isaac joked to himself, *this is precisely why it's better to have genetically engineered children. This guy's personality is a birth-defect. Wonder if it was his mom or his dad who's responsible?*

Isaac didn't want anything to do with sobriety. He really wanted to get intoxicated and stay that way for the remainder of his life. That, and to drown himself in other methods of self-medication, but he gave into a glass of sweet tea instead. Reaching into the cabinet for three glasses, he gingerly placed them on the table where his guests sat. He poured the tea and took a seat at the head of the table, flanked by both visitors.

"What have you brought me?"

After a few silent sips from his glass, Franklin stood and unzipped the duffle bag, which unfolded in three directions, containing numerous firearms and countless rounds of ammunition. "This is your rifle."

"A Scar, hm? Very nice. Wow!" Isaac stood and took the gun from the taller man, holding it in his hands, inspecting it. The gun was fully stocked with attachments; a tactical light, an angled foregrip, and a holographic sight. He quickly began daydreaming of all the damage and death that he could dish out with such a weapon. "Where'd you acquire such a beauty?" He grinned, worshipping the elegant modeling of the Scar.

"There are very few things Unity can't do. Obtaining arms is amongst the easiest of requests." The man also showed him the flashbangs, extended mags, and the sidearm packed along with it. Isaac could see by the immaculate finish on the weapons that they were likely brand new, not yet fired. Only the military and law enforcement had access to firearms, so these weapons must have been procured from their supply, or at least repurposed, as the supply had been blessed by Unity's and, like all things, flowed from him.

"What's the plan then? We just waiting for your initiation?" Isaac asked Reginald after placing the rifle back into the opened duffle bag.

"No, we need to take this slow and collect data on them for a couple of weeks at least." Reginald sipped his tea, hoping Isaac would be easy to work with.

"No offense or anything, but I don't know if I have the patience for it. I want these animals put down. We could just raid the house afterward, do a sweep for data." Normally, Isaac would have no problem with Reginald's plan, but after the events of the past few days, he lost all tolerance for time -- for waiting. Bloodthirst filled his dreams and every waking moment's imagination.

"If, for some reason, it turns out there's no physical data, then we would lose everything worth using." Reginald felt silly explaining such basic things, now fearing Isaac might prove difficult to control. Isaac nodded in agreement, determining the best way to approach the Zealots. He sat back in the chair, it's backing rose a foot higher than his head. Closing his eyes, he meditated, envisioning the best plan of action. Rather than his usual clear thinking, all he felt was only an immense hatred and bloodlust for the Zealots. Plans and meetings like this just slowed him down. He wanted to terminate them. The weeks of manipulation and the loss of Susan would gain a new meaningful purpose in an instant of spraying bullets and attaining his revenge.

"We could save one for interrogation if there isn't anything to raid, but I promise you, they'll leave stuff behind. They always do."

"Yeah," Franklin chuckled sarcastically, "the department's done a great job tracking them down after the raid in Avondale, hasn't it?"

"Well," Isaac ignored the comment, "this time we can use much harsher interrogation techniques."

"Who's going to torture them?"

"I can," Franklin volunteered flatly, picking at his fingernails.

"You've experience?"

Franklin's dark and lifeless eyes looked up from his hands and stared directly into Isaac's soul, like a look from the Reaper himself, "Lifetime of experiences."

"I see." Franklin's shortness irritated Isaac. His patience thinned even further as he started to resent working with the man.

"Honey, listen to Reginald," Susan's voice resonated in his Auris. Still, like a visit from a ghost, it unnerved him when he didn't expect to hear it. *"You'll soon have your chance, but listen to his plan. He's been working very hard on this and it's extremely time-consuming. It would be a waste if you were to ruin it before we got anything out of it."*

"Okay, darling, okay. I'll leave it alone."

"Excuse me?" Reginald asked, his eyebrows pushed together in confusion.

"We'll go with your plan. I'll have my fun, eventually."

"Good. Very good."

They remained there, seated around the table, the rest of the night. The men discussed numerous plan variations and possibilities, including multiple contingencies. They conspired and schemed about ways to eliminate the terrorists once and for all in the Birmingham area. They had a short window of time before the Zealots would execute another attack. They felt an urgency to act quickly before the STORK headquarters tower itself fell.

Everything had changed for Isaac. He now lived only to see a modern holocaust carried out against the Zealots, especially those in the Birmingham area for they were directly responsible for taking Susan's life. Soon, he would satisfy his craving and peace will then abound in his life. All of his foes will be as worm food.

Unity smiled down upon their meeting, watching and listening to their every move and word. His will would soon be done, returning the Earth to the heaven he envisioned for it. Many groups, in every major area of the world were doing the same things as these three men. They met and developed plans to eliminate the Zealots, but the Birmingham team held his entire favor and joy. They were the heroes he needed -- the turn of destiny to protect the future of his kingdom.

CHAPTER SEVENTEEN

The faces, names, and lives played infinitely in Stone's head. They were on loops, whether the news had been turned on or not, there wasn't a moment of peace for the young man. Stone had chewed his nails away until there was nothing left to bite or tear away. Cigarettes had been smoked constantly, as Stone appeared to be a sort of human-chimney releasing an uninterrupted cloud of smoke into the air. The faces, the dead, the murdered men, women, and children Stone had killed never left his attention. Tears only fell from his face in secret, when he had gone on walks around the block to clear his mind with no success. Clarity was impossible for him to obtain, thoughts of his future were clouded with smoke, and his retrospection flooded with the blood of a hundred people.

The words that his friends and mentors had offered him had done nothing to help clear his conscience. He thought more of what they had done, and as horrible as their actions had been against the unborn, many of them may have been forced to visit the clinics. Stone was unable to shake the idea, that there may have been a couple of innocent lives destroyed or the idea that in a sense, he and his friends had carried out the abortions themselves. They were just as guilty killing the unborn as the doctors had been, but Jeremy said they were preventing it from happening in the future. No answers made a difference to Stone, although many believed he had been coming around as he kept his remorse secret.

Stone missed his family. Throughout the days since the bombing, Stone imagined returning home to the embrace of his incredible and forgiving kin. The thought had been the only thing that lifted his spirits until he was turned to remember that they likely knew what he had done. He wasn't sure he could ever face them again; Stone believed God Himself wouldn't forgive him for his crimes. However, the idea of running to them, and attempting repentance grew until he could no longer take it. It had grown until it was impossible for him to ignore the desire to go home.

He unlocked the downstairs apartment after his morning walk and entered. The air outside had been so frosty that as soon as he entered it he began to overheat and needed to strip immediately of his coat and over shirt. Debra sat on the couch in the living room, submerged into her virtual reality. She often visited the place in the clouds with Nelson in the simulated realm. There wasn't a limit to what she could do with her companion as they snooped through people's private information and lost articles scattered about the internet.

Stone began packing his duffle bag with all the same items Cole had placed in there an eternity ago. Most of which had always remained in the bag, as Stone had practically lived out of it ever since his brother had tossed it from the window. Once it was packed, he placed it back where it had been sitting before. If he was going to leave the Zealots, he would return once more for the bag, but at that time he simply wanted to attempt to rejoin his true family. Stone sat beside Debra on the couch.

"Stone?" She asked, still unable to see as she was placed elsewhere virtually, but could still feel his weight land beside her on the couch and the stench of cigarettes filling the air.

"Yes, Debs," he answered, his voice was choked and depressed.

"What's wrong?" She withdrew from the virtual place, to see him sitting beside her with his face drooping towards the floor, "Are you alright?"

He responded by the gentle left to right shaking of his head, "I'm about to head out for a little while...but I'll be back."

"Where are you going?"

Stone didn't want to tell her or raise any suspicions. She looked at him with great concern, her amber-brown eyes sparkled with sincerity as she searched him visually for clues. "I've got a couple of errands to run and need to return something to Cole," he lied.

"Is that all?"

"Yeah, ...just didn't want to be gone for so long without you knowing."

"But are you okay? It seems like you're holding back. You look troubled."

"Well, I ain't happy, but that doesn't matter...just how things are," Stone said, standing from the couch.

"You haven't been yourself ever since the bombings."

Stone didn't answer immediately, he just watched the cat stalking him from under a chair. "I don't know. Just feel like we're still not fighting the war I signed up for. Don't you ever think about it? About what we've actually done to date?"

"I think about it all the time. We had great success last week and thanks to you for helping us pull it off. Couldn't have gone better."

"Yeah, it was an incredible victory. God smiles upon us," his words dripped with sarcasm and he rolled his eyes. "I'll be back in a couple hours. Maybe sooner."

"God does smile upon you. You're working towards sainthood and your bravery will be remembered forever."

"There isn't anything brave about what we did." Stone shook his head and frowned, deciding to open up to her a bit more than he had before. "Our attack was carried out miles away in the comfort of this apartment. There wasn't any danger for us...a security officer that we awakened from a nap was the greatest threat we faced. I'm not the crusader I thought I would be when I joined and this branding makes me feel ridiculous. I'm a living lie wearing it."

"Oh? So, you think we're all liars too?" Debra fired back, "Think we should all feel ridiculous?"

"That's not what I mean. It's just how I feel about myself, you know?" Stone slowly shook his head as he continued to frown.

"You really coming back?" she asked, her voice held hints and notes of anger in it.

"Yeah. I told you I'm just going to run some errands." He started to walk away from the couch, with his back turned towards her.

"You just sound like someone that's giving up."

"I'm not giving up," he lied.

"We've been over this several times, Stone." She shifted from her position of comfort on the couch, sitting up, "When are you going to remember the vow you made? We told you that there would be difficult times -- times you wouldn't feel proud of the sacrifices we make."

"You guys forgot to mention that I wouldn't feel proud of any of them." Stone exited the apartment, leaving her behind as she called for him to return.

...

He still loved her, loved her more than he ever had, but reality began exposing it all to him. He was heartbroken over her, not wanting to abandon her in the basement, but unwilling to listen to her attempts to comfort him any longer. It was always the same speech, always the same points, promises of the future that remained nowhere in sight. STORK tower still stretched into the sky, visible to all in the city, and Unity still menacing above it invisibly ruling the masses. Nothing had been done it seemed, but the vain attempts to end abortions; the attempts to stop something that was continued without the slightest hiccup in progress.

The entire train ride over, his eyes watched every passerby, paranoid that they knew who he was and what he had done. Everywhere he went in public, even as he wore coats and long sleeves, he kept guard over the branding on his arm. It was a mark of shame, a mark of his youthful ignorance and a sign that he had been duped into believing the lies others had successfully sold him. His family, the people he had once started to loathe, had always been right. Michael had always told him the truth, with his words and his fists, and even at Ruffner they told him, attempted to save him from his own thick-headedness. The train ride seemed to last an eternity as he felt the dread that he would be too late reaching them. None of his texts or calls had been answered. He thought that perhaps Cole had been afraid to associate with him. It was possible, he believed, that his family had officially detached themselves from him, that repentance was too late and that his journey to Irondale would be for nothing.

Finally, after a time of trembling upon the train, the Irondale stop approached and he stood before the train had even halted. Stone began walking towards the doors, exiting them as soon as they had opened, and took a deep breath of the foul air that hung in the town. The sea of blue sparkled like the tears that had pooled along his eye-lids. He ran down the stairs of the platform and raced all the way to the house in which he had been raised. There was something odd about it, something different, and his worst fears made themselves a reality in an instant.

He began knocking rapidly on the door and rang the doorbell repeatedly until someone answered angrily. "Ronny?" he asked, confused.

"Stone! I was getting ready to open a can on someone," the new tenant greeted him with laughter. "Where you been, man?"

"Been living in the city. Where's everyone?" He skipped the pleasantries.

"You mean Mikey and them?" The young man stood towering in perplexity.

"They left already, didn't they?" Stone resisted the emotions that crashed against him like rogue waves against a ship.

"Yeah, man. I thought they would've told you. They left a couple nights ago." Opening the door wider, "Wanna come in?"

Stone wanted to turn away immediately and run, but he realized there wasn't anywhere he wanted to go,

"Maybe for a minute." His voice was choked and the words were difficult for him to form. "Did they leave anything?" He hoped a note would have been left or perhaps he could get a clue somehow, of where they had actually gone.

"Come in, come in!" Ronny invited him again, oblivious to Stone's hidden emotions. "Not sure if they left anything. They locked up some stuff in the basement. Did you need to get something?"

Cardboard boxes lined the walls of the hallway and living room. The place that had been Stone's home at one time was now made alien to him. The entire place seemed different even though some of the same furniture remained in place. The photos that hung from the walls had changed and the abandonment by its previous tenants left the house sad, it seemed to Stone. There was a darkness to it, a somberness, more like a lack of light that once shone within it. The visitor looked over the kids' height marks along the door frame. The black and blue names of his family had faded over time, yet left their impression in the wood.

"Did you hear me, Stone?" Ronny laughed uncomfortably, watching his guest inspect the room.

"I was hoping they'd still be here." Stone wasn't sure what to do. "I guess...I don't know...I guess I should go then."

"You don't have to leave! Stay a while, tell me what's up. Feels like forever since I've seen you." Ronny quickly made his way into the kitchen and grabbed two beers and returned with them opened, handing one to Stone.

"Thanks." Stone sat on the couch in the corner, the one that Cole had always taken for himself. Ronny sat across from him on the long couch, waiting to hear Stone begin as he sipped his beer.

"I've been living with some friends -- past few months, I guess. It's been a minute, now that I think about it. What about you?"

"Just holding the place down, until they return."

"If ever they return, you mean."

For the first time, perhaps because of the beer's relaxing effect, Stone revealed his sadness a little more. Or maybe Ronny had just finally detected the sadness in his voice. Ronny suddenly understood there was something the matter with Stone.

"Mass starts in a couple hours if you'd like to stay a while and attend. Whole neighborhood is bringing food to welcome the new priest."

"I don't know. I'd catch fire if I attended a Mass right now."

"Why do you say that?"

"Just done things recently -- things that have me hellbound, surely."

"Father James will be here in an hour. He'll be hearing confessions in the shed outside, just as Burns did in the winter. I already got the space heater ready in there so it won't be cold. I'm sure there's nothing too grave. Priests hear all sorts of wild things."

"Maybe," the invite tempted Stone; however, he couldn't imagine the penance that would be required. The possibility that the priest would tell him to turn himself in terrified him. There was no telling what the penance would be and whatever it was, he would need to honor it.

"I promise man. I can't tell you how many times I've done disgusting things and the priest just says. Is that everything?"

"It's a bit different with me. You don't know what I've done."

"Give it a shot, Stone! Don't worry about it. You might just leave here in a state of grace tonight, you know!" Ronny chuckled lightly, trying his best to encourage the sad young man.

The two of them continued talking about things regarding the family and if they left any messages for him. Soon after the topics ran dry, Ronny took Stone into the basement to look around for anything packed away that belonged to him. Stone found a few small things, things he had forgotten he even owned. For a moment, he was tempted to take them, but then he realized that they had been out of his possession, unnoticed for so long, that it didn't make a difference if he took them. *This basement is a sort of time capsule*, he thought. *If they ever return, even years from now, everything would be sitting there just as they left it.* He decided against taking anything, even his own effects.

Choosing, instead, to leave it all untouched -- to gather dust while the items waited for a light to hit them again.

"I want to leave a note down here."

"Yeah, sure man. Cole's got some sketchbooks and pens over here. Surely there's an unused page in one of them." Ronny thought it strange that Stone wanted to leave a note in a basement. A note that would likely be old news before anyone ever read it. It would be easier to text or call his family, surely.

"Unlikely, Cole fills everything, but maybe so!"

Stone flipped through the sketchbook left on the top of the stack, it's dating was fresh, finished just weeks ago. The book had been filled with sketches Stone had never seen, some of them speaking loudly to him as if the markings themselves shouted. They all looked so familiar, but he didn't have time to inspect them in the dark basement with Ronny hovering over him. Stone tore a page out and wrote his note to the family. He put everything in there, but only hinting at certain incriminating things. Once he finished, he folded it and left it resting in the frame of a family photo, leaning against a dresser that had been moved down there.

"I'm going to take this sketchbook with me. It has a bunch of new art and I haven't seen any of it."

"Alright." Ronny laughed, not caring what Stone did. He thought it funny that he even mentioned it as if he were asking for permission.

The doorbell rang throughout the house, resonating down the stairs into the grim basement. "Must be the priest! You sure you don't want to stay?"

Stone's heart fluttered excitedly, as he felt a sudden inclination to stay. The paintings of the saints along the walls of the basement pushed him, filled him with confidence. Church history had always been a bloody matter, surely his confession wasn't anything new. Stone was still uncertain about the penance, but felt assurance that whatever it was would be alright by him. He had nothing to lose, other than his eternal soul, and the pains of Hell would be far worse than incarceration.

"I think I'll give it a shot," Stone said and he followed Ronny up the stairs to greet the priest inside.

Father James placed his collar on just as he entered the house and smiled as he shook hands with both the young men. He was shorter, nearly the same height as Stone, and he had dark skin. "Nice to finally meet you face to face, Ronny! I'm really looking forward to holding Mass here. You'll probably see some new faces from my previous mission."

"The more the merrier! We've got the whole neighborhood coming and they're bringing dinner."

"Wonderful!" The priest studied his surroundings, taking it all in, "So, perhaps I should take my place in the shed? That's where confessions have been heard in the past, correct?"

"Yes, there's going to be a line developing any minute now, once people start to arrive."

"Oh, I'm sure of it." The priest passed through the house, to the back door by Ronny's direction, and exited quickly, leaving the two boys alone.

Stone became nervous. His body shivered as he convinced himself to receive the sacrament. *I don't know...I'm a terrorist...there's no way this will end well. There's no hope...there's nothing for me out there, but a jail cell or excommunication.* Now that reality was setting in, he knew there was more to it than the brief confidence that the saint's images had offered him.

"You going, or should I go first?"

"You go first, I'll be next."

...

Ronny exited the house and joined the priest in the dimly lit shed. Stone began to pace around the kitchen nervously, chewing at his nails again, wishing he could smoke a cigarette before he went. Ronny took hardly any time at all, returning no more than two minutes later.

"You're up!" He smiled until Stone turned and presented himself, eyes bloodshot and filled with tears.

"Hey man, it's okay!"

"Can't believe I'm about to do this."

"Hey, I've been binge watching porn the past couple weeks. I'm sure you'll be fine."

If Stone hadn't been lost in a sea of regret and deep sorrow he would have laughed hysterically at Ronny's announcement, as he compared the sins. Anyone following Stone's confession that night would surely have an easy penance, he imagined. No one could top his sins. Everyone in the neighborhood either drank too much or had common sins of the flesh, but none of them were terrorists.

He became dizzy as the room seemed to spin around him when he turned for the door and gripped the knob tightly. He pushed and cracked the door away from the frame to make his exit into the chilling wind, blowing towards him. It was winter's kiss, almost freezing the tears against his cheeks. It was the cold air that stormed against the hellfire which awaited him -- two extremes that he had not fully prepared himself for.

The shed had a little window in the side of it and an orange light radiated from it. It was the light from the heater, warm and inviting it would be to other confessors; but, to him, it represented the awful eternity awaiting him. He hesitantly opened the shed's door and entered the silence within. The wind blew noisily against the sides of the wooden walls and the priest waited for his visitor to speak.

"Forgive me, Father, for I have sinned." Stone's voice shook as he crossed himself and the tears poured out of him like a fountain. "It's been months since my last confession." He withheld the loud weeping sound that he wanted to make, yet violently shook with nervousness in his chair.

"Peace be with you, child. There's nothing to fear here." The priest heard his sniffling and shakiness, unable to see him fully through the screening that had been propped between the two chairs.

"I've done horrible things, Father. Horrible, horrible things, and I'm unsure how to even say them. It hurts to even speak on what I've done." The words came out just as Stone felt the floodgate of emotions bursting within him. He knew he'd be wrecked as soon as he opened himself fully. The pressure in his head began to build and build until there wasn't any strength in him left to hold it back. He fell prostrate onto the floor moaning loudly as he wailed with lamentations.

"Son," the priest waited until the most violent cries passed and Stone calmed himself, "there's no limit to the sins many have committed and yet when they've confessed, however severe they may be, the Lord returns to them His forgiveness. He pours out His Divine Mercy for all who seek to find it." The priest encouraged Stone, his voice calm behind the screen. The wind howled against the window to his left, as he sat between the two.

"A few months ago, I joined the Zealots." Stone rolled up his sleeve to look at the branding on his arm. He rubbed the scars as he recalled all that happened since.

"I see."

"I thought we were going to change the world...save our people from persecution." Stone sniffled and cleared his throat, the torrential tears and cries had ended. His voice calmed greatly, "Destroy STORK and Unity. I thought we were crusaders, waging war against the hordes of Hell." The priest was silent beyond the screen, Stone had expected more of a reaction -- a major reaction. He continued his story, "I've been living with them. And at first, I was only running errands and passing messages between them...vandalizing buildings with their propaganda." Stone took a deep breath before continuing, wondering how the priest was taking it all in. "Then I was officially initiated. They branded my arm with the Jerusalem cross." Stone unrolled his sleeve and covered the marking. He looked towards the screen to see if the priest was peering through. The priest's silhouette showed his head leaning against the support of his hand, slouched against the screen. "After that night, they gave me more serious jobs, and I, uh, I was...was trained..." Stone began to weep, unable to control himself any longer. His heart tore open with every syllable, "...on how to make...bombs." He shook his head, "And I...I, uh, I even helped plant the bombs the night before the attacks last week." Once he uttered the words, the torment poured out in his voice, "I'm responsible for their deaths...every one of them...all those faces on the news...I killed those people. Some of them most likely not even wanting to be there...I ended them." Stone's voice cracked once again as more tears came, "I don't have the slightest clue what to do Father. I've committed a sin so grave that I'm drowning in it. A hundred lives lost because of me. A hundred. Men, women, children, the unborn. I killed them all, Father...and I'm not sure there's anything I could ever do to make up for it."

The priest remained silent for some time, Stone could almost hear a sniffling from beyond the screen, as if the priest himself had begun to cry. The silence between them seemed to last an eternity. Nothing spoken, no comfort given. Stone was afraid to speak, afraid to impatiently interrupt the priest's contemplation.

"I see," the priest said after the long nerve-racking silence, clearly searching for what to say. "It's a horrible, horrible sin you've committed, but yet somehow it isn't unforgivable to Christ." The priest's voice was pained, he strained as he spoke to the penitent. "Jesus was crucified for our sins, Stone." Hearing the priest speak his name made him uneasy. "God Himself, the Creator of the universe, came down in flesh to die for you. You must understand, that no matter how horrible the sin is, nothing is greater than His sacrifice. If you're truly repentant, there's nothing that stands in your way. You must have faith in His forgiveness." Every word shocked Stone. He had expected the priest to immediately alert the authorities or command him to turn himself over. The words were like honey when he had expected a bitter poison, a searing of ears.

"How though? God will surely cast me into Hell. There's no place in Heaven for someone that's done what I've done."

"Are you not listening?" The priest spoke sharply, "God allowed Himself to be sacrificed for you! To doubt His forgiveness is to belittle that sacrifice. It blasphemes the love our Father has for us. Never doubt His mercy, Stone. His purpose was to die for your sins. He even died for the sins of the people whose murder you contributed to."

"Yes, Father. I'm sorry. I'm sorry, I'm so sorry." Stone broke out in tears after hearing the reproach.

"There are also people who have done similar things to what you've confessed and they're saints now. Saint Paul, as I mentioned earlier, murdered Christians, before God blinded him. Saint Olga, massacred an entire tribe before selling the rest of them into slavery. And then her grandson followed a similar path as well until he converted. Even King David was a man after God's heart, and the Bible is filled with atrocities he committed. Believe me, if it were entirely up to me, I wouldn't offer such extreme and radical forgiveness. It's not in my heart. In fact, I can't say that I'd ever be able to forgive you, but I am a small man and God is greater than the weight of all the world's sins. No matter how great they are, He's large enough to destroy them."

"What must I do, then?"

"It's a very serious crime, that you've confessed. Possibly the gravest sin I've heard confessed." The priest's words began to singe Stone's heart. He felt as if he were burning and the wait brought great suffering to him. "Don't let my words allow you to believe it wasn't anything, because it is. What you did is as horrible as the things they do. You mustn't become one of them when you fight. In fact," the priest sounded as if he wept, "if things were any different I would ask you to turn yourself in tonight. I'm absolutely certain, however, that Unity would execute you and perhaps hunt down your entire family. Your crimes would endanger the entire neighborhood here and I can't let that happen." Stone continued to cry and wipe snot and tears away as they drained from his face. "The entire community should not perish because of your sin. But, you must mend your relationship with God and turn away from the Zealots immediately."

"Yes." Stone wiped more of his tears away.

"But, I can see how some of your intentions may have been righteous. Unity is forcing abortions upon all who conceive. Make no mistake, there is a war to be waged in these days, these days that Christians are hunted and the innocent are slain." The words the priest spoke shocked Stone yet again; he had not expected to hear such things coming from within the confessional. "Terrorism is by no means a just method for warfare, but defending your people and tearing down a tyrannical government is. Unity and those who, as we speak, conspire on ways to destroy us, must be stopped. You must study the words of Saint Augustine and Saint Aquinas as part of your journey. Pray to them that they may intercede on your behalf before God. There are those out there who have the same fire as you, who need leadership and guidance in these dark hours of the Church. Pray, son, pray and listen to the Lord. Do not shed innocent blood and do not wage war blindly. And if you can't find a just way to wage this war, then the fight isn't for you. Some of us make better martyrs than warriors, when it comes to our salvation, and there's nothing wrong with that."

"Yes, Father." Stone's voice sounded weak.

"Are there any other sins that are pressing?" The question baffled Stone, and in an instant, his other sins came forward to the front of his mind, things that seemed to have lost their importance while he lived with such great guilt.

"Masturbation, use of pornography, lustful thoughts towards a woman I love, um," Stone couldn't remember all the things he had done, "disobedience, doubting the mercy of God, speaking ill to clergy, fighting those that love me, vandalism, and casting judgment and hate on others."

"These are also things you must learn to turn from. Guilt for grave sins often makes us lose sight of all that is wrong in our lives. For your penance, I want you to study Saint Aquinas and Saint Augustine. You must also begin the Chaplet to Saint Michael the Archangel tonight, to defeat your demons, to protect you, and to give you a Pure Heart."

"Yes, Father."

"Remember, if things were any different, you'd be turning yourself in tonight. I want you to never forget the severity of your crime. If this war is won, if Unity is overthrown, I want you to turn yourself in afterward. I just can't bring down all who know you because of what you've done, but I also can't tell you not to face judgment in this life either."

Stone nodded his head, "I understand, Father. Don't think I'd ever truly find peace within myself. I promise, once Unity is overthrown, I will turn myself in. I give you my word."

"Now recite the Act of Contrition."

"O my God, I am heartily sorry for having offended Thee," Stone's words once again broke forth with tears and sadness, "and I detest all my sins, because I dread the loss of heaven and the pains of hell, but most of all because they offend Thee, my God, Who art all-good and deserving of all of my love." Stone paused, wanting to speak the words as sincerely as possible, feeling each syllable in his soul, "I firmly resolve, with the help of Thy grace, to confess my sins, to do penance, and to amend my life. Amen."

The priest waited for him to finish and soon after responded with absolution in Latin, ending with, "Et ego te absolvo a peccatis tuis in nominee Patris, et Filii, et Spiritus Sancti. Amen."

Stone replied, "Amen," and he was absolved of all that he had done. All stain of sin and blood he had spilled was washed clean of his soul. Everything he had ever done since his last confession was removed from him. A great peace came upon him, the pressure and remorse lifted and eased off of him. In a way, it felt as if a great weight had been immediately released from him. Stone would feel the pain still, he knew, likely for the rest of his life, but the priest's words filled him with momentary bliss.

"Go in peace," the priest said, his voice deeply resonating in the shed.

"Thank you, Father." Stone's voice was flat, solemn.

"Give thanks to God, it's all due to Him."

...

Stone stood from the chair and exited the tiny room. He faced into the wind that immediately bit at him as he opened the door. He felt as light as a feather, as if he floated rather than stepped towards the backdoor of the house. An impatient line of people greeted him as he entered the kitchen and the first in line immediately sprinted towards the shed behind him.

"Stone! I'm so happy to see you!" one of them greeted him. His neighbors and fellow parishioners hadn't seen him since the night he and Michael fought and were thrilled that he was visiting.

He hugged and shook hands with all of them. They had questions about his family and if they had made their trip safely, to which Stone had no news. He awkwardly responded to them, without any idea if or when they had reached their destination. Stone broke away from them eventually and took his place in another room of the house to pray. After which he decided he would wait and attend the Mass, and while he waited he looked through the sketchbook that Cole had left behind.

It was filled with works of art created using various mediums and techniques, from gold leaf to sketches in pen, and even darker ones that had been done in charcoal. One of the drawings he saw looked familiar, perhaps it was the concept image Cole sketched for the painting he gave him at Ruffner -- the one depicting the Angel of Death and the inflamed woman with red hair. He hadn't looked at the painting since that night, leaving it rolled beside his things in Jeremy's apartment. For once, he understood the painting; and, at that moment, he realized it depicted the results of his actions.

Stone felt the pain again, as he stared into the agony-stricken face of the woman being dragged to Hell, unforgiven for her crimes against her unborn. The baby was going somewhere peaceful, but the woman was carried away before ever having the chance to repent of what she had done. That was the worst effect, he thought, of his evil choices and actions. It wasn't simply the murder of the sinners, but the fact that it prevented them from getting a chance to repent. Stone ended their journeys to God before they were completed. The Zealots' mission served death to the wrong ones -- to the sinners -- victims of the cruel ways of this world. He wiped his tears away again and turned the page to the next piece of art.

It was a portrait of him -- Stone. In it, his face looked hard and expressed a rugged quality. The branding was harshly drawn onto his forearm -- the line strokes almost tore through the page, it seemed. The portrait had two sides: one was his past, the side with the branding; the other was of his present and future, holding a crucifix in his hand with his head illuminated by a semi halo that glowed behind him in gold leaf. This part of the sketch had much cleaner lines than the other side -- empty of shadowy charcoal smears and smudges. The piece filled him with hope and Stone wanted its image never to leave his mind. It portrayed the part of himself that he wanted to kill and the person he desired to become.

Below the portrait, Cole included a Latin inscription, "*Et dabo vobis cor novum et spiritum novum ponam in medio vestri et AUFERAM cor lapideum de carne vestra et dabo vobis cor carneum.*"

Which when Stone read the inscription, he turned on a translation overlay within his Visum, to see it in English. Cole had always loved and studied Latin, but Stone never found the time or interest to learn it fluently. It read: "*And I will give you a new heart, and put a new spirit within you: and I will take away the STONY heart out of your flesh, and will give you a heart of flesh.*" The verse from Ezekiel rattled him, shook him to his very bones, causing every nerve to fire as he saw his name.

"I'm so sorry...God," Stone knelt and wrapped his face with his sweaty hands, "please, Lord, please heal me. Help me find the path that delights You. Give me an honorable purpose, work within me so that I may protect Your people." Stone searched himself for words, feeling the tides of them crash against his heart, like a sea of heat. His soul burned with passion, every part of his being blurred in a dizzied act of the prayer. At the moment, he wasn't simply the flesh and bone he felt, but for the first time in a long time, he felt his spirit curl and strike within him, quaking before the glory of God. "Work within me so that I may have the wisdom to do Your will, send Your angels to protect me. Help me Lord, use me as a tool for the rescue of Your people. Give me the strength to do what many cannot; give me the strength to do what I've failed to do. Amen." Stone crossed himself and continued kneeling, enjoying the intensity of his moment with God. It was the most incredible sensation he had ever felt -- greater than anything he had ever experienced. It was a glimpse of Heaven and his surroundings melted away from his consciousness.

He never wanted to leave. He wanted the moment to last forever. He felt he could remain in that spot on his bedroom floor for eternity. Stone knew, however, that he couldn't so he stood to join the people on the floor below him for Mass. It saddened him to leave the moment behind.

But, the Mass was just as glorious to him. It seemed every word was spoken directly to him. Every verse and every moment imprinted upon his mind and heart as he opened himself entirely to it. When the Eucharist, the flesh and blood of Christ, had been consecrated, Stone bowed. He felt, although absolved, he still wasn't worthy of the sight, but the priest's eyes beckoned him forward to partake of the Sacrament and Stone did, kneeling.

The Blood of Christ burned within him like supernatural fuel. His already heightened passion inflamed with the consumption of the Precious Body and Blood and Stone felt truly changed. Everything that occurred in that Mass became a fresh experience as if he had never experienced it before. A wave of great peace and patience covered him and he was delivered from the scars and wounds that plagued his life.

He left the house after Mass concluded, choosing not to stay for dinner. The others implored him to remain a little longer, but he refused, giving the honest excuse that he had important things awaiting him, which needed immediate attention. He took the train back to Birmingham and returned to Jeremy's apartment. It would be his last time to cross the Zealot's threshold.

...

Once he arrived, he fumbled around in the dark looking for the keyhole. The porch light had burned out earlier that night and it was extremely dark, so he had to feel it out. He wasn't sure what he was going to say or do upon entering. He wasn't positive about how to leave or where to go when he did. His heart ached at the idea of leaving Debra behind. But he knew there was no chance the woman would leave with him.

"Stone," a deep voice called after he entered, "where've you been?" Jeremy loomed in his bedroom doorway.

"I went to Mass." Stone felt numb to the fear that would have engulfed him under different circumstances.

"Well, you missed the initiation." He was clearly enraged and his face soured as he eyed Stone from head to toe. "There's a new Zealot named Reggie. But, you should have known that without me saying so. You were told to be present tonight."

"I hadn't been to Mass in months. I needed to go, now that we're all targets -- or will be soon."

"You have a duty here." Jeremy crossed his arms, his muscles exaggerated in size as his arms pressed against each other. "A duty to God here. He'd prefer you be present and find time for Mass on your own clock."

"Zealots serve themselves," Stone replied, his tone flat and even. He turned his back and caught sight of Debra asleep in the living room.

"Excuse me?" His eyes widened, a fire raged in his piercing pupils as they expanded across his irises like flames consuming grassy fields.

"It's true."

"Our service to God is greater than any of the others with their silly gatherings and empty intentions. They hide in their homes and hold their Masses, but where are they when the innocents are sacrificed?"

"They're at Mass, praying for them. If we served God as we should, then we'd also go to Mass on every occasion possible. When's the last time you went? When's the last time you did anything other than devise methods to kill women?" Stone's retort caught Jeremy off guard -- the man who believed his intimidation was too much for the young man.

"Praying? Pft. And you watch the way you talk to me."

"What?" Stone searched for his things, making sure that he wouldn't leave anything behind.

"When has prayer ever done any good?"

"That's how I know Zealots serve themselves. We've failed to uphold the very traditions that we've claimed to protect." Stone's face grimaced and he shook his head, looking up at him. "You're ruled by your past trauma and the resulting rage. Your hate for what others did to you and your family consumes you. You don't serve God. You serve your own intentions to seek revenge."

"Who the hell do you think you're talking to?" Jeremy followed him aggressively as he packed. His shouting awakened Debra. Nelson had also begun listening, in secret, from the device he dwelt within.

"What's going on? Stone? Jeremy?" She opened her eyes wide, trying to discern what was taking place.

"Stone's looking for an ass-kicking. He's been enlightened all of a sudden and if he doesn't watch it, I swear--"

"Calm down," she yelled, rising from the couch. "What is it, Stone?"

"I'm done pretending we're doing a good thing here."

"What do you mean?"

"I'm fighting y'all's war and you guys aren't even fighting the right people. You're not even fighting the right way." He stood between the two of them, unafraid of Jeremy's menacing glare and Debra's heartbroken face. "I know why too. I know why y'all fight the way you do. It wasn't clear to me before, but now I know. It all makes sense."

"What do you think you know?" Jeremy mocked, crossing his arms again.

"The terrorism...the attacks on STORK clinics...you guys are waging the same war with the same methods others used to wage it on you. Your actions are no different from the monsters that burned down that church when you were kids. They did it in secret...they killed everyone within, just like we did at the clinic. You're not interested in saving anybody. You just want the world to burn like the church burned.

"How could you possibly compare the two?" Debra butted in, shocked that he dared defend the abortionists.

"We could've destroyed the clinics while no one was inside. Could have knocked the guards out and dragged them to safety before detonation." Stone's words flooded forth, unconstrained, "or used our resources to overthrow Unity...the source of all our problems. Instead, you thought it reasonable to kill women. Some of which in all likelihood didn't want to be there anyway and felt forced by pressure of the law or their husbands. You thought it reasonable to kill women who carried innocence within them, just as the men who burned down the church."

Debra began to cry, tears poured from her eyes and Jeremy's fists clenched as he caught sight of her reaction. He was seconds away from unrepressed brutality. Stone waited for the retort -- whatever argument came next -- and he also prepared to defend himself, if attacked.

"Look at what you've done to her!" Jeremy screamed, his face turned red and he spat with each word.

"Debra, you don't have to continue this. Neither of you have to continue fighting like this. We can figure something out -- a fight to be proud of." Stone's heart spilled out his passion. He hoped they would change, just as he did.

"I've got nowhere to go."

"Come with me. We'll find someplace safe. We'll go south or something."

"I can't, Stone. This is my life." Debra lowered her eyes. Part of her wished to leave, but she was a fugitive. If she left the apartment, they would find and arrest her before the night ended.

"So, you're just going to spend the rest of your life down here?"

"You're the one that needs to change, not us," Jeremy bellowed, jabbing his index finger against Stone's chest.

"Don't you put another finger on me!"

"Oh yeah?" Jeremy stepped into the boy's face, his chest pressing against his. "What's up? What you gonna do, boy?"

"Stop it!" Debra begged, trying to push them away from each other. Her arms were far too weak to put distance between the two riled, testosterone-filled men. The heat was building in the room as if a fire grew between them, while they stared into each other's faces. Jeremy was larger than Stone, yet the young man showed no sign that he felt intimidated. The grace granted to him through reconciliation and the Eucharist filled him with confidence. If he died, he'd be headed too paradise, and he felt no dread.

Jeremy bumped against him, pushing him back. He repeated this a couple of times before Stone lost all control and dove into his mentor, knocking him against the dining room furniture. The table fell back onto its side scattering chairs across the floor. Somewhere, behind the curtain of Stone's instinctual rage and the fight for his life, he wondered how he had gotten himself into this position yet again. Again, he found himself fighting, tossing, and scrambling on the floor as he swung his fists and received punches along all parts of his body. They exchanged blows on the floor and Stone realized that this fight could be it for him. Jeremy wasn't his caretaker or his family. He had to protect the safety and secrets of his clan; he wouldn't let Stone leave alive.

"Stop!" Debra shouted, her cries unheeded by the men bloodying each other upon the floor.

Jeremy's size gave him an advantage over the young man and he started to choke the life from Stone. Soon his face changed in hue, from pale white to a violet red. He twisted violently onto his side, kicked his leg out from beneath Jeremy and flung it out and around the bigger man's head. Stone immediately brought it back down against him and slammed against the floor. This allowed him to catch him in an armbar, as he pushed into the air against Jeremy's arm. A loud and clear snap thundered into the room followed by a loud moaning made by one of the men.

Stone broke away and jumped to his feet, pacing to and fro before Jeremy who was on his knees, looking at his right arm, which pointed in an awkward, unnatural direction. He tried to move the arm, but it simply flopped. The bones were out of place and pushed against his skin in all the wrong places. Jeremy's rage continued, at least momentarily, until his shock was fully realized and dizziness caused him to sway from left to right, until he quickly lost consciousness. Debra jumped to his side, checking to make sure he hadn't landed in a way to cause himself any more harm.

"Debra," Stone started, approaching her as she checked over Jeremy's body and arm.

"Don't Stone. Just leave. Leave before he wakes up and kills you."

"Debra, please..." his heart sank, "just come with me. Leave this all behind. There's nothing but death waiting for you here."

"I can't leave," Debra sighed, as Jeremy's eyes opened and rolled lethargically. "My place is with him, as it has always been. Just get out. Leave. And please, Stone, don't ever try to come back. He will never let this slide."

Stone reached down and lifted his duffle bag from the ground to place it over his shoulder as he watched Jeremy begin to mumble. He didn't plan on leaving this way, not able to say goodbye to her the way he intended. He wanted to hold her, express his love, but it wouldn't be so.

"Guess this is it, then." Stone refused to allow his emotions to show. He wanted to rush her with his arms wide open and drag her away, but it was her decision to stay. In that moment, he realized that she didn't share the love he held for her. She was Jeremy's the whole time. Jeremy probably allowed him to believe the lie too as a way to seduce him to their will.

"Good luck out there, Stone."

"As if you really care." He departed just as Jeremy regained consciousness. By the time the Zealot rose to his feet, the young man had already vanished from the apartment.

...

The night was cold, as cold as any night had been that winter, and Stone was without a home. He had no friends left to run to and his family was hundreds of miles away. His tears were cold against his cheeks as he jogged through the dimly lit streets and alleys of Glen Iris. Life had, once again, forced him out into the wild of the city, bleeding and abandoned, the ever-revolving wheel kept turning as he searched for his place and peace in the world. Snow began to fall from the grey sky illuminated by the distant city lights and the moon hanging behind them. The fire burning within his chest fizzled out and he shivered the entire night through, filled with nightmares and regret over what he had done to so many.

He eventually found himself not far from the police department, desiring nothing more than to walk in with his hands up, but he knew what the priest said was true. He couldn't risk the well-being of his family and that of the good neighbors of Irondale. His pain would continue, his suffering wouldn't recede, and he would continue to freeze until sunrise, struggling to find even the slightest bit of warmth.

Homeless, friendless, and alone, the only thing that brightened his spirits was the rosary he held within his pocket and the sketchbook he had to look through. That night he fell asleep within a dumpster pad. At least it had four walls and a roof to shield him from the winter. He bundled up beneath any material he could find, continuing to pray and shiver until the night grew late, silent, and ever more still beneath the white covering accumulating across the landscape.